THE THEORY OF OPTICS

THE THEORY OF OPTICS

BY

PAUL DRUDE

TRANSLATED FROM THE GERMAN

BY

C. RIBORG MANN AND ROBERT A. MILLIKAN

DOVER PUBLICATIONS, INC.
NEW YORK

This new Dover edition first published in 1959 is an unabridged and unaltered republication of the last English translation.

Manufactured in the United States of America

Dover Publications, Inc.
180 Varick Street
New York 14, New York

PREFACE TO THE ENGLISH TRANSLATION

THERE does not exist to-day in the English language a general advanced text upon Optics which embodies the important advances in both theory and experiment which have been made within the last decade.

Preston's "Theory of Light" is at present the only general text upon Optics in English. Satisfactory as this work is for the purposes of the general student, it approaches the subject from the historical standpoint and contains no fundamental development of some of the important theories which are fast becoming the basis of modern optics. Thus it touches but slightly upon the theory of optical instruments—a branch of optics which has received at the hands of Abbe and his followers a most extensive and beautiful development; it gives a most meagre presentation of the electromagnetic theory—a theory which has recently been brought into particular prominence by the work of Lorentz, Zeeman, and others; and it contains no discussion whatever of the application of the laws of thermodynamics to the study of radiation.

The book by Heath, the last edition of which appeared in 1895, well supplies the lack in the field of Geometrical Optics, and Basset's "Treatise on Physical Optics" (1892) is a valuable and advanced presentation of many aspects of the wave theory. But no complete development of the electromagnetic theory in all its bearings, and no comprehensive discussion of the relation between the laws of radiation and the principles of thermodynamics, have yet been attempted in any general text in English.

It is in precisely these two respects that the "Lehrbuch der Optik" by Professor Paul Drude (Leipzig, 1900) particularly excels. Therefore in making this book, written by one who has contributed so largely to the progress which has been made in Optics within the last ten years, accessible to the English-speaking public, the translators have rendered a very important service to English and American students of Physics.

No one who desires to gain an insight into the most modern aspects of optical research can afford to be unfamiliar with this remarkably original and consecutive presentation of the subject of Optics.

A. A. MICHELSON.

UNIVERSITY OF CHICAGO,
February, 1902.

AUTHOR'S PREFACE

THE purpose of the present book is to introduce the reader who is already familiar with the fundamental concepts of the differential and integral calculus into the domain of optics in such a way that he may be able both to understand the aims and results of the most recent investigation and, in addition, to follow the original works in detail.

The book was written at the request of the publisher—a request to which I gladly responded, not only because I shared his view that a modern text embracing the entire domain was wanting, but also because I hoped to obtain for myself some new ideas from the deeper insight into the subject which writing in book form necessitates. In the second and third sections of the Physical Optics I have advanced some new theories. In the rest of the book I have merely endeavored to present in the simplest possible way results already published.

Since I had a text-book in mind rather than a compendium, I have avoided the citation of such references as bear only upon the historical development of optics. The few references which I have included are merely intended to serve the reader for more complete information upon those points which can find only brief presentation in the text, especially in the case of the more recent investigations which have not yet found place in the text-books.

In order to keep in touch with experiment and attain the simplest possible presentation of the subject I have chosen a synthetic method. The simplest experiments lead into the domain of geometrical optics, in which but few assumptions need to be made as to the nature of light. Hence I have begun with geometrical optics, following closely the excellent treatment given by Czapski in "Winkelmann's Handbuch der Physik" and by Lommer in the ninth edition of the "Müller-Pouillet" text.

The first section of the Physical Optics, which follows the Geometrical, treats of those general properties of light from which the conclusion is drawn that light consists in a periodic change of condition which is propagated with finite velocity in the form of transverse waves. In this section I have included, as an important advance upon most previous texts, Sommerfeld's rigorous solution of the simplest case of diffraction, Cornu's geometric representation of Fresnel's integrals, and, on the experimental side, Michelson's echelon spectroscope.

In the second section, for the sake of the treatment of the optical properties of different bodies, an extension of the hypotheses as to the nature of light became for the first time necessary. In accordance with the purpose of the book I have merely mentioned the mechanical theories of light; but the electromagnetic theory, which permits the simplest and most consistent treatment of optical relations, I have presented in the following form:

Let X, Y, Z, and α, β, γ represent respectively the components of the electric and magnetic forces (the first measured in electrostatic units); also let j_x, j_y, j_z, and s_x, s_y, s_z represent the components of the electric and magnetic current densities, i.e. $\frac{1}{4\pi}$ times the number of electric or magnetic lines of force which pass in unit time through a unit surface at rest with reference to the ether; then, if c represent the ratio of the electromagnetic to the electrostatic unit, the following *fundamental equations* always hold:

$$\frac{4\pi j_x}{c} = \frac{\partial \gamma}{\partial y} - \frac{\partial \beta}{\partial z}, \text{ etc.,} \quad \frac{4\pi s_x}{c} = \frac{\partial Y}{\partial z} - \frac{\partial Z}{\partial y}, \text{ etc.}$$

The number of lines of force is defined in the usual way. The particular optical properties of bodies first make their appearance in the equations which connect the electric and magnetic current densities with the electric and magnetic forces. Let these equations be called the *substance equations* in order to distinguish them from the above *fundamental equations*. Since these substance equations are developed for non-homogeneous bodies, i.e. for bodies whose properties vary from point to point, and since the fundamental equations hold in *all* cases, both the differential equations of the electric and magnetic forces and the equations of condition which must be fulfilled at the surface of a body are immediately obtained.

In the process of setting up "substance and fundamental equations" I have again proceeded synthetically in that I have deduced them from the simplest electric and magnetic experiments. Since the book is to treat mainly of optics this process can here be but briefly sketched. For a more complete development the reader is referred to my book "Physik des Aethers auf elektromagnetische Grundlage" (Enke, 1894).

In this way however, no explanation of the phenomena of dispersion is obtained because pure electromagnetic experiments lead to conclusions in what may be called the domain of *macrophysical* properties only. For the explanation of optical dispersion a hypothesis as to the *microphysical* properties of bodies must be made. As such I have made use of the ion-hypothesis introduced by Helmholtz because it seemed to me the simplest, most intelligible, and most consistent way of presenting not only dispersion, absorption, and rotary polarization, but also magneto-optical phenomena and the optical properties of bodies in motion. These two last-named subjects I have thought it especially necessary to consider because the first has acquired new interest from Zeeman's discovery, and the second has received at the hands of H. A. Lorentz a development as comprehensive as it is elegant. This theory of Lorentz I have attempted to simplify by the elimination of all quantities which are not necessary to optics. With respect to magneto-optical phenomena I have pointed out that it is, in general, impossible to explain them by the mere supposition that ions set in motion in a magnetic field are subject to a deflecting force, but that in the case of the strongly magnetic metals the ions must be in such a *continuous* motion as to produce Ampère's molecular currents. This supposition also disposes at once of the hitherto unanswered question as to why the permeability of iron and, in fact, of all other substances must be assumed equal to that of the free ether for those vibrations which produce light.

The application of the ion-hypothesis leads also to some new dispersion formulæ for the natural and magnetic rotation of the plane of polarization, formulæ which are experimentally verified. Furthermore, in the case of the metals, the ion-hypothesis leads to dispersion formulæ which make the continuity of the optical and electrical properties of the metals depend essentially upon the inertia of the ions, and which have also been experimentally verified within the narrow limits thus far accessible to observation.

The third section of the book is concerned with the relation of optics to thermodynamics and (in the third chapter) to the kinetic theory of gases. The pioneer theoretical work in these subjects was done by Kirchhoff, Clausius, Boltzmann, and W. Wien, and the many fruitful experimental investigations in radiation which have been more recently undertaken show clearly that theory and experiment reach most perfect development through their mutual support.

Imbued with this conviction, I have written this book in the endeavor to make the theory accessible to that wider circle of readers who have not the time to undertake the study of the original works. I can make no claim to such completeness as is aimed at in Mascart's excellent treatise, or in Winkelmann's Handbuch. For the sake of brevity I have passed over many interesting and important fields of optical investigation. My purpose is attained if these pages strengthen the reader in the view that optics is not an old and worn-out branch of Physics, but that in it also there pulses a new life whose further nourishing must be inviting to every one.

Mr. F. Kiebitz has given me efficient assistance in the reading of the proof.

LEIPZIG, January, 1900.

INTRODUCTION

MANY optical phenomena, among them those which have found the most extensive practical application, take place in accordance with the following fundamental laws:

1. The law of the rectilinear propagation of light;

2. The law of the independence of the different portions of a beam of light;

3. The law of reflection;

4. The law of refraction.

Since these four fundamental laws relate only to the geometrical determination of the propagation of light, conclusions concerning certain geometrical relations in optics may be reached by making them the starting-point of the analysis without taking account of other properties of light. Hence these fundamental laws constitute a sufficient foundation for so-called *geometrical optics*, and no especial hypothesis which enters more closely into the nature of light is needed to make the superstructure complete.

In contrast with geometrical optics stands *physical optics*, which deals with other than the purely geometrical properties, and which enters more closely into the relation of the physical properties of different bodies to light phenomena. The best success in making a convenient classification of the great multitude of these phenomena has been attained by devising particular hypotheses as to the nature of light.

From the standpoint of physical optics the four above-mentioned fundamental laws appear only as very close approximations. However, it is possible to state within what limits the laws of geometrical optics are accurate, i.e. under what circumstances their consequences deviate from the actual facts.

This circumstance must be borne in mind if geometrical optics is to be treated as a field for real discipline in physics rather than one for the practice of pure mathematics. The truly complete theory of optical instruments can only be developed from the standpoint of physical optics; but since, as has been already remarked, the laws of geometrical optics furnish in most cases very close approximations to the actual facts, it seems justifiable to follow out the consequences of these laws even in such complicated cases as arise in the theory of optical instruments.

TABLE OF CONTENTS

PART I.—GEOMETRICAL OPTICS

CHAPTER I

THE FUNDAMENTAL LAWS

CHAPTER II

GEOMETRICAL THEORY OF OPTICAL IMAGES

CHAPTER III

PHYSICAL CONDITIONS FOR IMAGE FORMATION

CHAPTER IV

APERTURES AND THE EFFECTS DEPENDING UPON THEM

CHAPTER V

OPTICAL INSTRUMENTS

PART II.—PHYSICAL OPTICS

SECTION I

GENERAL PROPERTIES OF LIGHT

CHAPTER I

THE VELOCITY OF LIGHT

CHAPTER II

INTERFERENCE OF LIGHT

CHAPTER III

HUYGENS' PRINCIPLE

CHAPTER IV

DIFFRACTION OF LIGHT

CHAPTER V

POLARIZATION

SECTION II

OPTICAL PROPERTIES OF BODIES

CHAPTER I

THEORY OF LIGHT

CHAPTER II

TRANSPARENT ISOTROPIC MEDIA

CHAPTER III

OPTICAL PROPERTIES OF TRANSPARENT CRYSTALS

CHAPTER IV

ABSORBING MEDIA

CHAPTER V

DISPERSION

CHAPTER VI

OPTICALLY ACTIVE SUBSTANCES

CHAPTER VII

MAGNETICALLY ACTIVE SUBSTANCES

A. *Hypothesis of Molecular Currents*

B. *Hypothesis of the Hall Effect*

CHAPTER VIII

BODIES IN MOTION

PART III.—RADIATION

CHAPTER I

ENERGY OF RADIATION

CHAPTER II

APPLICATION OF THE SECOND LAW OF THERMODYNAMICS TO PURE TEMPERATURE RADIATION

CHAPTER III

INCANDESCENT VAPORS AND GASES

THE THEORY OF OPTICS

PART I

GEOMETRICAL OPTICS

CHAPTER I

THE FUNDAMENTAL LAWS

1. **Direct Experiment.**—The four fundamental laws stated above are obtained by direct experiment.

The rectilinear propagation of light is shown by the shadow of an opaque body which a point source of light P casts upon a screen S. If the opaque body contains an aperture L, then the edge of the shadow cast upon the screen is found to be the intersection of S with a cone whose vertex lies in the source P and whose surface passes through the periphery of the aperture L.

If the aperture is made smaller, the boundary of the shadow upon the screen S contracts. Moreover it becomes indefinite when L is made very small (e.g. less than *1 mm.*), for points upon the screen which lie within the geometrical shadow now receive light from P. However, it is to be observed that a true point source can never be realized, and, on account of the finite extent of the source, the edge of the shadow could never be perfectly sharp even if light were propagated in straight lines (umbra and penumbra). Nevertheless, in the case of a very small opening L (say of about one tenth *mm.* diameter) the light is spread out behind L upon the screen so far that *in this case the propagation cannot possibly be rectilinear.*

The same result is obtained if the shadow which an opaque body S' casts upon the screen S is studied, instead of the spreading out of the light which has passed through a hole in an opaque object. If S' is sufficiently small, rectilinear propagation of light from P does not take place. It is therefore necessary to bear in mind that the law of the rectilinear propagation of light holds only when the free opening through which the light passes, or the screens which prevent its passage, are not too small.

In order to conveniently describe the propagation of light from a source P to a screen S, it is customary to say that P sends *rays* to S. The path of a ray of light is then defined by the fact that its effect upon S can be cut off only by an obstacle that lies in the path of the ray itself. When the propagation of light is rectilinear the rays are straight lines, as when light from P passes through a sufficiently large opening in an opaque body. In this case it is customary to say that P sends a beam of light through L.

Since by diminishing L the result upon the screen S is the same as though the influence of certain of the rays proceeding from P were simply removed while that of the other rays remained unchanged, it follows that *the different parts of a beam of light are independent of one another.*

This law too breaks down if the diminution of the opening L is carried too far. But in that case the conception of light rays propagated in straight lines is altogether untenable.

The concept of light rays is then merely introduced for convenience. It is altogether impossible to isolate a single ray and prove its physical existence. For the more one tries to attain this end by narrowing the beam, the less does light proceed in straight lines, and the more does the concept of light rays lose its physical significance.

If the homogeneity of the space in which the light rays exist is disturbed by the introduction of some substance, the rays undergo a sudden change of direction at its surface: each ray splits up into two, a reflected and a refracted ray. If the surface of the body upon which the light falls is plane, then the *plane of incidence* is that plane which is defined by the incident ray and the normal N to the surface, and the *angle of incidence* ϕ is the angle included between these two directions.

The following laws hold: *The reflected and refracted rays both lie in the plane of incidence. The angle of reflection* (the angle included between N and the reflected ray) *is equal to the angle of incidence. The angle of refraction* ϕ' (angle included between N and the refracted ray) *bears to the angle of incidence the relation*

$$\frac{\sin \phi}{\sin \phi'} = n, \qquad \qquad (1)$$

in which n is a constant for any given color, and is called the *index of refraction* of the body with reference to the surrounding medium.—Unless otherwise specified the index of refraction with respect to air will be understood.—For all transparent liquids and solids n is greater than *1*.

If a body A is separated from air by a thin plane parallel plate of some other body B, the light is refracted at both surfaces of the plate in accordance with equation (1); i.e.

$$\frac{\sin \phi}{\sin \phi'} = n_b, \quad \frac{\sin \phi'}{\sin \phi''} = n_{ab},$$

in which ϕ represents the angle of incidence in air, ϕ' the angle of refraction in the body B, ϕ'' the angle of refraction in the body A, n_b the index of refraction of B with respect to air, n_{ab} the index of refraction of A with respect to B; therefore

$$\frac{\sin \phi}{\sin \phi''} = n_b \cdot n_{ab}.$$

If the plate B is infinitely thin, the formula still holds. The case does not then differ from that at first considered, viz. that of simple refraction between the body A and air. The last equation in combination with (1) then gives, n_a denoting the index of refraction of A with respect to air,

$$\left.\begin{aligned} n_a &= n \cdot n_{ab}, \\ \text{or} \qquad n_{ab} &= n_a : n_b, \end{aligned}\right\} \quad . \quad . \quad . \quad . \quad . \quad . \quad (2)$$

i.e. *the index of refraction of A with respect to B is equal to the ratio of the indices of A and B with respect to air.*

If the case considered had been that of an infinitely thin plate A placed upon the body B, the same process of reasoning would have given

$$n_{ba} = n_b : n_a.$$

Hence

$$n_{ab} = 1 : n_{ba},$$

i.e. *the index of A with respect to B is the reciprocal of the index of B with respect to A.*

The law of refraction stated in (1) permits, then, the conclusion that ϕ' may also be regarded as the angle of incidence in the body, and ϕ as the angle of refraction in the surrounding medium; i.e. *that the direction of propagation may be reversed without changing the path of the rays.* For the case of reflection it is at once evident that this principle of reversibility also holds.

Therefore equation (1), which corresponds to the passage of light from a body A to a body B or the reverse, may be put in the symmetrical form

$$n_a \cdot \sin \phi_a = n_b \cdot \sin \phi_b, \quad . \quad . \quad . \quad . \quad . \quad . \quad (3)$$

in which ϕ_a and ϕ_b denote the angles included between the normal N and the directions of the ray in A and B respectively, and n_a and n_b the respective indices with respect to some medium like air or the free ether.

The difference between the index n of a body with respect to air and its index n_0 with respect to a vacuum is very small. From (2)

$$n_0 = n : n', \quad . \quad . \quad . \quad . \quad . \quad . \quad . \quad . \quad . \quad (4)$$

in which n' denotes the index of a vacuum with respect to air. Its value at atmospheric pressure and 0° C. is

$$n' = 1 : 1.00029. \quad . \quad . \quad . \quad . \quad . \quad . \quad (5)$$

According to equation (3) there exists a refracted ray (ϕ_b) to correspond to every possible incident ray ϕ_a only when $n_a < n_b$; for if $n_a > n_b$, and if

$$\sin \phi_a > \frac{n_b}{n_a}, \quad . \quad . \quad . \quad . \quad . \quad . \quad (6)$$

then $\sin \phi_b > 1$; i.e. there is no real angle of refraction ϕ_b. In that case no refraction occurs at the surface, but reflection only. The whole intensity of the incident ray must then be contained in the reflected ray; i.e. there is *total reflection.*

In all other cases (*partial reflection*) the intensity of the incident light is divided between the reflected and the refracted rays according to a law which will be more fully considered later (Section 2, Chapter II). Here the observation must suffice that, in general, for transparent bodies the refracted ray contains much more light than the reflected. Only in the case of the metals does the latter contain almost the entire intensity of the incident light. It is also to be observed that the law of reflection holds for very opaque bodies, like the metals, but the law of refraction is no longer correct in the form given in (1) or (3). This point will be more fully discussed later (Section 2, Chapter IV).

The different qualities perceptible in light are called *colors.* The refractive index depends on the color, and, when referred to air, increases, for transparent bodies, as the color changes from red through yellow to blue. The spreading out of white light into a spectrum by passage through a prism is due to this change of index with the color, and is called *dispersion.*

If the surface of the body upon which the light falls is not plane but curved, it may still be looked upon as made up of very small elementary planes (the tangent planes), and the paths of the light rays may be constructed according to the above laws. However, this process is reliable only when the curvature of the surface does not exceed a certain limit, i.e. when the surface may be considered smooth.

Rough surfaces exhibit irregular (diffuse) reflection and refraction and act as though they themselves emitted light. The surface of a body is visible only because of diffuse reflection and refraction. The surface of a perfect mirror is invisible. Only objects which lie outside of the mirror, and whose rays are reflected by it, are seen.

2. Law of the Extreme Path.*—All of these experimental facts as to the direction of light rays are comprehended in the law of the extreme path. If a ray of light in passing from a point P to a point P' experiences any number of reflections and refractions, then the sum of the products of the index of refraction of each medium by the distance traversed in it, i.e. Σnl, has a maximum or minimum value; i.e. it differs from a like sum for all other paths which are infinitely close to the actual path by terms of the second or higher order. Thus if δ denotes the variation of the first order,

$$\delta \Sigma nl = 0. \qquad (7)$$

The product, index of refraction times distance traversed, is known as the *optical length* of the ray.

In order to prove the proposition for a single refraction let POP' be the actual path of the light (Fig. 1), OE the intersection of the plane of incidence PON with the surface (tangent plane) of the refracting body, O' a point on the surface of the refracting body infinitely near to O, so that OO' makes any angle θ with the plane of incidence, i.e. with the line OE. Then it is to be proved that, to terms of the second or higher order,

$$n \cdot PO + n' \cdot OP' = n \cdot PO' + n' \cdot O'P', \qquad (8)$$

* 'Extreme' is here used to denote either greatest or least (maximum or minimum).—TR.

in which n and n' represent the indices of refraction of the adjoining media.

If a perpendicular OR be dropped from O upon PO' and a perpendicular OR' upon $P'O'$, then, to terms of the second order,

$$PO' = PO + RO', \quad O'P' = OP' - O'R'. \quad . \quad . \quad (9)$$

Also, to the same degree of approximation,

$$RO' = OO' \cdot \cos POO', \quad O'R' = OO' \cdot \cos P'OO'. \quad (10)$$

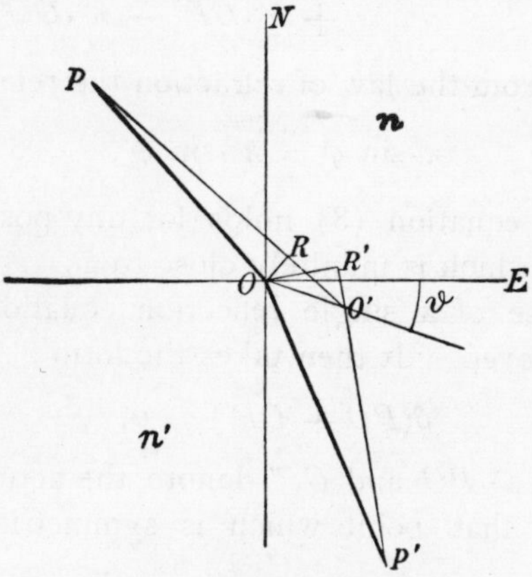

FIG. 1.

In order to calculate $\cos POO'$ imagine an axis OD perpendicular to ON and OE, and introduce the direction cosines of the lines PO and OO' referred to a rectangular system of coordinates whose axes are ON, OE, and OD. If ϕ represent the angle of incidence PON, then, disregarding the sign, the direction cosines of PO are

$$\cos \phi, \quad \sin \phi, \quad 0,$$

those of OO are

$$0, \quad \cos \vartheta, \quad \sin \vartheta.$$

According to a principle of analytical geometry the cosine of the angle between any two lines is equal to the sum of the products of the corresponding direction cosines of the lines with reference to a system of rectangular coordinates, i.e.

$$\cos POO' = \sin \phi \cdot \cos \vartheta,$$

and similarly

$$\cos P'OO' = \sin \phi' \cdot \cos \vartheta,$$

in which ϕ' represents the angle of refraction.

Then, from (9) and (10),

$$n \cdot PO' + n' \cdot O'P' = n \cdot PO + n \cdot OO' \cdot \sin \phi \cdot \cos \vartheta + n' \cdot OP' - n' \cdot OO' \cdot \sin \phi' \cdot \cos \vartheta.$$

Since now from the law of refraction the relation exists

$$n \cdot \sin \phi = n' \cdot \sin \phi',$$

it follows that equation (8) holds for any position whatever of the point O' which is infinitely close to O.

For the case of a single reflection equation (7) may be more simply proved. It then takes the form

$$\delta(PO + OP') = 0, \quad . \quad . \quad . \quad . \quad . \quad (11)$$

in which (Fig. 2) PO and OP' denote the actual path of the ray. If P_1 be that point which is symmetrical to P with

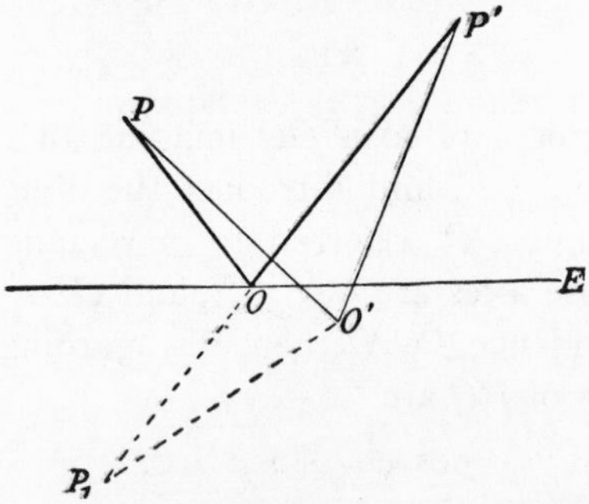

FIG. 2.

respect to the tangent plane OE of the refracting body, then for every point O' in the tangent plane, $PO' = P_1O'$. The length of the path of the light from P to P' for a single reflection at the tangent plane OE is, then, for every position of the point O', equal to $P_1O' + O'P'$. Now this length is a minimum if P_1, O', and P' lie in a straight line. But in that case the point O' actually coincides with the point O which is determined by the law of reflection. But since the property of a minimum (as well as of a maximum) is expressed by the vanishing of the first derivative, i.e. by equation (11), therefore equation (7) is proved for a single reflection.

It is to be observed that the vanishing of the first derivative is the condition of a maximum as well as of a minimum. In the case in which the refracting body is actually bounded by a plane, it follows at once from the construction given that the path of the light in reflection is a minimum. It may also be proved, as will be more fully shown later on, that in the case of refraction the actual path is a minimum if the refracting body is bounded by a plane. Hence this principle has often been called the *law of least path.*

When, however, the surface of the refracting or reflecting body is curved, *then the path of the light is a minimum or a maximum according to the nature of the curvature.* The vanishing of the first derivative is the only property which is common to all cases, and this also is entirely sufficient for the determination of the path of the ray.

A clear comprehension of the subject is facilitated by the introduction of the so-called *aplanatic surface*, which is a surface such that from every point upon it the sum of the optical paths to two points P and P' is constant. For such a surface the derivative, not only of the first order, but also of any other order, of the sum of the optical paths vanishes.

In the case of reflection the aplanatic surface, defined by

$$PA + P'A = \text{constant } C, \quad . \quad . \quad . \quad . \quad (12)$$

is an ellipsoid of revolution having the points P and P' as foci.

If SOS' represents a section of a mirror (Fig. 3) and O a point upon it such that PO and $P'O$ are incident and reflected rays, then the aplanatic surface AOA', which passes through the point O and corresponds to the points P and P', must evidently be tangent to the mirror SOS' at O, since at this point the first derivative of the optical paths vanishes for both surfaces. If now, as in the figure, the mirror SOS' is more concave than the aplanatic surface, then the optical path $PO + OP'$ is a maximum, otherwise a minimum.

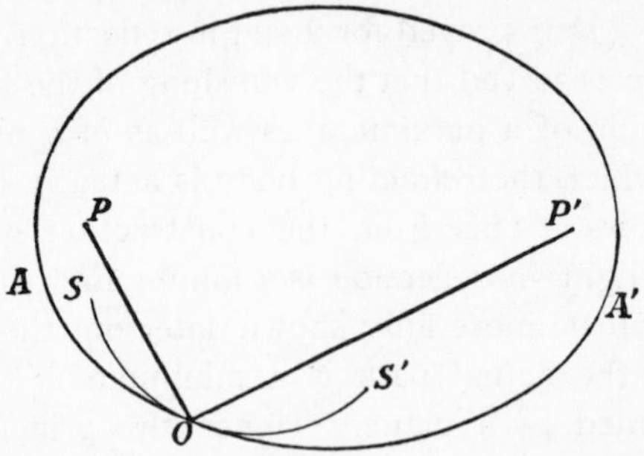

FIG. 3.

The proof of this appears at once from the figure, since for all points O' within the ellipsoid AOA' whose equation is given in (12), the sum $PO + OP'$ is smaller than the constant C, while for all points outside, this sum is larger than C, and for the actual point of reflection O, it is equal to C.

In the case of refraction the aplanatic surface, defined by

$$n \cdot PA + n' \cdot P'A = \text{constant } C,$$

is a so-called Cartesian oval which must be convex towards the less refractive medium (in Fig. 4 $n < n'$), and indeed more convex than a sphere described about P' as a centre.

This aplanatic surface also separates the regions for whose points O' the sum of the optical paths $n \cdot PO' + n' \cdot P'O' > C$ from those for which that sum $< C$. The former regions lie on the side of the aplanatic surface toward the less refractive medium (left in the figure), the latter on the side toward the more refractive medium (right in the figure).

If now SOS' represents a section of the surface between the two media, and PO, $P'O$ the actual path which the light takes in accordance with the law of refraction, then the length of the path through O is a maximum or a minimum according as SOS' is more or less convex toward the less refracting medium

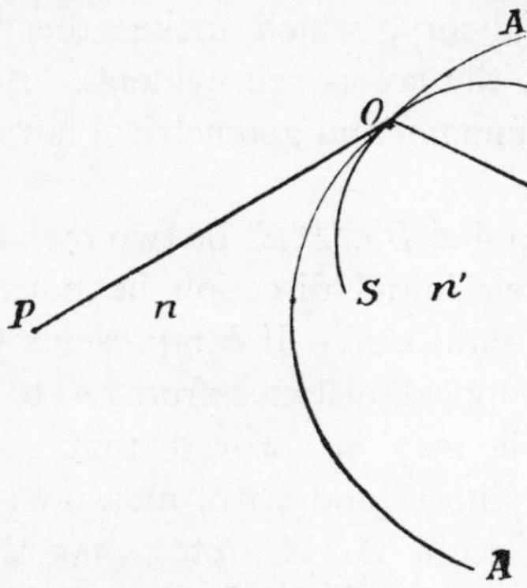

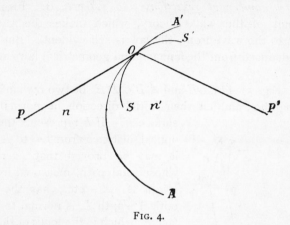

FIG. 4.

than the aplanatic surface AOA'. The proof appears at once from the figure.

If, for example, SOS' is a plane, the length of the path is a minimum. In the case shown in the figure the length of the path is a maximum.

Since, as will be shown later, the index of refraction is inversely proportional to the velocity, the optical path nl is proportional to the time which the light requires to travel the distance l. *The principle of least path is then identical with Fermat's principle of least time*, but it is evident from the above that, under certain circumstances, the time may also be a maximum.

Since $\delta \Sigma nl = 0$ holds for each single reflection or refraction, the equation $\delta \Sigma nl = 0$ may at once be applied to the case of any number of reflections and refractions.

3. The Law of Malus.—Geometrically considered there are two different kinds of ray systems: those which may be cut at right angles by a properly constructed surface F (orthotomic system), and those for which no such surface F can be found (anorthotomic system). With the help of the preceding principle the law of Malus can now be proved. This law is stated thus: *An orthotomic system of rays remains orthotomic after any number of reflections and refractions.* From the standpoint of the wave theory, which makes the rays the normals to the wave front, the law is self-evident. But it can also be deduced from the fundamental geometrical laws already used.

Let (Fig. 5) $ABCDE$ and $A'B'C'D'E'$ be two rays infinitely close together and let their initial direction be normal to a surface F. If L represents the total optical distance from A to E, then it may be proved that every ray whose total path, measured from its origin A, A', etc., has the same optical length L, is normal to a surface F' which is the locus of the ends E, E', etc., of those paths. For the purpose of the proof let $A'B$ and $E'D$ be drawn.

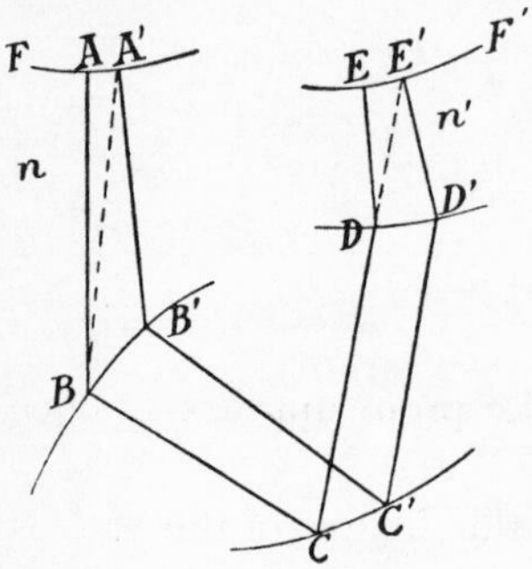

FIG. 5.

According to the law of extreme path stated above, the length of the path $A'B'C'D'E'$ must be equal to that of the infinitely near path $A'BCDE'$, i.e. equal to L, which is also the length of the path $ABCDE$. If now from the two optical distances $A'BCDE'$ and $ABCDE$ the common portion BCD be subtracted, it follows that

$$n \cdot AB + n' \cdot DE = n \cdot A'B + n' \cdot DE',$$

in which n represents the index of the medium between the surfaces F and B, and n' that of the medium between D and F'. But since $AB = A'B$, because AB is by hypothesis normal to F, it follows that

$$DE = DE',$$

i.e. DE is perpendicular to the surface F'. In like manner it may be proved that any other ray $D'E'$ is normal to F'.

Rays which are emitted by a luminous point are normal to a surface F, which is the surface of any sphere described about the luminous point as a centre. Since every source of light may be looked upon as a complex of luminous points, it follows that *light rays always form an orthotomic system.*

CHAPTER II

GEOMETRICAL THEORY OF OPTICAL IMAGES

1. **The Concept of Optical Images.**—If in the neighborhood of a luminous point P there are refracting and reflecting bodies having any arbitrary arrangement, then, in general, there passes through any point P' in space one and only one ray of light, i.e. the direction which light takes from P to P' is completely determined. Nevertheless certain points P' may be found at which two or more of the rays emitted by P intersect. If a large number of the rays emitted by P intersect in a point P', then P' is called the *optical image* of P. The intensity of the light at P' will clearly be a maximum. If the actual intersection of the rays is at P', the image is called *real;* if P' is merely the intersection of the backward prolongation of the rays, the image is called *virtual*. The simplest example of a virtual image is found in the reflection of a luminous point P in a plane mirror. The image P' lies at that point which is placed symmetrically to P with respect to the mirror. Real images may be distinguished from virtual by the direct illumination which they produce upon a suitably placed rough surface such as a piece of white paper. In the case of plane mirrors, for instance, no light whatever reaches the point P'. Nevertheless virtual images may be transformed into real by certain optical means. Thus a virtual image can be seen because it is transformed by the eye into a real image which illumines a certain spot on the retina.

The cross-section of the bundle of rays which is brought together in the image may have finite length and breadth or may be infinitely narrow so as in the limit to have but one dimension. Consider, for example, the case of a single refraction. If the surface of the refracting body is the aplanatic surface for the two points P and P', then a beam of any size which has its origin in P will be brought together in P'; for all rays which start from P and strike the aplanatic surface must intersect in P', since for all of them the total optical distance from P to P' is the same.

If the surface of the refracting body has not the form of the aplanatic surface, then the number of rays which intersect in P is smaller the greater the difference in the form of the two surfaces (which are necessarily tangent to each other, see page 10). In order that an infinitely narrow, i.e. a plane, beam may come to intersection in P', the curvature of the surfaces at the point of tangency must be the same at least in one plane. If the curvature of the two surfaces is the same at O for two and therefore for all planes, then a solid elementary beam will come to intersection in P'; and if, finally, a finite section of the surface of the refracting body coincides with the aplanatic surface, then a beam of finite cross-section will come to intersection in P'.

Since the direction of light may be reversed, it is possible to interchange the source P and its image P', i.e. a source at P' has its image at P. On account of this reciprocal relationship P and P' are called *conjugate points*.

2. General Formulæ for Images.—Assume that by means of reflection or refraction all the points P of a given space are imaged in points P' of a second space. The former space will be called the *object space*; the latter, the *image space*. From the definition of an optical image it follows that for every ray which passes through P there is a conjugate ray passing through P'. Two rays in the object space which intersect at P must correspond to two conjugate rays which intersect in the image space, the intersection being at the point P' which is conjugate to P. For every point P there is then but one conjugate point P'. If four points $P_1P_2P_3P_4$ of the object space lie in a plane, then the rays which connect any two pairs of these points intersect, e.g. the ray P_1P_2 cuts the ray P_3P_4 in the point A. Therefore the conjugate rays $P'_1P'_2$ and $P'_3P'_4$ also intersect in a point, namely in A' the image of A. Hence the four images $P_1'P_2'P_3'P_4'$ also lie in a plane. In other words, to every point, ray, or plane in the one space there corresponds one, and but one, point, ray, or plane in the other. Such a relation of two spaces is called in geometry a *collinear relationship.*

The analytical expression of the collinear relationship can be easily obtained. Let x, y, z be the coordinates of a point P of the object space referred to one rectangular system, and x', y', z' the coordinates of the point P' referred to another rectangular system chosen for the image space; then to every x, y, z there corresponds one and only one x', y', z', and *vice versa.* This is only possible if

$$\left.\begin{aligned} x' &= \frac{a_1x + b_1y + c_1z + d_1}{ax + by + cz + d}, \\ y' &= \frac{a_2x + b_2y + c_2z + d_2}{ax + by + cz + d}, \\ z' &= \frac{a_3x + b_3y + c_3z + d_3}{ax + by + cz + d}, \end{aligned}\right\} \quad . \quad . \quad . \quad . \quad (1)$$

in which a, b, c, d are constants. That is, for any given x', y', z', the values of x, y, z may be calculated from the three linear equations (1); and inversely, given values of x, y, z determine x', y', z'. If the right-hand side of equations (1) were not the quotient of two linear functions of x, y, z, then for every x', y', z' there would be several values of x, y, z. Furthermore the denominator of this quotient must be one and the same linear function $(ax + by + cz + d)$, since otherwise a plane in the image space

$$A'x' + B'y' + C'z' + D' = 0$$

would not again correspond to a plane

$$Ax + By + Cz + D = 0$$

in the object space.

If the equations (1) be solved for x, y, and z, forms analogous to (1) are obtained; thus

$$x = \frac{a_1'x' + b_1'y' + c_1'z' + d_1'}{a'x' + b'y' + c'z' + d'}, \text{ etc.} \quad . \quad . \quad . \quad (2)$$

From (1) it follows that for

$$ax + by + cz + d = 0: \quad x' = y' = z' = \infty .$$

Similarly from (2) for

$$a'x' + b'y' + c'z' + d' = 0: \quad x = y = z = \infty .$$

The plane $ax + by + cz + d = 0$ is called the *focal plane* $\mathfrak{F}$ *of the object space.* The images P' of its points P lie at infinity. Two rays which originate in a point P of this focal plane correspond to two parallel rays in the image space.

The plane $a'x' + b'y' + c'z' + d' = 0$ is called the *focal plane* $\mathfrak{F}'$ *of the image space.* Parallel rays in the object space correspond to conjugate rays in the image space which intersect in some point of this focal plane $\mathfrak{F}'$.

In case $a = b = c = 0$, equations (1) show that to finite values of x, y, z correspond finite values of x', y', z'; and, inversely, since, when a, b, and c are zero, a', b', c' are also zero, to finite values of x', y', z' correspond finite values of x, y, z. In this case, which is realized in telescopes, there are no focal planes at finite distances.

3. Images Formed by Coaxial Surfaces.—In optical instruments it is often the case that the formation of the image takes place symmetrically with respect to an axis; e.g. this is true if the surfaces of the refracting or reflecting bodies are surfaces of revolution having a common axis, in particular, surfaces of spheres whose centres lie in a straight line.

From symmetry the image P' of a point P must lie in the plane which passes through the point P and the axis of the system, and it is entirely sufficient, for the study of the image formation, if the relations between the object and image in such a meridian plane are known.

If the xy plane of the object space and the $x'y'$ plane of the image space be made to coincide with this meridian plane, and if the axis of symmetry be taken as both the x and the x' axis, then the z and z' coordinates no longer appear in equations (1). They then reduce to

$$x' = \frac{a_1x + b_1y + d_1}{ax + by + d}, \quad y' = \frac{a_2x + b_2y + d_2}{ax + by + d} \quad . \quad . \quad (3)$$

The coordinate axes of the xy and the $x'y'$ systems are then parallel and the x and x' axes lie in the same line. The origin O' for the image space is in general distinct from the origin O for the object space. The positive direction of x will be taken as the direction of the incident light (from left to

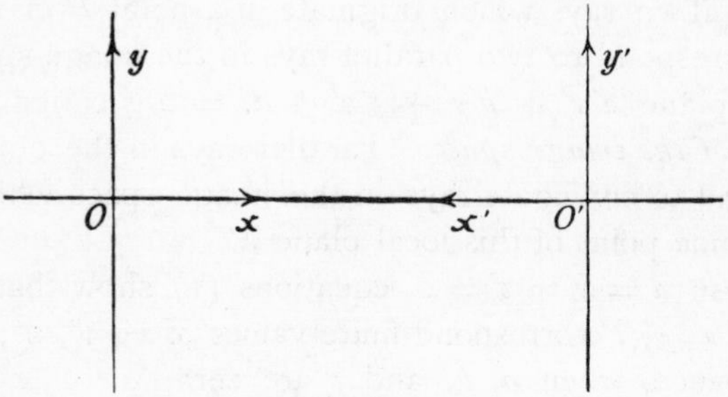

FIG. 6.

right); the positive direction of x', the opposite, i.e. from right to left. The positive direction of y and y' will be taken upward (see Fig. 6).

From symmetry it is evident that x' does not change its value when y changes sign. Therefore in equations (3) $b_1 = b = 0$. It also follows from symmetry that a change in sign of y produces merely a change in sign of y'. Hence $a_2 = d_2 = 0$ and equations (3) reduce to

$$x' = \frac{a_1x + d_1}{ax + d}, \quad y' = \frac{b_2y}{ax + d} \quad . \quad . \quad . \quad . \quad (4)$$

Five constants thus remain, but their ratios alone are sufficient to determine the formation of the image. Hence *there are in general four characteristic constants which determine the formation of images by coaxial surfaces.*

The solution of equations (4) for x and y gives

$$x = \frac{dx' - d_1}{a_1 - ax'}, \quad y = \frac{a_1 d - ad_1}{b_2} \cdot \frac{y'}{a_1 - ax'}. \quad . \quad . \quad . \quad (5)$$

The equation of the focal plane of the object space is $ax + d = 0$, that of the focal plane of the image space $ax' - a_1 = 0$. The intersections F and F' of these planes with the axis of the system are called the *principal foci*.

If the principal focus F of the object space be taken as the origin of x, and likewise the principal focus F' of the image space as the origin of x', then, if x_0, x_0' represent the coordinates measured from the focal planes, ax_0 will replace $ax + d$ and $-ax_0'$, $a_1 - ax'$. Then from equations (4)

$$x_0 x_0' = \frac{ad_1 - a_1 d}{a^2}, \quad \frac{y'}{y} = \frac{b_2}{ax_0}. \quad . \quad . \quad . \quad . \quad (6)$$

Hence only two characteristic constants remain in the equations. The other two were taken up in fixing the positions of the focal planes. For these two complex constants simpler expressions will be introduced by writing (dropping subscripts)

$$xx' = ff', \quad \frac{y'}{y} = \frac{f}{x} = \frac{x'}{f'}. \quad . \quad . \quad . \quad . \quad (7)$$

In this equation x and x' are the distances of the object and the image from the principal focal planes $\mathfrak{F}$ and $\mathfrak{F}'$ respectively.

The ratio $y' : y$ is called the *magnification*. It is 1 for $x = f$, i.e. $x' = f'$. This relation defines two planes $\mathfrak{H}$ and $\mathfrak{H}'$ which are at right angles to the axis of the system. These planes are called the unit planes. Their points of intersection H and H' with the axis of the system are called *unit points*.

The unit planes are characterized by the fact that the distance from the axis of any point P in one unit plane is equal to that of the conjugate point P' in the other unit plane. The two remaining constants f and f' of equation (7) denote, in accordance with the above, the distance of the unit planes $\mathfrak{H}$, $\mathfrak{H}'$ from the focal planes $\mathfrak{F}$, $\mathfrak{F}'$. The constant f is called the *focal length of the object space; f', the focal length of the image space.* The direction of f is positive when the ray falls first upon the focal plane $\mathfrak{F}$, then upon the unit plane $\mathfrak{H}$; for f' the case is the reverse. In Fig. 7 both focal lengths are positive.

The significance of the focal lengths can be made clear in the following way: Parallel rays in the object space must have conjugate rays in the image space which intersect in some point in the focal plane $\mathfrak{F}'$ distant, say, y' from the axis. The value of y' evidently depends on the angle of inclination u of the incident ray with respect to the axis. If $u = 0$, it follows from symmetry that $y' = 0$, i.e. rays parallel to the axis have conjugate rays which intersect in the principal focus F'. But

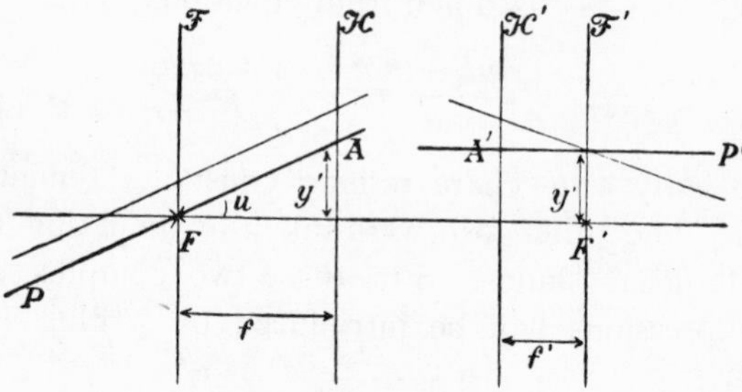

FIG. 7.

if u is not equal to zero, consider a ray PFA which passes through the first principal focus F, and cuts the unit plane $\mathfrak{H}$ in A (Fig. 7). The ray which is conjugate to it, $A'P'$, must evidently be parallel to the axis since the first ray passes through F. Furthermore, from the property of the unit planes, A and A' are equally distant from the axis. Consequently the distance from the axis y' of the image which is formed by a parallel beam incident at an angle u is, as appears at once from Fig. 7,

$$y' = f \cdot \tan u. \quad . \quad . \quad . \quad . \quad . \quad . \quad . \quad (8)$$

Hence the following law: *The focal length of the object space is equal to the ratio of the linear magnitude of an image formed in the focal plane of the image space to the apparent (angular) magnitude of its infinitely distant object.* A similar definition holds of course for the focal length f' of the image space, as is seen by conceiving the incident beam of parallel rays to pass first through the image space and then to come to a focus in the focal plane $\mathfrak{F}$.

If in Fig. 7 $A'P'$ be conceived as the incident ray, so that the functions of the image and object spaces are interchanged, then the following may be given as the definition of the focal length f, which will then mean the focal length of the image space:

The focal length of the image space is equal to the distance between the axis and any ray of the object space which is parallel to the axis divided by the tangent of the inclination of its conjugate ray.

Equation (8) may be obtained directly from (7) by making $\tan u = y : x$ and $\tan u' = y' : x'$. Since x and x' are taken positive in opposite directions and y and y' in the same direction, it follows that u and u' are positive in different directions. *The angle of inclination u of a ray in the object space is positive if the ray goes upward from left to right; the angle of inclination u' of a ray in the image space is positive if the ray goes downward from left to right.*

The magnification depends, as equation (7) shows, upon x, the distance of the object from the principal focus F, and upon f, the focal length. It is, however, independent of y, i.e. the image of a plane object which is perpendicular to the axis of the system is similar to the object. On the other hand the image of a solid object is not similar to the object, as is evident at once from the dependence of the magnification upon x. Furthermore it is easily shown from (7) that the *magnification in depth*, i.e. the ratio of the increment dx' of x' to an increment dx of x, is proportional to the *square* of the lateral magnification.

Let a ray in the object space intersect the unit plane $\mathfrak{H}$ in

A and the axis in P (Fig. 8). Its angle of inclination u with respect to the axis is given by

$$\tan u = \frac{AH}{PH} = \frac{AH}{f - x},$$

if x taken with the proper sign represents the distance of P from F.

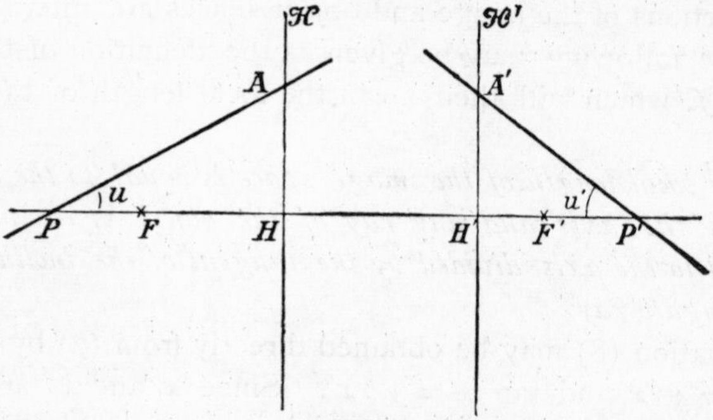

FIG. 8.

The angle of inclination u' of the conjugate ray with respect to the axis is given by

$$\tan u' = \frac{A'H'}{P'H'} = \frac{A'H'}{f' - x'},$$

if x' represent the distance of P' from F', and P' and A' are the points conjugate to P and A. On account of the property of the unit planes $AH = A'H'$; then by combination of the last two equations with (7),

$$\frac{\tan u'}{\tan u} = \frac{f - x}{f' - x'} = -\frac{x}{f'} = -\frac{f}{x'}. \quad . \quad . \quad . \quad (9)$$

The ratio of the tangents of inclination of conjugate rays is called the *convergence ratio* or the *angular magnification*. It is seen from equation (9) that it is independent of u and u'.

The angular magnification $= -1$ for $x = f'$ or $x' = f$. The two conjugate points K and K' thus determined are called the *nodal points* of the system. *They are characterized by the fact that a ray through one nodal point K is conjugate and parallel to a ray through the other nodal point K′.* The position of the nodal points for positive focal lengths f and f' is

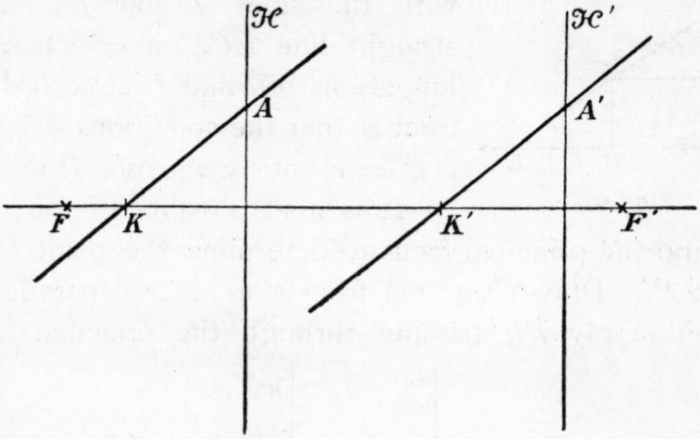

FIG. 9.

shown in Fig. 9. KA and $K'A'$ are two conjugate rays. It follows from the figure that *the distance between the two nodal points is the same as that between the two unit points.* If $f = f'$, the nodal points coincide with the unit points.

Multiplication of the second of equations (7) by (9) gives

$$\frac{y' \tan u'}{y \tan u} = -\frac{f}{f'}. \quad . \quad . \quad . \quad . \quad . \quad (10)$$

If e be the distance of an object P from the unit plane $\mathfrak{H}$, and e' the distance of its image from the unit plane $\mathfrak{H}'$, e and e' being positive if P lies in front of (to the left of) $\mathfrak{H}$ and P' behind (to the right of) $\mathfrak{H}'$, then

$$e = f - x, \quad e' = f' - x'.$$

Hence the first of equations (7) gives

$$\frac{f}{e} + \frac{f'}{e'} = 1. \quad . \quad . \quad . \quad . \quad . \quad . \quad (11)$$

The same equation holds if e and e' are the distances of P and P' from any two conjugate planes which are perpendicular to the axis, and f and f' the distances of the principal foci from these planes. This result may be easily deduced from (7).

4. Construction of Conjugate Points.—A simple graphical interpretation may be given to equation (11). If $ABCD$ (Fig. 10) is a rectangle with the sides f and f', then any straight line ECE' intersects the prolongations of f and f' at such distances from A that the conditions $AE = e$ and $AE' = e'$ satisfy equation (11).

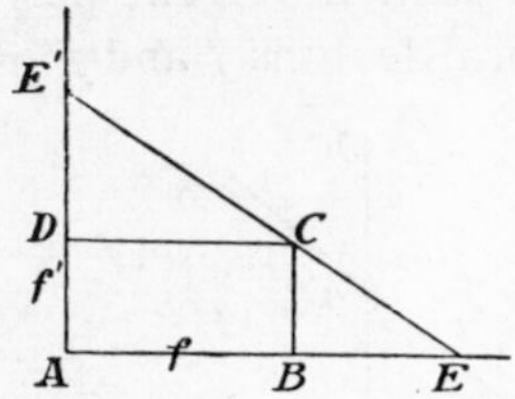

FIG. 10.

It is also possible to use the unit plane and the principal focus to determine the point P' conjugate to P. Draw (Fig. 11) from P a ray PA parallel to the axis and a ray PF passing through the principal focus F.

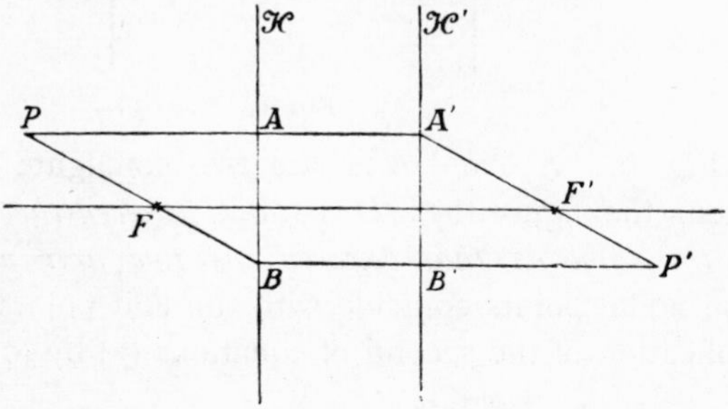

FIG. 11.

$A'F'$ is conjugate to PA, A' being at the same distance from the axis as A; also $P'B'$, parallel to the axis, is conjugate to PFB, B' being at the same distance from the axis as B. The intersection of these two rays is the conjugate point sought. The nodal points may also be conveniently used for this construction.

The construction shown in Fig. 11 cannot be used when P and P' lie upon the axis. Let a ray from P intersect the focal plane $\mathfrak{F}$ at a distance g and the unit plane $\mathfrak{H}$ at a distance h from the axis (Fig. 12). Let the conjugate ray intersect $\mathfrak{H}'$ and $\mathfrak{F}$ at the distances $h'(= h)$ and g'. Then from the figure

$$\frac{g}{h} = \frac{PF}{f + PF} = \frac{-x}{f - x}, \quad \frac{g'}{h} = \frac{P'F'}{f' + P'F'} = \frac{-x'}{f' - x'};$$

and by addition, since from equation (7) $xx' = ff'$,

$$\frac{g + g'}{h} = \frac{2xx' - fx' - f'x}{ff' + xx' - fx' - f'x} = 1, \quad . \quad . \quad (12)$$

P' may then be found by laying off in the focal plane $\mathfrak{F}'$ the distance $g' = h - g$, and in the unit plane $\mathfrak{H}'$ the distance

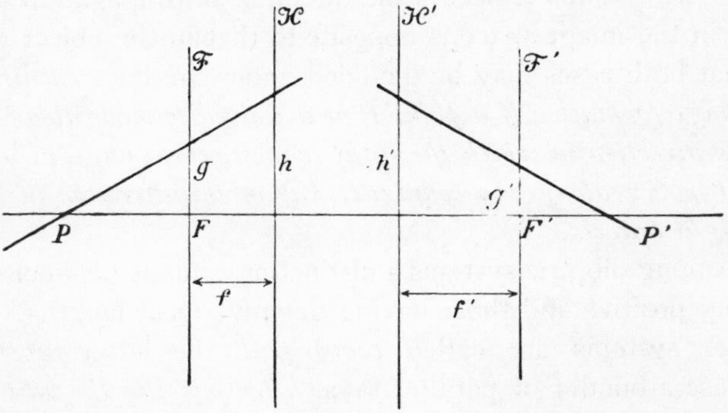

FIG. 12.

$h' = h$, and drawing a straight line through the two points thus determined. g and g' are to be taken negative if they lie below the axis.

5. Classification of the Different Kinds of Optical Systems.—The different kinds of optical systems differ from one another only in the signs of the focal lengths f and f'.

If the two focal lengths have the same sign, the system is concurrent, i.e. if the object moves from left to right (x increases), the image likewise moves from left to right (x' decreases). This follows at once from equation (7) by taking into account the directions in which x and x' are considered positive (see above, p. 18). It will be seen later that this kind of image formation occurs if the image is due to refraction alone or to an even number of reflections or to a combination of the two. Since this kind of image formation is most frequently produced by refraction alone, it is also called *dioptric*.

If the two focal lengths have opposite signs the system is contracurrent, i.e. if the object moves from left to right, the image moves from right to left, as appears from the formula $xx' = ff'$. This case occurs if the image is produced by an odd number of reflections or by a combination of an odd number of such with refractions. This kind of image formation is called *katoptric*. When it occurs the direction of propagation of the light in the image space is opposite to that in the object space, so that both cases may be included under the law: *In all cases of image formation if a point P be conceived to move along a ray in the direction in which the light travels, the image P′ of that point moves along the conjugate ray in the direction in which the light travels.*

Among dioptric systems a distinction is made between those having positive and those having negative focal lengths. The former systems are called *convergent*, the latter *divergent*, because a bundle of parallel rays, *after passing the unit plane* $\mathfrak{H}'$ *of the image space*, is rendered *convergent* by the former, *divergent* by the latter. No distinction between systems on the ground that their foci are real or virtual can be made, for it will be seen later that many divergent systems (e.g. the microscope) have real foci.

By similar definition katoptric systems which have a negative focal length in the image space are called convergent,—for in reflection the direction of propagation of the light is reversed.

There are therefore the four following kinds of optical systems:

Dioptric... { *a*. Convergent: $+f$, $+f'$.
{ *b*. Divergent: $-f$, $-f'$.

Katoptric.. { *a*. Convergent: $+f$, $-f'$.
{ *b*. Divergent: $-f$, $+f'$.

6. Telescopic Systems.—Thus far it has been assumed that the focal planes lie at finite distances. If they lie at infinity the case is that of a telescopic system, and the coefficient a vanishes from equations (4), which then reduce by a suitable choice cf the origin of the x coordinates to

$$x' = \alpha x, \quad y' = \beta y. \quad . \quad . \quad . \quad . \quad . \quad (13)$$

Since $x' = 0$ when $x = 0$, it is evident that any two conjugate points may serve as origins from which x and x' are measured. It follows from equation (13) that the magnification in breadth and depth are constant. The angular magnification is also constant, for, given any two conjugate rays OP and $O'P'$, their intersections with the axis of the system may serve as the origins. If then a point P of the first ray has the coordinates x, y, and its conjugate point P' the coordinates x', y', the tangents of the angles of inclination are

$$\tan u = y : x, \quad \tan u' = y' : x'.$$

Hence by (13)

$$\tan u' : \tan u = \beta : \alpha. \quad . \quad . \quad . \quad . \quad (14)$$

α must be positive for katoptric (contracurrent) systems, negative for dioptric (concurrent) systems. For the latter it is evident from (14) and a consideration of the way in which u and u' are taken positive (see above, p. 21) that for positive β erect images of infinitely distant objects are formed, for negative β, inverted images. There are therefore four different kinds of telescopic systems depending upon the signs of α and β.

Equations (14) and (13) give

$$\frac{y' \tan u'}{y \tan u} = \frac{\beta^2}{\alpha}. \quad . \quad . \quad . \quad . \quad . \quad . \quad (15)$$

A comparison of this equation with (10) (p. 23) shows that for telescopic systems the two focal lengths, though both infinite, have a finite ratio. Thus

$$\frac{f}{f'} = -\frac{\beta^2}{\alpha}. \quad . \quad . \quad . \quad . \quad . \quad . \quad (16)$$

If $f = f'$, as is the case in telescopes and in all instruments in which the index of refraction of the object space is equal to that of the image space (cf. equation (9), Chapter III), then $\alpha = -\beta^2$. Hence from (14)

$$\tan u' : \tan u = -1 : \beta.$$

This convergence ratio (angular magnification) is called in the case of telescopes merely the magnification Γ. From (13)

$$y : y' = -\Gamma, \quad \ldots \ldots \quad (14')$$

i.e. *for telescopes the reciprocal of the lateral magnification is numerically equal to the angular magnification.*

7. Combinations of Systems.—A series of several systems must be equivalent to a single system. Here again attention will be confined to coaxial systems. If f_1 and f_1' are the focal lengths of the first system alone, and f_2 and f_2' those of the second, and f and f' those of the combination, then both the focal lengths and the positions of the principal foci of the combination can be calculated or constructed if the distance $F_1'F_2 = \Delta$ (Fig. 13) is known. This distance will be called for brevity the *separation* of the two systems 1 and 2, and will be considered positive if F_1' lies to the left of F_2, otherwise negative.

A ray S (Fig. 13), which is parallel to the axis and at a

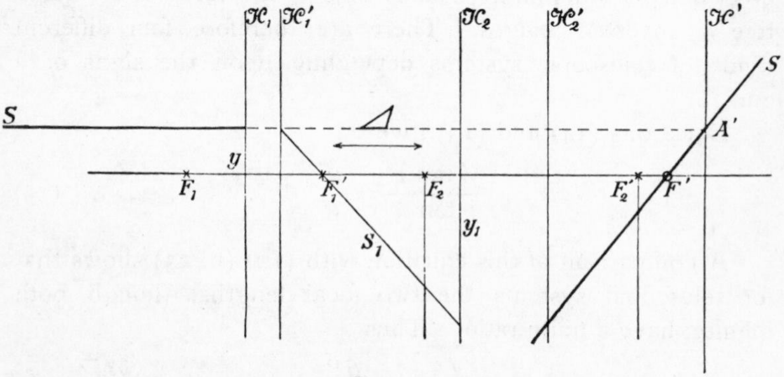

FIG. 13.

distance y from it, will be transformed by system 1 into the ray S_1, which passes through the principal focus F_1' of that system. S_1 will be transformed by system 2 into the ray S'.

The point of intersection of this ray with the axis is the principal focus of the image space of the combination. Its position can be calculated from the fact that F_1' and F' are conjugate points of the second system, i.e. (cf. eq. 7)

$$F_2'F' = \frac{f_2 f_2'}{\Delta}, \quad . \quad . \quad . \quad . \quad . \quad . \quad . \quad (17)$$

in which $F_2'F$ is positive if F' lies to the right of F_2'. F' may be determined graphically from the construction given above on page 25, since the intersection of S_1 and S' with the focal planes F_2 and F_2' are at such distances g and g' from the axis that $g + g' = y_1$.

The intersection A' of S' with S must lie in the unit plane $\mathfrak{H}'$ of the image space of the combination. Thus $\mathfrak{H}'$ is determined, and, in consequence, the focal length f' of the combination, which is the distance from $\mathfrak{H}'$ of the principal focus F' of the combination. From the construction and the figure it follows that f' is negative when Δ is positive.

f' may be determined analytically from the angle of inclination u' of the ray S'. For S_1 the relation holds:

$$\tan u_1 = y : f_1',$$

in which u_1 is to be taken with the opposite sign if S_1 is considered the object ray of the second system. Now by (9),

$$\frac{\tan u'}{\tan u_1} = \frac{\Delta}{f_2'}$$

or since $\tan u_1 = -y : f_1'$,

$$\tan u' = -y \cdot \frac{\Delta}{f_1' f_2'}.$$

Further, since (cf. the law, p. 21) $y : f' = \tan u'$, it follows that

$$f' = -\frac{f_1' f_2'}{\Delta}. \quad . \quad . \quad . \quad . \quad . \quad . \quad (18)$$

A similar consideration of a ray parallel to the axis in the image space and its conjugate ray in the object space gives

$$f = -\frac{f_1 f_2}{\Delta}, \quad . \quad . \quad . \quad . \quad . \quad . \quad (19)$$

and for the distance of the principal focus F of the combination from the principal focus F_1,

$$FF_1 = \frac{f_1 f_1'}{\Delta}, \quad . \quad . \quad . \quad . \quad . \quad . \quad (20)$$

in which FF_1 is positive if F lies to the left of F_1.

Equations (17), (18), (19), and (20) contain the characteristic constants of the combination calculated from those of the systems which unite to form it.

Precisely the same process may be employed when the combination contains more than two systems.

If the separation Δ of the two systems is zero, the focal lengths f and f' are infinitely great, i.e. the system is telescopic. The ratio of the focal lengths, which remains finite, is given by (18) and (19). Thus

$$\frac{f}{f'} = \frac{f_1}{f_1'} \cdot \frac{f_2}{f_2'}. \quad . \quad . \quad . \quad . \quad . \quad (21)$$

From the consideration of an incident ray parallel to the axis the lateral magnification $y' : y$ is seen to be

$$y' : y = \beta = -f_2 : f_1'. \quad . \quad . \quad . \quad . \quad (22)$$

By means of (21), (22), and (16) the constant α, which represents the magnification in depth (*cf.* equation (13)) is found. Thus

$$\frac{x'}{x} = \alpha = -\frac{f_2 f_2'}{f_1 f_1'}. \quad . \quad . \quad . \quad . \quad . \quad (23)$$

Hence by (14) the angular magnification is

$$\tan u' : \tan u = \beta : \alpha = f_1 : f_2'. \quad . \quad . \quad . \quad (24)$$

The above considerations as to the graphical or analytical determination of the constants of a combination must be somewhat modified if the combination contains one or more telescopic systems. The result can, however, be easily obtained by constructing or calculating the path through the successive systems of an incident ray which is parallel to the axis.

CHAPTER III

PHYSICAL CONDITIONS FOR IMAGE FORMATION

ABBE'S geometrical theory of the formation of optical images, which overlooks entirely the question of their physical realization, has been presented in the previous chapter, because the general laws thus obtained must be used for every special case of image formation no matter by what particular physical means the images are produced. The concept of focal points and focal lengths, for instance, is inherent in the concept of an image no matter whether the latter is produced by lenses or by mirrors or by any other means.

In this chapter it will appear that the formation of optical images as described ideally and without limitations in the previous chapter is physically impossible, e.g. the image of an object of finite size cannot be formed when the rays have too great a divergence.

It has already been shown on page 15 that, whatever the divergence of the beam, the image of one point may be produced by reflection or refraction at an aplanatic surface. Images of other points are not produced by widely divergent rays, since the form of the aplanatic surface depends upon the position of the point. For this reason the more detailed treatment of special aplanatic surfaces has no particular physical interest. In what follows only the formation of images by refracting and reflecting spherical surfaces will be treated, since, on account of the ease of manufacture, these alone are used in optical instruments; and since, in any case, for the reason mentioned above, no other forms of reflecting or refracting surfaces furnish ideal optical images.

It will appear that the formation of optical images can be practically accomplished by means of refracting or reflecting spherical surfaces if certain limitations are imposed, namely, limitations either upon the size of the object, or upon the divergence of the rays producing the image.

1. Refraction at a Spherical Surface.—In a medium of index n, let a ray PA fall upon a sphere of a more strongly refractive substance of index n' (Fig. 14). Let the radius of

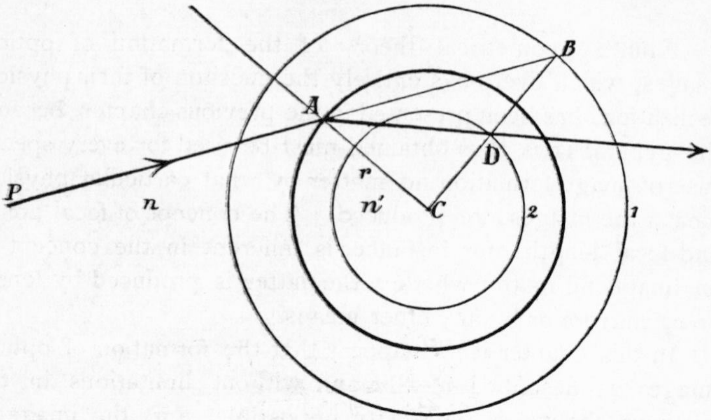

FIG. 14.

the sphere be r, its centre C. In order to find the path of the refracted ray, construct about C two spheres 1 and 2 of radii $r_1 = \frac{n'}{n}r$ and $r_2 = \frac{n}{n'}r$ (method of Weierstrass).

Let PA meet sphere 1 in B; draw BC intersecting sphere 2 in D. Then AD is the refracted ray. This is at once evident from the fact that the triangles ADC and BAC are similar. For $AC : CD = BC : CA = n' : n$. Hence the $\measuredangle DAC = \measuredangle ABC = \phi'$, the angle of refraction, and since $\measuredangle BAC = \phi$, the angle of incidence, it follows that

$$\sin \phi : \sin \phi' = BC : AC = n' : n,$$

which is the law of refraction.

If in this way the paths of different rays from the point P

be constructed, it becomes evident from the figure that these rays will not all intersect in the same point P'. Hence no image is formed by widely divergent rays. Further it appears from the above construction that all rays which intersect the sphere at any point, and whose prolongations pass through B, are refracted to the point D. Inversely all rays which start from D have their virtual intersection in B. *Hence upon every straight line passing through the centre C of a sphere of radius r, there are two points at distances from C of* $r\frac{n'}{n}$ *and* $r\frac{n}{n'}$ *respectively which, for all rays, stand in the relation of object and virtual (not real) image.* These two points are called the *aplanatic points* of the sphere.

If u and u' represent the angles of inclination with respect to the axis BD of two rays which start from the aplanatic points B and D, i.e. if

$$\sphericalangle ABC = u, \quad \sphericalangle ADC = u',$$

then, as was shown above, $\sphericalangle ABC = \sphericalangle DAC = u$. From a consideration of the triangle ADC it follows that

$$\sin u' : \sin u = AC : CD = n' : n. \quad . \quad . \quad . \quad (1)$$

In this case then the ratio of the sines of the angles of inclination of the conjugate rays is independent of u, not, as in equation (9) on page 22, the ratio of the tangents. The difference between the two cases lies in this, that, before, the image of a portion of space was assumed to be formed, while now only the image of a surface formed by widely divergent rays is under consideration. The two concentric spherical surfaces 1 and 2 of Fig. 14 are the loci of all pairs of aplanatic points B and D. To be sure, the relation of these two surfaces is not collinear in the sense in which this term was used above, because the surfaces are not planes. If s and s' represent the areas of two conjugate elements of these surfaces, then, since their ratio must be the same as that of the entire spherical surfaces 1 and 2,

$$s' : s = n^4 : n'^4.$$

Hence equation (1) may be written:

$$\sin^2 u \cdot s \cdot n^2 = \sin^2 u' \cdot s' \cdot n'^2. \quad . \quad . \quad . \quad . \quad (2)$$

It will be seen later that this equation always holds for two surface elements s and s' which have the relation of object and image no matter by what particular arrangement the image is produced.

In order to obtain the image of a portion of space by means of refraction at a spherical surface, the divergence of the rays which form the image must be taken very small. Let PA (Fig. 15) be an incident ray, AP' the refracted ray, and PCP'

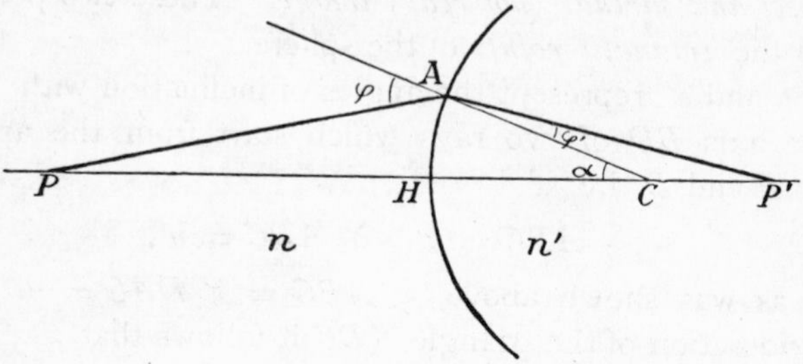

FIG. 15.

the line joining P with the centre of the sphere C. Then from the triangle PAC,

$$\sin \phi : \sin \alpha = PH + r : PA,$$

and from the triangle $P'AC$,

$$\sin \phi' : \sin \alpha = P'H - r : P'A.$$

Hence by division,

$$\frac{\sin \phi}{\sin \phi'} = \frac{n'}{n} = \frac{PH + r}{P'H - r} \cdot \frac{P'A}{PA}. \quad . \quad . \quad . \quad (3)$$

Now assume that A lies infinitely near to H, i.e. that the angle APH is very small, so that PA may be considered equal to PH, and $P'A$ to $P'H$. Also let

$$PH = e, \quad P'H = e'.$$

Then from (3)

$$\frac{e+r}{e'-r}\cdot\frac{e'}{e}=\frac{n'}{n},$$

or

$$\frac{n}{e}+\frac{n'}{e'}=\frac{n'-n}{r}. \quad . \quad . \quad . \quad . \quad . \quad (4)$$

In which r is to be taken positive if the sphere is convex toward the incident light, i.e. if C lies to the right of H. e is positive if P lies to the left of H; e' is positive if P' lies to the right of H. To every e there corresponds a definite e' which is independent of the position of the ray PA, i.e. an image of a portion of space which lies close to the axis PC is formed by rays which lie close to PC.

A comparison of equation (4) with equation (11) on page 23 shows that the focal lengths of the system are

$$f=r\frac{n}{n'-n}, \quad f'=r\frac{n'}{n'-n}. \quad . \quad . \quad . \quad . \quad (5)$$

and that the two unit planes $\mathfrak{H}$ and $\mathfrak{H}'$ coincide and are tangent to the sphere at the point H. Since f and f' have the same sign, it follows, from the criterion on page 25 above, that the system is dioptric or concurrent. If $n' > n$, a convex curvature (positive r) means a convergent system. Real images ($e' > 0$) are formed so long as $e > f$. Such images are also inverted.

Equation (10) on page 23 becomes

$$\frac{y' \tan u'}{y \tan u}=-\frac{n}{n'}. \quad . \quad . \quad . \quad . \quad . \quad . \quad (6)$$

By the former convention the angles of inclination u and u' of conjugate rays are taken positive in different ways. If they are taken positive in the same way the notation $'u$ will be used instead of u', i.e. $'u = -u'$. Hence the last equation may be written:

$$ny \tan u = n'y' \tan {}'u. \quad . \quad . \quad . \quad . \quad . \quad (7)$$

In this equation a quantity which is not changed by refraction appears,—an *optical invariant.* This quantity remains constant when refraction takes place at any number of coaxial spherical surfaces. For such a case let n be the index of refraction of the first medium, n' that of the last; then equation (7) holds. But since in general for every system, from equation (10), page 23,

$$\frac{y' \tan u'}{y \tan u} = \frac{f}{f'}, \quad . \quad . \quad . \quad . \quad . \quad . \quad (8)$$

there results from a combination with (7)

$$f : f' = n : n', \quad . \quad . \quad . \quad . \quad . \quad . \quad (9)$$

i.e. *In the formation of images by a system of coaxial refracting spherical surfaces the ratio of the focal lengths of the system is equal to the ratio of the indices of refraction of the first and last media.* If, for example, these two media are air, as is the case with lenses, mirrors, and most optical instruments, the two focal lengths are equal.

2. Reflection at a Spherical Surface.—Let the radius r be considered positive for a convex, negative for a concave mirror.

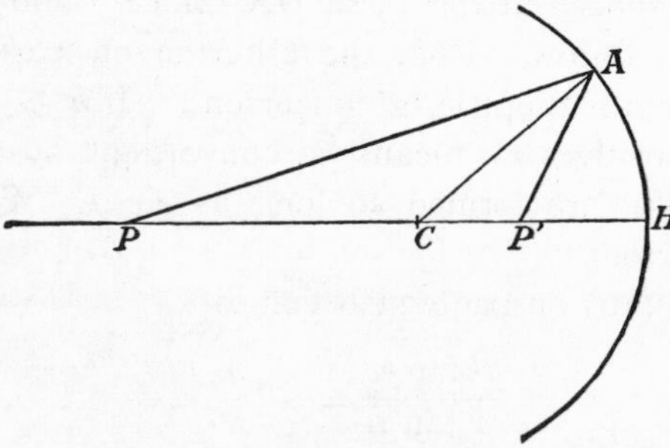

FIG. 16.

By the law of reflection (Fig. 16) $\sphericalangle PAC = \sphericalangle P'AC$. Hence from geometry

$$PA : P'A = PC : P'C. \quad . \quad . \quad . \quad . \quad (10)$$

If the ray PA makes a large angle with the axis PC, then the position of the point of intersection P' of the conjugate ray with the axis varies with the angle. In that case no image of the point P exists. But if the angle APC is so small that the angle itself may be used in place of its sine, then for every point P there exists a definite conjugate point P', i.e. an image is now formed. It is then permissible to set $PA = PH$, $P'A = P'H$, so that (10) becomes

$$PH : P'H = PC : P'C, \quad . \quad . \quad . \quad . \quad (11)$$

or if $PH = e$, $P'H = -e'$, then, since r in the figure is negative,

$$-\frac{1}{e} + \frac{1}{e'} = \frac{2}{r} . \quad . \quad . \quad . \quad . \quad . \quad . \quad (12)$$

A comparison of this with equation (11) on page 23 shows that the focal lengths of the system are

$$f = -\frac{1}{2}r, \quad f' = +\frac{1}{2}r \, ; \quad . \quad . \quad . \quad . \quad (13)$$

that the two unit planes $\mathfrak{H}$ and $\mathfrak{H}'$ coincide with the plane tangent to the sphere at the vertex H; that the two principal foci coincide in the mid-point between C and H; and that the nodal points coincide at the centre C of the sphere. The signs of e and e' are determined by the definition on page 23.

Since f and f' have opposite signs, it follows, from the criterion given on page 25, that the system is katoptric or contracurrent. By the conventions on page 26 a negative r, i.e. a concave mirror, corresponds to a convergent system; on the other hand a convex mirror corresponds to a divergent system.

A comparison of equations (13) and (5) shows that the results here obtained for reflection at a spherical surface may be deduced from the former results for refraction at such a surface by writing $n' : n = -1$. In fact when $n' : n = -1$, the law of refraction passes into the law of reflection. Use may be made of this fact when a combination of several refracting or reflecting surfaces is under consideration. Equation (9) holds for all such cases and shows that a positive ratio $f : f'$

always results from a combination of an even number of reflections from spherical surfaces or from a combination of any number of refractions, i.e. such systems are dioptric or concurrent (cf. page 25).

The relation between image and object may be clearly brought out from Fig. 17, which relates to a concave mirror. The numbers *1*, *2*, *3*, . . . *8* represent points of the object at a constant height above the axis of the system. The numbers *7* and *8* which lie behind the mirror correspond to *virtual objects*, i.e. the incident rays start toward these points, but fall upon the mirror and are reflected before coming to an intersection at them. Real rays are represented in Fig. 17 by

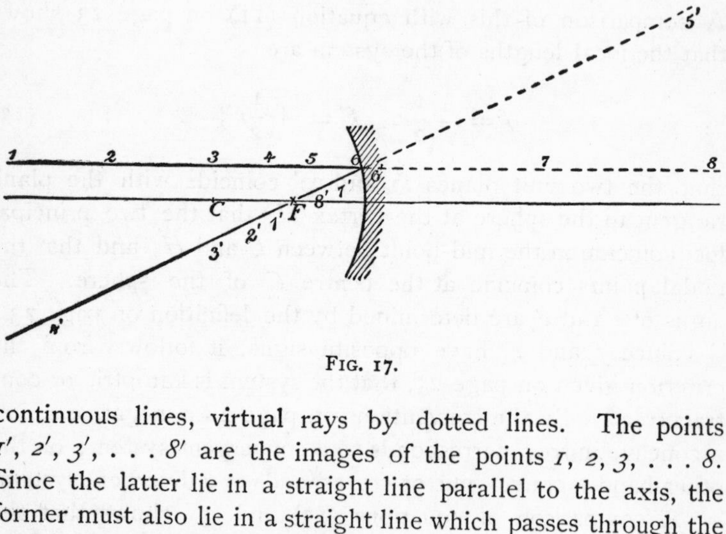

FIG. 17.

continuous lines, virtual rays by dotted lines. The points *1'*, *2'*, *3'*, . . . *8'* are the images of the points *1*, *2*, *3*, . . . *8*. Since the latter lie in a straight line parallel to the axis, the former must also lie in a straight line which passes through the principal focus F and through point *6*, the intersection of the object ray with the mirror, i.e. with the unit plane. The continuous line denotes real images; the dotted line, virtual images. Any image point *2'* may be constructed (cf. page 24) by drawing through the object *2* and the principal focus F a straight line which intersects the mirror, i.e. the unit plane, in some point A_2. If now through A_2 a line be drawn parallel to the axis, this line will intersect the previously constructed image line in the point sought, namely *2′*. From the figure it may be clearly seen that the images of distant objects are real and inverted, those of objects which lie in front of the mirror within the focal length are virtual and erect, and those of virtual objects behind the mirror are real, erect, and lie in front of the mirror.

Fig. 18 shows the relative positions of object and image

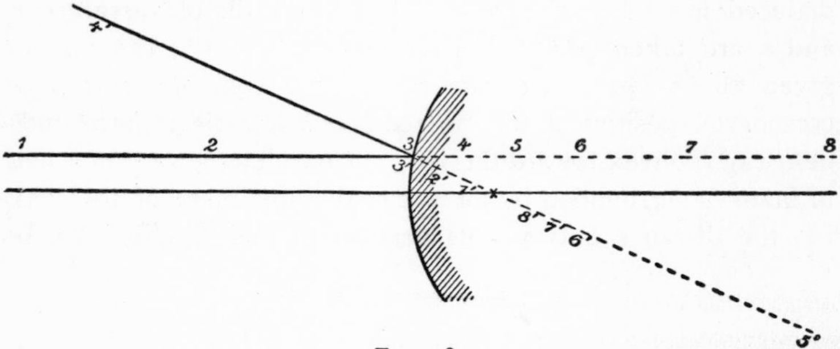

FIG. 18.

for a convex mirror. It is evident that the images of all real objects are virtual, erect, and reduced; that for virtual objects which lie within the focal length behind the mirror the images are real, erect, and enlarged; and that for more distant virtual objects the images are also virtual.

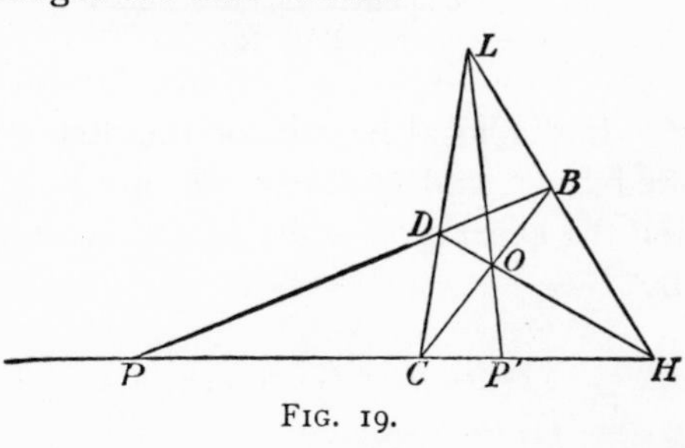

FIG. 19.

Equation (11) asserts that $PCP'H$ are four harmonic points. The image of an object P may, with the aid of a proposition of synthetic geometry, be constructed in the following way:

From any point L (Fig. 19) draw two rays LC and LH, and then draw any other ray PDB. Let O be the intersection of DH with BC: then LO intersects the straight line PH in a point P' which is conjugate to P. For a convex mirror the construction is precisely the same, but the physical meaning of the points C and H is interchanged.

3. Lenses.—The optical characteristics of systems composed of two coaxial spherical surfaces (lenses) can be directly deduced from § 7 of Chapter II. The radii of curvature r_1 and r_2 are taken positive in accordance with the conventions given above (§ 1); i.e. the radius of a spherical surface is considered positive if the surface is convex toward the incident ray (convex toward the left). Consider the case of a lens of index n surrounded by air. Let the thickness of the lens, i.e. the distance between its vertices S_1 and S_2 (Fig. 20), be

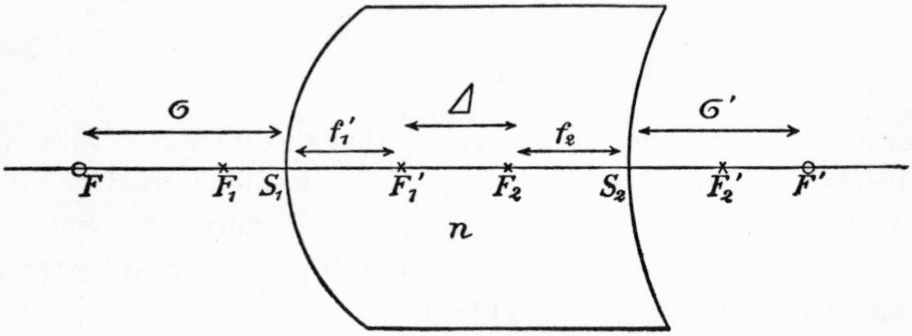

FIG. 20.

denoted by d. If the focal lengths of the first refracting surface are denoted by f_1 and f_1', those of the second surface by f_2 and f_2', then the separation Δ of the two systems (cf. page 28) is given by

$$\Delta = d - f_1' - f_2, \quad . \quad . \quad . \quad . \quad . \quad (14)$$

and, by (5),

$$f_1 = r_1 \frac{1}{n-1}, \quad f_1' = r_1 \frac{n}{n-1}, \quad f_2 = r_2 \frac{n}{1-n}, \quad f_2' = r_2 \frac{1}{1-n}. \quad (15)$$

Hence by equations (19) and (18) of Chapter II (page 29) the focal lengths of the combination are

$$f = f' = \frac{n}{n-1} \cdot \frac{r_1 r_2}{d(n-1) - nr_1 + nr_2}, \quad . \quad . \quad (16)$$

while the positions of the principal foci F and F' of the combination are given by equations (17) and (20) of Chapter II (page 29). By these equations the distance σ of the principal focus F in front of the vertex S_1, and the distance σ' of the principal focus F' behind the vertex S_2 are, since $\sigma = FF_1 + f$, and $\sigma' = F_2'F' + f_2'$,

$$\sigma = \frac{r_1}{n-1} \cdot \frac{d(n-1) + nr_2}{d(n-1) - nr_1 + nr_2}, \quad . \quad . \quad . \quad (17)$$

$$\sigma' = \frac{r_2}{n-1} \cdot \frac{-d(n-1) + nr_1}{d(n-1) - nr_1 + nr_2}. \quad . \quad . \quad . \quad (18)$$

If h represents the distance of the first unit plane $\mathfrak{H}$ in front of the vertex S_1, and h' the distance of the second unit plane $\mathfrak{H}'$ behind the vertex S_2, then $f + h = \sigma$ and $f' + h' = \sigma'$, and, from (16), (17), and (18), it follows that

$$h = \frac{r_1 d}{d(n-1) - nr_1 + nr_2}, \quad . \quad . \quad . \quad . \quad (19)$$

$$h' = \frac{-r_2 d}{d(n-1) - nr_1 + nr_2}. \quad . \quad . \quad . \quad . \quad (20)$$

Also, since the distance p between the two unit planes $\mathfrak{H}$ and $\mathfrak{H}'$ is $p = d + h + h'$, it follows that

$$p = d(n-1)\frac{d - r_1 + r_2}{d(n-1) - nr_1 + nr_2}. \quad . \quad . \quad . \quad (21)$$

Since $f = f'$, the nodal and unit points coincide (cf. page 23).

From these equations it appears that the character of the system is not determined by the radii r_1 and r_2 alone, but that the thickness d of the lens is also an essential element. For example, a double convex lens (r_1 positive, r_2 negative), of not too great thickness d, acts as a convergent system, i.e. possesses a positive focal length; on the other hand it acts as a divergent system when d is very great.

4. Thin Lenses.—In practice it often occurs that the thickness d of the lens is so small that $d(n-1)$ is negligible in comparison with $n(r_1 - r_2)$. Excluding the case in which $r_1 = r_2$, which occurs in concavo-convex lenses of equal radii, equation (16) gives for the focal lengths of the lens

$$\left.\begin{aligned} f = f' &= \frac{-r_1 r_2}{(n-1)(r_1 - r_2)}, \quad \text{or} \\ \frac{1}{f} &= (n-1)\left(\frac{1}{r_1} - \frac{1}{r_2}\right), \end{aligned}\right\} \quad . \quad . \quad . \quad . \quad (22)$$

while equations (19), (20), and (21) show that the unit planes nearly coincide with the nearly coincident tangent planes at the two vertices S_1 and S_2.

More accurately these equations give, when $d(n-1)$ is neglected in comparison to $n(r_1 - r_2)$,

$$h = -\frac{d}{n}\cdot\frac{r_1}{r_1 - r_2}, \quad h' = +\frac{d}{n}\cdot\frac{r_2}{r_1 - r_2}, \quad p = d\frac{n-1}{n}. \quad (23)$$

Thus the distance p between the two unit planes is independent of the radii of the lens. For $n = 1.5$, $p = \frac{1}{3}d$. For both double-convex and double-concave lenses, since h and h' are negative, the unit planes lie inside of the lens. For equal curvature $r_1 = -r_2$, and for $n = 1.5$, $h = h' = -\frac{1}{3}d$, i.e. the distance of the unit planes from the surface is one third the thickness of the lens. When r_1 and r_2 have the same sign the lens is concavo-convex and the unit planes may lie outside of it.

Lenses of positive focal lengths (convergent lenses) include

Double-convex lenses ($r_1 > 0$, $r_2 < 0$),
Plano-convex lenses ($r_1 > 0$, $r_2 = \infty$)
Concavo-convex lenses ($r_1 > 0$, $r_2 > 0$, $r_2 > r_1$),

in short all lenses which are thicker in the middle than at the edges.

Lenses of negative focal length (divergent lenses) include

Double-concave lenses ($r_1 < 0, \ r_2 > 0$),

Plano-concave lenses ($r_1 = \infty, \ r_2 > 0$),

Convexo-concave lenses ($r_1 > 0, \ r_2 > 0, \ r_2 < r_1$),

i.e. all lenses which are thinner in the middle than at the edges.*

The relation between image and object is shown diagrammatically in Figs. 21 and 22, which are to be interpreted in

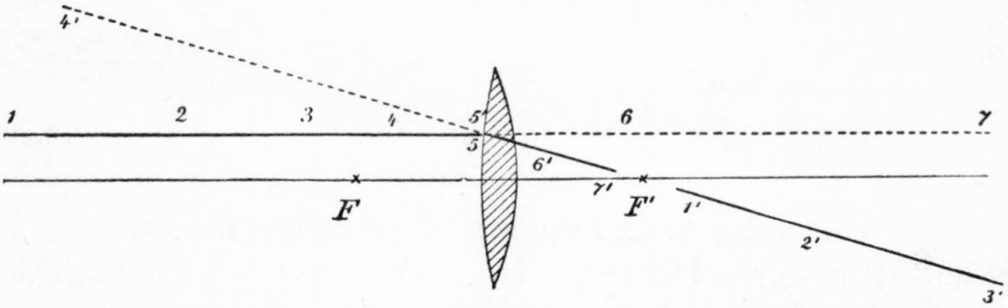

FIG. 21.

the same way as Figs. 17 and 18. From these it appears that whether convergent lenses produce real or virtual images of

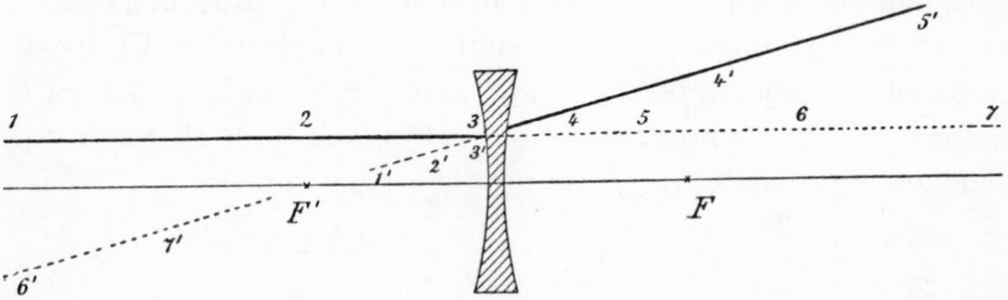

FIG. 22.

real objects depends upon the distance of the object from the lens; but divergent lenses produce only virtual images of real

---

* The terms collective (dioptric), for systems of positive focal length, dispersive, for those of negative focal length, have been chosen on account of this property of lenses. A lens of positive focal length renders an incident beam more convergent, one of negative focal length renders it more divergent. When images are formed by a system of lenses, or, in general, when the unit planes do not coincide, say, with the first refracting surface, the conclusion as to whether the system is convergent or divergent cannot be so immediately drawn. Then recourse must be had to the definition on page 26.

objects. However, divergent lenses produce real, upright, and enlarged images of virtual objects which lie behind the lens and inside of the principal focus.

If two thin lenses of focal lengths f_1 and f_2 are united to form a coaxial system, then the separation Δ (cf. page 40) is $\Delta = -(f_1 + f_2)$. Hence, from equation (19) of Chapter II (page 29), the focal length of the combination is

$$f = \frac{f_1 f_2}{f_1 + f_2} = f',$$

or

$$\frac{1}{f} = \frac{1}{f_1} + \frac{1}{f_2}. \qquad (24)$$

It is customary to call the reciprocal of the focal length of a lens its power. Hence the law: *The power of a combination of thin lenses is equal to the sum of the powers of the separate lenses.*

5. Experimental Determination of Focal Length.—For thin lenses, in which the two unit planes are to be considered as practically coincident, it is sufficient to determine the positions of an object and its image in order to deduce the focal length. For example, equation (11) of Chapter II, page 23, reduces here, since $f = f'$, to

$$\frac{1}{e} + \frac{1}{e'} = \frac{1}{f}. \qquad (25)$$

Since the positions of real images are most conveniently determined by the aid of a screen, concave lenses, which furnish only virtual images of real objects, are often combined with a convex lens of known power so that the combination furnishes a real image. The focal length of the concave lens is then easily obtained from (24) when the focal length of the combination has been experimentally determined. This procedure is not permissible for thick lenses nor for optical systems generally. The positions of the principal foci are readily determined by means of an incident beam of parallel rays. If then the positions of an object and its image with respect to the principal foci be determined, equations (7), on page 19, or (9), on page 22, give at once the focal length $f\ (=f')$.

Upon the definition of the focal length given in Chapter II, page 20 (cf. equation (8)), viz.,

$$f = y' : \tan u, \quad . \quad . \quad . \quad . \quad . \quad . \quad (26)$$

it is easy to base a rigorous method for the determination of focal length. Thus it is only necessary to measure the angular magnitude u of an infinitely distant object, and the linear magnitude y' of its image. This method is particularly convenient to apply to the objectives of telescopes which are mounted upon a graduated circle so that it is at once possible to read off the visual angle u.

If the object of linear magnitude y is not at infinity, but is at a distance e from the unit plane $\mathfrak{H}$, while its image of linear magnitude y' is at a distance e' from the unit plane $\mathfrak{H}'$, then

$$y' : y = -e' : e, \quad . \quad . \quad . \quad . \quad . \quad (27)$$

because, when $f = f'$, the nodes coincide with the unit points, i.e. object and image subtend equal angles at the unit points.

By eliminating e and e' from (25) and (27) it follows that

$$f = \frac{e}{1 - \frac{y}{y'}} = \frac{e'}{1 - \frac{y'}{y}}. \quad . \quad . \quad . \quad . \quad . \quad (28)$$

Now if either e or e' are chosen large, then without appreciable error the one so chosen may be measured from the centre of the optical system (e.g. the lens), at least unless the unit planes are very far from it. Then either of equations (28) may be used for the determination of the focal length f when e or e' and the magnification $y' : y$ have been measured.

The location of the positions of the object or image may be avoided by finding the magnification for two positions of the object which are a measured distance l apart. For, from (7), page 19,

$$\left(\frac{y}{y'}\right)_1 = \frac{x}{f}, \quad \left(\frac{y}{y'}\right)_2 = \frac{x+l}{f},$$

hence

$$f = \frac{l}{\left(\frac{y}{y'}\right)_2 - \left(\frac{y}{y'}\right)_1}, \quad . \quad . \quad . \quad . \quad . \quad (29)$$

in which $(y:y')_1$ denotes the reciprocal of the magnification for the position x of the object, $(y:y')_2$ the reciprocal of the magnification for a position $x+l$ of the object. l is positive if, in passing to its second position, the object has moved the distance l in the direction of the incident light (i.e. from left to right).

Abbe's *focometer*, by means of which the focal lengths of microscope objectives can be determined, is based upon this principle. For the measurement of the size of the image y' a second microscope is used. Such a microscope, or even a simple magnifying-glass, may of course be used for the measurement of a real as well as of a virtual image, so that this method is also applicable to divergent lenses, in short to all cases.*

6. Astigmatic Systems.—In the previous sections it has been shown that elementary beams whose rays have but a small inclination to the axis and which proceed from points either on the axis or in its immediate neighborhood may be brought to a focus by means of coaxial spherical surfaces. In this case all the rays of the beam intersect in a single point of the image space, or, in short, the beam is *homocentric* in the image space. What occurs when one of the limitations imposed above is dropped will now be considered, i.e. an

* A more detailed account of the focometer and of the determination of focal lengths is given by Czapski in Winkelmann, Handbuch der Physik, Optik, pp. 285-296.

elementary beam *having any inclination to the axis* will now be assumed to proceed from a point P.

In this case the beam is, in general, no longer homocentric in the image space. An elementary beam which has started from a luminous point P and has suffered reflections and refractions upon surfaces of any arbitrary form is so constituted that, by the law of Malus (cf. page 12), it must be classed as an orthotomic beam, i.e. it may be conceived as made up of the normals N to a certain elementary surface Σ. These normals, however, do not in general intersect in a point. Nevertheless geometry shows that upon every surface Σ there are two systems of curves which intersect at right angles (the so-called lines of curvature) whose normals, which are also at right angles to the surface Σ, intersect.

If a *plane* elementary beam whose rays in the image space are normal to an element l_1 of a line of curvature be alone considered, it is evident that an image will be formed. The image is located at the centre of curvature of this element l_1, since its normals intersect at that point. Since every element l_1 of a line of curvature is intersected at right angles by some other element l_2 of another line of curvature, a second elementary beam always exists which also produces an image, but the positions of these two images do not coincide, since in general the curvature of l_1 is different from that of l_2.

What sort of an image of an object P will then in general be formed by any elementary beam of *three* dimensions? Let *1*, *2*, *3*, *4* (Fig. 23) represent the four intersections of the four lines of curvature which bound the element $d\Sigma$ of the surface Σ. Let the curves *1–2* and *3–4* be horizontal, *2–3* and *1–4* vertical. Let the normals at the points *1* and *2* intersect at *12*, those at *3* and *4* at *34*. Since the curvature of the line *1–2* differs by an infinitely small amount from that of the line *3–4*, the points of intersection *12* and *34* lie at almost the same distance from the surface Σ. Hence the line p_1 which connects the points *12* and *34* is also nearly perpendicular to the ray S which passes through the middle of $d\Sigma$ and is normal to it.

This ray is called the *principal ray* of that elementary beam which is composed of the normals to $d\Sigma$. From the symmetry of the figure it is also evident that the line p_1 must be parallel to the lines *2–3* and *1–4*, i.e. it is vertical. The normals to any horizontal line of curvature intersect at some point of the line p_1.

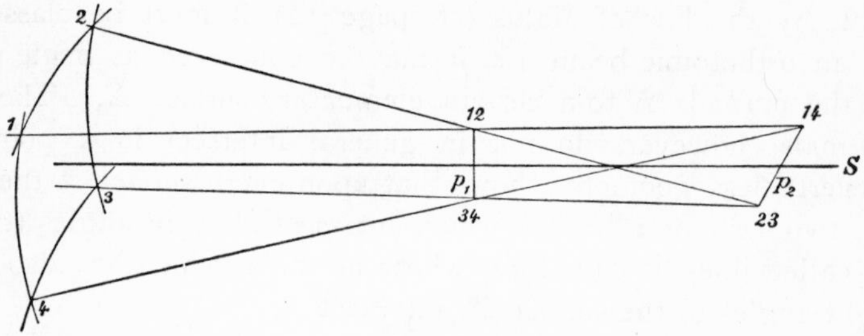

FIG. 23.

Likewise the normals to any vertical line of curvature intersect at some point of the line p_2 which connects *14* and *23*. Also, p_2 must be horizontal and at right angles to S. These two lines p_1 and p_2, which are perpendicular both to one another and to the principal ray, are called the two *focal lines* of the elementary beam. The planes determined by the principal ray S and the two focal lines p_1 and p_2 are called the *focal planes* of the beam. It can then be said that in general the image of a luminous point P, formed by any elementary beam, consists of two focal lines which are at right angles to each other and to the principal ray, and lie a certain distance apart. This distance is called the *astigmatic difference*. Only in special cases, as when the curvatures of the two systems of lines of curvature are the same, does a homocentric crossing of the rays and a true image formation take place. This present more general kind of image formation will be called *astigmatic* in order to distinguish it from that considered above.*

A sharp, recognizable image of a collection of object points P is not formed by an astigmatic system. Only when the

* Stigma means focus, hence an astigmatic beam is one which has no focus.

object is a straight line can a straight-line image be formed; and only then when the line object is so placed that all the focal lines which are the images of all the points P of the line object coincide. Since the image of every point consists of two focal lines p_1 and p_2 which are at right angles to each other, there are also two positions of the line object 90° apart which give rise to a line image. These two images lie at different distances from the surface Σ.

Similarly there are two orientations of a system of parallel straight lines which give rise to an image consisting of parallel straight lines.

If the object is a right-angled cross or a network of lines at right angles, there is one definite orientation for which an image of one line of the cross or of one system of parallel lines of the network is formed in a certain plane $\mathfrak{P}_1$ of the image space; while in another plane $\mathfrak{P}_2$ of the image space an image of the other line of the cross or of the other system of lines of the network is formed. This phenomenon is a good test for astigmatism.

Astigmatic images must in general be formed when the elementary refracting or reflecting surface has two different curvatures. Thus cylindrical lenses, for example, show marked astigmatism. Reflection or refraction at a spherical surface also renders a homocentric elementary beam astigmatic when the incidence is oblique.

In order to enter more fully into the consideration of this case, let the point object P, the centre C of the sphere, and the point A in which the principal ray of the elementary beam emitted by P strikes the spherical surface, lie in the plane of the figure (Fig. 24). Let the line PA be represented by s, the line AP_2 by s_2. Now since

$$\Delta PAP_2 = \Delta PAC + \Delta CAP_2,$$

it follows that

$$ss_2 \sin(\phi - \phi') = sr \sin\phi + s_2 r \sin\phi',$$

in which ϕ and ϕ' denote the angles of incidence and refraction respectively, and r the radius of the sphere. Since now by the law of refraction $\sin\phi = n\sin\phi'$, it follows from the last equation that

$$ss_2(n\cos\phi' - \cos\phi) = srn + s_2 r, \quad \text{or}$$

$$\frac{1}{s} + \frac{n}{s_2} = \frac{n\cos\phi' - \cos\phi}{r} \quad . \quad . \quad (30)$$

It is evident that all rays emitted by P which have the same angle of inclination u with the axis must, after refraction, cross

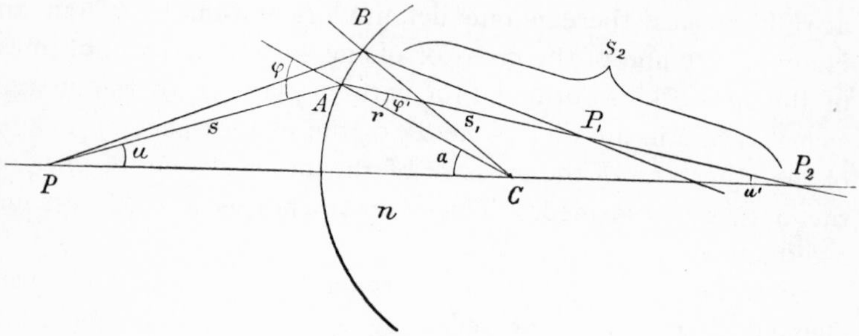

FIG. 24.

the axis at the same point P_2. The beam made up of such rays is called a *sagittal beam*. It has a focal point at P_2.

On the other hand a *meridional beam*, i.e. one whose rays all lie in the plane PAC, has a different focal point P_1. Let PB be a ray infinitely near to PA, and let its angle of inclination to the axis be $u + du$ and its direction after refraction BP_1. Then $\measuredangle BP_1A$ is to be considered as the increment du' of u', and $\measuredangle BCA$ as the increment $d\alpha$ of α. It is at once evident that

$$s \,.\, du = AB\cos\phi, \quad s_1 \,.\, du' = AB \,.\, \cos\phi', \quad r \,.\, d\alpha = AB. \quad (31)$$

But since

$$\phi = \alpha + u, \quad \phi' = \alpha - u',$$

it follows that

$$d\phi = d\alpha + du = AB\left(\frac{1}{r} + \frac{\cos\phi}{s}\right),$$

$$d\phi' = d\alpha - du' = AB\left(\frac{1}{r} - \frac{\cos\phi'}{s_1}\right). \quad . \quad . \quad . \quad . \quad (32)$$

But a differentiation of the equation of refraction $\sin\phi = n\sin\phi'$ gives

$$\cos\phi \, . \, d\phi = n\cos\phi' \, . \, d\phi'.$$

Substituting in this the values of $d\phi$ and $d\phi'$ taken from (32), there results

$$\frac{\cos^2\phi}{s} + \frac{n\cos^2\phi'}{s_1} = \frac{n\cos\phi' - \cos\phi}{r}. \quad . \quad . \quad . \quad (33)$$

From (33) and (30) different values s_1 and s_2 corresponding to the same s are obtained, i.e. P is imaged astigmatically. The astigmatic difference is greater the greater the obliquity of the incident beam, i.e. the greater the value of ϕ. It appears from (30) and (33) that this astigmatic difference vanishes, i.e. $s_1 = s_2 = s'$, only when $s = -ns'$. This condition determines the two aplanatic points of the sphere mentioned on page 33.

The equations for a reflecting spherical surface may be deduced from equations (30) and (33) by substituting in them $n = -1$, i.e. $\phi' = -\phi$ (cf. page 37). Thus for this case *

$$\frac{1}{s} - \frac{1}{s_2} = -2\frac{\cos\phi}{r}, \quad \frac{1}{s} - \frac{1}{s_1} = -\frac{2}{r\cos\phi}. \quad . \quad (34)$$

Or by subtraction,

$$\frac{1}{s_1} - \frac{1}{s_2} = \frac{2}{r}\left(\frac{1}{\cos\phi} - \cos\phi\right),$$

or

$$\frac{s_2 - s_1}{s_1 s_2} = \frac{2}{r}\sin\phi\tan\phi, \quad . \quad . \quad . \quad . \quad . \quad . \quad (35)$$

* For a convex mirror r is positive; for a concave, negative.

an equation which shows clearly how the astigmatism increases with the angle of incidence. This increase is so rapid that the astigmatism caused by the curvature of the earth may, by suitable means, be detected in a beam reflected from the surface of a free liquid such as a mercury horizon. Thus if the reflected image of a distant rectangular network be observed in a telescope of 7.5 m. focal length and $\frac{1}{2}$ m. aperture, the astigmatic difference amounts to $\frac{1}{10}$ mm., i.e. the positions in which the one or the other system of lines of the network is in sharp focus are $\frac{1}{10}$ mm. apart. In the giant telescope of the Lick Observatory in California this astigmatic difference amounts to $\frac{7}{10}$ mm. Thus the phenomena of astigmatism may be made use of in testing the accuracy of the surface of a plane mirror. Instead of using the difference in the positions of the images of the two systems of lines of the network, the angle of incidence being as large as possible, the difference in the sharpness of the images of the two systems may be taken as the criterion. For this purpose a network of dotted lines may be used to advantage.

7. Means of Widening the Limits of Image Formation.—It has been shown above that an image can be formed by refraction or reflection at coaxial spherical surfaces only when the object consists of points lying close to the axis and the inclination to the axis of the rays forming the image is small. If the elementary beam has too large an inclination to the axis, then, as was shown in the last paragraph, no image can be formed unless all the rays of the beam lie in one plane.

Now such arrangements as have been thus far considered for the formation of images would in practice be utterly useless. For not only would the images be extremely faint if they were produced by single elementary beams, but also, as will be shown in the physical theory (cf. Section 1, Chapter IV), single elementary beams can never produce sharp images, but only diffraction patterns.

Hence it is necessary to look about for means of widening the limits hitherto set upon image formation. In the first place the limited sensitiveness of the eye comes to our assistance: we are unable to distinguish two luminous points as separate unless they subtend at the eye an angle of at least one minute. Hence a mathematically exact point image is not necessary, and for this reason alone the beam which produces the image does not need to be elementary in the mathematical sense, i.e. one of infinitely small divergence.

By a certain compromise between the requirements it is possible to attain a still further widening of the limits. Thus it is possible to form an image with a broadly divergent beam if the object is an element upon the axis, or to form an image of an extended object if only beams of small divergence are used. The realization of the first case precludes the possibility of the realization of the second at the same time, and *vice versa*.

That the image of a point upon the axis can be formed by a widely divergent beam has been shown on page 33 in connection with the consideration of aplanatic surfaces. But this result can also be approximately attained by the use of a suitable arrangement of coaxial spherical surfaces. This may be shown from a theoretical consideration of so-called *spherical aberration.* To be sure the images of adjacent points would not in general be formed by beams of wide divergence. In fact the image of a surface element perpendicular to the axis can be formed by beams of wide divergence only if the so-called *sine law* is fulfilled. The objectives of microscopes and telescopes must be so constructed as to satisfy this law.

The problem of forming an image of a large object by a relatively narrow beam must be solved in the construction of the eyepieces of optical instruments and of photographic systems. In the latter the beam may be quite divergent, since, under some circumstances (portrait photography), only fairly sharp images are required. These different problems in image formation will be more carefully considered later. The formation of images in the ideal sense first considered, i.e. when the objects have any size and the beams any divergence, is, to be sure, impossible, if for no other reason, simply because, as will be seen later, the sine law cannot be simultaneously fulfilled for more than one position of the object.

8. Spherical Aberration.—If from a point P on the axis two rays S_1 and S_2 are emitted of which S_1 makes a very small angle with the axis, while S_2 makes a finite angle u, then, after refraction at coaxial spherical surfaces, the image rays S_1' and S_2' in general intersect the axis in two different points P_1' and P_2'. The distance between these two points is known as the *spherical aberration* (longitudinal aberration). In case the angle u which the ray S_2 makes with the axis is not too great, this aberration may be calculated with the aid of a series of ascending powers of u. If, however, u is large, a direct trigonometrical determination of the path of each ray is to be preferred. This calculation will not be given here in detail.* For relatively thin convergent lenses, when the object is distant, the image P_1 formed by rays lying close to the axis is farther from the lens than the image P_2 formed by the more oblique rays. Such a lens, i.e. one for which P_2 lies nearer to the object than P_1, is said to be *undercorrected*. Inversely, a lens for which P_2 is more remote from the object than P_1 is said to be *overcorrected*. Neglecting all terms of the power series in u save the first, which contains u^2 as a factor, there results for this so-called *aberration of the first order*, if the object P is very distant,

$$\epsilon = P_1'P_2' = -\frac{h^2\{2-2n^2+n^3+\sigma(n+2n^2-2n^3)+\sigma^2n^3\}}{f.\,2n(n-1)^2(1-\sigma)^2}, \quad (36)$$

in which h represents the radius of the aperture of the lens, f its focal length, n its index of refraction, and σ the ratio of its radii of curvature, i.e.

$$\sigma = r_1 : r_2. \quad . \quad . \quad . \quad . \quad . \quad . \quad (37)$$

* For a more complete discussion cf. Winkelmann's Handbuch der Physik, Optik, p. 99 sq.; Müller-Pouillet's Lehrbuch d. Physik, 9th Ed. p. 487; or Heath, Geometrical Optics.

The signs of r_1 and r_2 are determined by the conventions adopted on page 40; for example, for a double-convex lens r_1 is positive, r_2 negative. $P_1'P_2'$ is negative for an undercorrected lens, positive for an overcorrected one. Further, the ratio $h:f$ is called the relative aperture of the lens. It appears then from (36) that if σ remains constant, the ratio of the aberration $P_1'P_2'$ to the focal length f is directly proportional to the square of the relative aperture of the lens.

For given values of f and h the aberration reaches a minimum for a particular value σ' of the ratio of the radii.* By (36) this value is

$$\sigma' = -\frac{4+n-2n^2}{n(1+2n)}. \qquad (38)$$

For $n = 1.5$, $\sigma = -1:6$. This condition may be realized either with a double-convex or a double-concave lens. The surface of greater curvature must be turned toward the incident beam. But if the object lies near the principal focus of the lens, the best image is formed if the surface of lesser curvature is turned toward the object; for this case can be deduced from that above considered, i.e. that of a distant object, by simply interchanging the rôles of object and image.† For $n = 2$, (38) gives $\sigma' = +\frac{1}{5}$. This condition is realized in a convexo-concave lens whose convex side is turned toward a distant object P.

The following table shows the magnitude of the longitudinal aberration ϵ for two different indices of refraction and for different values of the ratio σ of the radii. f has been assumed equal to 1 m. and $h:f = \frac{1}{10}$, i.e. $h = 10$ cm. The so-called *lateral aberration* ζ, i.e. the radius of the circle which the rays passing through the edge of a lens form upon

---

* This minimum is never zero. A complete disappearance of the aberration of the first order can only be attained by properly choosing the thickness of the lens as well as the ratio of the radii.

† It follows at once that the form of the lens which gives minimum aberration depends upon the position of the object.

a screen placed at the focal point P_1', is obtained, as appears at once from a construction of the paths of the rays, by multiplication of the longitudinal aberration by the relative aperture $h:f$, i.e. in this case by $\frac{1}{10}$. Thus the lateral aberration determines the radius of the illuminated disc which the outside rays from a luminous point P form upon a screen placed in the plane in which P is sharply imaged by the axial rays.

$$f = 1 \text{ m.} \quad h = 10 \text{ cm.}$$

	$n = 1.5$			$n = 2$		
Form of lens	σ	$-\epsilon$	ζ	σ	$-\epsilon$	ζ
Front face plane	∞	4.5 cm	4.5 mm	∞	2 cm	2 mm
Both sides alike	-1	1.67 "	1.67 "	-1	1 "	1 "
Rear face plane	0	1.17 "	1.17 "	0	0.5 "	0.5 "
Most advantageous form	$-\frac{1}{6}$	1.07 "	1.07 "	$+\frac{1}{5}$	0.44 "	0.44 "

That a plano-convex lens produces less aberration when its convex side is turned toward a distant object than when the sides are reversed seems probable from the fact that in the first case the rays are refracted at both surfaces of the lens, in the second only at one; and it is at least plausible that the distribution of the refraction between two surfaces is unfavorable to aberration. The table further shows that the most favorable form of lens has but little advantage over a suitably placed plano-convex lens. Hence, on account of the greater ease of construction, the latter is generally used.

Finally the table shows that the aberration is very much less if, for a given focal length, the index of refraction is made large. This conclusion also holds when the aberration of a higher order than the first is considered, i.e. when the remaining terms of the power series in u are no longer neglected. Likewise the aberration is appreciably diminished when a single lens is replaced by an equivalent system of several lenses.* By selecting for the compound system lenses of different form, it is possible to cause the aberration not only of the first but also of still higher orders to vanish.† One system can be made to accomplish this for more than one position of the object on the axis, but never for a finite length of the axis.

When the angle of inclination u is large, as in microscope objectives in which u sometimes reaches a value of 90°, the power series in u cannot be used for the determination of the aberration. It is then more practicable to determine the paths of several rays by trigonometrical calculation, and to find by trial the best form and arrangement of lenses. There is, however, a way, depending upon the use of the aplanatic points of a sphere mentioned on page 33, of diminishing the divergence of rays proceeding from near objects without introducing aberration, i.e. it is possible to produce virtual images of any size, which are free from aberration.

Let lens *1* (Fig. 25) be plano-convex, for example, a hemi-

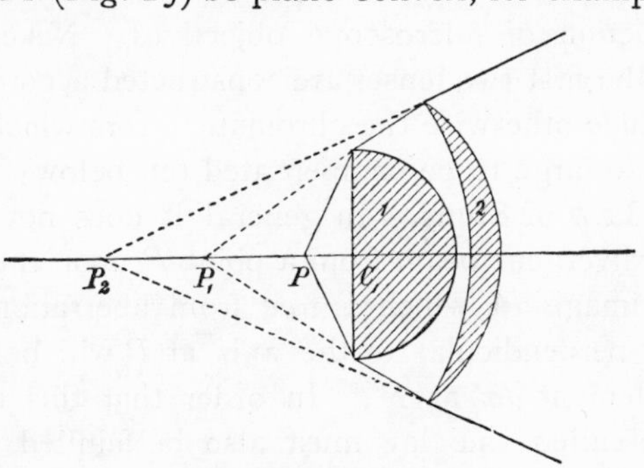

FIG. 25.

spherical lens of radius r_1, and let its plane surface be turned toward the object P. If the medium between P and this lens has the same index n_1 as the lens, then refraction of the rays

* In this case, to be sure, the brightness of the image suffers somewhat on account of the increased loss of light by reflection.

† Thus the aberration of the first order can be corrected by a suitable combination of a convergent and a divergent lens.

proceeding from the object first takes place at the rear surface of the lens; and if the distance of P from the centre of curvature C_1 of the back surface is $r_1 : n_1$, then the emergent rays produce at a distance $n_1 r_1$ from C_1 a virtual image P_1 free from aberration. If now behind lens *1* there be placed a second concavo-convex lens *2* whose front surface has its centre of curvature in P_1 and whose rear surface has such a radius r_2 that P_1 lies in the aplanatic point of this sphere r_2 (the index of lens *2* being n_2), then the rays are refracted only at this rear surface, and indeed in such a way that they form a virtual image P_2 which lies at a distance $n_2 r_2$ from the centre of curvature C_2 of the rear surface of lens *2*, and which again is entirely free from aberration. By addition of a third, fourth, etc., concavo-convex lens it is possible to produce successive virtual images P_3, P_4, etc., lying farther and farther to the left, i.e. it is possible to diminish successively the divergence of the rays without introducing aberration.

This principle, due to Amici, is often actually employed in the construction of microscope objectives. Nevertheless no more than the first two lenses are constructed according to this principle, since otherwise the chromatic errors which are introduced are too large to be compensated (cf. below).

9. The Law of Sines.—In general it does not follow that if a widely divergent beam from a point P upon the axis gives rise to an image P' which is free from aberration, a surface element $d\sigma$ perpendicular to the axis at P will be imaged in a surface element $d\sigma'$ at P'. In order that this may be the case the so-called sine law must also be fulfilled. This law requires that if u and u' are the angles of inclination of any two conjugate rays passing through P and P', $\sin u : \sin u' = \text{const.}$

According to Abbe systems which are free from aberration for two points P and P' on the axis and which fulfil the sine law for these points are called *aplanatic systems.* The points P and P' are called the *aplanatic points* of the system. The aplanatic points of a sphere mentioned on page 33 fulfil these conditions, since by equation (2), page 34, the ratio of the sines is constant. The two foci of a concave mirror whose surface is an ellipsoid of revolution are not aplanatic points although they are free from aberration.

It was shown above (page 22, equation (9), Chapter II) that when the image of an object of any size is formed by a collinear system, $\tan u : \tan u' = \text{const}$. Unless u and u' are very small, this condition is incompatible with the sine law, and, since the latter must always be fulfilled in the formation of the image of a surface element, it follows that *a point-for-point imaging of objects of any size by widely divergent beams is physically impossible.*

Only when u and u' are very small can both conditions be simultaneously fulfilled. In this case, whenever an image P' is formed of P, an image $d\sigma'$ will be formed at P' of the surface element $d\sigma$ at P. But if u is large, even though the spherical aberration be entirely eliminated for points on the axis, unless the sine condition is fulfilled the images of points which lie to one side of the axis become discs of the same order of magnitude as the distances of the points from the axis. According to Abbe this blurring of the images of points lying off the axis is due to the fact that the different zones of a spherically corrected system produce images of a surface element of different linear magnifications.

The mathematical condition for the constancy of this linear magnification is, according to Abbe, the sine law.* The same conclusion was reached in different ways by Clausius † and v. Helmholtz ‡. Their proofs, which rest upon considerations of energy and photometry, will be presented in the third division of the book. Here a simple proof due to Hockin § will be given which depends only on the law that the optical lengths of all rays between two conjugate points must be equal (cf.

---

* Carl's Repert. f. Physik, 1881, 16, p. 303.

† R. Clausius, Mechanische Wärmetheorie, 1887, 3d Ed. 1, p. 315.

‡ v. Helmholtz, Pogg. Ann. Jubelbd. 1874, p. 557.

§ Hockin, Jour. Roy. Microsc. Soc. 1884, (2), 4. p. 337.

page 9).* Let the image of P (Fig. 26) formed by an axial ray PA and a ray PS of inclination u lie at the axial point P'. Also let the image of the infinitely near point P_1 formed by a ray P_1A_1 parallel to the axis, and a ray P_1S_1 parallel to PS, lie at the point P_1'. The ray $F'P_1'$ conjugate to P_1A_1 must evidently pass through the principal focus F' of the image space. If now the optical distance between the points P and P' along the path through A be represented by (PAP'), that

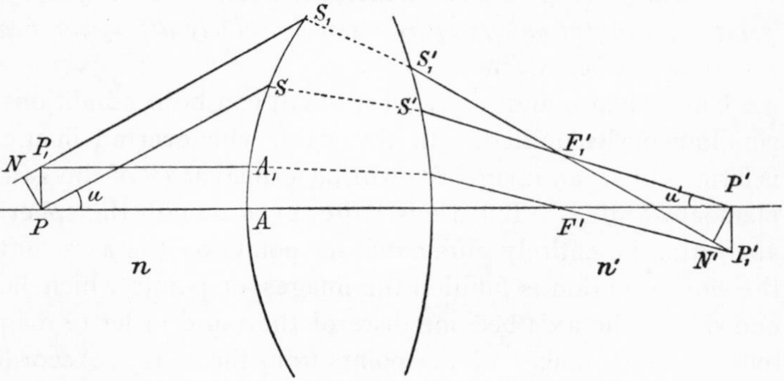

FIG. 26.

along the path through SS' by $(PSS'P')$, and if a similar notation be used for the optical lengths of the rays proceeding from P_1, then the principle of extreme path gives

$$(PAP') = (PSS'P'); \quad (P_1A_1F'P_1') = (P_1S_1S_1'P_1'),$$

and hence

$$(PAP') - (P_1A_1F'P_1') = (PSS'P') - (P_1S_1S_1'P_1'). \quad . \quad (39)$$

Now since F' is conjugate to an infinitely distant object T on the axis, $(TPAF') = (TP_1A_1F')$. But evidently $TP = TP_1$, since PP_1 is perpendicular to the axis. Hence by subtraction

$$(PAF') = (P_1A_1F'). \quad . \quad . \quad . \quad . \quad . \quad (40)$$

* According to Bruns (Abh. d. sachs. Ges. d. Wiss. Bd. 21, p. 325) the sine law can be based upon still more general considerations, namely, upon the law of Malus (cf. p. 12) and the existence of conjugate rays.

Further, since $P'P_1'$ is perpendicular to the axis, it follows that when $P'P_1'$ is small $F'P' = F'P_1'$. Hence by addition

$$(PAF'P') = (P_1A_1F'P_1'),$$

i.e. the left side of equation (39) vanishes. Thus

$$(PSS'P') = (P_1S_1S_1'P_1'). \quad . \quad . \quad . \quad . \quad (41)$$

Now if F_1' is the intersection of the rays $P'S'$ and $P_1'S_1'$, then F_1' is conjugate to an infinitely distant object T_1, the rays from which make an angle u with the axis. Hence if a perpendicular PN be dropped from P upon P_1S_1, an equation similar to (40) is obtained; thus

$$(PSS'F_1') = (NS_1S_1'F_1'). \quad . \quad . \quad . \quad . \quad (42)$$

By subtraction of this equation from (41),

$$(F_1'P') = -(NP_1) + (F_1'P_1'). \quad . \quad . \quad . \quad (43)$$

If now n is the index of the object space, n' that of the image space, then, if the unbracketed letters signify geometrical lengths,

$$(NP_1) = n \cdot NP_1 = n \cdot PP_1 \cdot \sin u. \quad . \quad . \quad . \quad (44)$$

Further, if $P'N'$ be drawn perpendicular to $F_1'P'$, then, since $P'P_1'$ is infinitely small,

$$(F_1'P_1') - (F_1'P') = n' \cdot N'P_1' = n' \cdot P'P_1' \cdot \sin u'. \quad . \quad (45)$$

Equation (43) in connection with (44) and (45) then gives

$$n \cdot PP_1 \cdot \sin u = n' \cdot P'P_1' \cdot \sin u'.$$

If y denote the linear magnitude PP_1 of the object, and y' the linear magnitude $P'P_1'$ of the image, then

$$\frac{\sin u}{\sin u'} = \frac{n'y'}{ny}. \quad . \quad . \quad . \quad . \quad . \quad . \quad (46)$$

Thus it is proved that if the linear magnification is constant the ratio of the sines is constant, and, in addition, the value of this constant is determined. This value agrees with that obtained in equation (2), page 34, for the aplanatic points of a sphere.

The sine law cannot be fulfilled for two different points on the axis. For if P' and P_1' (Fig. 27) are the images of P and P_1, then, by the principle of equal optical lengths,

$$(PAP') = (PSS'P'), \quad (P_1AP_1') = (P_1S_1S_1'P_1'), \quad . \quad (47)$$

in which PS and P_1S_1 are any two parallel rays of inclination u.

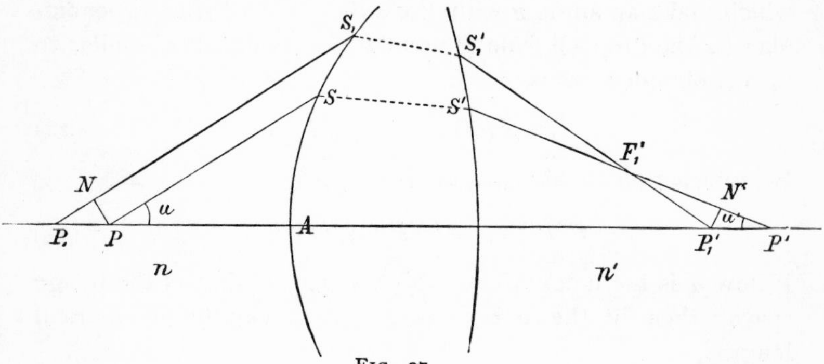

FIG. 27.

Subtraction of the two equations (47) and a process of reasoning exactly like the above gives

$$(P_1'P') - (P_1P) = -(P_1N) + (N'P'),$$

or

$$n \cdot P_1P(1 - \cos u) = n' \cdot P_1'P' \; (1 - \cos u'),$$

i.e.

$$\frac{\sin^2 \frac{1}{2}u}{\sin^2 \frac{1}{2}u'} = \frac{n' \cdot P'P_1'}{n \cdot PP_1} \quad . \quad . \quad . \quad . \quad . \quad . \quad (48)$$

This equation is then the condition for the formation, by a beam of large divergence, of the image of two neighboring points upon the axis, i.e. an image of an element of the axis.

However this condition and the sine law cannot be fulfilled at the same time. *Thus an optical system can be made aplanatic for but one position of the object*

The fulfilment of the sine law is especially important in the case of microscope objectives. Although this was not known from theory when the earlier microscopes were made, it can be experimentally proved, as Abbe has shown, that these old microscope objectives which furnish good images actually satisfy the sine law although they were constructed from purely empirical principles.

10. Images of Large Surfaces by Narrow Beams.—It is necessary in the first place to eliminate astigmatism (cf. page 46). But no law can be deduced theoretically for accomplishing this, at least when the angle of inclination of the rays with respect to the axis is large. Recourse must then be had to practical experience and to trigonometric calculation. It is to be remarked that the astigmatism is dependent not only upon the form of the lenses, but also upon the position of the stop.

Two further requirements, which are indeed not absolutely essential but are nevertheless very desirable, are usually im-

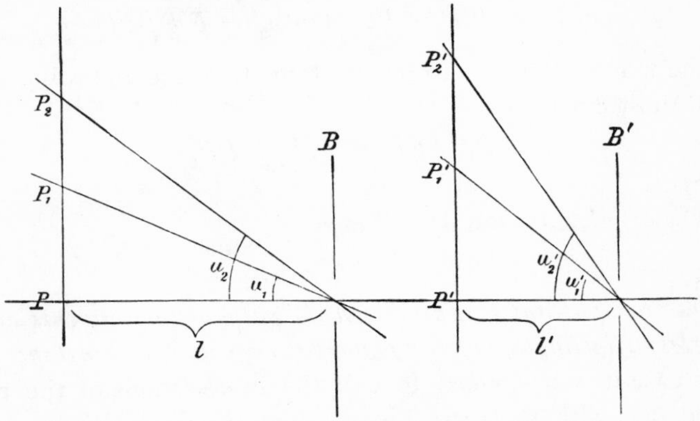

FIG. 28.

posed upon the image. First it must be plane, i.e. free from bulging, and second its separate parts must have the same magnification, i.e. it must be free from distortion. The first requirement is especially important for photographic objectives.

For a complete treatment of the analytical conditions for this requirement cf. Czapski, in Winkelmann's Handbuch der Physik, Optik, page 124.

The analytical condition for freedom from distortion may be readily determined. Let PP_1P_2 (Fig. 28) be an object plane, $P'P_1'P_2'$ the conjugate image plane. The beams from the object are always limited by a stop of definite size which may be either the rim of a lens or some specially introduced diaphragm. This stop determines the position of a virtual aperture B, the so-called *entrance-pupil*, which is so situated that the principal rays of the beams from the objects P_1, P_2, etc., pass through its centre. Likewise the beams in the image space are limited by a similar aperture B', the so-called *exit-pupil*, which is the image of the entrance-pupil.* If l and l' are the distances of the entrance-pupil and the exit-pupil from the object and image planes respectively, then, from the figure,

$$\tan u_1 = PP_1 : l, \qquad \tan u_2 = PP_2 : l,$$
$$\tan u_1' = P'P_1' : l', \quad \tan u_2' = P'P_2' : l'.$$

If the magnification is to be constant, then the following relation must exist:

$$P'P_1' : PP_1 = P'P_2' : PP_2,$$

hence

$$\frac{\tan u_1'}{\tan u_1} = \frac{\tan u_2'}{\tan u_2} = \text{const.} \quad . \quad . \quad . \quad . \quad (49)$$

Hence for constant magnification the ratio of the tangents of the angles of inclination of the principal rays must be constant. In this case it is customary to call the intersections of the principal rays with the axis, i.e. the centres of the pupils, *orthoscopic* points. Hence it may be said that, *if the image is to be free from distortion, the centres of perspective of object and image must be orthoscopic points.* Hence the positions of the pupils are of great importance.

* For further treatment see Chapter IV.

An example taken from photographic optics shows how the condition of orthoscopy may be most simply fulfilled for the case of a projecting lens. Let R (Fig. 29) be a stop on either side of which two similar lens systems *1* and *2* are symmetrically placed. The whole system is then called a symmetrical double objective. Let S and S' represent two conjugate principal rays. The optical image of the stop R with respect to the system *1* is evidently the entrance-pupil, for, since all principal rays must actually pass through the centre of the stop R, the prolongations of the incident principal rays S must pass through the centre of B, the optical image of R with respect to *1*. Likewise B', the optical image of R with respect to *2*, is the exit-pupil. It follows at once from the symmetry of arrangement that u is always equal to u', i.e. the condition of orthoscopy is fulfilled.

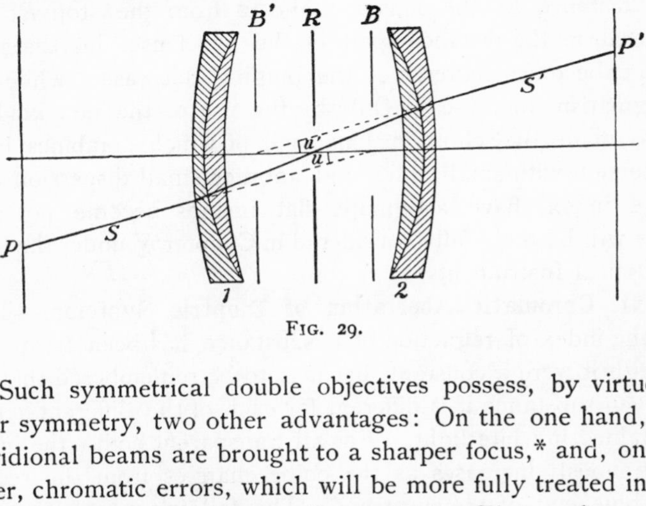

FIG. 29.

Such symmetrical double objectives possess, by virtue of their symmetry, two other advantages: On the one hand, the meridional beams are brought to a sharper focus,* and, on the other, chromatic errors, which will be more fully treated in the next paragraph, are more easily avoided. The result $u = u'$, which means that conjugate principal rays are parallel, is altogether independent of the index of refraction of the system,

* The elimination of the error of coma is here meant. Cf. Müller-Pouillet, Optik, p. 774.

and hence also of the color of the light. If now each of the two systems *1* and *2* is achromatic with respect to the position of the image which it forms of the stop *R*, i.e. if the positions of the entrance- and exit-pupils are independent of the color,* then the principal rays of one color coincide with those of every other color. But this means that the images formed in the image plane are the same size for all colors. To be sure, the position of sharpest focus is, strictly speaking, somewhat different for the different colors, but if a screen be placed in sharp focus for yellow, for instance, then the images of other colors, which lie at the intersections of the principal rays, are only slightly out of focus. If then the principal rays coincide for all colors, the image will be nearly free from chromatic error.

The astigmatism and the bulging of the image depend upon the distance of the lenses *1* and *2* from the stop *R*. In general, as the distance apart of the two lenses increases the image becomes flatter, i.e. the bulging decreases, while the astigmatism increases. Only by the use of the new kinds of glass made by Schott in Jena, one of which combines large dispersion with small index and another small dispersion with large index, have astigmatic flat images become possible. This will be more fully considered in Chapter V under the head of Optical Instruments.

11. Chromatic Aberration of Dioptric Systems.—Thus far the index of refraction of a substance has been treated as though it were a constant, but it is to be remembered that for a given substance it is different for each of the different colors contained in white light. For all transparent bodies the index continuously increases as the color changes from the red to the blue end of the spectrum. The following table contains the indices for three colors and for two different kinds of glass. n_C is the index for the red light corresponding to the Fraun-

* As will be seen later, this achromatizing can be attained with sufficient accuracy; on the other hand it is not possible at the same time to make the sizes of the different images of *R* independent of the color.

hofer line C of the solar spectrum (identical with the red hydrogen line), n_D that for the yellow sodium light, and n_F that for the blue hydrogen line.

Glass.	n_C	n_D	n_F	$\nu = \frac{n_F - n_C}{n_D - 1}$
Calcium-silicate-crown......	1.5153	1.5179	1.5239	0.0166
Ordinary silicate-flint......	1.6143	1.6202	1.6314	0.0276

The last column contains the so-called *dispersive power* ν, of the substance. It is defined by the relation

$$\nu = \frac{n_F - n_C}{n_D - 1}. \quad . \quad . \quad . \quad . \quad . \quad . \quad (50)$$

It is practically immaterial whether n_D or the index for any other color be taken for the denominator, for such a change can never affect the value of ν by more than 2 per cent.

Since now the constants of a lens system depend upon the index, an image of a white object must in general show colors, i.e. the differently colored images of a white object differ from one another in position and size.

In order to make the red and blue images coincide, i.e. in order to make the system *achromatic* for red and blue, it is necessary not only that the focal lengths, but also that the unit planes, be identical for both colors. In many cases a partial correction of the chromatic aberration is sufficient. Thus a system may be achromatized either by making the focal length, and hence the magnification, the same for all colors; or by making the rays of all colors come to a focus in the same plane. In the former case, though the magnification is the same, the images of all colors do not lie in one plane; in the latter, though these images lie in one plane, they differ in size. A system may be achromatized one way or the other according to the purpose for which it is intended, the choice depending upon whether the magnification or the position of the image is most important.

A system which has been achromatized for two colors, e.g. red and blue, is not in general achromatic for all other colors, because the ratio of the dispersions of different substances in different parts of the spectrum is not constant. The chromatic errors which remain because of this and which give rise to the so-called *secondary spectra* are for the most part unimportant for practical purposes. Their influence can be still farther reduced either by choosing refracting bodies for which the lack of proportionality between the dispersions is as small as possible, or by achromatizing for three colors. The chromatic errors which remain after this correction are called spectra of the third order.

The choice of the colors which are to be used in practice in the correction of the chromatic aberration depends upon the use for which the optical instrument is designed. For a system which is to be used for photography, in which the blue rays are most effective, the two colors chosen will be nearer the blue end of the spectrum than in the case of an instrument which is to be used in connection with the human eye, for which the yellow-green light is most effective. In the latter case it is easy to decide experimentally what two colors can be brought together with the best result. Thus two prisms of different kinds of glass are so arranged upon the table of a spectrometer that they furnish an almost achromatic image of the slit; for instance, for a given position of the table of the spectrometer, let them bring together the rays C and F. If now the table be turned, the image of the slit will in general appear colored; but there will be one position in which the image has least color. From this position of the prism it is easy to calculate what two colors emerge from the prism exactly parallel. These, then, are the two colors which can be used with the best effect for achromatizing instruments intended for eye observations.

Even a single thick lens may be achromatized either with reference to the focal length or with reference to the position of the focus. But in practice the cases in which thin lenses are used are more important. When such lenses are combined, the chromatic differences of the unit planes may be neglected without appreciable error, since, in this case, these planes always lie within the lens (cf. page 42). If then the focal lengths be achromatized, the system is almost perfectly achromatic, i.e. both for the position and magnitude of the image.

Now the focal length f_1 of a thin lens whose index for a given color is n_1 is given by the equation (cf. eq. (22), page 42)

$$\frac{1}{f_1} = (n_1 - 1)\left(\frac{1}{r_1} - \frac{1}{r_1'}\right) = (n_1 - 1)k_1, \quad . \quad . \quad (51)$$

in which k_1 is an abbreviation for the difference of the curvatures of the faces of the lens.

Also, by (24) on page 44, the focal length f of a combination of two thin lenses whose separate focal lengths are f_1 and f_2 is given by

$$\frac{1}{f} = \frac{1}{f_1} + \frac{1}{f_2}. \quad . \quad . \quad . \quad . \quad . \quad . \quad (52)$$

For an increment dn_1 of the index n_1 corresponding to a change of color, the increment of the reciprocal of the focal length is, from (51),

$$d\left(\frac{1}{f_1}\right) = dn_1 \cdot k_1 = \frac{dn_1}{n_1 - 1} \cdot \frac{1}{f_1} = \frac{\nu_1}{f_1}, \quad . \quad . \quad (53)$$

in which ν_1 represents the dispersive power of the material of lens 1 between the two colors which are used. If the focal ength f of the combination is to be the same for both colors, it follows from (52) and (53) that

$$d\frac{1}{f} = d\left(\frac{1}{f_1}\right) + d\left(\frac{1}{f_2}\right) = \frac{\nu_1}{f_1} + \frac{\nu_2}{f_2} = 0. \quad . \quad . \quad (54)$$

This equation contains the condition for achromatism. It also shows, since ν_1 and ν_2 always have the same sign no matter what materials are used for 1 and 2, that *the separate focal lengths of a thin double achromatic lens always have opposite signs.*

From (54) and (52) it follows that the expressions for the separate focal lengths are

$$\frac{1}{f_1} = \frac{1}{f}\frac{\nu_2}{\nu_2 - \nu_1}, \quad \frac{1}{f_2} = -\frac{1}{f}\frac{\nu_1}{\nu_2 - \nu_1}. \quad . \quad . \quad (55)$$

Hence in a combination of positive focal length the lens with the smaller dispersive power has the positive, that with the larger dispersive power the negative, focal length.

If f is given and the two kinds of glass have been chosen, then there are four radii of curvature at our disposal to make f_1 and f_2 correspond to (55). Hence two of these still remain arbitrary. If the two lenses are to fit together, r_1' must be equal to r_2. Hence one radius of curvature remains at our disposal. This may be so chosen as to make the spherical aberration as small as possible.

In microscopic objectives achromatic pairs of this kind are very generally used. Each pair consists of a plano-concave lens of flint glass which is cemented to a double-convex lens of crown glass. The plane surface is turned toward the incident light.

Sometimes it is desirable to use two thin lenses at a greater distance apart; then their optical separation is (cf. page 28)

$$\Delta = a - (f_1 + f_2).$$

Hence, from (19) on page 29, the focal length of the combination is given by

$$\frac{1}{f} = \frac{1}{f_1} + \frac{1}{f_2} - \frac{a}{f_1 f_2}. \quad . \quad . \quad . \quad . \quad (56)$$

If the focal length is to be achromatic, then, from (56) and (53),

$$0 = \frac{\nu_1}{f_1} + \frac{\nu_2}{f_2} - \frac{a(\nu_1 + \nu_2)}{f_1 f_2},$$

or

$$a = \frac{\nu_2 f_1 + \nu_1 f_2}{\nu_1 + \nu_2}. \quad . \quad . \quad . \quad . \quad . \quad . \quad . \quad (57)$$

If the two lenses are of the same material ($\nu_1 = \nu_2$), *then, when they are at the distance*

$$a = \frac{f_1 + f_2}{2}, \quad . \quad . \quad . \quad . \quad . \quad . \quad (58)$$

they form a system which is achromatic with respect to the focal length. Since $\nu_1 = \nu_2$, this achromatism holds for all colors.

If it is desired to achromatize the system not only with reference to the focal length, but completely, i.e. in respect to both position and magnification of the image, then it follows from Fig. 30 that

$$\frac{y_1}{y} = -\frac{e_1'}{e_1}, \quad \frac{y'}{y_1} = -\frac{e_2'}{e_2},$$

i.e. the ratio of the magnifications is

$$y' : y = e_1'e_2' : e_1e_2. \quad . \quad . \quad . \quad . \quad . \quad (59)$$

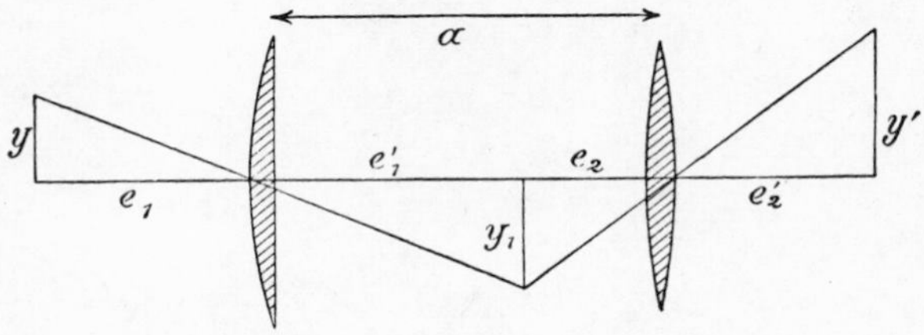

FIG. 30.

If, therefore, the image is to be achromatic both with respect to magnitude and position, then, since e_1 is constant for all colors,

$$d\left(\frac{e_1'e_2'}{e_2}\right) = 0, \quad de_2' = 0. \quad . \quad . \quad . \quad . \quad (60)$$

But since $e_1' + e_2 = a$ (distance between the lenses) is also constant for all colors, it follows that $de_1' = -de_2$, while, from (60), $d(e_1'/e_2) = 0$. Hence $de_1' = 0$ and $de_2 = 0$, i.e. each of the two separate lenses must be for itself achromatized, i.e. must consist of an achromatic pair.

Hence the following general conclusion may be drawn: *A combination which consists of several separated systems is only perfectly achromatic* (i.e. with respect to both position and magnification of the image) *when each system for itself is achromatic.*

When the divergence of the pencils which form the image becomes greater, complete achromatism is not the only condition for a good image even with monochromatic light. The spherical aberration for two colors must also be corrected as far as possible; and, when the image of a surface element is to be formed, the aplanatic condition (the sine law) must be fulfilled for the two colors. Abbe calls systems which are free from secondary spectra and are also aplanatic for several colors "*apochromatic*" systems. Even such systems have a chromatic error with respect to magnification which may, however, be rendered harmless by other means (cf. below under the head Microscopes).

CHAPTER IV

APERTURES AND THE EFFECTS DEPENDING UPON THEM.

1. Entrance- and Exit-pupils.—The beam which passes through an optical system is of course limited either by the dimensions of the lenses or mirrors or by specially introduced diaphragms. Let P be a particular point of the object (Fig. 31); then, of the stops or lens rims which are present, that one which most limits the divergence of the beam is found in the following way: Construct for every stop B the optical image B_1 formed by that part S_1 of the optical system which lies between B and the object P. That one of these images B_1 which subtends the smallest angle at the object point P is evidently the one which limits the divergence of the beam. This image is called the *entrance-pupil* of the whole system. The stop B is itself called the *aperture* or *iris*.* The angle $2U$ which the entrance-pupil subtends at the object, i.e. the angle included between the two limiting rays in a meridian plane, is called the *angular aperture* of the system.

The optical image B_1' which is formed of the entrance-pupil by the entire system is called the *exit-pupil*. This evidently limits the size of the emergent beam which comes to a focus in P', the point conjugate to P. The angle $2U'$ which the exit-pupil subtends at P' is called the *angle of projection* of the system. Since object and image are interchangeable, it follows at once that the exit-pupil B_1' is the image of the

* If the iris lies in front of the front lens of the system, it is identical with the entrance-pupil.

stop B formed by that part S_2 of the optical system which lies between B and the image space. In telescopes the rim of the objective is often the stop, hence the image formed of this rim by the eyepiece is the exit-pupil. The exit-pupil may be seen, whether it be a real or a virtual image, by holding the

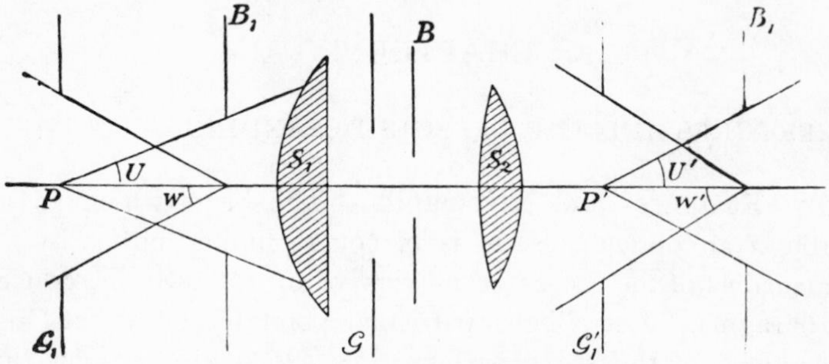

FIG. 31.

instrument at a distance from the eye and looking through it at a bright background.

Under certain circumstances the iris of the eye of the observer can be the stop. The so-called pupil of the eye is merely the image of the iris formed by the lens system of the eye. It is for this reason that the general terms entrance-pupil and iris have been chosen.

As was seen on page 52, the position of the pupils is of importance in the formation of images of extended objects by beams of small divergence. If the image is to be similar to the object, the entrance- and exit-pupils must be orthoscopic points. Furthermore the position of the pupils is essential to the determination of the *principal rays*, i.e. the central rays of the pencils which form the image. If, as will be assumed, the pupils are circles whose centres lie upon the axis of the system, then the rays which proceed from any object point P toward the centre of the entrance-pupil, or from the centre of the exit-pupil toward the image point P', are the principal rays of the object and image pencils respectively. When the paths of the rays in any system are mentioned it will be understood that the paths of the principal rays are meant.

2. **Telecentric Systems.**—Certain positions of the iris can be chosen for which the entrance- or the exit-pupils lie at infinity (in telescopic systems both lie at infinity). To attain this it is only necessary to place the iris behind S_1 at its principal focus or in front of S_2 at its principal focus (Fig. 31). The system is then called *telecentric*,—in the first case, *telecentric on the side of the object;* in the second, *telecentric on the side of the image*. In the former all the principal rays in the object space are parallel to the axis, in the latter all those of the image space. Fig. 32 represents a system which is telecentric on the side of the image. The iris B lies in front of and at the principal focus of the lens S which forms the real image $P_1'P_2'$ of the object P_1 and P_2. The principal rays

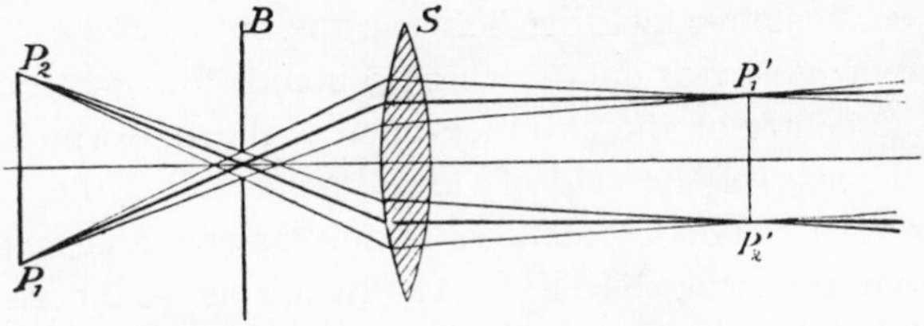

FIG. 32.

from the points P_1 and P_2 are drawn heavier than the limiting rays. This position of the stop is especially advantageous when the image $P_1'P_2'$ is to be measured by any sort of a micrometer. Thus the image $P_1'P_2'$ always has the same size whether it coincides with the plane of the cross-hairs or not. For even with imperfect focussing it is the intersection of the principal rays with the plane of the cross-hairs which determines for the observer the position of the (blurred) image. If then the principal rays of the image space are parallel to the axis, even with improper focussing the image must have the same size as if it lay exactly in the plane of the cross-hairs. But when the principal rays are not parallel in the image space, the apparent size of the image changes rapidly with a change in the position of the image with respect to the plane of the cross-hairs.

If the system be made telecentric on the side of the object, then, for a similar reason, the size of the image is not dependent upon an exact focussing upon the object. This arrangement is therefore advantageous for micrometer microscopes, while the former is to be used for telescopes, in which the distance of the object is always given (infinitely great) and the adjustment must be made with the eyepiece.

3. Field of View.—In addition to the stop B (the iris), the images of which form the entrance- and exit-pupils, there are always present other stops or lens rims which limit the size of the object whose image can be formed, i.e. which limit the *field of view*. That stop which determines the size of the field of view may be found by constructing, as before, for all the stops the optical images which are formed of them by that part S_1 of the entire lens system which lies between the object and each stop. Of these images, that one G_1 which subtends the smallest angle $2w$ at the centre of the entrance-pupil is the one which determines the size of the field of view. $2w$ is called the *angular field of view*. The correctness of this assertion is evident at once from a drawing like Fig. 31. In this figure the iris B, the rims of the lenses S_1 and S_2, and the diaphragm G are all pictured as actual stops. The image of G formed by S_1 is G_1; and since it will be assumed that G_1 subtends at the centre of the entrance-pupil a smaller angle than the rim of S_1 or the image which S_1 forms of the rim of the lens S_2, it is evident that G acts as the field-of-view stop. The optical image G_1' which the entire system $S_1 + S_2$ forms of G_1 bounds the field of view in the image space. The angle $2w'$ which G_1' subtends at the centre of the exit-pupil is called the *angle of the image*.

In Fig. 31 it is assumed that the image G_1 of the field-of-view stop lies in the plane of the object. This case is characterized by the fact that the limits of the field of view are perfectly sharp, for the reason that every object point P can either completely fill the entrance-pupil with rays or else can send none to it because of the presence of the stop G_1. If the plane of the object does not coincide with the image G_1, the boundary of the field of view is not sharp, but is a zone of continuously diminishing brightness. For in this case it is evident that there are object points about the edge of the field whose rays only *partially* fill the entrance-pupil.

In instruments which are intended for eye observation it is of advantage to have the pupil of the eye coincide with the exit-pupil of the instrument, because then the field of view is wholly utilized. For if the pupil of the eye is at some distance from the exit-pupil, it itself acts as the field-of-view stop, and the size of the field is thus sometimes greatly diminished. For this reason the exit-pupil is often called the *eye-ring*, and its centre is called the *position of the eye*.

Thus far the stops have been discussed only with reference to their influence upon the geometrical configuration of the rays, but in addition they have a very large effect upon the brightness of the image. The consideration of this subject is beyond the domain of geometrical optics; nevertheless it will be introduced here, since without it the description of the action of the different optical instruments would be too imperfect.

4. The Fundamental Laws of Photometry.—By the *total quantity of light M* which is emitted by a source Q is meant the quantity which falls from Q upon any *closed* surface S completely surrounding Q. S may have any form whatever, since the assumption, or better the definition, is made that the total quantity of light is neither diminished nor increased by propagation through a perfectly transparent medium.*

It is likewise assumed that the quantity of light remains constant for every cross-section of a tube whose sides are made up of light rays (tube of light).† If Q be assumed

* In what follows perfect transparency of the medium is always assumed.

† The definitions here presented appear as necessary as soon as light quantity is conceived as the energy which passes through a cross-section of a tube in unit time. Such essentially physical concepts will here be avoided in order not to forsake entirely the domain of geometrical optics.

to be a point source, then the light-rays are straight lines radiating from the point Q. A tube of light is then a cone whose vertex lies at Q. By angle of aperture (or solid angle) Ω of the cone is meant the area of the surface which the cone cuts out upon a sphere of radius 1 (1 cm.) described about its apex as centre.

If an elementary cone of small solid angle $d\Omega$ be considered, the quantity of light contained in it is

$$dL = K\ d\Omega. \quad . \quad . \quad . \quad . \quad . \quad . \quad (61)$$

The quantity K is called the *candle-power* of the source Q in the direction of the axis of the cone. It signifies physically that quantity of light which falls from Q upon unit surface at unit distance when this surface is normal to the rays, for in this case $d\Omega = 1$.

The candle-power will in general depend upon the direction of the rays. Hence the expression for the total quantity of light is, by (61),

$$M = \int K \cdot d\Omega, \quad . \quad . \quad . \quad . \quad . \quad (62)$$

in which the integral is to be taken over the entire solid angle about Q. If K were independent of the direction of the rays, it would follow that

$$M = 4\pi K,$$

since the integral of $d\Omega$ taken over the entire solid angle about Q is equal to the surface of the unit sphere described about Q as a centre, i.e. is equal to 4π. The mean candle-power K_m is defined by the equation

$$K_m = \frac{\int K d\Omega}{\int d\Omega} = \frac{M}{4\pi}. \quad . \quad . \quad . \quad . \quad (63)$$

If now the elementary cone $d\Omega$ cuts from an arbitrary surface S an element dS, whose normal makes an angle Θ with the axis of the cone, and whose distance from the apex Q of the cone, i.e. from the source of light, is r, then a simple geometrical consideration gives the relation

$$d\Omega \cdot r^2 = dS \cdot \cos \Theta. \quad . \quad . \quad . \quad . \quad . \quad . \quad (64)$$

Then, by (61), the quantity of light which falls upon dS is

$$dL = K\frac{dS \cdot \cos \Theta}{r^2}. \quad . \quad . \quad . \quad . \quad . \quad (65)$$

The quantity which falls upon unit surface is called the *intensity of illumination B*. From (65) this intensity is

$$B = K\frac{\cos \Theta}{r^2}, \quad . \quad . \quad . \quad . \quad . \quad . \quad . \quad (66)$$

i.e. *the intensity of illumination is inversely proportional to the square of the distance from the point source and directly proportional to the cosine of the angle which the normal to the illuminated surface makes with the direction of the incident rays.*

If the definitions here set up are to be of any practical value, it is necessary that all parts of a screen appear to the eye equally bright when they are illuminated with equal intensities. Experiment shows that this is actually the case. Thus it is found that one candle placed at a distance of 1 m. from a screen produces the same intensity of illumination as four similar candles placed close together at a distance of 2 m.

Hence a simple method is at hand for comparing light intensities. Let two sources Q_1 and Q_2 illuminate a screen from such distances r_1 and r_2 (Θ being the same for both) that the intensity of the two illuminations is the same. Then the candle-powers K_1 and K_2 of the two sources are to each other as the squares of the distances r_1 and r_2. A photometer is used for making such comparisons accurately. The most perfect form of this instrument is that constructed by Lummer and Brodhun.*

* A complete treatment of this instrument, as well as of all the laws of photometry, is given by Brodhun in Winkelmann's Handbuch der Physik, Optik, p. 450 sq.

The most essential part of this instrument is a glass cube which consists of two right-angled prisms *A* and *B* (Fig. 33) whose hypothenuses are polished so as to fit accurately together. After the hypothenuse of prism *A* has been ground upon a concave spherical surface until its polished surface has been reduced to a sharply defined circle, the two prisms are pressed so tightly together that no air-film remains between them. An eye at *O*, which with the help of a lens *w* looks

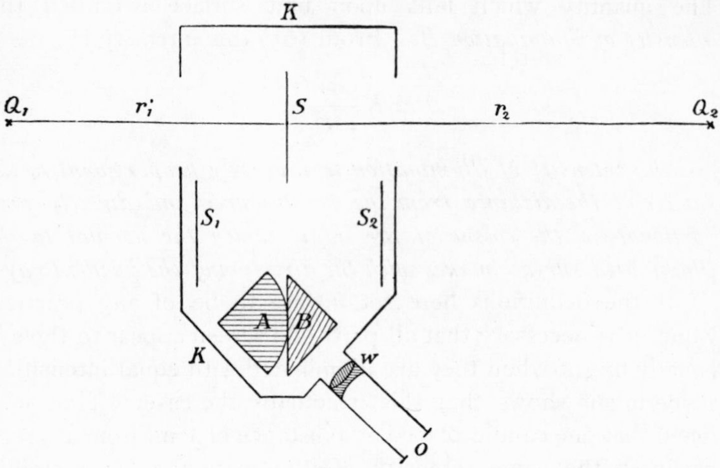

Fig. 33.

perpendicularly upon one of the other surfaces of the prism *B*, receives transmitted and totally reflected light from immediately adjoining portions of the field of view. Between the two sources Q_1 and Q_2 which are to be compared is placed a screen *S* of white plaster of Paris, whose opposite sides are exactly alike. The light diffused by *S* is reflected by the two mirrors S_1 and S_2 to the glass cube *AB*. If the intensities of illumination of the two sides of *S* are exactly equal, the eye at *O* sees the glass cube uniformly illuminated, i.e. the figure which distinguishes the transmitted from the reflected light vanishes. The sources Q_1 and Q_2 are then brought to such distances r_1 and r_2 from the screen *S* that this vanishing of the figure takes place. In order to eliminate any error which might arise from a possible inequality in the two sides of S, it is desirable to make a second measurement with the positions of the two sources Q_1 and Q_2 interchanged. The screen S, together with the mirrors S_1 and S_2 and the glass cube, are rigidly held in place in the case KK.

As unit of candle-power it is customary to use the flame of a standard paraffine candle burning 50 mm. high, or, better still, because reproducible with greater accuracy, the Hefner light. This light was introduced by v. Hefner-Alteneck and is produced by a lamp which burns amyl-acetate and is regulated to give a flame 40 mm. high.

When the candle-power of any source has been measured, the intensity at any distance can be calculated by (66). The unit of intensity is called the candle-meter. It is the intensity of illumination produced by a unit candle upon a screen standing 1 m. distant and at right angles to the direction of the rays. Thus, for example, an intensity of 50 candle-meters, such as is desirable for reading purposes, is the intensity of illumination produced by 50 candles upon a book held at right angles to the rays at a distance of 1 m., or that produced by $12\frac{1}{2}$ candles at a distance of $\frac{1}{2}$ m., or that produced by one candle at a distance of $\frac{1}{7}$ m.

Photometric measurements upon lights of different colors are attended with great difficulties. According to Purkinje the difference in brightness of differently colored surfaces varies with the intensity of the illumination.*

If the source Q must be looked upon as a surface rather than as a point, the amount of light emitted depends not only upon the size of the surface, but also upon the inclination of the rays.

A glowing metal ball appears to the eye uniformly bright. Hence the same quantity of light must be contained in all ele-

* Even when the two sources appear colorless, if they are composed of different colors physiological effects render the measurement uncertain. Cf. A. Tschermak, Arch. f. ges. Physiologie, 70, p. 297, 1898.

mentary cones of equal solid angle $d\omega$ whose vertices lie at the eye and which intersect the sphere. But since these cones cut out upon the metal sphere (cf. eq. (64)) surface elements ds such that

$$ds = \frac{d\omega \cdot r^2}{\cos \vartheta}, \quad . \quad . \quad . \quad . \quad . \quad . \qquad (67)$$

in which ϑ is the angle of inclination of ds with the axis of the cone, it follows that the surface elements which send a given quantity of light to the eye increase in size as the angle included between the normal and the direction of the rays to the eye increases, i.e. the surfaces are proportional to $1 : \cos \theta$.

Hence (cf. eq. (65)) the quantity of light dL which a surface element ds sends to another surface element dS is

$$dL = \frac{i \cdot ds \cdot dS \cdot \cos \vartheta \cdot \cos \Theta}{r^2},* \quad . \quad . \quad . \qquad (68)$$

in which r represents the distance between the surface elements, and θ and Θ represent the inclinations of the normals at ds and dS to the line joining the elements. i is called the *intensity of radiation* of the surface ds. It is the quantity which unit surface radiates to another unit surface at unit distance when both surfaces are at right angles to the line joining them.

The symmetry of eq. (68) with respect to the surface element which sends forth the radiations and that upon which they fall is to be noted. This symmetry can be expressed in the following words: *The quantity of light which a surface element radiating with an intensity i sends to another surface element is the same as the former would receive from the latter if it were radiating with the intensity i.*

Equation (68) can be brought into a simpler form by introducing the solid angle $d\Omega$ which dS subtends at ds. The

* This equation, which is often called the cosine law of radiation, is only approximately correct. Strictly speaking, i always varies with θ, and this variation is different for different substances. The subject will be treated more fully when considering Kirchhoft's law (Part III, Chapter II). This approximate equation will, however, be used here, i.e. i will be regarded as constant.

relation existing bewteen $d\Omega$ and dS is expressed in equation (64). Hence (68) may be written

$$dL = i \cdot ds \cdot \cos \vartheta \cdot d\Omega. \quad . \quad . \quad . \quad . \quad (69)$$

On the other hand it is possible to introduce the solid angle $d\omega$ which ds subtends at dS. A substitution in (68) of its value taken from (67) gives

$$dL = i \cdot dS \cdot \cos \Theta \cdot d\omega. \quad . \quad . \quad . \quad . \quad (70)$$

The relation which the intensity of radiation i bears to the total quantity M which is emitted by ds is easily obtained.

Thus a comparison of equations (61) and (69) shows that the candle-power K of the surface ds in a direction which makes an angle ϑ with its normal has the value

$$K = ids \cos \vartheta. \quad . \quad . \quad . \quad . \quad . \quad (71)$$

Let now the quantity of light be calculated which is contained between two cones whose generating lines make the angles ϑ and $\vartheta + d\vartheta$ respectively with the normal to the surface ds. The volume enclosed between the two cones is a conical shell whose aperture is

$$d\Omega = 2\pi \sin \vartheta \, d\vartheta, \quad . \quad . \quad . \quad . \quad . \quad (72)$$

for it cuts from a sphere of radius 1 a zone whose width is $d\vartheta$ and whose radius is $\sin \vartheta$. Hence, from equations (69) and (72), the quantity of light contained in the shell is

$$dL = 2\pi ids \sin \vartheta \cos \vartheta \, d\vartheta.$$

Hence the quantity contained in a cone of finite size whose generating line makes the angle U with the normal to ds is

$$L = 2\pi ids \int_0^U \sin \vartheta \cos \vartheta \, d\vartheta = \pi ids \sin^2 U. \quad . \quad (73)$$

In order to obtain the total quantity M, U must be set equal to $\frac{\pi}{2}$ and the result multiplied by 2 in case the surface element ds radiates with intensity i on both sides. Hence

$$M = 2\pi ids. \quad . \quad . \quad . \quad . \quad . \quad . \quad (74)$$

5. The Intensity of Radiation and the Intensity of Illumination of Optical Images.—Upon the axis of a coaxial optical system let there be placed perpendicular to the axis a surface element which radiates with intensity i. Let U be the angle between the axis of the system and the limiting rays, i.e. those which proceed from ds to the rim of the entrance-pupil; then, by (73), the quantity of light which enters the system is

$$L = \pi i ds \sin^2 U. \quad . \quad . \quad . \quad . \quad . \quad (75)$$

Thus this quantity increases as U increases, i.e. as the entrance-pupil of the system increases. If now ds' is the optical image of ds, and U' the angle between the axis and the limiting rays of the image, i.e. the rays proceeding from the exit-pupil to the image, then the problem is to determine the intensity of radiation i' of the optical image. According to (73) the quantity of light which radiates from the image would be

$$L' = \pi i' ds' \sin^2 U'. \quad . \quad . \quad . \quad . \quad . \quad (76)$$

Now L' cannot be greater than L, and can be equal to it only when there are no losses by reflection and absorption; for then, by the definitions on page 77, the quantity within a tube of light remains constant. If this most favorable case be assumed, it follows from (75) and (76) that

$$i' = i \frac{ds \sin^2 U}{ds' \sin^2 U'}. \quad . \quad . \quad . \quad . \quad . \quad (77)$$

But if ds' is the optical image of ds, it follows from the sine law (equation (46), page 61) that

$$\frac{ds \sin^2 U}{ds' \sin^2 U'} = \frac{n'^2}{n^2}, \quad . \quad . \quad . \quad . \quad . \quad (78)$$

in which n is the index of the object space, and n' that of the image space. Hence, from (77),

$$i' = i \frac{n'^2}{n^2}. \quad . \quad . \quad . \quad . \quad . \quad (79)$$

Hence if the indices of the object and image spaces are the same, the intensity of radiation of the image is at best equal to the intensity of radiation of the object.

For example, the intensity of radiation of the real image of the sun produced by a burning-glass cannot be greater than that of the sun. Nevertheless the intensity of illumination of a screen placed in the plane of the image is greatly intensified by the presence of the glass, and is proportional directly to the area of the lens and inversely to its focal length. This intensity of illumination B is obtained by dividing the value of L' as given in (76) by ds'. If $n = n'$, it follows that $B = \pi i' \sin^2 U'$. The fact that an optical system produces an increase in the intensity of illumination is made obvious by the consideration that all the tubes of light which pass through the image ds' must also pass through the exit-pupil. Hence the total quantity of light which is brought together in the image ds' is, by the proposition of page 82, the same as though the whole exit-pupil radiated with the intensity i of the sun upon the element ds'. The effect of the lens is then exactly the same as though the element ds' were brought without a lens so near to the sun that the angle subtended by the sun at ds' became the same as the angle subtended by the exit-pupil of the lens at its focus.

The same consideration holds for every sort of optical instrument. Therefore *no arrangement for concentrating light can accomplish more than to produce, with the help of a given source of light which is small or distant, an effect which would be produced without the arrangement by a larger or nearer source of equal intensity of radiation.*

In case n and n' have different values, an increase of the intensity of radiation of the image can be produced provided $n < n'$. For example, this is done in the immersion systems used with microscopes in which the light from a source Q in a medium of index unity is brought together by a condenser in front of the objective in a medium (immersion fluid) of greater index n'. The quantity of light which therefore enters the microscope is proportional to $n^2 \sin^2 U$, in which U represents the angle between the limiting rays which enter the entrance-pupil. The product

$$n \sin U = a \tag{80}$$

is called by Abbe the *numerical aperture* of the instrument. Then the quantity of light received is proportional to the square of the numerical aperture. The intensity of radiation in the image, which again lies in air, is, of course, never more than the intensity of the source Q.

6. Subjective Brightness of Optical Images.—It is necessary to distinguish between the (objective) *intensity of illumination* which is produced at a point O by a luminous surface s and the (subjective) *brightness* of such a surface as it appears to an observer. The sensation of light is produced by the action of radiation upon little elements of the retina which are sensitive to light. If the object is a luminous surface s, then the image upon the retina covers a surface s' within which these sensitive elements are excited. The *brightness* of the surface s is now defined as the quantity of light which falls upon unit surface of the retina, i.e. it is the intensity of illumination of the retina.

If no optical system is introduced between the source of light and the eye, then the eye itself is to be looked upon as an optical system to which the former considerations are applicable. The illumination upon the retina may be obtained from equations (76) and (79); but in this case it is to be remembered that n, the index of the object space, and n', that of the image space, have in general different values. Hence the brightness H_0 which is produced when no optical instruments are present and when the source lies in a medium of index $n = 1$ is called the *natural brightness* and has the value

$$H_0 = \pi i n'^2 \sin^2 W_0' \quad . \quad . \quad . \quad . \quad . \quad . \tag{81}$$

i here is the intensity of radiation of the source (losses due to the passage of the rays through the eye are neglected). W_0' is the angle included between the axis of the eye and lines drawn to the middle point of the image upon the retina from the rim of the pupil. Therefore $2W_0'$ is the *angle of projection in the eye* (cf. page 73). If the size of the pupil remains constant, W_0' is also constant. *Hence the brightness H_0 depends only upon the intensity of radiation i of the source and is altogether independent of the distance of the source from the eye.*

This result actually corresponds within certain limits with physiological experience. To be sure when the source of light is very close to the eye, so that the image upon the retina is very much larger, a blinding sensation which may be interpreted as an increase in brightness is experienced. As the pupil is diminished in size W_0' becomes smaller and hence H_0 decreases.

If now an optical instrument is introduced before the eye, the two together may be looked upon as a single system for which the former deductions hold. Let the eye be made to coincide with the exit-pupil, a position which (cf. page 77) gives the largest possible field of view. Then two cases are to be distinguished:

1. The exit-pupil is equal to or greater than the pupil of the eye. Then the angle of projection $2W'$ of the image in the eye is determined by the pupil of the eye, i.e. $W' = W_0'$. The brightness is given by equation (81), in which i is the intensity of radiation of the source (all losses in the instrument and in the eye are neglected and the source is assumed to be in a medium of index $n = 1$). If this index differs from unity, H must be divided by n^2. This case is, however, never realized in actual instruments. The source always lies in air or (as the sun) in space. This is also the case with the immersion systems used in microscopes, for the source is not the object immersed in the fluid, as this is merely illuminated from without. The real source is the bright sky, the sun, a lamp, etc. In what follows it will always be assumed that the source lies in a medium of index $n = 1$. Hence the result: Provided no losses take place by reflection and absorption in the instrument, *the brightness of the optical image produced by an instrument is equal to the natural brightness of the source.*

2. *The exit-pupil is smaller than the pupil of the eye.* Then the brightness is given by an equation analogous to (81), namely,

$$H = \pi i n'^2 \sin^2 W', \quad . \quad . \quad . \quad . \quad . \quad (82)$$

in which i is the intensity of radiation of the source, and $2W'$ is the angle of projection of the image in the eye. But now $W' < W_0'$, i.e. *the brightness of the image is less than the natural brightness of the source.* The ratio of these two brightnesses as obtained from (81) and (82) is

$$H : H_0 = \sin^2 W' : \sin^2 W_0' . \quad . \quad . \quad . \quad . \quad (83)$$

Since now W_0' is a small angle and W' even smaller (in the human eye W_0' is about 5°), the *sine* may be replaced by the *tangent*, so that the right-hand side of (83), i.e. *the ratio of the brightness of the image to the natural brightness of the source, is equal to the ratio of the size of the exit-pupil of the instrument to the size of the pupil of the eye* (or, better, to the size of the image of the iris formed by the crystalline lens and the front chamber of the eye). In short: *In the case of extended objects an optical instrument can do no more than increase the visual angle under which the object appears without increasing its brightness.*

This result could have been obtained as follows: By the principle on page 85, the intensity of radiation of the image is equal to that of the source (when $n = n' = 1$ and reflection and absorption losses are neglected). An optical instrument then produces merely an apparent change of position of the source. But since, by the principle of page 87, the brightness of the source is entirely independent of its position provided the whole pupil of the eye is filled with rays, it follows that the brightness of the image is equal to the natural brightness of the source. But if the exit-pupil is smaller than the pupil of the eye, the latter is not entirely filled with rays, i.e. the brightness of the image must be smaller than the natural brightness. The ratio $H : H_0$ comes out the same in this case as before, since the inclination to the axis of the image rays is small when the image lies at a sufficient distance from the eye to be clearly visible.

If the image ds' of a luminous surface ds lies at the distance δ from the exit-pupil (i.e. from the eye, since the latter is to be placed at the position of the exit-pupil), then $\delta \tan U'$ is the radius of the exit-pupil, $2U'$ being the angle of projection of the image (in air). Hence, replacing $\sin U'$ by $\tan U'$, the ratio of the brightness H of the image to the natural brightness H_0 of the source when the radius of the exit-pupil is smaller than the radius p of the pupil of the eye is

$$\frac{H}{H_0} = \frac{\delta^2 \sin^2 U'}{p^2}.$$

Now by the law of sines (equation (78)), the index n' of the image space being equal to unity,

$$\frac{H}{H_0} = \frac{\delta^2 n^2 \sin^2 U}{p^2} \cdot \frac{ds}{ds'}, \quad . \quad . \quad . \quad . \quad (84)$$

in which ds is the element conjugate to ds' and whose limiting rays make an angle U with the axis of the instrument. Let n be the index of refraction of the medium about ds, then (cf. (80)) $n \sin U = a$ is equal to the numerical aperture of the system. $ds' : ds$ is the square of the lateral magnification of the instrument. Representing this by V, (84) becomes

$$\frac{H}{H_0} = \frac{\delta^2 a^2}{p^2 V^2}. \quad . \quad . \quad . \quad . \quad . \quad (85)$$

This equation holds only when $H < H_0$. It shows clearly the influence of the numerical aperture upon the brightness of the image, and is of great importance in the theory of the microscope.

The magnification which is produced by an optical instrument when its exit-pupil is equal to the pupil of the eye, i.e.

when the image has the natural brightness of the source, is called the *normal magnification*. If the radius p of the pupil be taken as 2 mm. and the distance δ of the image from the eye as 25 cm. (distance of most distinct vision), then, from (85), the normal magnifications V_n corresponding to different numerical apertures are

$$\begin{aligned} &\text{when } a = 0.5 \qquad V_n = 62; \\ &\text{"} \quad a = 1.0 \qquad V_n = 125; \\ &\text{"} \quad a = 1.5 \qquad V_n = 187. \end{aligned}$$

When the magnification V is equal to $2V_n$ the brightness H is a quarter of the natural brightness H_0. $2V_n$ may be looked upon as about the limit to which the magnification can be carried without diminishing the clearness of the image. For $a = 1.5$ this would be, then, a magnification of about 380. For a magnification of 1000 and $a = 1.5$ the brightness H is $\frac{1}{27}$ of the natural brightness H_0.

For telescopes equation (85) is somewhat modified in practice. Thus if h is the radius of the objective of the telescope, then, by equation (14′) on page 28, the radius of its exit-pupil is equal to $h : \Gamma$, in which Γ is the angular magnification of the telescope. Hence the ratio of the area of the exit-pupil to that of the pupil of the eye is (cf. p. 87, eq. (83 et seq.)

$$\frac{H}{H_0} = \frac{h^2}{p^2\Gamma^2}. \quad . \quad . \quad . \quad . \quad . \quad . \qquad (86)$$

For a normal magnification Γ_n the radius of the objective of a telescope must be $p \cdot \Gamma_n$, i.e. it must be 2, 4, 6, 8, etc., mm. if the normal magnification has the value 1, 2, 3, 4, etc., and p is taken as 2 mm. Thus, for example, if the normal magnification is 100, the radius of the objective must be 20 cm.

7. The Brightness of Point Sources.—The laws for the brilliancy of the optical images of surfaces do not hold for the images of point sources such as the fixed stars. On account of diffraction at the edges of the pupil, the size of the image upon the retina depends only on the diameter of the pupil, being altogether independent of the magnification. (Cf. Chapter IV, Section I of Physical Optics.) As long as the visual angle of an object does not exceed one minute the source is to be regarded as a point.

The brightness of a point source P is determined by the quantity of light which reaches the eye from P. The natural brightness H_0 is therefore proportional directly to the size of the pupil and inversely to the square of the distance of P from the eye. By the help of an optical instrument all the light from P which passes through the entrance-pupil of the instrument is brought to the eye provided the exit-pupil is smaller than the pupil of the eye, i.e. provided the normal magnification of the instrument is not exceeded. If the rim of the objective is the entrance-pupil of the instrument, then the brightness of a distant source such as a star exceeds the natural brightness in the ratio of the size of the objective to the size of the pupil of the eye.*

But if the natural magnification of the telescope has not yet been reached, i.e. if its exit-pupil is larger than the pupil of the eye, then in the use of the instrument the latter constitutes the exit-pupil and its image formed by the telescope the entrance-pupil. According to equation (14′) on page 28 this entrance-pupil is Γ^2 times as great as the pupil of the eye, Γ representing the magnification of the telescope. Hence the brightness of the star is Γ^2 times the natural brightness.

Since, then, the brightness of stars may be increased by the use of a telescope, while the brightness of the background is not increased but even diminished (in case the normal magnification is exceeded), stars stand out from the background more clearly when seen through a telescope than otherwise and, with a large instrument, may even be seen by day.

8. The Effect of the Aperture upon the Resolving Power of Optical Instruments.—Thus far the effect of the aperture upon the geometrical construction of the rays and the bright-

* The length of the telescope must be negligible in comparison with the distance of the source.

ness of the image has been treated. But the aperture also determines the *resolving power* of the instrument, i.e. its ability to optically separate two objects which the unaided eye is unable to distinguish as separate. It has already been remarked on page 52 that, on account of diffraction phenomena, very narrow pencils produce poor images. These diffraction phenomena also set a limit to the resolving power of optical instruments, and it is at once clear that this limit can be pushed farther and farther on by increasing the width of the beam which forms the image, i.e. by increasing the aperture of the instrument. The development of the numerical relations which exist in this case will be reserved for the chapter on the diffraction of light. But here it may simply be remarked that two objects a distance d apart may be separated by a microscope if

$$d \geqq \frac{\lambda}{2a}, \qquad (87)$$

in which λ is the wave-length (to be defined later) of light in air, and a the numerical aperture of the microscope. A telescope can separate two objects if the visual angle ϕ which they subtend is

$$\phi \geqq 0.6\frac{\lambda}{h}, \qquad (88)$$

in which h is the radius of the aperture of the telescope.

CHAPTER V

OPTICAL INSTRUMENTS*

1. Photographic Systems.—In landscape photography the optical system must throw a real image of a very extended object upon the sensitive plate. The divergence of the pencils which form the image is relatively small. The principal sources of error which are here to be avoided have already been mentioned on page 63. Attention was there called to the advantage of the symmetrical double objective as well as to the influence of suitably placed stops upon the formation of a correct image. But the position of the stop has a further influence upon the flatness of the image.

For the case of a combination of two thin lenses of focal length f_1 and f_2 and of indices n_1 and n_2 the greatest flatness of image can be obtained † when

$$n_1 f_1 = -n_2 f_2. \qquad (1)$$

The condition for achromatism for two thin lenses is, by equation (54) on page 69,

$$\nu_2 f_1 = -\nu_1 f_2. \qquad (2)$$

The two conditions (1) and (2) can be simultaneously fulfilled only when the lens of larger index n has the smaller dispersive power ν.

---

* For a more complete treatment cf. Winkelmann's Handbuch der Physik Optik, p. 203 sq. Müller-Pouillet, 9th Ed. Optik, p. 721 sq.

† For a deduction of this condition, first stated by Petzval in the year 1843, cf. Lummer, Ztschr. f. Instrk., 1897, p. 231, where will be found in three articles (pps. 208, 225, 264) an excellent review of photographic optics.

Formerly no kinds of glass were known which fulfilled this condition, namely, that the one with larger index have the smaller dispersion. For crown glass both the refraction and the dispersion were small; for flint glass they were both large. Only recently has Schott in Jena produced glasses which show in some degree the reverse relation,* and hence it has become possible to obtain at the same time achromatism and flatness of the image. Such systems of lenses are called the new achromats to distinguish them from the old achromats.

For another reason the use of these new kinds of glass, which combine a large n with a small ν, is advantageous for photographic optics. Astigmatism may be corrected by combining an old achromat with a new, because the former, on account of the dispersive effect at the junction between the lenses, produces an astigmatic difference of opposite sign from that produced by the latter, which has a convergent effect at the junction. Such symmetrical double objectives which have on both sides a combination of old and new achromats are called anastigmatic aplanats.

In order to produce as large images as possible of a distant object, the focal length of the system must be as great as possible. This would necessitate, if the lenses of the system lie close together, an inconvenient lengthening of the camera, since its length b must be approximately equal to the focal length f. This difficulty can be avoided by the use of a so-called teleobjective, which consists of a combination of a convergent and a divergent system placed at a distance a apart. The latter forms (cf. Fig. 22, page 43) erect, enlarged images of virtual objects which lie behind it but in front of its second principal focus F_2. The principal focus F_1' of the convergent lens must also lie in front of F_2. As is shown in Fig. 34, the focal length f of the whole system is greater than the distance of the convergent system from the position of the

* The barium-silicate glasses produce larger refraction but smaller dispersion than crown glass.

image, i.e. than the camera length. For example, in order to be able to use a focal length f of 37 cm. in a camera whose length is about 20 cm., a convergent lens of focal length 10 cm. must be combined with a divergent lens of focal length 5 cm. so that the optical separation Δ is 1.35 cm., i.e. the dis-

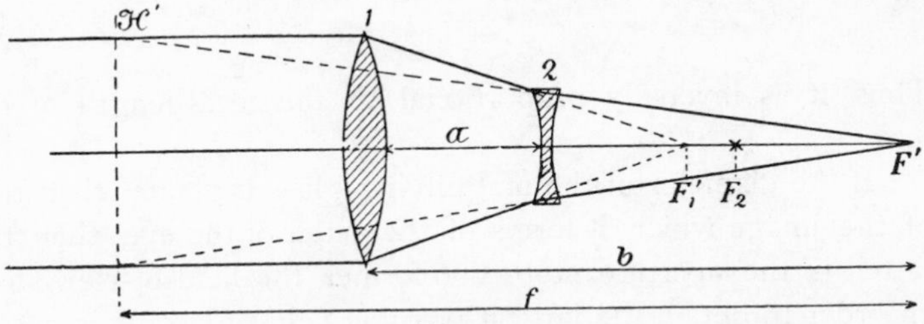

FIG. 34.

tance between the lenses must be 6.35 cm. These values are obtained from the equations (17) and (19) for a compound system given on page 29.

In a portrait lens the size of the aperture is of the greatest importance because it is desirable to obtain as much light as possible. Hence the first consideration is to eliminate spherical aberration and to fulfil the sine law.

2. Simple Magnifying-glasses.—The apparent size of an object depends upon the size of the angle which it subtends at the eye. This visual angle may be increased by bringing the object nearer to the eye, but only up to a certain limit, since the object cannot lie closer to the eye than the limit of distinct vision (25 cm.). But the visual angle may be still further increased by the use of a magnifying-glass.

The simplest form of magnifying-glass is a single convergent lens. This produces (cf. Fig. 21, page 43) an erect enlarged virtual image of an object which lies between the lens and its principal focus. If this image is at a distance of $\delta\theta$ from the eye, then, by equation (7) on page 19, the magnification V of the lens is

$$V = \frac{y'}{y} = \frac{x'}{f} = \frac{\delta + a}{f}, \quad . \quad . \quad . \quad . \quad . \quad (3)$$

in which x' denotes the distance of the image from the second principal focus, and a that of the eye. Generally a may be neglected in comparison with δ, in which case the magnification produced by the lens is

$$V = \frac{\delta}{f}. \quad . \quad . \quad . \quad . \quad . \quad . \quad . \quad (4)$$

Thus it is inversely proportional to the focal length of the lens.

If the diameter of the magnifying-glass is greater than that of the image which it forms of the pupil of the eye, then the latter is the aperture stop, the former the field-of-view stop. In order to obtain the largest possible field of view it is necessary to bring the eye as near as possible to the lens. As the distance of the lens from the eye is increased, not only does the field of view become smaller, but also the configuration of the rays changes in that the images of points off the axis are formed by portions of the lens which lie to one side of the axis. This is evident at once from a graphical construction of the entrance-pupil of the system, i.e. a construction of the image of the pupil of the eye formed by the lens. The orthoscopy is in this way generally spoiled, i.e. the image appears blurred at the edges.

A simple plano-convex lens gives good images for magnifications of less than eight diameters, i.e. for focal lengths greater than 3 cm. The plane side of the lens must be turned toward the eye. Although this position gives a relatively large spherical aberration on the axis (cf. page 55), because the object lies near its principal focus of the lens, nevertheless it is more satisfactory than the inverse position on account of the smaller aberration off the axis.

The image may be decidedly improved by the use of two simple lenses because the distribution of the refraction over several lenses greatly diminishes the spherical aberration on the axis. Figs. 35 and 36 show the well-known Fraunhofer and Wilson magnifying-glasses. In the latter the distance between the lenses is much greater than in the former. In this way the advantage is gained that the differences in the magnifications for the different colors is diminished, although at the cost of the distance of the object from the lens.*

Achromatization is attained in Steinheil's so-called aplanatic magnifying-glass by a choice of different kinds of glass (Fig. 37). In this a double-convex lens of crown glass is cemented between two convexo-concave lenses of flint glass.

FIG. 35.

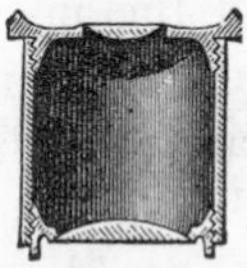
FIG. 36.

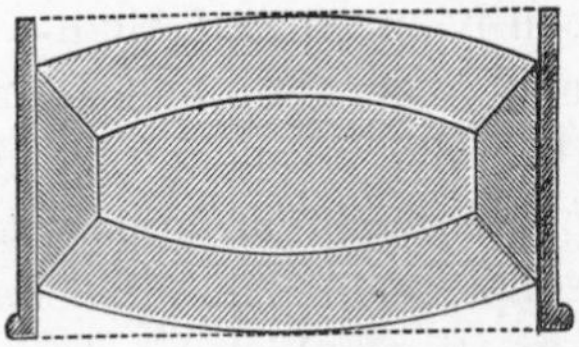
FIG. 37.

The Brücke magnifying-glass, which consists of a convergent achromatic front lens and at some distance from it a simple divergent lens, is characterized by the fact that the object lies at a considerable distance. The divergent lens produces inverted, enlarged, virtual images of virtual objects which lie behind its second principal focus (cf. Fig. 22, page 43). The arrangement of the lenses may be the same as in the teleobjective (Fig. 34), i.e. the optical separation of the convergent and the divergent lenses may be positive. Nevertheless, if the object is sufficiently close, the image formed by the convergent lens may lie behind the second focus of the divergent lens. Like the simple magnifying-glass this combination furnishes erect images, for the image formed by the convergent lens alone would be inverted were another inversion not produced by the divergent lens. The objectionable feature of this instrument is the smallness of the field of view.

3. The Microscope.—*a. General Considerations.*—In order to obtain greater magnification it is advantageous to replace

* The effect of the distance between the lenses upon achromatism has been treated above, p. 71. The subject will come up again when the eyepieces of telescopes and microscopes are under consideration.

the magnifying-glass of short focal length by a microscope. This consists of two convergent systems relatively far apart. The first system (the objective) produces a real, inverted, enlarged image of an object which lies just beyond its first principal focus. This image is again enlarged by the second system (the eyepiece) which acts as a magnifying-glass. Apart from the fact that, on account of the greater distance apart of the two systems of the microscope, a greater magnification can be produced than with a single system used as a simple magnifier, the chief advantage of the instrument lies in this, that the problem of forming the image is divided into two parts which can be solved separately by the objective and the eyepiece. This division of labor is made as follows: the objective, which has the greatest possible numerical aperture,* forms an image of a surface element, while the eyepiece, like any magnifying-glass, forms the image of a large field of view by means of pencils which must be of small divergence, since they are limited by the pupil of the eye. It has been shown above (Chapter III, §§ 8, 9, 10) that these two problems may be separately solved.

b. The Objective.—The principal requirements which an objective must fulfil are as follows:

1. That with a large numerical aperture the spherical aberration upon the axis be eliminated and the aplanatic condition, i.e. the sine law, be fulfilled.

2. That chromatic errors be corrected. This requires that the aplanatic condition be fulfilled for at least two colors, and that a real achromatic image of the object be formed by the objective. If only partial achromatism is required it is sufficient to make the objective achromatic with respect to the first principal focus; for the position of the image of an object which lies near this focal point F would vary rapidly with the color if the position of F depended upon the color. If a system has been achromatized thus with respect to the focus F, i.e.

* This requirement is introduced not only for the sake of increased brightness but also of increased resolving power. Cf. above, pp. 90, 92.

with respect to the position of the image, it is not achromatic with respect to the focal length. The different colors, therefore, produce images of different sizes, i.e. chromatic differences in magnification still remain. These must be corrected by means of the eyepiece.

It is customary to distinguish between *dry* and *immersion* systems. In the latter the space between the front lens of the objective and the cover-glass under which the object lies is filled with a liquid. The advantages of this method of increasing the numerical aperture are evident. Furthermore, by the use of the so-called homogeneous immersions, in which the liquid has the same index and dispersion as the cover-glass and the front lens, the formation of aplanatic images by a hemispherical front lens may be attained in accordance with the principle of Amici (cf. page 58). Fig. 38 shows, in double the natural size, an objective designed by Abbe, called an *aprochromat*, in which the above conditions are fulfilled by a combination of ten different lenses used with a homogeneous immersion. The aprochromat, being achromatic for three colors, is free from secondary spectra, and the aplanatic conditions are fulfilled for two colors. The focal length of the system is 2 mm. and its numerical aperture $a = 1.40$. The light-collecting and dioptric excellence of this objective is such that the limit of resolving power of a microscope (equation (87), page 92) may be considered as actually attained by it.

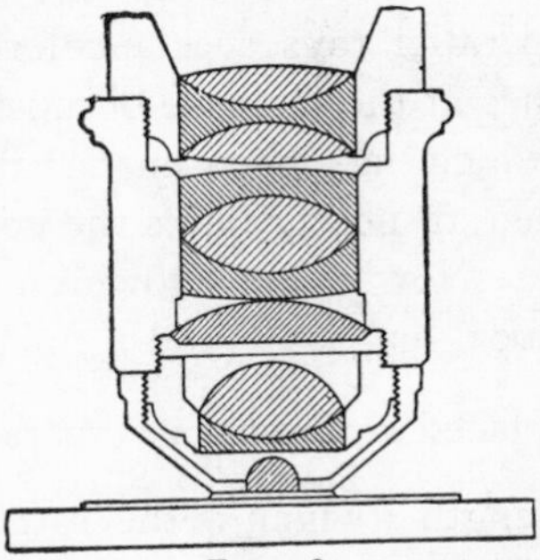

FIG. 38.

c. The Eyepiece.—The chief requirements for the eyepiece are those for the formation of the image of an extended object by means of narrow pencils, namely:

1. The elimination of astigmatism in the oblique pencils.
2. The formation of orthoscopic images.
3. The formation of achromatic images.

The first two points have been discussed in Chapter III, § 10, page 63; as to the last, partial achromatization is sufficient. Consider the case in which the image formed by an objective is free from chromatic errors. On account of the length of the microscope tube, i.e. on account of the relatively large distance between the real image formed by the objective and the exit-pupil of the objective, the principal rays which fall upon the eyepiece have but a small inclination to the axis of the instrument. If now the eyepiece is made achromatic with respect to its focal length, then it is evident from the construction of conjugate rays given on page 24, as well as from the property of the focal length given on page 20, that a ray of white light which falls upon the eyepiece is split up into colored rays all of which emerge from the eyepiece with the same inclination to the axis. Hence an eye focussed for parallel rays sees a colorless image. Even when the image lies at the distance of most distinct vision (25 cm.) an eyepiece which has been made achromatic with respect to its focal length nearly fulfils the conditions 71 for a colorless image.

Now it was shown on page 71 that two simple lenses of focal lengths f_1 and f_2, made of the same kind of glass, when placed at a distance apart $a = \frac{f_1 + f_2}{2}$, have a resultant focal length f which is the same for all colors. Since, in addition, the construction of an eyepiece from two lenses produces an improvement of the image in the matter of astigmatism, eyepieces are usually made according to this principle. The lens which is nearer the objective is called the *field-lens*, that next the eye the *eye-lens*.

The two most familiar forms of achromatic eyepiece are the following:

1. *The Ramsden eyepiece* (cf. Fig. 40, page 109). This consists of two equal plano-convex lenses which have their curved sides turned toward each other. Since $f_1 = f_2$, the distance a between the lenses is $a = f_1 = f_2$. But this arrangement has the disadvantage that the field-lens lies at the prin-

cipal focus of the eye-lens, and hence any dust-particles or scratches upon the former are seen magnified by the latter. Hence the field-lens is placed somewhat nearer to the eye-lens, for instance, $a = \frac{2}{3}f_1$. In this way a further advantage is obtained. When $a = \frac{2}{3}f_1$, the optical separation of the two lenses (cf. page 28) $\Delta = -\frac{4}{3}f_1$. Hence, by equation (20) on page 30, the focal length F of the combination lies at a distance $\frac{1}{4}f_1$ before the field-lens; while, when $a = f_1$, i.e. $\Delta = -f_1$, it would fall in the objective lens itself. Since the real image formed by the objective of the microscope lies near the principal focus F of the eyepiece, if $a = \frac{2}{3}f_1$, it is still in front of the field-lens; hence the image in the microscope may be measured by introducing in front of the field-lens, at the position of the real image formed by the objective, a micrometer consisting of fine graduations upon glass or a cross-hair movable by means of a screw.

2. *The Huygens eyepiece* (Fig. 39). In this the focal length f_1 of the field-lens is larger than that f_2 of the eye-lens. Generally $f_1 = 3f_2$. Then from $a = \dfrac{f_1 + f_2}{2}$ it follows that $a = \frac{2}{3}f_1 = 2f_2$. The optical separation has the value $\Delta = -\frac{2}{3}f_1$, hence by (20) on page 30 the focal length F of the combination lies a distance $\frac{1}{2}f_1$ behind the field-lens. The real image formed by the objective must, therefore, fall behind the field-lens as a virtual object, and a micrometrical measurement of it is not easily made since both the lenses in the eye-piece take part in the formation of the image of the object, while the image of the micrometer is formed by the eye-lens alone. This eyepiece also consists of two plano-convex lenses but their curved surfaces are both turned toward the object. The advantage of the combination of a weak field-lens with an eye-lens three times as powerful lies in the fact that the bending of the rays at the two lenses is uniformly distributed between them.*

* For this calculation cf. Heath, Geometrical Optics, Cambr., 1895.

If chromatic errors exist in the image formed by the objective, they may be eliminated by constructing the eyepiece to have chromatic errors of opposite sign. It was shown above (page 99) that the chromatic errors of magnification are not eliminated in the aprochromat objective, the blue image being larger than the red. Abbe then combines with such objectives the so-called compensating eyepieces which are not achrometized with respect to focal length, i.e. with respect to magnification, but which produce larger red images than blue.

d. The Condenser.—In order that full advantage may be taken of the large numerical aperture of the objective, the rays incident upon it must be given a large divergence. To obtain such divergence there is introduced under the stage of the microscope a condenser which consists of one or more convergent lenses of short focal length arranged as in an objective, but in the inverse order. From the discussion above on page 85 it is evident that such a condensation of the light does not increase the intensity of the source but merely has the effect of bringing it very close to the objective.

e. Geometrical Configuration of the Rays.—If the normal magnification (cf. page 90) has not been reached, the pupil of the eye is the exit-pupil of the entire microscope, and the image of the pupil of the eye formed by the instrument is the entrance-pupil. If the normal magnification is exceeded, a stop or the rim of a lens in the microscope is the aperture stop. This stop always lies in the objective, not in the eyepiece. Fig. 39 shows a case of very frequent occurrence in which the rim B_1B_2 of the hemispherical front lens of the objective is both aperture stop and entrance-pupil. The image $B_1'B_2'$ of B_1B_2 formed by the whole microscope is the exit-pupil. If the length of the tube is not too small, this image lies almost at the principal focus of the eyepiece. The eyepiece shown in Fig. 39 is a Huygens eyepiece. The real image of the object P_1P_2 formed by the objective and the field-lens of the eyepiece is $P_1'P_2'$. The field-of-view stop GG is placed at $P_1'P_2'$. In this way the edge of the field of view becomes sharply defined, because the image of G formed by the field-lens and the objective lies in the plane of the object P_1P_2 (cf. remark on page 76). The points $P_1'P_2'$ must lie on the edge of the field-of-view stop. Then P_1P_2 is the size of the field of view on the side of the object. The virtual image $P_1''P_2''$ formed by the eye-lens of the real image $P_1'P_2'$ is the image seen by the observer. If this image is at a distance δ from the exit-pupil,

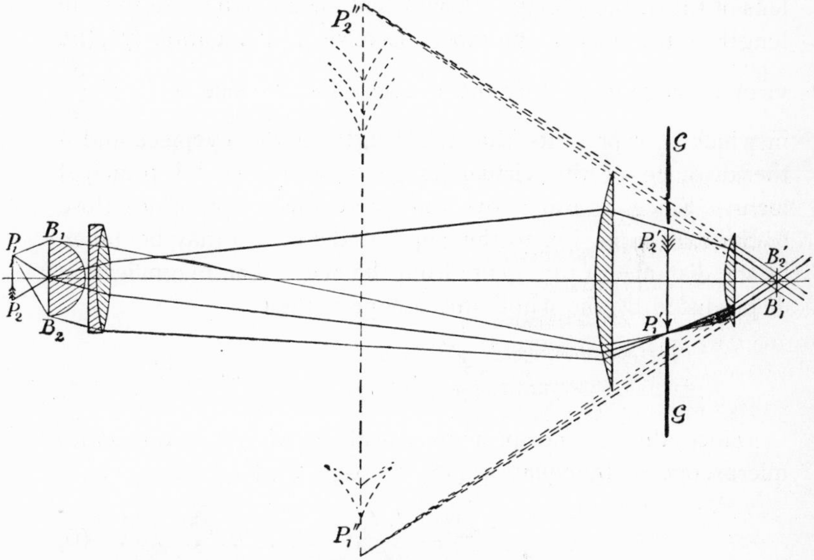

FIG. 39.

then the observer, the pupil of whose eye ought to be coincident with the exit-pupil $B_1'B_2'$ (cf. page 77), must focus his eye for this distance δ. By a slight raising or lowering of the whole microscope with respect to the object P_1P_2 the image $P_1''P_2''$ may easily be brought to any desired distance δ. It is usually assumed that δ is the distance of most distinct vision, namely, 25 cm.

In Fig. 39 the principal and the limiting rays which proceed from P_1 are shown. From P_2 the principal ray only is drawn, the limiting rays being introduced behind the eye-lens.

f. The Magnification.—Let the object have the linear magnitude y. By equation (7) on page 19, the objective forms a real image of size $y' = y \cdot \frac{l}{f_1'}$, in which f_1' is the second focal length of the objective,* and l the distance of the image from the second principal focus. Since, as was shown above, this image y' lies immediately in front of or behind the field-lens of the ocular, l may with sufficient accuracy be taken as the length of the microscope tube. Likewise, by equation (7), the virtual image formed by the eyepiece has the size $y'' = y' \cdot \frac{\delta}{f_2}$, in which f_2 represents the focal length of the eyepiece and δ the distance of the virtual image from its second principal focus. Since, as was above remarked, this eyepiece lies close to the exit-pupil, i.e. to the pupil of the eye, δ may be taken as the distance of the image from the eye. The magnification V produced by the whole microscope is then

$$V = \frac{y''}{y} = \frac{\delta \cdot l}{f_1' f_2}. \quad \ldots \ldots \quad (5)$$

Since the second principal focal length f' of the entire microscope is, by equation (18) on page 29, †

$$f' = -\frac{f_1' f_2}{l}, \quad \ldots \ldots \quad (6)$$

Δ, the optical separation between the objective and the eyepiece being almost equal to l, it follows that, disregarding the sign, (5) may be written

$$V = \frac{\delta}{f'}. \quad \ldots \ldots \quad (7)$$

Thus the magnification depends upon three factors which are entirely arbitrary, namely, upon f_1', f_2, and l. The length

* A distinction between first and second principal foci is only necessary for immersion systems.

† For the eyepiece $f_2 = f_2'$.

l of the tube cannot be increased beyond a certain limit without making the instrument cumbrous. It is more practicable to obtain the effect of a longer l by increasing the power of the eyepiece. Furthermore the focal length of the objective is always made smaller than that of the eyepiece. In this way not only may the lenses in the objective be made relatively small even for high numerical aperture, but also a certain quality of image (near the axis) may be more easily obtained for a given magnification the smaller the focal length of the objective. But since, with the diminution of the focal length of the objective, the errors in the final image formed by the eyepiece increase for points off the axis, the shortening of f_1' cannot be carried advantageously beyond a certain limit (1.5–2 mm. in immersion systems).

g. The Resolving Power.—This is not to be confused with magnification, for, under certain circumstances, a microscope of smaller magnifying power may have the larger resolving power, i.e. it may reveal to the eye more detail in the object than a more powerfully magnifying instrument. The resolving power depends essentially upon the construction of the objective: the detail of the image formed by it depends (cf. page 92) on the one hand upon the numerical aperture of the objective, on the other upon the size of the discs which arise because the focussing is not rigorously homocentric. If two points P_1 and P_2 of an object be considered such that the discs to which they give rise in the image formed by the objective do not overlap, they may be distinguished as two distinct points or round spots in case the eyepiece has magnified the image formed by the objective to such an extent that the visual angle is at least 1′. But if these discs in the image formed by the objective overlap, then the most powerful eyepiece cannot separate the points P_1 and P_2. For every objective there is then a particular ocular magnification, which will just suffice to bring out completely the detail in the image formed by the objective. A stronger magnification may indeed be conveniently used in bringing out this detail, but it adds no new element to the picture. From the focal length of the objective, the length of the tube, and the focal length of the eyepiece which is just sufficient to bring out the detail in the image, it is possible to calculate from (5) the smallest permissible magnification for complete resolution. This magnification is greater the greater the resolving power of the objective. Assuming a perfect objective, the necessary magnification of the whole instrument depends only upon the numerical aperture. This has not yet been pushed beyond the limit (for immersion systems) $a = 1.6$. Hence, by equation (87) on page 92, *the smallest interval d which can be optically resolved is*

$$d = \frac{\lambda}{2a} = \frac{0.00053 \text{ mm.}}{3.2} = 0.00016 \text{ mm.}$$

if λ be the wave-length of green light. Now at a distance $\delta = 25$ cm. from the eye an interval $d' = 0.145$ mm. has a visual angle of $2'$, which is the smallest angle which can be easily distinguished. Since $d' : d = 905$, *the limit of resolution of the microscope is attained when the total magnification is about 900.* Imperfections in the objective reduce this required magnification somewhat. By equation (85) on page 89 the ratio of the brightness of the image to the normal brightness is for this case

$$H : H_0 = \frac{\delta^2 \cdot a^2}{p^2 \cdot V^2} = \left(\frac{250 \cdot 1.6}{2 \cdot 900}\right)^2 = \frac{1}{20},$$

the radius p of the pupil of the eye being assumed as 2 mm.

h. Experimental Determination of the Magnification and the Numerical Aperture.—The magnification may be determined by using as an object a fine glass scale and drawing with the help of a camera lucida its image upon a piece of paper placed at a distance of 25 cm. from the eye. The simplest form of camera lucida consists of a little mirror mounted obliquely to the axis of the instrument, from the middle of which the silvering has been removed so as to leave a small hole of about 2 mm. diameter. The image in the microscope is seen through the hole, while the drawing-paper is at the same time visible in the mirror.* The ratio of the distances between the divisions in the drawing to those upon the glass scale is the magnification of the instrument.

From the magnification and a measurement of the exit-pupil of the microscope its numerical aperture may be easily found. Since, according to the discussion on page 88, the ratio of the brightness of the image to the normal brightness is equal to the ratio of the exit-pupil to the pupil of the eye, it follows, from (85) on page 89, that

$$\frac{H}{H_0} = \frac{b^2}{p^2} = \frac{\delta^2 a^2}{p^2 V^2}, \quad . \quad . \quad . \quad . \quad . \quad . \quad (8)$$

in which b represents the radius of the exit-pupil. Hence the numerical aperture is

$$a = \frac{bV}{\delta}. \quad . \quad . \quad . \quad . \quad . \quad . \quad . \quad . \quad (9)$$

A substitution of the value of V from (7) gives

$$a = b : f', \quad . \quad . \quad . \quad . \quad . \quad . \quad (10)$$

i.e. *the numerical aperture is equal to the ratio of the radius of the exit-pupil to the second focal length of the whole microscope.*

Abbe has constructed an apertometer which permits the determination of the numerical aperture of the objective directly.†

4. The Astronomical Telescope.—This consists, like the microscope, of two convergent systems, the objective and the eyepiece. The former produces at its principal focus a real inverted image of a very distant object. This image is enlarged by the eyepiece, which acts as a simple magnifier. If the eye of the observer is focussed for parallel rays, the first focal plane of the eyepiece coincides with the second focal plane of the

* Other forms of camera lucida are described in Müller-Pouillet, Optik, p. 839.

† A description of it will be found in the texts referred to at the beginning of this chapter.

objective, and the image formation is telescopic in the sense used above (page 26), i.e. both the object and the image lie at infinity. The magnification Γ means then the ratio of the convergence of the image rays to the convergence of the object rays. But, by (24) on page 30,

$$\Gamma = \tan u' : \tan u = f_1 : f_2, \quad . \quad . \quad . \quad . \quad (11)$$

in which f_1 is the focal length of the objective and f_2 that of the eyepiece. Hence for a powerful magnification f_1 must be large and f_2 small.

The magnification may be experimentally determined by measuring the ratio of the entrance-pupil to the exit-pupil of the instrument. For when the image formation is telescopic, the lateral magnification is constant (cf. page 26), i.e. it is independent of the position of the object and, by (14′) on page 28, is equal to the reciprocal of the angular magnification. Now (without reference to the eye of the observer, cf. below) the entrance-pupil is the rim of the objective, hence the exit-pupil is the real image (eye-ring) of this rim formed by the eyepiece. Hence if the diameter of this eye-ring be measured with a micrometer, the ratio between it and the diameter of the objective is the reciprocal of the angular magnification of the telescope.

Fig. 40 shows the configuration of the rays when a Ramsden eyepiece is used (cf. page 100). B_1B_2 is the entrance-pupil (the rim of the objective), $B_1'B_2'$ the exit-pupil, and P_1 is the real image formed by the objective of an infinitely distant point P. The principal ray is drawn heavy, the limiting ray light. P_1 lies somewhat in front of the field-lens of the eyepiece. The field-of-view stop GG is placed at this point. Since its image on the side of the object lies at infinity, the limits of the field of view are sharp when distant objects are observed. P' is the infinitely distant image which the eyepiece forms of P_1. When the eye of the observer is taken into consideration, it is necessary to distinguish between the case in which the exit-pupil of the instrument is smaller than the pupil of the eye and that in which it is greater. Only in the first case do the conclusions reached above hold, while in the second the pupil of the eye is the exit-pupil for the whole system of rays, and the image of the pupil of the eye formed by the telescope is the entrance-pupil.

The objective is an achromatic lens which is corrected for spherical aberration. In making the eyepiece achromatic the

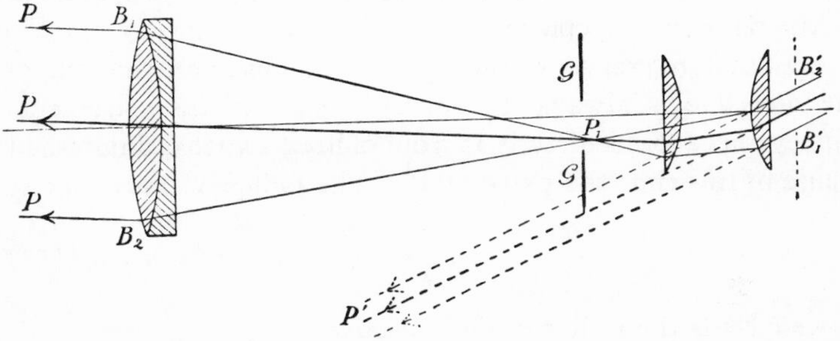

FIG. 40.

same conditions must be fulfilled which were considered in the case of the microscope. Since the principal rays which fall upon the eyepiece are almost parallel to the axis, it is sufficient if it be achromatized with respect to the focal length. Hence the same eyepiece may be used for both microscope and telescope, but the Ramsden eyepiece is more frequently employed in the latter because it lends itself more readily to micrometric measurements.

Here, as in the microscope, in order to bring out all the detail, the magnification must reach a certain limit beyond which no advantage is obtained in the matter of resolving power. In telescopes the aperture of the objective corresponds to the numerical aperture in microscopes.

5. The Opera-glass.—If the convergent eyepiece of the astronomical telescope be replaced by a divergent one, the instrument becomes an opera-glass. In order that the image formation may be telescopic, the second principal focus of the eyepiece must coincide with the second principal focus of the objective. Thus the length of the telescope is not equal to the sum, as in the astronomical form, but rather to the difference of the focal lengths of the eyepiece and the objective.

Since equation (11) of this chapter holds for all cases of telescopic image formation, the angular magnification Γ of the opera-glass may be obtained from it. This instrument, however, unlike the astronomical telescope, produces erect images, for the inverted image formed by the objective is again inverted by the dispersive eyepiece.

Without reference to the eye of the observer, the rim of the objective is always the entrance-pupil of the instrument. The eyepiece forms directly in front of itself a virtual diminished image of this rim (the exit-pupil). The radius of this image is

$$b = h \cdot \frac{f_2}{f_1} = \frac{h}{\Gamma}, \quad . \quad . \quad . \quad . \quad . \quad (12)$$

in which h is the radius of the objective.

Since this exit-pupil lies before rather than behind the eyepiece, the pupil of the eye of the observer cannot be brought into coincidence with it; consequently the pupil of the eye acts as a field-of-view stop in case the quantity b determined by

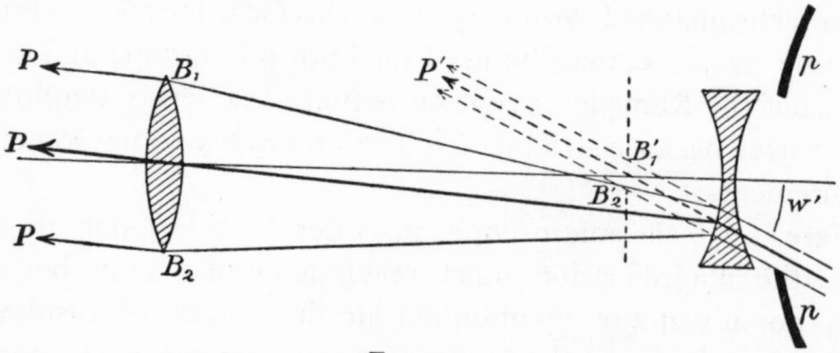

FIG. 41.

equation (12), i.e. the exit-pupil of the instrument, is smaller than the eye, which means that the normal magnification is exceeded. Hence for large magnifications the field of view is very limited. Fig. 41 shows the geometrical configuration of the rays for such a case. p, p represents the pupil of the eye, w' the angular field of view of the image. Since the image of the field-of-view stop (the pupil of the eye), formed by the whole telescope lies at a finite distance, i.e. since it is not at infinity with the object, the edge of the field of view is not sharp (cf. page 76).

But if the exit-pupil $B_1'B_2' = 2b$ of the instrument is larger than the pupil of the eye, i.e. if the normal magnification has not been reached, then, taking into account the eye of the observer, the pupil of his eye is the exit-pupil for all the rays, and the rim of the objective acts as the field-of-view stop. The field of view on the side of the image is bounded by the image $2b$ of the rim of the objective (in Fig. 42 this is represented by $B_1'B_2'$). Hence in this case the field of view may be enlarged by the use of a large objective. But again, for the same reason as above, the limits of the field of view are not sharp. Fig. 42 shows this case, w' being the angular field of view on the side of the image.

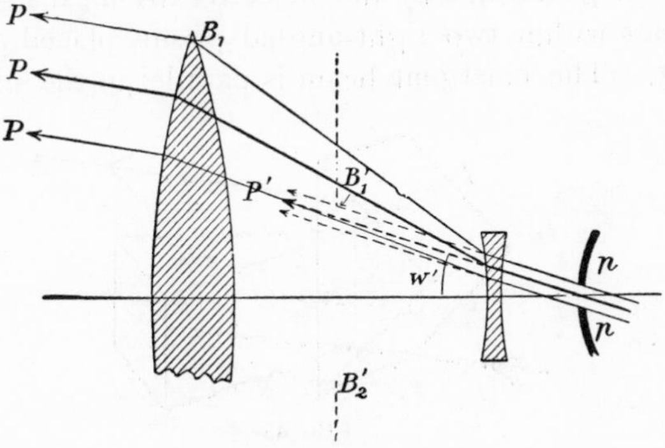

FIG. 42.

If the radius of the pupil of the eye is assumed as 2 mm., then the paths of the rays will be those shown in 41 or 42, according as *

$$h \lessgtr 2\Gamma \text{ mm};$$

* The difference between these cases may be experimentally recognized by shading part of the objective with an opaque screen and observing whether the brightness of the image or the size of the field is diminished.

for example, for a magnification of eight diameters, $2h = 32$ mm. is the critical size of the objective.

6. The Terrestrial Telescope.—For observation of objects on the earth it is advantageous to have the telescope produce an erect image. If the magnification need not be large, an opera-glass may be used. But since for large magnifications this has a small field of view, the so-called terrestrial telescope is often better. This latter consists of an astronomical telescope with an inverting eyepiece. The image is then formed as follows: the objective produces a real inverted image of the object; this image is then inverted without essential change in size by a convergent system consisting of two lenses. The erect image thus formed is magnified either by a Ramsden or a Huygens eyepiece.

7. The Zeiss Binocular.—The terrestrial eyepiece has an inconvenient length. This difficulty may be avoided by inverting the image formed by the objective by means of four total reflections within two right-angled prisms placed as shown in Fig. 43. The emergent beam is parallel to the incident, but

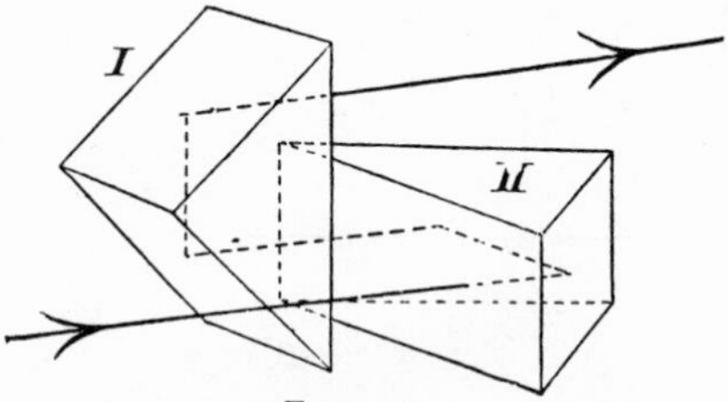

FIG. 43.

has experienced a lateral displacement. Otherwise the construction is the same as that of the astronomical telescope.

The telescope may be appreciably shortened by separating the two prisms I and II, since the ray of light traverses the distance between the prisms three times. By a suitable division and arrangement of the prisms the lateral displacement between the incident and the emergent rays may be made as large as desired. In this way a binocular may be constructed in which the exit-pupils (the lenses of the objective) are much farther apart than the pupils of the eyes. Thus the stereoscopic effect due to binocular vision is greatly increased.

8. The Reflecting Telescope.—This differs from the refracting telescope in that a concave mirror instead of a lens is used to produce the real image of the object. For observing this image various arrangements of the eyepiece are used.* Reflecting telescopes were of great importance before achromatic objectives were invented, for it is evident that concave mirrors are free from chromatic errors.

To obtain the greatest possible magnification large mirrors with large radii of curvature must be used. Herschel built an enormous concave mirror of 16 m. radius of curvature. Since the visual angle of the sun is about 32′, the image of the sun formed by it was 7 cm. in diameter.

* For further details cf. Heath, Geometrical Optics, Cambr., 1895.

PART II

PHYSICAL OPTICS

SECTION I

GENERAL PROPERTIES OF LIGHT

CHAPTER I

THE VELOCITY OF LIGHT

1. Römer's Method.—Whether light is propagated with finite velocity or not is a question of great theoretical importance. On account of the enormous velocity with which light actually travels, a method depending on terrestrial distances which was first tried by Galileo, gave a negative result. For the small distances which must be used in terrestrial methods the instruments employed must be extremely delicate.

Better success was attained by astronomical methods, which permit of the observation of the propagation of light over very great distances. The first determination of the velocity of light was made by Olaf Römer in 1675. He observed that the intervals of time between the eclipses of one of Jupiter's satellites increased as the earth receded from Jupiter and decreased as it approached that planet. This change in the interval between eclipses can be very accurately determined by observing a large number of consecutive eclipses. Römer found that the sum of these intervals taken over a period extending from the opposition to the conjunction of the earth and Jupiter differed by 996 seconds from the product of the number of eclipses and the mean interval between eclipses taken throughout the whole year. He ascribed this difference to the finite velocity of light. According to this view, then, light requires 996 seconds to traverse the earth's diameter. Glasenapp's more recent observations make the correct value of this interval 1002 seconds. The diameter of the earth's orbit may be obtained from the radius of the earth and the solar parallax, i.e. the angle which the radius of the earth subtends at the sun. According to the most recent observations the most probable value of the solar parallax is 8.85″. The radius of the earth is 6378 km., so that the diameter, d, of its orbit is

$$d = \frac{2 \cdot 6378}{8.85} \cdot \frac{180 \cdot 60 \cdot 60}{\pi} = 2973 \cdot 10^5 \text{ km.}$$

Hence the velocity of light V is

$$V = 296\,700 \,{}^{\text{km.}}/_{\text{sec.}} = 2.967 \cdot 10^{10} \,{}^{\text{cm.}}/_{\text{sec.}}$$

On account of errors in the determination of the solar parallax this value is uncertain by from $\frac{1}{2}$ to 1 per cent.

2. **Bradley's Method.**—Imagine that a ray of light from a distant source P reaches the eye of an observer after passing successively through two holes S_1 and S_2 which lie upon the axis of a tube R. If the tube R moves with a velocity v in a direction at right angles to its axis, while the source P remains at rest, then if the light requires a finite time to traverse the length of the tube R a ray of light which has passed through the first hole S_1 will no longer fall upon the hole S_2. Therefore the observer no longer sees the source P. In order to see it again he must turn the tube R through an angle α. Thus the line of sight to P appears inclined in the direction of the motion of the observer an angle ζ such that

$$\tan \zeta = v : V, \quad . \quad . \quad . \quad . \quad . \quad . \quad (1)$$

in which V represents the velocity of light.

This consideration furnished the explanation of the aberration of the fixed stars, a phenomenon discovered in 1727 by Bradley. He found that if the line of sight and the motion of the earth are at right angles, the line of sight is displaced a small angle in the direction of the earth's motion. According to the most recent observations the value of this angle is 20.5″. Since the velocity v of the earth in its orbit is known from the size of the orbit, equation (1) gives as the velocity of light

$$V = 2.982 \cdot 10^{10}\ \mathrm{cm.}/_{\mathrm{sec.}}$$

This method, like Römer's or any astronomical method, is subject to the uncertainty which arises from the imperfect knowledge of the solar parallax and hence of the size of the earth's orbit.

The result agrees well with that obtained by Römer, a fact which justifies the assumption made in both calculations, that the rays, in passing through the atmosphere which is moving with the earth, receive from it no lateral velocity. Nevertheless aberration cannot be completely explained in this simple way. From the considerations here given it would be expected that when a fixed star is viewed through a telescope filled with water the aberration would be greater, since, as will be shown later, the velocity of light in water is less than in air. As a matter of fact, however, the aberration is independent of the medium in the tube. In order to explain this a more complete investigation of the effect of the motion of a body upon the propagation of light within it is necessary. This will be given farther on. It is sufficient here to note that the phenomenon of aberration is capable of giving the velocity of light in space, i.e. in vacuo.

3. Fizeau's Method.—The first successful determination of the velocity of light by a method employing terrestrial distances was made by Fizeau in the year 1849. An image of a source of light P is formed at f by means of a convergent lens and a glass plate p inclined to the direction of the rays (Fig. 44). The rays are then made parallel by a lens L_1 and pass to the second lens L_2 distant from L_1 8.6 km. A real image is formed upon a concave mirror *s* whose centre of curvature lies in the middle of the lens L_2. The mirror *s* returns the light back over the same path so that the reflected rays also form a real image at *f*. This image is observed through the obliquely inclined plate *p* by means of the eyepiece *o*. At *f*,

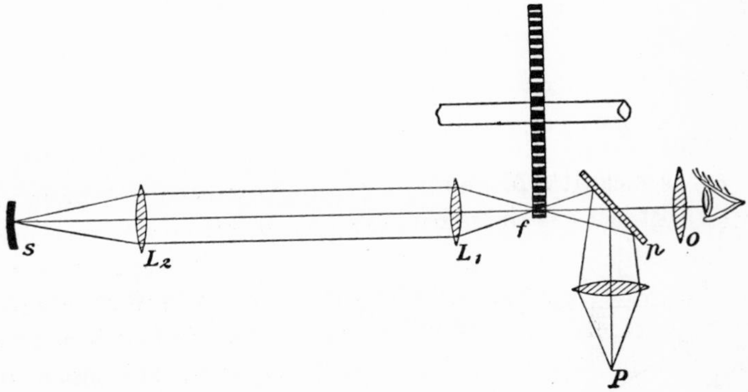

FIG. 44.

where the real image is formed, the rim of a toothed wheel is so placed that the light passes freely through an opening, but is cut off by a tooth. If the wheel is rotated with small velocity, the image alternately appears and disappears. When the velocity is increased, the image is seen continuously on account of the persistence of vision. As the velocity of the wheel is still further increased, a point is reached at which the image slowly disappears. This occurs when, in the time required by the light to travel from *f* to *s* and back, the wheel has turned so that a tooth is in the position before occupied by an opening. When the velocity is twice as great the light again appears, when it is three times as great it disappears, etc. From the velocity of rotation of the wheel, the number of teeth, and the distance between *f* and *s*, the velocity of light can easily be calculated. Fizeau used a wheel having 720 teeth. The first disappearance occurred when the rate of rotation was 12.6

revolutions per second. Since the distance between L_1 and L_2 was 8.633 km., the velocity of light was calculated as

$$V = 3.13 \cdot 10^{10}\ \text{cm.}/_{\text{sec.}}$$

The principal difficulty in the method lies in the production and measurement of a uniform velocity of rotation. By using more refined methods of measurement Cornu obtained the value

$$V = 2.9995 \cdot 10^{10}\ \text{cm.}/_{\text{sec.}},$$

Young and Forbes the value

$$V = 3.013 \cdot 10^{10}\ \text{cm.}/_{\text{sec.}}$$

4. Foucault's Method.—This method does not require so large distances as the above and is in several respects of great importance in optical work. Rays from a source P pass through an inclined plate p (Fig. 45) and fall upon the rotating mirror m. When this mirror m is in a certain position, the rays are reflected through the lens L,* which is close to m and so placed that a real image of the source P is formed at a distance D upon a concave mirror s whose centre of curvature is at m. The mirror s reflects the rays back over the same path provided the mirror m has not appreciably changed its position in the time required for the light to travel the distance $2D$. An image P' of the source P is then formed by the rays reflected from m, s, and p. But if, in the time required for the light to travel the distance $2D$, the rotating mirror has turned through an angle α, then the ray returning from m to p makes an angle 2α with the original ray and a displaced image P'' is produced after reflection at p.

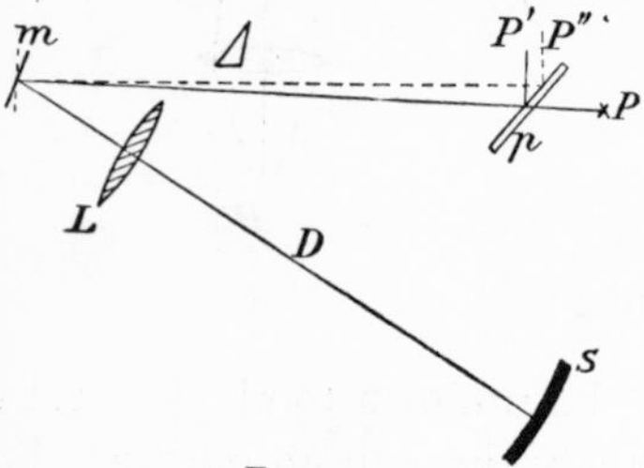

FIG. 45.

* In Foucault's experiment the lens L was actually between the source P and the mirror m, instead of between m and s; but the discussion is essentially the same for either arrangement so long as L is close to m.—TR.

From the displacement $P'P''$, the velocity of rotation of the mirror m, and the distances D and Δ, the velocity of light may be easily obtained.

If $\Delta = 1$ m., $D = 4$ m., and the mirror m makes 1000 revolutions a second, then the displacement $P'P''$ is 0.34 mm. By reflecting the light back and forth between five mirrors slightly inclined to one another, Foucault made the distance D 20 m. instead of 4.

Theoretically this method is not so good as Fizeau's, since it is necessary to measure not only the number of revolutions but also the small displacement $P'P''$. However, by increasing the distance D to 600 m. Michelson materially improved the method, since in this way he obtained a displacement $P'P''$ of 13 cm. without using a rate of revolution greater than 200 a second. With Foucault's arrangement it was not possible to materially increase D, because the light returned would be too faint unless the concave mirror s were of enormous dimensions. Michelson avoided this difficulty by placing the lens L so that m lay at its principal focus. In this way the principal rays of all beams which are reflected by m to the lens L are made parallel after passage through L, so that D can be taken as large as desired and a plane mirror s perpendicular to the axis of L used for reflection. Thus the mirror need be no larger than the lens. From a large number of measurements Michelson obtained

$$V = 2.999 \cdot 10^{10} \text{ cm.}/_{\text{sec.}}$$

Newcomb also, by the method of the rotating mirror, obtained a result in close agreement with this.

The mean of the values obtained by Cornu, Michelson, and Newcomb is

$$V = 2.9989 \cdot 10^{10} \text{ cm.}/_{\text{sec.}},$$

the probable error being only 1 : 10,000. Because of the errors introduced into the astronomical methods by the uncertainty of the solar parallax the results of these methods which depend on terrestrial distances are much more reliable.

In spite of this extraordinary velocity with which light travels, a velocity 900,000 times greater than that of sound in air, the time required for light to travel astronomical distances is sometimes considerable. This appears, for instance, from the observations of Römer, which show that it requires 8 minutes for light to travel from the sun to the earth. Since many years are required for the light of the nearest fixed stars to reach the earth (from α Centauri $3\frac{3}{4}$ years, from Sirius 17 years), these great interstellar distances are usually reckoned in light-years.

5. Dependence of the Velocity of Light upon the Medium and the Color.—The velocity of light is independent of the intensity of the source. This has been proved by very delicate interference experiments made by Lippich and Ebert. On the other hand the velocity does depend upon the medium in which the light is propagated. Foucault compared by his method the velocities in air and in water by placing two mirrors s_1 and s_2 in front of the rotating mirror m and inserting between m and s_2 a tube of water 2 m. long. It was found that when the mirror m was rotated, the image reflected from the mirror s_2 experienced a greater displacement than that reflected from s_1, a proof *that light travels slower in water than in air.*

Quantitative measurements of the velocity of light in water and in carbon bisulphide have been made by Michelson. For the ratio of the velocities in air and in water he obtained 1.33; in air and in carbon bisulphide, white light being used, 1.77. The first number agrees exactly, the last approximately, with the observed indices of refraction. It is assumed (and in fact the wave theory demands it) that this result holds for all bodies. Hence the velocity of light in air must be somewhat smaller than in vacuum, since the index of air $n = 1.00029$. The number given above for the velocity of light which was obtained as a mean from the methods using terrestrial distances was reduced to vacuum by means of this factor.

Since the index of all transparent media is smaller for the red rays than for the blue, it is to be expected that the velocities of the different colors in the same medium will be inversely proportional to the absolute index, provided the velocity in vacuum is independent of the color. This, too, was proved directly by Michelson, who found the velocity of the red ray in water 1.4 per cent, in carbon bisulphide 2.5 per cent greater than that of the blue. This agrees approximately with the results obtained by refraction.

That the velocity in vacuum is independent of the color is very decisively proved by the fact that at the beginning or the end of an eclipse Jupiter's satellites show no color; also from the fact that temporary stars show no changes in color.

Because of the small dispersion of air there is practically no difference in the velocity of propagation of the different colors in it.

6. The Velocity of a Group of Waves.—In the investigation of the velocity of light in a strongly dispersive medium, like carbon bisulphide, there is an important correction to be made, as was first pointed out by Rayleigh. As will be seen in the next chapter, interference phenomena necessitate the assumption that light consists in a periodic change of a certain quantity s, characteristic of the ether or the body considered, which, in view of the fact that the velocity of light is finite, may be written in the form

$$s = A \cdot \sin \frac{2\pi}{T}\left(t - \frac{x}{V}\right). \quad . \quad . \quad . \quad . \quad (2)$$

This is the equation of a so-called plane wave which is propagated with a velocity V along the x-axis. T is the period, which determines the color of the light, and A is the amplitude, which determines the intensity. It is necessary to distinguish between the velocity V of a single wave and the velocity U of a group of waves. For example, in Fizeau's method, at a definite point g in the path of the rays the light is alternately cut off and let through because of the rotation of the toothed wheel. Even when the velocity of rotation of the wheel is great, the period T is so small that a large number of waves pass g at each interval of transmission. It is the velocity of such a complex of waves which is measured by the experiment. The phenomenon can be approximately represented mathematically if it be assumed that two waves of equal amplitude but of slightly different periods T_1 and T_2 and different velocities V_1 and V_2 are superimposed. Then the following relation exists:

$$s = A \cdot \left\{ \sin \frac{2\pi}{T_1}\left(t - \frac{x}{V_1}\right) + \sin \frac{2\pi}{T_2}\left(t - \frac{x}{V_2}\right) \right\} =$$

$$2A \cdot \sin \frac{2\pi}{T}\left(t - \frac{x}{V}\right) \cos \pi \left[t\left(\frac{1}{T_1} - \frac{1}{T_2}\right) - x\left(\frac{1}{T_1 V_1} - \frac{1}{T_2 V_2}\right) \right], \quad (3)$$

in which

$$\frac{1}{T} = \frac{1}{2}\left(\frac{1}{T_1} + \frac{1}{T_2}\right), \quad \frac{1}{TV} = \frac{1}{2}\left(\frac{1}{T_1 V_1} + \frac{1}{T_2 V_2}\right). \quad (4)$$

Equation (3) now represents a light vibration of period T and periodically changing amplitude. The period T_0 of this change of amplitude is

$$\frac{1}{T_0} = \frac{1}{T_1} - \frac{1}{T_2}. \quad . \quad . \quad . \quad . \quad . \quad . \quad (5)$$

Furthermore, if

$$\frac{1}{T_0 U} = \frac{1}{T_1 V_1} - \frac{1}{T_2 V_2}, \quad . \quad . \quad . \quad . \quad . \quad (6)$$

it follows from (3) that at a point $x = l$ a maximum amplitude of the group of waves occurs $l : U$ seconds after it has occurred at the point $x = 0$. Hence U is the velocity of propagation of the group, the quantity which was measured in Fizeau's experiment.

Setting now $T_2 = T_1 + dT_1$, $V_2 = V_1 + dV_1$, and developing to terms of the first order in dT_1 and dV_1, there results from (5) and (6)

$$U = V_1\left(1 - \frac{T_1}{V_1}\frac{dV_1}{dT_1}\right). \quad . \quad . \quad . \quad . \quad . \quad (7)$$

In this equation T_1 and V_1 may, with the same degree of accuracy, be replaced by T and V, i.e. by the period and velocity of a single wave.

Equation (7) shows that the velocity U of a group of waves such as is actually observed is somewhat smaller than the true velocity of light V, since in all transparent bodies V increases with T. This correction is negligible for air on account of the smallness of $dV : dT$, but for the strongly dispersive medium carbon bisulphide it amounts to 7.5 per cent. Since a careful analysis shows that the method of the rotating mirror gives the value U, it is easily understood why Michelson obtained the velocity in carbon bisulphide 1.77 times as great as the velocity in air, although the relative index of the two media is only 1.64. Increasing 1.64 by 7.5 per cent gives a value in close agreement with Michelson's observation, namely, 1.76.

Römer's method also gives the velocity U of a group of waves, while the astronomical aberration gives V directly. In these cases, however, there is no difference between the two quantities U and V, since there is no dispersion in space, i.e. no dependence of V upon color.

CHAPTER II

INTERFERENCE OF LIGHT

1. General Considerations.—Experiment shows that under certain circumstances two parallel or nearly parallel beams do not produce when superposed increased intensity, but rather disturb each other's effects in such a way that darkness results. In such cases the light-waves are said to *interfere*.

Interference phenomena are divided into two classes: the first, that in which the beams have experienced only regular reflections and refractions; the second, that in which they have been bent from their straight path by diffraction. The former will be considered in this chapter, the latter under Diffraction. Nevertheless some of the interference phenomena discussed in this chapter, namely, those which are treated in §§ 3 and 4, and happen to be most easily produced, are somewhat modified by diffraction, while §§ 5, 7, 8, and 9 treat only of pure interference phenomena, i.e. such as are not connected with diffraction.

2. Hypotheses as to the Nature of Light.—Theories as to the nature of light and the mathematical deductions depending upon them have in the course of time undergone many changes. So long as nothing was known of the conservation of energy, every active agent which had the power of propagating itself and of persisting under changed conditions was looked upon as a substance. The fact that light travels in straight lines supported the assumption of its material nature, for light may indeed be stopped in its progress, but in general, when no obstacle is interposed, it moves on in straight lines. It was natural to look upon this as a consequence of the inertia of a material body. Hence Newton supported the emission theory of light, according to which light consists of material particles which are thrown off with enormous velocities from luminous bodies and move in straight lines through space. In order to explain refraction it was necessary to assume that the more refractive bodies exert a greater attraction upon the light corpuscles, so that, at the instant at which such a particle falls obliquely upon the surface of a denser medium, it experiences an attraction which gives to the component of its velocity perpendicular to the surface a larger value, and hence causes its path to approach the perpendicular. According to this theory, then, the velocity of light must be greater within a strongly refracting body than in the surrounding medium. This fact alone suffices for the overthrow of the emission theory, for it was shown on page 120 that the velocity of light is less in water than in air. Besides, the difficulties of explaining the phenomena of interference from the standpoint of the emission theory are enormous. But these very interference phenomena furnish a direct confirmation of an essentially different theory as to the nature of light, namely, the *undulatory theory* developed by Huygens.

According to this theory, light possesses properties similar to sound. It consists in a periodic change of a certain quantity s characteristic of the body (or of empty space) through which the light is passing. This change is propagated with finite velocity so that, if the values which s has at any instant along the path of the ray be plotted as ordinates, the ends of these ordinates form a wave-shaped curve.

What is the nature of this quantity s whose periodic changes are the essence of light can be left for the present altogether undecided. In accordance with the mechanical theory of light, space is conceived to be filled with a subtle elastic medium, the ether, and s is the displacement of the ether particles from their position of equilibrium. But so specific an assumption is altogether unnecessary. It is sufficient if, in order to analytically represent the light disturbance produced by a source Q at any point P in space, the periodic variation of the quantity s at the point P be introduced by means of an equation of the form

$$s = A \sin\left(2\pi\frac{t}{T} + \delta\right), \quad . \quad . \quad . \quad . \quad . \quad (1)$$

in which t is the time, while A, T, and δ are constants. A is the amplitude, T the period of the quantity s. T varies with the color of the light, while A determines the intensity of illumination J* of a screen placed at P. It may in fact be shown that

$$J = A^2. \quad . \quad . \quad . \quad . \quad . \quad . \quad . \quad . \quad . \quad (2)$$

For it follows from all theories of light that the amplitude A of the light emitted from a point source is inversely proportional to the distance r from the source Q. Since now experiment shows that the intensity of illumination is inversely proportional to r^2 (cf. page 79), it follows that J is represented by the square of the amplitude.

If the light travels with a velocity V from a point P to a point P' at a distance r from P, the time required to traverse this distance r is $t' = r : V$. If (1) represents the condition at P, then the condition at P' is represented by

$$s' = A' \sin\left(2\pi\frac{t - r/V}{T} + \delta\right), \quad . \quad . \quad . \quad . \quad (3)$$

for s' is always in a given condition of vibration $r : V$ seconds after s has been in that same condition. The condition of the vibration, i.e. the argument of the periodic function, is called the *phase*.

If from a point source Q light radiates uniformly in all directions, equation (3) evidently holds for every point P' which is at a distance r from Q. Any spherical surface described about Q as a centre contains, then, only points in the same

---

* This quantity J is called the intensity of light at the point P. It is important to distinguish between J and the intensity of radiation i of the source Q as defined on page 82.

phase. Such surfaces, which contain only points in the same phase, are called wave surfaces. The wave surfaces spreading out from a point source Q are then concentric spherical surfaces, and the rays emanating from Q are the radii of these surfaces and are therefore perpendicular to them. The greater the distance of the source, the less curved are the wave surfaces and the more nearly parallel the rays. The wave surfaces of a parallel beam are planes perpendicular to the rays and parallel to each other. Hence such waves are called plane waves. They exist when the source Q is infinitely distant or at the focus of a convergent lens which renders the emergent rays parallel.

Introducing the term λ defined by

$$T \cdot V = \lambda, \quad . \quad . \quad . \quad . \quad . \quad . \quad . \quad (4)$$

(3) becomes

$$s' = A' \sin\left[2\pi\left(\frac{t}{T} - \frac{r}{\lambda}\right) + \delta\right], \quad . \quad . \quad . \quad (5)$$

i.e. at a given time, s' is periodic with respect to r and its period is λ. This period λ, which is the distance at a given instant between any two points along r which are in the same phase, is called the wave length.

The table on page 128 gives the wave lengths in air of various light, heat, and electrical waves. These values are determined from interference or diffraction phenomena.

The wave theory furnishes the simplest possible explanation of interference phenomena. On the other hand it has considerable difficulty in explaining the rectilinear propagation of light. In this respect the analogy between sound and light seems to break down, for sound does not travel in straight lines. The explanation of these difficulties will be considered in detail in the next chapter. This analogy between sound and light presents still further contradictions when polarization phenomena are under consideration. It was these contradictions which prevented for a long time the general recognition of the wave theory in spite of the simple explanation which it offers of interference. The difficulties were not removed until a too close analogy between sound and light was given up. This point, too, will be considered in a later chapter. Here the explanation of refraction as furnished by the wave theory will be briefly presented.

If a plane wave is incident obliquely upon the surface of a refracting body, the normal to the wave front is bent toward the perpendicular to the surface if the velocity of light in the body is less than in the surrounding medium, which will in general be assumed to be air. Upon the incident wave front consider one point A which lies upon the surface, and another

WAVE LENGTHS.

Kind of Light.	λ in mm.
Limit of the photographic rays in vacuum	0.000100
Limit of the photographic rays in air	0.000185
Limit of visible light in the blue	0.000330
Blue hydrogen line	0.000486
Yellow sodium line	0.000589
Red hydrogen line	0.000656
Limit of visible light in the red	0.000812
Longest heat-waves as yet detected	0.06
Shortest electric waves	6

point B which is still outside in the air. If now the wave from A travels more slowly than that from B, it is evident that the wave front, which is the locus of the points at which the light has arrived in a given time, must be bent upon entrance into the refracting medium in such a way that the normal to the wave front (the ray) is turned toward the perpendicular. Hence the wave theory requires the result given by experiment that the velocity of light is smaller in water than in air. The more exact determination of the position of the refracted wave front will be given in connection with the discussion of Huygens' principle, and again more rigorously in Chapter I of Section 2. Here but one important result will be mentioned, namely: *When light passes from a medium A to a medium B*

the index of refraction is equal to the ratio of the velocities of light in A and B.

It was shown on page 6 that the fundamental laws of geometrical optics are all included in the one principle of the extreme path. This principle gains a peculiar significance from the wave theory. Since the index of a body with respect to air is inversely proportional to the velocity of light in the body, the optical path nl is proportional to the time which the light requires to travel the distance l. The law of extreme path asserts, then, that light in travelling between any two points P and P' chooses that path which is so situated that all infinitely near paths would be traversed in the same time. *Thus the law of least path becomes the law of least time.*

The nature of a ray of light may be looked upon from the standpoint of the wave theory in the following way: Elementary disturbances travel from P to P' over all possible paths. But in general they arrive at P' at different times, so that the phases of the individual disturbances do not agree at P', and hence no appreciable effect is produced. Such an effect will, however, immediately appear as soon as the beam is made infinitely narrow, for then the time of propagation between P and P' is the same, so that the elementary disturbances all have the same phase at P'. Hence such an infinitely thin beam marks out the path of the light, i.e. the effect at P' is cut off by introducing an obstacle in the way of the beam.

These considerations, however, are not so conclusive as to make it superfluous to place the fundamental laws of geometrical optics upon a more rigorous analytical basis. The first question to be answered is this: If light and sound are both wave motions why is there a difference in the laws of their propagation? This question will be answered in the next chapter.

The wave theory makes it possible to drop altogether the concept of rays and to calculate the optical effect of reflecting and refracting bodies from a consideration of the wave surface. In the case of a point source P, for example, the wave surfaces in the medium surrounding P are spherical. If the rays are to be homocentrically focussed at P' by means of refraction by a lens, the wave surfaces must after passage through the lens be concentric spherical surfaces with their centre at P'.

Since the rays are the normals to the wave surfaces, the law of Malus follows at once from the wave theory, because reflections and refractions can have no other effect than to deform in some way the wave surfaces.

3. Fresnel's Mirrors.—From the standpoint of the wave theory interference phenomena are explained simply by the principle of the superposition of simultaneous values of the quantity s. Thus if a source Q_1 produces at a point P a disturbance

$$s_1 = A_1 \sin 2\pi\left(\frac{t}{T} - \frac{r_1}{\lambda}\right), \quad . \quad . \quad . \quad . \quad (6)$$

while a source Q_2 produces at the same point a disturbance

$$s_2 = A_2 \sin 2\pi\left(\frac{t}{T} - \frac{r_2}{\lambda}\right), \quad . \quad . \quad . \quad . \quad (7)$$

then, by the principle of superposition, which is applicable provided the rays passing from Q_1 and Q_2 to P have a small inclination to one another,* the resultant disturbance is

$$s = s_1 + s_2. \quad . \quad . \quad . \quad . \quad . \quad . \quad . \quad (8)$$

Now this sum may be put into the form

$$s = A \sin\left(2\pi\frac{t}{T} - \delta\right), \quad . \quad . \quad . \quad . \quad . \quad (9)$$

by setting

$$\left.\begin{aligned} A \cos \delta &= A_1 \cos 2\pi\frac{r_1}{\lambda} + A_2 \cos 2\pi\frac{r_2}{\lambda}, \\ A \sin \delta &= A_1 \sin 2\pi\frac{r_1}{\lambda} + A_2 \sin 2\pi\frac{r_2}{\lambda}, \end{aligned}\right\} \quad . \quad (10)$$

* That this limitation is necessary will be evident from a later discussion in which it will be proved that s is a directed quantity, i.e. a vector.

in which the quantity A represents the amplitude of the resulting disturbance.

Squaring and adding the two equations (10) gives for the intensity of the resultant light at the point P

$$J = A^2 = A_1^2 + A_2^2 + 2A_1A_2 \cos 2\pi\left(\frac{r_1 - r_2}{\lambda}\right). \quad . \quad (11)$$

The quantity $2\pi \frac{r_1 - r_2}{\lambda} = \Delta$ is, by (6) and (7), seen to be the phase difference of the separate disturbances, and the meaning of equation (11) may be stated as follows (Fig. 46): *The resultant amplitude A is equal to the third side of a triangle whose other two sides are A_1 and A_2 and include between them the angle $\pi - \Delta$, in which Δ is the difference of phase between the two disturbances.*

According to this proposition it is evident that maxima and minima of light intensity depend upon the difference of phase Δ, the former occurring when $\Delta = 0, + 2\pi, + 4\pi$, etc., the latter when $\Delta = + \pi, + 3\pi$, etc. Entire darkness must result at a minimum if $A_1 = A_2$.

These conditions are realized in the Fresnel-mirror experiment in which two virtual sources Q_1 and Q_2 (Fig. 47) are produced by reflecting light from a single source Q upon two mirrors S and S' which are slightly inclined to one another. In the space illuminated by both of the sources interference occurs.* From the calculation above there will be darkness at a point P if

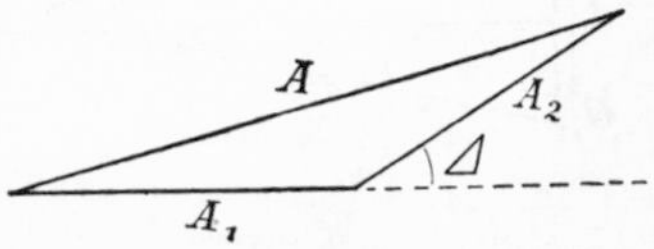

FIG. 46.

$$r_1 - r_2 = \pm \frac{\lambda}{2}, \quad \pm \frac{3\lambda}{2}, \quad \text{etc.} \quad . \quad . \quad . \quad . \quad (12)$$

Considering only such positions of the point P as lie on a line parallel to Q_1Q_2 (Fig. 47), then if d represent the distance

* This space will be considerably diminished if the mirror S projects in front of the mirror S'. Hence care must be taken that the common edge of the mirrors coincides with their line of intersection.

between Q_1 and Q_2, a the distance of the line d from the line P_0P, and p the distance of a point P from the point P_0, which lies on the perpendicular erected at the middle of d,

$$r_1^2 = a^2 + (\tfrac{1}{2}d + p)^2, \quad r_2^2 = a^2 + (\tfrac{1}{2}d - p)^2,$$

i.e. $$r_1^2 - r_2^2 = (r_1 + r_2)(r_1 - r_2) = 2dp,$$

or since $r_1 + r_2$ is approximately equal to $2a$ when p and d are small in comparison with a, it follows that

$$r_1 - r_2 = dp : a,$$

i.e. darkness occurs at the points

$$p = \pm\frac{a}{d}\cdot\frac{\lambda}{2}, \quad \pm\frac{a}{d}\cdot\frac{3\lambda}{2}, \quad \pm\frac{a}{d}\cdot\frac{5\lambda}{2}, \quad \text{etc.} \qquad (13)$$

Hence, if the light be monochromatic, interference fringes will appear on a screen held at a distance a from the line d, and the constant distance between these fringes will be $a\lambda : d$.

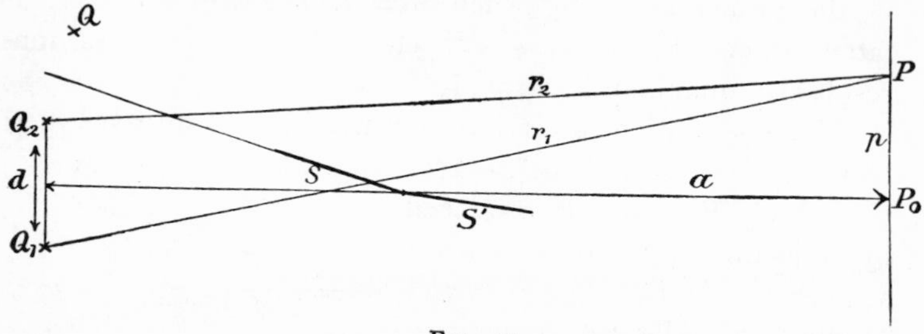

FIG. 47.

If white light is used, colored fringes will appear upon the screen since the different colors contained in white light, on account of their different wave lengths, produce points of maximum and minimum brightness at different places upon the screen. But at the point P_0 there will be no color, since there all the colors have a maximum brightness ($r_1 - r_2 = 0$).

The distance d between the virtual sources may be calculated from the position of the actual source Q with respect to the mirrors and the angle between the mirrors. This angle must be very small (only a few minutes) in order that d may be small enough to permit of the separation of the interference fringes. Since (13) contains only the ratio $a : d$, it is merely necessary to measure the angle subtended at P_0 by the two images Q_1 and Q_2.

Instead of receiving the interference pattern upon a screen, it is possible to observe it by means of a lens or by the eye itself, if it be placed in the path of the rays coming from Q_1 and Q_2 and focussed upon a point P at a distance a from those sources.* Fig. 48 shows an arrangement for making quantitative measurements such as the determination of wave lengths. A cylindrical lens l brings to a line focus the rays from a lamp. This, acting as a source Q, sends rays to both mirrors S and

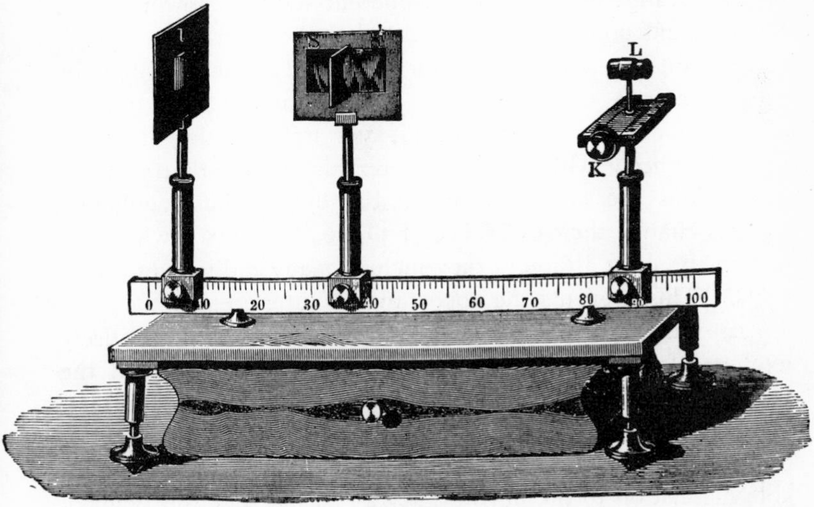

FIG. 48.

S', whose line of intersection is made parallel to the axis of the cylindrical lens. The direct light from Q is cut off by a screen attached to the mirrors and at right angles to them. The

*If the eye be focussed with or without a lens upon P, the two interfering beams reach the image of P upon the retina with the same difference of phase which they have at P itself, since the optical paths between P and the retinal image are the same for all the rays. Hence the intensity upon the retina is zero if it would be zero upon the corresponding point of a screen placed at P.

interference fringes are observed by means of a micrometer eyepiece L which is movable by the micrometer screw K.

The question arises whether interference fringes might not be more simply produced by using as sources not the two virtual images of a real source, but two small adjacent openings in a screen placed before a luminous surface.

In this case no interference phenomena are obtained even with monochromatic light such as a sodium flame. For if two sources are to produce interference, their phases must always be either exactly the same or else must have a constant difference. Such sources are called coherent. They may always be obtained by dividing a single source into two by any sort of optical arrangement. With incoherent sources, however, like two different points of a flame, although the difference of phase is constant for a large number of periods, since, as will be shown later, a monochromatic source emits a large number of vibrations of constant period, yet irregularities in these vibrations occur within so short intervals of time that separate impressions are not produced in the eye. Thus incoherent sources change their difference of phase at intervals which are extremely short although they include many millions of vibrations. This prevents the appearance of interference.

As was remarked on page 124, diffraction is not entirely excluded from this simple interference experiment. All the boundaries of the mirrors can give rise to diffraction, but especially the edge in which the two touch. In order to avoid this effect it is desirable that the incident light have a considerable inclination to the mirrors (say 45°), and that the point of observation be at a considerable distance from them. Also the angle between the mirrors must not be made too small. In this way it is possible to arrange the experiment so that the extreme rays which proceed from Q_1 and Q_2 to the common edge of the mirrors are removed as far as possible from the point of observation P.

4. Modifications of the Fresnel Mirrors.—The considerations advanced in paragraph 3 are typical of all cases in which interference is produced by the division of a single source into two coherent sources Q_1 and Q_2. This division may be brought about in several other ways. The Fresnel bi-prism, shown in cross-section in Fig. 49, is particularly convenient. The light

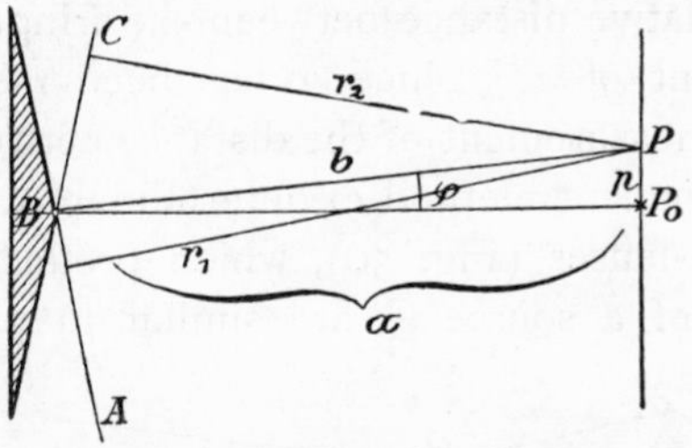

FIG. 49.

from a line source Q which is parallel to the edge B is refracted by the prism in such a way that two coherent line sources Q_1 and Q_2 are produced.

If such a prism be placed upon the table of a spectrometer so that the edge B is vertical, and if the vertical slit of the collimator focussed for parallel rays be used for the source, then two separate images of the slit appear in the telescope of the spectrometer. The angle α between these images may be read off upon the graduated circle of the spectrometer when the cross-hairs have been set successively upon the two images. This angle α is the supplement of the angle ABC (Fig. 49) which the two refracted wave fronts AB and BC make with each other after passage through the prism. If the telescope be removed, dark fringes may be observed at any point P for which (cf. 12) $r_1 - r_2 = \pm \frac{1}{2}\lambda, \frac{3}{2}\lambda$, etc., in which r_1 and r_2 are the distances of the point P from the wave fronts AB and BC. From the figure it is evident that

$$r_1 = b \sin (ABP), \quad r_2 = b \sin (CBP),$$

hence

$$r_1 - r_2 = 2b \cos \frac{ABC}{2} \cdot \sin \phi.$$

The angle ϕ is very small so that $\sin\phi = \tan\phi = p : a$. Furthermore $ABC = \pi - \alpha$, and since $b = a$ approximately, and $\sin\alpha = \alpha$, it follows finally that

$$r_1 - r_2 = \alpha \cdot p.$$

Thus the relative distance between the fringes is $\lambda : \alpha$, i.e. it is independent of a. Since α has been measured by the telescope, the measurement of the distance between the fringes furnishes a convenient method of determining λ.

Billet's half-lenses (Fig. 50), which produce two real or virtual images of a source Q, are similar in principle to the

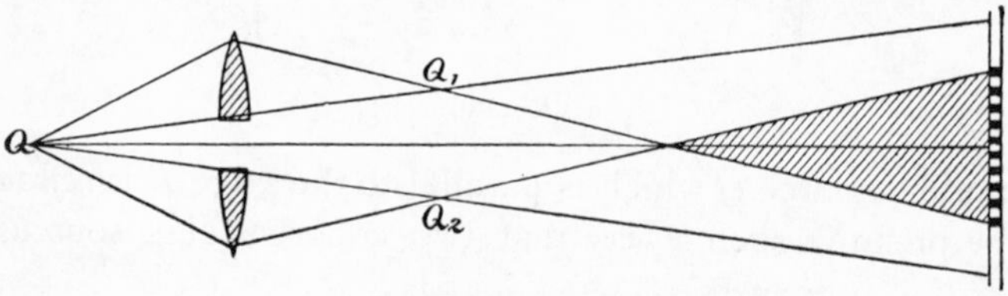

FIG. 50.

Fresnel bi-prism. The space within which interference occurs is shaded in the figure.

5. Newton's Rings and the Colors of Thin Plates.—Sufficiently thin films of all transparent bodies show brilliant colors. These may be most easily observed in soap-bubbles, or in thin films of oil upon water, or in the oxidation films formed upon the heated surfaces of polished metals.

The explanation of these phenomena is at once evident as soon as they are attributed to interference taking place between the light reflected from the front and the rear surface of the film.

Consider a ray AB of homogeneous light (Fig. 51) incident at an angle ϕ upon a thin plane parallel plate of thickness d. At the front surface of the plate AB divides into a reflected ray BC and a refracted ray BD. At the rear surface the latter is partially reflected to B' and passes out of the plate as the ray $B'C'$. The essential elements of the phenomena can be presented by discussing the interference between the two rays

BC and $B'C'$ only. If these two rays are brought together at a point on the retina, as is done when the eye is focussed for parallel rays, the impression produced is a minimum if the phase of the ray BC differs from that of $B'C'$ by π, 3π, 5π, etc.

Of course for a complete calculation of the intensity of the reflected light all the successive reflections which take place between the two surfaces must be taken into account. This

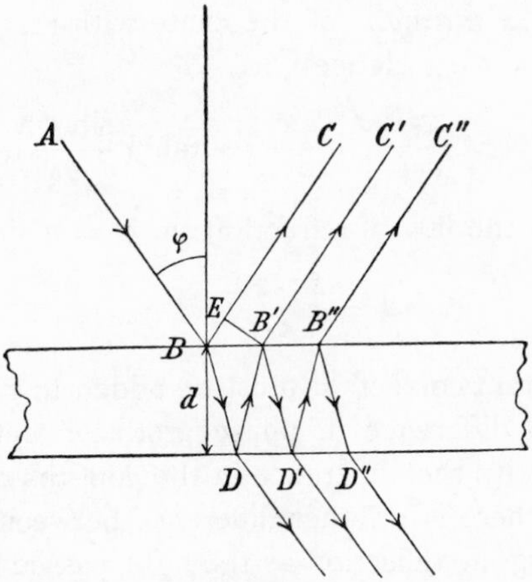

FIG. 51.

rigorous discussion will be given in Section II, Chapter II, § 11. It is at once apparent that the introduction of these repeated reflections will not essentially modify the result, since the intensity of these rays is much smaller than that of BC and $B'C'$, which have experienced but one reflection.

If a perpendicular $B'E$ be dropped from B' upon BC, the two rays BC and $B'C'$ would have no difference of phase if the phase at B' were the same as that at E. The two rays would then come together at a point upon the retina in the same phase. The difference of phase between the points E and B' is identical with the difference of phase between the rays BC and $B'C'$.

But the difference of phase between B' and E is

$$\Delta = 2\pi\left(\frac{BD+DB'}{\lambda'} - \frac{BE}{\lambda}\right),$$

provided λ' represents the wave length of the light within the plate, λ its wave length in the surrounding medium. If now the angle of refraction be denoted by χ, then

$$BD = B'D = d : \cos\chi, \quad BE = BB' \sin\phi = 2d \tan\chi \sin\phi;$$

further, $\lambda : \lambda' = n$ (index of the plate with respect to the surrounding medium). Hence

$$\Delta = \frac{2\pi \cdot 2d}{\lambda'}\left(\frac{1}{\cos\chi} - \tan\chi \frac{\sin\phi}{n}\right),$$

or, since from the law of refraction $\sin\phi = n \sin\chi$,

$$\Delta = \frac{2\pi \cdot 2d}{\lambda'} \cos\chi. \quad . \quad . \quad . \quad . \quad . \quad (14)$$

An important correction must be added to this expression. (14) gives the difference in phase produced between the rays BC and $B'C'$ by the difference in the lengths of their optical paths. But there is another difference between the two rays. BC has undergone reflection as the light passed from air to the plate, $B'C'$ as it passed from the plate to air. Now in general a change of phase is introduced by reflection; and since the reflection of the two rays occurs under different conditions, a quantity Δ' must be added to the difference in phase as given in (14). This quantity Δ' depends solely upon the reflection itself and not at all upon the difference in the lengths of the optical paths. Hence (14) becomes

$$\Delta = 2\pi \cdot \frac{2d}{\lambda'} \cos\chi + \Delta'. \quad . \quad . \quad . \quad . \quad (15)$$

A definite assertion may be made with respect to this quantity Δ' without entering any farther into the theory of light. Consider first the case in which the thickness d of the plate gradually approaches zero. According to (14) no difference of phase would then occur between BC and $B'C'$; they should therefore reinforce each other. But this effect cannot take place, because a plate of thickness $d = 0$ is no plate at all and the homogeneity of the space would not be disturbed if, as will be assumed, the medium above and below the plate is the same, for instance air; and hence no reflection of light can take place. For reflection can only take place when there is a change in the homogeneity of the medium; otherwise light could never travel with undiminished intensity through a homogeneous transparent medium like the ether. Hence for $d = 0$ complete interference of the two rays BC and $B'C'$ must take place so that no reflected light whatever is obtained. Since in this case $(d = 0)$ $\Delta = \pm \pi$, it follows from (15) that

$$\Delta' = \pm \pi. \quad \ldots \ldots \quad (16)$$

Whether Δ be taken as equal to $+ \pi$, or $- \pi$, or $+ 3\pi$, etc., is immaterial for this discussion, since the addition of 2π to the phase of a ray produces no change whatever in its condition of vibration.

In consideration of (16) and (15) it is evident that a minimum of intensity occurs when

$$\frac{2d}{\lambda'} \cos \chi = 0, 1, 2, \ldots \quad \ldots \ldots \quad (17)$$

The light transmitted by the plate must likewise show interference effects. Since it is assumed that no absorption takes place within the plate, the transmitted light must be of the same intensity as the incident light if the intensity of the reflected light is zero. On the other hand, the transmitted light must have a minimum of intensity when the reflected light is a maximum. This occurs for plates whose thicknesses lie midway between the thicknesses determined by (17), for then the two reflected rays BC and $B'C'$ are in the same phase. Nevertheless the minima in the transmitted light are never marked, since the reflected light is always but a small portion of the incident light. The quantitative relations between the reflected and the transmitted portions can only be deduced after a more complete treatment of the theory (cf. Section II, Chapter II).

If the plate be wedge-shaped instead of plane parallel, it must be crossed, when viewed by reflected light, by dark interference bands which are parallel to the edge of the wedge and lie at those places where the thickness d of the wedge corresponds to (17). In order that the fringes may appear separate it is evident that, because of the smallness of λ', the angle of the wedge must be small. Nevertheless these fringes cannot be perceived unless a broad source be used, for light from a point source is reflected to an eye placed at a particular point and focussed for parallel rays only from a single point of the wedge.

By proper focussing of the eye sharp interference fringes may be seen when the source is broad. In order to be able to form a judgment as to the *visibility of the interference fringes* in this case it is necessary to bear in mind the fundamental law stated above in accordance with which only those rays are capable of interfering which are emitted from one and the same point of the source, since only such rays are coherent.

Now it is evident that every point P situated anywhere in front of the plate or the wedge will be the intersection of two coherent rays emitted from a point Q of the source, the one reflected from the front, the other from the rear, surface. In general these rays start from Q in slightly different directions, but they are brought together at a point P' upon the retina if the eye is focussed upon the point of intersection P. In this case an interference between these two waves might be detected. But there are many other pairs of coherent rays emitted from other points Q', Q'', etc., of the source, which intersect at the same point P. In general these rays pass through the wedge at different places and with different inclinations, and hence have various differences of phase at P. Therefore when the eye is focussed upon P the interference phenomena are either indistinct or else disappear entirely. Interference is perceived with the greatest clearness only when all the pairs of coherent rays which proceed from the different points of the source and intersect at P have the same difference of phase. The locus of the points P for which this condition is fulfilled is the surface of best visibility of the interference pattern. This locus is a continuous surface and has a complicated form if the incident light is very oblique.

But, for nearly perpendicular incidence, the solution for a thin wedge is simple. In this case, with a broad source, the interference fringes appear most clearly when the eye is focussed

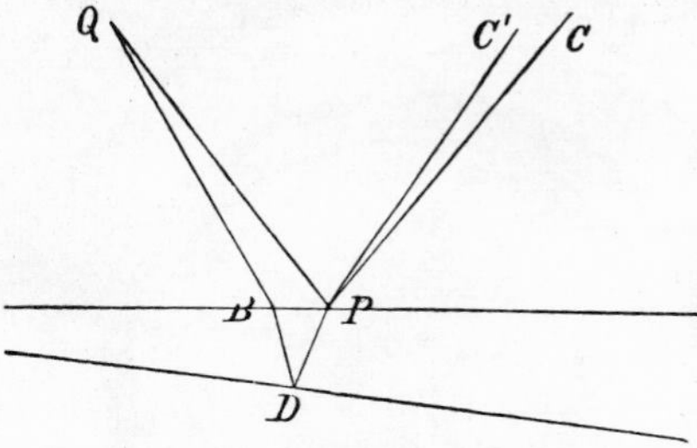

FIG. 52.

upon the wedge itself. If the eye is focussed upon a point P of the wedge (Fig. 52), QPC and $QBDPC'$ are two coherent rays which are brought together upon a point of the retina. These rays have a certain difference of phase, which depends only upon the thickness d of the wedge (say of glass) at the point P, and which from (15) and (16) may be written, since ϕ and therefore also (for a thin wedge) χ differ but little from zero,

$$\Delta = 2\pi\frac{2d}{\lambda'} + \pi.$$

But every pair of coherent rays emitted by the other points Q', Q'', etc., of the source, and intersecting in P, have the same difference in phase, since for all rays the angle of incidence ϕ and also χ is to be taken so small that $\cos\chi = 1$.*

* This is only permissible when the thickness d of the wedge is not too great. When d is very large, for example, several thousand wave lengths, the change in χ for the different pairs of wave lengths must still be taken into consideration. The interference then becomes indistinct.

Thus *with nearly perpendicular incidence and a broad source the interference figure lies within the wedge itself.*

In order to observe interference in a film of variable thickness, Newton pressed a slightly convex lens upon a plane glass surface. The thin layer of air between the lens and the plate gives rise to concentric interference circles whose diameters increase as the square roots of the even numbers. Fig. 53 is

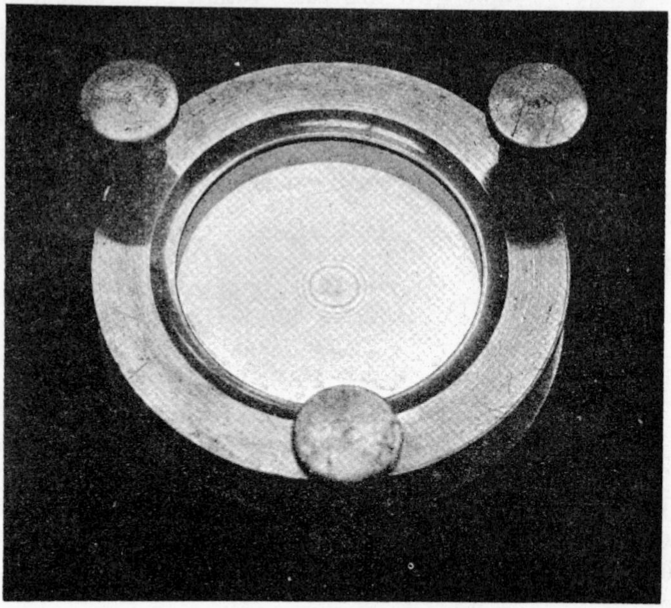

FIG. 53.

a photograph of the effect produced by white light. With homogeneous light the rings extend to the very edge of the plate.

Illuminated by white light, a thin plate appears colored; for all those colors whose wave lengths λ satisfy (17) are want ing. But when the thickness of the plate is considerable the colors which are cut out extend in close succession over the whole spectrum, hence the colors which remain produce a mixture which cannot be distinguished from white light. Also the color of the plate is not brilliant when it is too thin, because in this case all the colors are present to a greater or less extent. The colors are most brilliant for certain mean thicknesses, which for air films lie between 0.00016 mm. and 0.0008 mm. Such colors are naturally not pure spectral colors, since they arise from cutting out certain regions of color from the whole spectrum. In Newton's arrangement the rings show in close succession all the colors of thin plates.

If the incident light is made more oblique, the plate changes color. For the presence of the factor cos χ in (17) shows that increasing the obliquity of incidence of the light has the same effect as diminishing d in the case of perpendicular incidence.

The color of the light transmitted by the plate is complementary to that of the reflected light, since the sum of the two must be equal to the incident light. Nevertheless the color of the transmitted light is never so saturated as that of the reflected light, because in the transmitted light a color is never completely cut out, but only somewhat weakened.

The color shown by a thin film in reflected light furnishes a very delicate means of determining its thickness, provided the index of refraction of the film be known. Only the knowledge of the thickness of a film of air which shows the same color is required. This knowledge may be obtained from Newton's rings or, as will be seen later, from the optical properties of crystals.

Interference has also been applied to the determination of the thermal expansion of bodies in the *Abbe-Fizeau dilatometer*. With this instrument* the change caused by thermal expansion in the distance between the surface O_2 of a glass plate and a polished surface O_1 of the body is measured by the change in the interference figure which is formed between the two surfaces O_1 and O_2.

---

* Cf. Pulfrich, Ztschr. Instrk. 1893, or Müller-Pouillet, Optik, p. 924.

6. Achromatic Interference Bands.—In order that an interference band may be achromatic it is necessary that at the place at which it is formed the difference of phase Δ of the interfering rays be the same for all colors. Whether the band is bright or dark depends upon the value of Δ. Thus in Newton's apparatus the central spot is black in reflected light, since there the interfering rays of all colors have the same difference of phase $\Delta = \pi$. But if the interference pattern be observed through a prism, the central spot no longer appears achromatic, but the position of achromatism is at the point at which Δ varies very little or not at all with the color, i.e. at the point at which

$$\frac{\partial \Delta}{\partial \lambda} = 0, \quad . \quad . \quad . \quad . \quad . \quad . \quad . \quad (18)$$

in which λ is the wave length of the color in air.* With a strongly dispersive prism the achromatic position may be quite a distance from the central spot.

Likewise if a thin plate, for example mica, be introduced before one side of a Fresnel bi-prism, the interference pattern is changed. In this case, too, the achromatic fringe is not at the place for which $\Delta = 0$ as it was before the introduction of the plate, but at the place for which (18) is satisfied. The reason of this is that the thin plate, because of the dependence of its index upon the color, produces retardations of a different number of waves for the different colors.

7. The Interferometer.—Interference fringes due to small differences of path may be produced not only with thin films but also with thick plates by using differential effects between two of them. Jamin's form of instrument consists in two equally thick plane parallel glass plates P_1 and P_2 (cf. Fig. 54) placed almost parallel to each other and at a large distance apart. A ray of light LA is split up into two rays $ABCDE$

* More accurately this equation should be written $\frac{\partial \Delta}{\partial T} = 0$, in which T is the period. If the small dispersion of the air be neglected, this is identical with (18).

and $AB'C'D'E'$, which are in condition to interfere if the two emergent rays DE and $D'E'$ are again brought together at a point. Since these two rays are parallel, the eye or the telescope which receives them must be focussed for parallel rays. In order to obtain greatest intensity the source is placed in the focal plane of a convergent lens so that the beam LA which

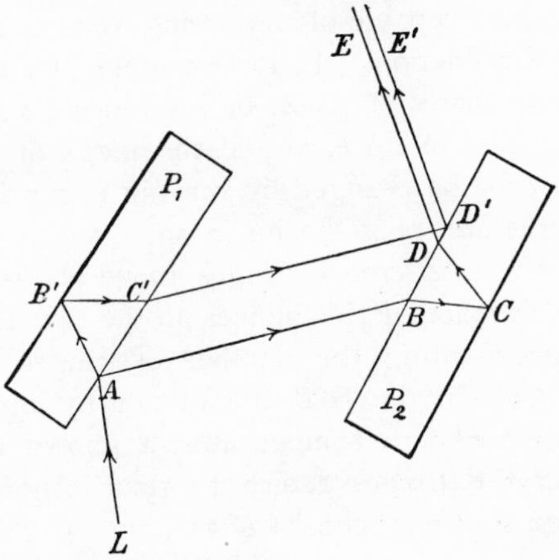

FIG. 54.

falls upon the plate P_1 is parallel. It is furthermore of advantage to silver the plates upon their rear surfaces. The difference of phase between the rays $C'D'$ and AB is, by (15), $\frac{4\pi d}{\lambda'} \cos \chi_1 + \Delta'$, in which χ_1 represents the angle of refraction in the plate P_1. The rays $D'E'$ and DE have, in addition, the difference of phase $-\left(\frac{4\pi d}{\lambda'} \cos \chi_2 + \Delta'\right)$, in which χ_2, the angle of refraction of the plate P_2, differs slightly from that of the plate P_1, since P_1 and P_2 are not exactly parallel. The total difference of phase between $D'E'$ and DE is therefore

$$\Delta = \frac{4\pi d}{\lambda'} (\cos \chi_1 - \cos \chi_2);$$

and since $\cos \chi_1 - \cos \chi_2$ varies somewhat with the inclination of the beam LA, the field of view at EE' will be crossed by interference fringes.

The chief advantage of this form of interferometer lies in the fact that the two interfering rays AB and $C'D'$ are separated considerably from one another provided thick plates are used and the incidence is oblique (50° is most advantageous). This instrument is capable of measuring very small variations in the index of refraction. If, for example, two tubes, closed at the ends with plates of glass, be introduced, the one in the path AB, the other in $C'D'$, and if the index of refraction of the air in one tube be changed by varying either the temperature or the pressure, or if the air in one tube be replaced by another gas, the interference fringes move across the field of view. The difference of the indices in the two tubes may be determined by counting the number of fringes which move across some mark in the field of view, or by introducing, by means of some sort of a compensator, a known difference of phase, so that the fringes return to their original position. Such a compensator may consist of two equally thick plates of glass, p_1 and p_2, which are movable about a common axis and make a small angle with one another (Jamin's compensator). The ray AB passes through p_1 alone, the ray $C'D'$ through p_2. The difference of phase which is thus introduced between the two rays depends upon the inclination of the plate p_1 to AB.*

With Jamin's instrument it is not possible to produce a separation between the two rays of more than 2 cm. A much larger separation may be obtained if, as in Zehnder's instrument,† four nearly parallel plates be used. According to Mach ‡ it is advantageous to replace two of these plates by metal mirrors S_1 and S_2. Fig. 55 shows Mach's arrangement. He also introduced a device for increasing the intensity of the

* For the more rigorous calculation cf. F. Neumann, Vorles. über theor. Optik (Leipzig, 1885), p. 286.

† Cf. Zehnder, Ztschr. Instrkd. 1891, p. 275.

‡ Mach, Wien. Ber. 101 (II.A.), p. 5, 1892. Ztschr. Instrkd. 1892, p. 89.

light. In the arrangements shown in Figs. 54 and 55, the rays coming to the eye at E are of small intensity because they have undergone one reflection at a glass surface and have thus been materially weakened. In Fig. 55 the rays from S_2 which

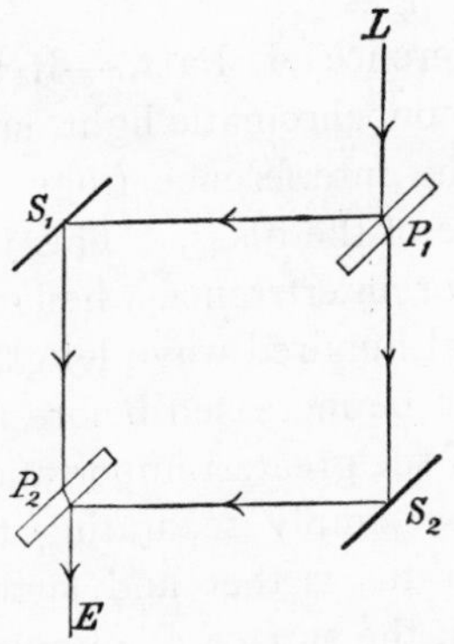

FIG. 55.

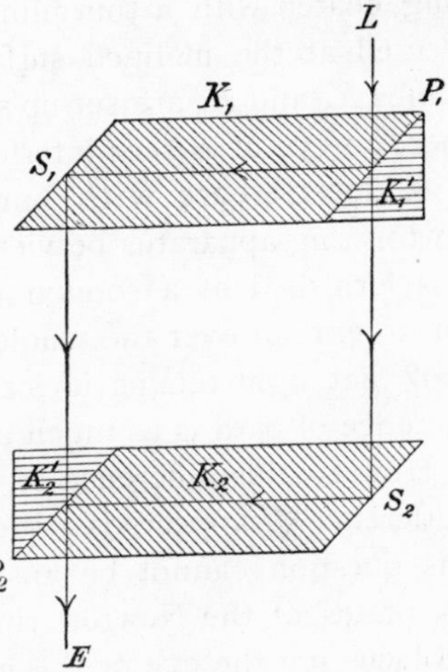

FIG. 56.

pass through PP_2 are much more intense than those which are reflected from PP_2 to E. This difficulty can be diminished by increasing the reflecting power of the glass surface. This is done by depositing a thin film of silver or gold upon the surface, the most favorable thickness of such a film being that for which the intensity of the reflected light is equal to that of the transmitted. But with the arrangement shown in Fig. 55 it is not necessary to use two plates P_1 and P_2 of finite thickness in order to produce interference; it is sufficient if, instead, the division of the ray into a reflected ray and a transmitted ray is accomplished by means of a thin film of metal. This may be done by pressing together the partially silvered hypothenuse surfaces of two right-angled glass prisms. The reflections upon the mirrors S_1 and S_2 may be replaced by total reflections upon the unsilvered surfaces of right-angled glass prisms. Finally these latter prisms may be united with the prisms which divide the light so as to form single pieces of glass. Thus Fig. 56 shows Mach's construction of the interferometer, in which to the two equal glass rhombs K_1 and K_2 the two prisms K_1' and K_2' are cemented with linseed oil, the surfaces of contact P_1 and P_2 being coated with a thin film of gold. The rays are totally reflected at the inclined surfaces S_1 and S_2. When the two rhombs K_1 and K_2 are set up so as to be nearly parallel to each other, an eye at E sees interference fringes.

8. Interference with Large Difference of Path.—If the Newton ring apparatus be viewed in monochromatic light, such as is furnished by a sodium flame, the interference rings are seen to extend over the whole surface of the glass. This is a proof that light retains its capacity for interference when the difference of path is as much as several hundred wave lengths.

How far this difference of path can be increased before the interference disappears is a question of the greatest importance. This question cannot be answered by simply separating the two plates of the Newton ring apparatus farther and farther and focussing the eye or the lens upon the surface O_1 of one of the plates, for, in accordance with the note on page 141, the interference fringes would soon become indistinct on account of the changing inclination of the coherent pairs of rays which intersect at a point of the surface O_1. It is necessary, therefore, to provide that all coherent pairs of rays which are brought together in the same point upon the retina of the observer have the same difference of phase.

This condition is fulfilled when the interference arises from reflections at two parallel surfaces O_1 and O_2, and the eye or the observing telescope is focussed for parallel rays. All the interfering coherent pairs of rays which are brought together at a point of the retina then traverse the interval of thickness d between the two surfaces at the same inclination to the common normal N to these two surfaces and hence have the same difference of phase, provided the distance d is constant. This difference of phase changes with the angle of inclination to N, so that the interference figure consists of concentric circles whose centres lie upon the perpendicular from the eye to the plates.* The interference rings thus produced are *curves of equal inclination*, rather than *curves of equal thickness*, such as are seen in a thin wedge or the Newton ring apparatus.

Such curves of equal inclination may be observed in monochromatic light in plane parallel plates several millimeters thick, so that interference takes place when the difference of path amounts to several thousand wave lengths. In order to be able to vary continuously the difference in path Michelson devised the following arrangement: †

The ray QA (Fig. 57) falls at an angle of 45° upon the half-silvered front face of a plane parallel glass plate, where it is divided into a transmitted ray, which passes on to the plane mirror D, and a reflected ray, which passes to the mirror C. These two mirrors return the ray to the point A, where the first is reflected, the second transmitted to E.

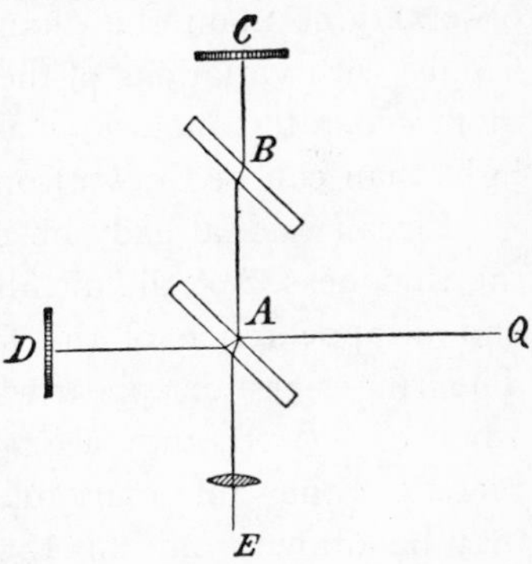

FIG. 57.

A second plane parallel glass plate B, of the same thickness as A, makes the difference in the paths of the two rays which come to interference at E equal to zero, provided the two mirrors D and C are symmetrically placed with respect to the plate A.

It is evident that, as far as interference is concerned, this arrangement is equivalent to a film of air between two plane surfaces O_1 and O_2, O_1 being the mirror C, and O_2 the image

* Lummer uses this phenomenon (cf. Müller-Pouillet, Optik, pp. 916–924) to test glass plates for parallelism. The curves of equal inclination vary from their circular form as soon as the distance d between the two reflecting surfaces O_1 and O_2 is not absolutely constant.

† A. A. Michelson, Am. J. Sci. (3) 34, p. 427, 1887. Travaux et Mém. du Bureau International d. Poids et Mes. 11, 1895, pp. 1–237. In this second work Michelson determined the value of the metre in wave lengths of light by the use of his interferometer.

of D in the plate A. This image O_2 must also be parallel to C if the interference curves of equal inclination are to be seen clearly when the difference of path is large. In order to vary the difference of path, one of the mirrors C is made movable in the direction AB by means of a micrometer-screw. With this apparatus, using as a source of light the red cadmium line from a Geissler tube, Michelson was able to obtain interference when the difference of path in air was 20 cm., a distance equal to about 300,000 wave lengths. Interference was obtained with the green mercury radiation when the difference of path was 540,000 wave lengths.*

These experiments are particularly instructive because observations upon the change of visibility of the interference fringes with variations of the difference of path furnish data for more accurate conclusions as to the homogeneity of a source of light than can be drawn from spectroscopic experiments.

Fizeau had already observed that a continuous change of the thickness d of the air film produced a periodic appearance and disappearance of the fringes produced by sodium light. The fringes first disappear when the thickness d is 0.1445 mm.; when $d = 0.289$ they are again clear; when $d = 0.4335$ they reach another minimum of clearness; etc. The conclusion may be drawn from this that the sodium line consists of two lines close together. The visibility of the fringes reaches a minimum when a bright fringe due to one line falls upon a dark fringe due to the other. Since the mean wave length of sodium light is 0.000589 mm., the thickness $d = 0.289$ mm. corresponds to 491 wave lengths. If the difference between the wave lengths of the two sodium lines be represented by $\lambda_1 - \lambda_2$, it follows that

$$(\lambda_1 - \lambda_2)\cdot 491 = \frac{\lambda}{2} = 0.000294 \text{ mm.},$$

i.e.

$$\lambda_1 - \lambda_2 = 0.000\,0006 \text{ mm.}$$

* A. Perot and Ch. Fabry (see C. R. 128, p. 1221, 1899), using a Geissler tube fed by a high-voltage battery, obtained interference for a difference of path of 790,000 wave lengths.

Michelson has given a more general solution of the problem.*

According to equation (11) on page 131 the intensity of illumination produced by two equally bright coherent rays whose difference of path is $2l$ is

$$J = 2A^2\left(1 + \cos 2\pi\frac{2l}{\lambda}\right). \quad . \quad . \quad . \quad . \qquad (19)$$

Instead of the wave length λ of light in air, its reciprocal

$$\frac{1}{\lambda} = m \quad . \quad . \quad . \quad . \quad . \quad . \qquad (20)$$

will be introduced. Then m denotes the number of waves in unit length.

If now the light is not strictly homogeneous, i.e. if it contains several wave lengths λ, or wave numbers m, then if the wave numbers lie between m and $m + dm$, the factor A^2 in equation (19) may be represented by $\psi(m) \cdot dm$. The intensity J obtained when interference is produced by an air film of thickness l is

$$J = 2\int_{m_1}^{m_2} \psi(m)[1 + \cos 4\pi\ lm]dm, \quad . \quad . \qquad (21)$$

in which the limits of integration are those wave numbers between which $\psi(m)$ differs appreciably from zero.

Assuming first that the source consists of a single spectral line of small width, and setting

$$m = \overline{m} + x, \quad m_1 = \overline{m} - a, \quad m_2 = \overline{m} + a, \quad . \qquad (22)$$

(21) becomes

$$J = 2\int_{-a}^{+a} \psi(x)[1 + \cos 4\pi l(\overline{m} + x)]dx;$$

* This development is found in Phil. Mag. 5th Ser., Vol. 31, p. 338, 1891; Vol. 34, pp. 380 and 407 (Rayleigh), 1892.

or setting

$$\left.\begin{aligned} 4\pi lm = \vartheta, \quad \int \psi(x)dx = P, \\ \int \psi(x)\cos(4\pi lx)\cdot dx = C, \quad \int \psi(x)\sin(4\pi lx)\cdot dx = S, \end{aligned}\right\} \quad (22')$$

$$\tfrac{1}{2}J = P + C\cos\vartheta - S\sin\vartheta. \quad . \quad . \quad . \quad . \quad (23)$$

If the thickness of the air-plate be slightly altered, J varies because ϑ does. On the other hand, C and S may be considered independent of small changes in l, provided the width of the spectral line, i.e. the quantity a, is small.

Hence, by (23), maxima and minima of the intensity J occur when

$$\tan\vartheta = -\frac{S}{C}, \quad . \quad . \quad . \quad . \quad . \quad . \quad (24)$$

the maxima being given by

$$\tfrac{1}{2}J_{\text{max.}} = P + \sqrt{C^2 + S^2}, \quad . \quad . \quad . \quad . \quad . \quad (25)$$

the minima by

$$\tfrac{1}{2}J_{\text{min.}} = P - \sqrt{C^2 + S^2}. \quad . \quad . \quad . \quad . \quad . \quad (25')$$

Hence no interference is visible when $C = S = 0$. But also when these two expressions are small there will be no perceptible interference. The visibility of the interference fringes is conveniently defined by

$$V = \frac{J_{\text{max.}} - J_{\text{min}}}{J_{\text{max.}} + J_{\text{min.}}}. \quad . \quad . \quad . \quad . \quad . \quad (26)$$

Hence, from (25) and (25'),

$$V^2 = \frac{C^2 + S^2}{P^2}. \quad . \quad . \quad . \quad . \quad . \quad (27)$$

This equation shows how the visibility of the fringes varies with the difference of path $2l$ of the two interfering beams when l is changed by the micrometer-screw.

If the distribution of brightness of the spectral line is symmetrical with respect to the middle, $S = 0$ and (27) becomes

$$V = C : P.$$

If it be assumed that $\psi(x) =$ constant $= c$, then

$$P = 2ac, \quad C = \frac{2c \sin 4\pi la}{4\pi l}, \quad V = \frac{\sin 4\pi la}{4\pi la}. \quad . \quad (28)$$

Thus the interference fringes vanish when $4la = 1, 2, 3$, etc., and the fringes are most distinct ($V = 1$) when $l = 0$. As l increases, the fringes, even for the most favorable values of l, become less and less distinct, e.g. for $4la = \frac{3}{2}$

$$V = 2 : 3\pi = 0.212.$$

Likewise a periodic vanishing and continual diminution in the distinctness of the maxima occur if, instead of $\psi(x) =$ constant,

$$\psi(x) = \cos^p \pi \frac{x}{2a}.$$

The smallest value of l for which the fringes vanish is given by $4l_1a = \frac{p}{2} + 1$; they vanish again when $4l_2a = \frac{p}{2} + 2$, $4l_3a = \frac{p}{2} + 3$, etc. Hence from the distances l_1, l_2, l_3, at which the visibility curve becomes zero, the width a of the line, as well as the exponent p, which gives its distribution of brightness, may be determined.

If $$\psi(x) = e^{-px^2} \text{*}$$

there is a gradual diminution of the visibility without periodic maxima and minima.

In like manner, when the source consists of several narrow spectral lines, the visibility curve may be deduced from (21). Thus, for example, two equally intense lines produce periodic

* This intensity law would follow from Maxwell's law of the distribution of velocities of the molecules as given in the kinetic theory of gases.

zero values of V. If the two lines are not equally intense, the visibility does not actually become zero, but passes through maxima and minima. This is the case of the double sodium line.

This discussion shows how, from any assumed intensity law $\psi(m)$, the visibility V of the fringes may be deduced. The inverse problem of determining $\psi(m)$ from V is much more difficult. Apart from the fact that the numerical values of V can only be obtained from the appearance of the fringes by a somewhat arbitrary process,* the problem is really not solvable, since, as follows from (27), only $C^2 + S^2$ can be determined from V, and not C and S separately.† Under the assumption that the distribution of brightness in the several spectral lines is symmetical with respect to the middle, a solution may indeed be obtained, since then, for a single line, $S = 0$, and for several lines similar simplifications may be made. Michelson actually observed the visibility curves V of numerous spectral lines and found them to differ widely.‡ He then found by trial what intensity law $\psi(m)$ best satisfied the observed forms of V. It must be admitted, however, that the resulting $\psi(m)$ is not necessarily the correct one, even though the distribution of intensity and the width of the several spectral lines are obtained from this valuable investigation of Michelson's with a greater degree of approximation than is possible with a spectroscope or a diffraction grating. In any case it is of great interest to have established the fact that lines exist which are so homogeneous that interference is possible when the difference of path is as much as 500,000 wave lengths.

9. Stationary Waves.—In the interference phenomena which have thus far been considered, the two interfering

---

* V might be determined rigorously if $J_{max.}$ and $J_{min.}$ were measured with a photometer or a bolometer.

† From Fourrier's theorem $\psi(m)$ could be completely determined if C and S were separately known for all values of l.

‡ Ebert has shown in Wied. Ann. 43, p. 790, 1891, that these visibility curves vary greatly with varying conditions of the source.

beams have had the same direction of propagation. But interference can also be detected when the two rays travel in opposite directions. If upon the train of plane waves

$$s_1 = A \sin 2\pi\left(\frac{t}{T} - \frac{z}{\lambda}\right),$$

which is travelling in the positive direction of the z-axis, there be superposed the train of plane waves

$$s_2 = A \sin 2\pi\left(\frac{t}{T} + \frac{z}{\lambda}\right),$$

which is travelling in the negative direction of the z-axis, there results

$$s = s_1 + s_2 = 2A \sin 2\pi\frac{t}{T} \cos 2\pi\frac{z}{\lambda}. \quad . \quad . \quad (29)$$

This equation represents a light vibration whose amplitude $2A \cos 2\pi z/\lambda$ is a periodic function of z. For $\frac{z}{\lambda} = \frac{1}{4}, \frac{3}{4}, \frac{5}{4}$, etc., the amplitude is zero, and the corresponding points are called *nodes*. For $\frac{z}{\lambda} = 0, \frac{1}{2}, \frac{2}{2}$, etc., the amplitude is a maximum, and the corresponding points are called *loops*. The distance between successive nodes or successive loops is therefore $\frac{1}{2}\lambda$. This kind of interference gives rise to waves called *stationary*, because the nodes and loops have fixed positions in space.

Wiener * proved the existence of such stationary waves by letting light fall perpendicularly upon a metallic mirror of high reflecting power. In this way stationary waves are produced by the interference of the reflected with the incident light. In order to be able to prove the existence of the nodes and loops Wiener coated a plate of glass with an extremely thin film of sensitized collodion, whose thickness was only $\frac{1}{30}$ of a light-wave = 20 millionths of a mm., and placed it nearly parallel to the front of the mirror upon which a beam of light from an electric arc was allowed to fall. The sensitized film

* O. Wiener, Wied. Ann. 40, p. 203, 1890.

then intersects the planes of the nodes and loops in a system of equidistant straight lines, whose distance apart is greater the smaller the angle between the mirror and the collodion film. Photographic development of the film actually shows this system of straight lines. This proves not only that photographic action may be obtained upon such a thin film, but also that such action is different at the nodes and the loops. These interesting interference phenomena may also be conveniently demonstrated by means of the fluorescent effects which take place in thin gelatine films containing fluorescin.* Such a film shows a system of equidistant green bands. It is a fact of great theoretical importance, as will be seen later, that the mirror itself lies at a node.

10. Photography in Natural Colors.—Lippmann has made use of these stationary light-waves in obtaining photographs in color. As a sensitive film he chose a transparent uniform layer of a mixture of collodion and albumen containing iodide and bromide of silver. This he laid upon mercury, which served as the mirror. When this plate has been exposed to the spectrum, developed, and fixed, it reproduces approximately the spectrum colors. The simplest explanation is that in that part of the film which was exposed to light whose wave length within the film was λ, thin layers of silver have been deposited at a distance apart of $\frac{1}{2}\lambda$. If now these parts of the film be observed in reflected white light, the light-waves are reflected from each layer of silver with a given intensity. But these reflected rays agree in phase, and hence give maximum intensity only for those waves whose wave lengths are equal to either λ, or $\frac{1}{2}\lambda$, or $\frac{1}{3}\lambda$, etc. Hence a spot which was exposed to green light, for instance, appears in white light essentially green, for the wave length $\frac{1}{2}\lambda$ lies outside the visible spectrum. But under some circumstances a part of the plate exposed to deep red appears violet, because in this case the wave length $\frac{1}{2}\lambda$ falls within the visible spectrum.

If such a photograph be breathed upon, the colors are dis-

* Drude and Nernst, Wied. Ann. 45, p. 460, 1892.

placed toward the red end of the spectrum, because the moisture thickens the collodion film, and the reflecting layers are a greater distance apart. If the plate be observed with light of more oblique incidence, the colors are displaced toward the violet end of the spectrum, for the same reason that the Newton's rings shift toward the lower orders as the incidence is more oblique. For, as is evident from (14) on page 138, the difference of phase Δ between two rays reflected from two surfaces a distance d apart is proportional to cos χ, in which χ is the angle of inclination of the rays between the two surfaces to the normal to the surfaces. When the angle of incidence increases Δ decreases; but in Newton's rings this effect is much more marked than in Lippmann's photographs, since, in the former, within the film of air which gives rise to the interference, χ varies much more rapidly with the incidence than it does in the collodion film, whose index is at least as much as 1.5.

Although the facts presented prove beyond a doubt that the colors are due to interference, yet the explanation of these colors by periodically arranged layers of silver is found, upon closer investigation, to be probably untenable. For Schütt* has made microscopic measurements upon the size of the particles of silver deposited in such photographic films, and found them to have a diameter of from 0.0007 to 0.0009 mm., which is much larger than a half wave length. According to Schütt, the stationary waves and the fixing of the sensitive film produce layers of periodically varying index of refraction, due to a periodic change in the arrangement of the silver molecules. This theory does not alter the principle underlying the explanation of the colors, for it also ascribes to the collodion film a variable reflecting power whose period is $\frac{1}{2}\lambda$.

This theory makes it possible to calculate the intensity of any color after reflection. The complete discussion will be omitted, especially as the calculation is complicated by the fact that it is not permissible to assume the number of periods

* F. Schütt, Wied. Ann. 57, 533, 1896.

in the photographic film as large.* The best color photographs are obtained when the thickness of the photographic film does not exceed 0.001 mm. This thickness corresponds to 3–5 half wave lengths. But without calculation it may be seen at once that the reflected colors are a mixture and not pure spectral colors,—a fact which can be verified by an analysis of the reflected light by the spectroscope.† For even if that color whose wave length is the same as that of the light to which the plate was exposed must predominate in the reflected light, yet the neighboring colors, and, for that matter, all the colors, must be present in greater or less intensity.

According to an experiment of Neuhauss,‡ the gradual reduction of the thickness of the film by friction causes the reflected colors to undergo certain periodic changes. This effect follows from theory if the small number of periods in the photographic film be taken into consideration.

A further peculiarity of these photographs is that, in reflected light, they do not show the same color when viewed from the front as from the back.§ Apart from the fact that the glass back gives rise to certain differences between the two sides, it is probable that the periodic variations in the optical character of the film are greater in amplitude on the side of the film which lay next to the metal mirror. On account of a slight absorption of the light, the stationary waves which, in the exposure of the plate, lie nearest the metal mirror are most sharply formed.

If this assumption be introduced into the theory, both the result of Neuhauss and the difference in the colors shown by the opposite sides of the plate are accounted for.

---

* The only calculations thus far made, namely those published by Meslin (Ann. de chim. et de phys. (6) 27, p. 369, 1892) and Lippmann (Jour. de phys. (3) 3, p. 97, 1894), not only make this untenable assumption, but they also lead to the impossible conclusion that under certain circumstances the reflected intensity can be greater than the incident.

† Cf., for instance, the above-mentioned article by Schütt.

‡ R. Neuhauss, Photogr. Rundsch. 8, p. 301, 1894. Cf. also the article by Schütt.

§ Cf. Wiener, Wied. Ann. 69, p. 488, 1899.

CHAPTER III

HUYGENS' PRINCIPLE

1. **Huygens' Principle as first Conceived.**—The fact has already been mentioned on page 127 that the explanation of the rectilinear propagation of light from the standpoint of the wave theory presents difficulties. To overcome these difficulties Huygens made the supposition that every point P which is reached by a light-wave may be conceived as the source of elementary light-waves, but that these elementary waves produce an appreciable effect only upon the surface of their envelope. If the spreading of the rays from a point source Q is hindered by a screen S_1S_2 containing an opening A_1A_2, then the wave surface at which the disturbance has arrived after the lapse of the time t may be constructed in the following way:

Consider all the points A_3 in the plane of the opening A_1A_2 as new centres of disturbance which send out their elementary waves into the space on both sides of the screen. These elementary wave surfaces are spheres described about the points A. These spheres have radii of different lengths, if they are drawn so as to touch the points at which the light from Q has arrived in the time t. Since, for instance, the disturbance from Q has reached A_3 sooner than A_1, the elementary wave about A_3 must be drawn larger than that about A_1 in proportion to the difference between these two times. It is evident that the radii of all the elementary waves, plus the distance from Q to their respective centres, have the same value. But in this way there is obtained, as the enveloping surface of these elementary waves, a spherical surface (drawn heavier in Fig. 58) whose centre is at Q, and which is limited by the points B_1, B_2, i.e. which lies altogether within the cone drawn from Q to the edge of the aperture S_1S_2. Inside this cone the light from Q is propagated as though the screen were not present, but outside of the cone no light disturbance exists.

Though the rectilinear propagation of light is thus actually obtained from this principle, yet its application in this form is subject to serious objection. First, it is evident from Fig. 58

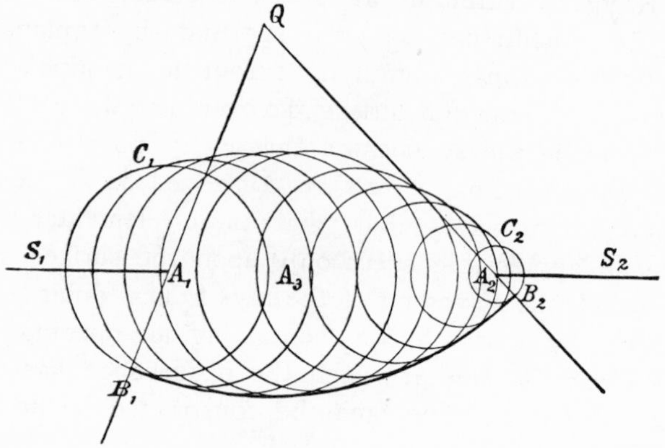

FIG. 58.

that the elementary waves from the points A have also an envelope C_1C_2 in the space between the screen and the source. Hence some light must also travel backward; but, as a matter of fact, in a perfectly homogeneous space, no such reflection takes place. Furthermore, the construction here given for the rectilinear propagation of light ought always to hold however small be the opening A_1A_2 in the screen. But it was shown on page 1 that, with very small apertures, light no longer travels in straight lines, but suffers so-called diffraction. Again, why do not these considerations hold also for sound, which is always diffracted, or, at least, never produces sharp shadows?

Before considering Fresnel's improvements upon Huygens' work, the latter's explanation of reflection and refraction will be presented. Let A_1A_2 be the bounding surface between two media I and II in which the velocities of light are respectively V_1 and V_2, and let a wave whose wave front at any time t_0

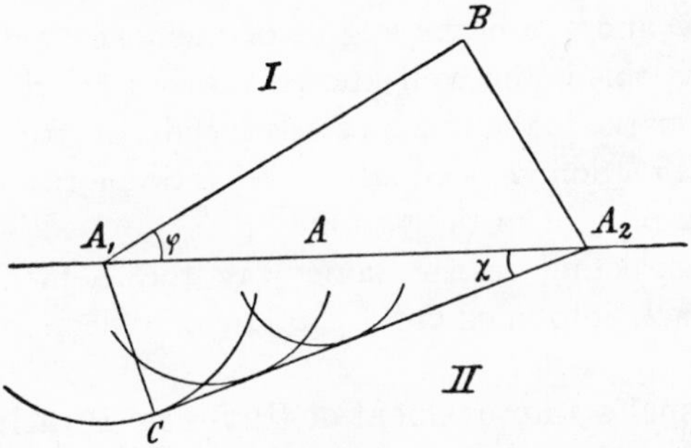

FIG. 59.

occupies the position A_1B fall obliquely upon the surface A_1A_2. What then is the position of the wave surface in medium II at the time $t_0 + t$? Conceive the points A of the bounding surface as centres of elementary waves which, as above, have different radii, since the points A are reached at different times by the wave front AB. Since the disturbance at A_1 begins at the time t_0, the elementary wave about A_1 must have a radius represented by the line $A_1C = V_2t$. Let the position of the point A_2 be so chosen that the disturbance reaches it at the time $t_0 + t$. This will be the case if the perpendicular dropped from A_2 upon the wave front has the length V_1t, since, according to Huygens' construction, in a homogeneous medium such as I any element of a plane wave is propagated in a straight line in the direction of the wave normal. The elementary wave about A_2 has then the radius zero. For any point A between A_1 and A_2 the elementary wave has a radius which diminishes from V_2t to zero proportionally to the distance A_1A. The envelope of the elementary waves in medium II is, therefore, the plane through A_2 tangent to the sphere about A_1. The angle A_2CA_1 is then a right angle. Since now $\sin\phi = BA_2 : A_1A_2 = V_1t : A_1A_2$, $\sin\chi = CA_1 : A_1A_2 = V_2t : A_1A_2$, it follows that

$$\frac{\sin\phi}{\sin\chi} = \frac{V_1}{V_2} = \text{const.}$$

But since ϕ and χ are the angles of incidence and refraction respectively, this is the well-known law of refraction. Hence, as was remarked though not deduced on page 129, the index of refraction n is equal to the ratio of the velocities of propagation of light in the two media.

By constructing in the same way the elementary waves reflected back into medium I the law of reflection is at once obtained.

2. Fresnel's Improvement of Huygens' Principle.—Fresnel replaced Huygens' arbitrary assumption that only the envelope of the elementary waves produces appreciable light effects by the principle that the elementary waves in their criss-crossing influence one another in accordance with the principle of interference. Light ought then to appear not only upon the enveloping surface, but everywhere where the elementary waves reinforce one another; on the other hand, there should be darkness wherever they destroy one another. Now as a matter of fact it is possible to deduce from this Fresnel-Huygens principle not only the laws of diffraction, but also those of straight-line propagation, reflection, and refraction.

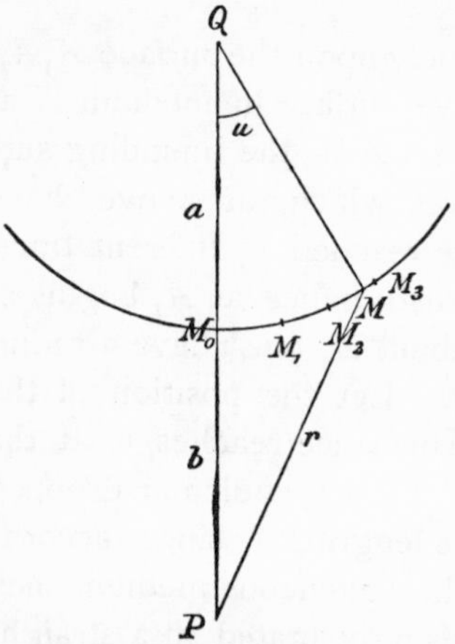

FIG. 60.

Consider the disturbance at a point P caused by light from a source Q, and at first assume that no screen is interposed between P and Q. A sphere of radius a described about Q

(Fig. 60) may be considered as the wave surface, and the disturbance which exists in the elements of this sphere may be expressed by (cf. page 127)

$$s = \frac{A}{a} \cos 2\pi\left(\frac{t}{T} - \frac{a}{\lambda}\right), \quad . \quad . \quad . \quad . \quad (1)$$

in which A represents the amplitude of the light at a distance $a = 1$ from the source Q. Fresnel now conceives the spherical surface to be divided in the following way into circular zones whose centres lie upon the straight line QP: The central zone reaches to the point M_1, at which the distance $M_1P = r_1$ is $\frac{1}{2}\lambda$ greater than the distance M_0P. Calling the latter b, $M_1P = r_1 = b + \frac{1}{2}\lambda$. The second zone reaches from M_1 to M_2, where $M_2P = r_2 = r_1 + \frac{1}{2}\lambda$. The third zone reaches from M_2 to M_3, where $M_3P = r_3 = r_2 + \frac{1}{2}\lambda$, etc. Consider now in any zone, say the third, an elementary ring which lies between the points M and M'. Let the distances $MP = r$, $M'P = r + dr$, and $\angle MQP = u$, $\angle M'QP = u + du$. The area of this elementary zone is

$$do = 2\pi a^2 \sin u \, du. \quad . \quad . \quad . \quad . \quad . \quad (2)$$

Also, since

$$r^2 = a^2 + (a + b)^2 - 2a(a + b) \cos u,$$

it follows by differentiation that

$$2r\, dr = 2a(a + b) \sin u \, du,$$

so that equation (2) may be written

$$do = 2\pi \frac{a}{a + b} r\, dr. \quad . \quad . \quad . \quad . \quad . \quad (3)$$

The disturbance ds' which is produced at P by this elementary zone must be proportional directly to do and inversely to r, since (cf. page 126) the amplitude of the disturbance due to an infinitely small source varies inversely as the distance from it. Hence, from (1),

$$ds' = \frac{kA}{ar} \cos 2\pi\left(\frac{t}{T} - \frac{a + r}{\lambda}\right) do, \quad . \quad . \quad . \quad . \quad (4)$$

or, in consideration of (3),

$$ds' = 2\pi \frac{k \cdot A}{a+b} \cos 2\pi\left(\frac{t}{T} - \frac{a+r}{\lambda}\right)dr. \quad . \quad . \quad (4')$$

In this equation k is a factor of proportionality which can depend only upon the inclination between the element do and the direction of r. Fresnel assumes that this factor k is smaller the greater the inclination between do and r. If this inclination be assumed to be constant over an entire Fresnel zone, i.e. between M_{n-1} and M_n, an assumption which is allowable if a and b are large in comparison with the wave length λ, it follows from (4′) that the effect of this nth zone is (k_n denoting the constant k under these circumstances)

$$s_n' = \int ds' = 2\pi \frac{k_n A}{a+b} \int_{r_{n-1}}^{r_n} \cos 2\pi\left(\frac{t}{T} - \frac{a+r}{\lambda}\right)dr, \quad . \quad (5)$$

or

$$s_n' = \frac{k_n \lambda A}{a+b} \left\{ \sin 2\pi\left(\frac{t}{T} - \frac{a+r_{n-1}}{\lambda}\right) - \sin 2\pi\left(\frac{t}{T} - \frac{a+r_n}{\lambda}\right) \right\}.$$

But since

$$r_{n-1} = b + \frac{n-1}{2}\lambda, \quad r_n = b + \frac{n}{2}\lambda,$$

it follows that

$$s_n' = (-1)^{n+1} \cdot \frac{2k_n \lambda A}{a+b} \sin 2\pi\left(\frac{t}{T} - \frac{a+b}{\lambda}\right). \quad . \quad (6)$$

From this it is evident that the successive zones give alternately positive and negative values for s'. If the absolute value of s_n' be represented by s_n, then by the principle of interference the whole effect s' at P due to the first n zones is given by the series

$$s' = s_1 - s_2 + s_3 - s_4 + \ldots + (-1)^{n+1} s_n. \quad (7)$$

If k_n were assumed equal for all zones, s_1, s_2, s_3, etc., would all be equal, and the value of the series (7) would vary with the number of terms n. But k_n and hence s_n diminish continuously as n increases, since the greater the value of n the greater the inclination between r and do. In this case the value of the series may be obtained in the following way:* If n is odd, the series may be written in the form:

$$s' = \frac{s_1}{2} + \left(\frac{s_1}{2} - s_2 + \frac{s_3}{2}\right) + \left(\frac{s_3}{2} - s_4 + \frac{s_5}{2}\right) + \dots$$
$$+ \left(\frac{s_{n-2}}{2} - s_{n-1} + \frac{s_n}{2}\right) + \frac{s_n}{2}, \quad . \quad . \quad . \quad . \quad (8)$$

or in the form:

$$s' = s_1 - \frac{s_2}{2} - \left\{\left(\frac{s_2}{2} - s_3 + \frac{s_4}{2}\right) + \left(\frac{s_4}{2} - s_5 + \frac{s_6}{2}\right) + \dots\right.$$
$$\left. + \left(\frac{s_{n-3}}{2} - s_{n-2} + \frac{s_{n-1}}{2}\right)\right\} - \frac{s_{n-1}}{2} + s_n. \quad . \quad (9)$$

If now every s_p is greater than the arithmetical mean of the two adjacent quantities s_{p-1} and s_{p+1}, the conclusion may be drawn from (8) that

$$s' < \frac{s_1}{2} + \frac{s_n}{2},$$

while it follows from (9) that

$$s' > s_1 - \frac{s_2}{2} + s_n - \frac{s_{n-1}}{2}.$$

These two limits between which s' is in this way contained are, however, equal to one another when, as is here the case, every s_p differs by an infinitely small amount both from s_{p-1} and s_{p+1}. Hence

$$s' = \frac{s_1}{2} + \frac{s_n}{2}. \quad . \quad . \quad . \quad . \quad . \quad (10)$$

A similar conclusion may be drawn when each s_p is smaller than the arithmetical mean between the two adjacent quantities s_{p-1} and s_{p+1}. In this latter case if at equal distances along an axis of abscissæ the s_p's be erected as successive ordinates,

---

* A. Schuster, Phil. Mag. (5), 31, p. 85, 1891.

the line connecting the ends of these ordinates is a curve which is convex toward the axis of abscissæ. In the former case this curve is concave toward this axis. These same conclusions may be drawn, i.e. equation (10) obtained, if the s_p curve consists of a finite number of concave and convex elements. Only when this number becomes infinitely large does equation (10) cease to hold. On account of the presence of the factor k_n this case can never occur.

If n is even, a similar argument, with a somewhat different arrangement of the terms of series (7), gives

$$s' = \frac{s_1}{2} - \frac{s_n}{2}. \quad . \quad . \quad . \quad . \quad . \quad . \quad . \quad (10')$$

According to Fresnel these zones are to be drawn until the radius vector r from P becomes tangent to the wave surface about Q. For the last zone r is perpendicular to QM and both k_n and s_n become zero. Hence the values of (10) and (10′) are identical and the light disturbance at P is

$$s' = \frac{s_1}{2} = \frac{k_1 \lambda A}{a+b} \sin 2\pi\left(\frac{t}{T} - \frac{a+b}{\lambda}\right). \quad . \quad . \quad . \quad (11)$$

Thus it may be looked upon as due solely to the effect of the elementary waves of half the central zone.

The effect at P of introducing any sort of a screen will depend upon whether the central zone and those immediately adjacent to it are covered or not. It might be expected that the effect at P would be completely cut off by a circular screen whose centre lies at M_0 and which covers half of the central zone. But this is not the case. For when a circular screen is introduced perpendicular to PQ with its centre at M_0, the construction of the Fresnel zones may begin at the edge of this screen. Then half of this first zone is still effective at P, i.e. equation (11) still holds, but b now represents the distance between P and the edge of the screen, and k_1 refers to the first zone about the edge of the screen. *Hence there can be darkness at no point along the central line M_0P. This surprising conclusion is actually verified by experiment.* However, for screens which are large in comparison with the wave length as well as in comparison with the distance b, the effect at P is small, because the factor k_n in equation (5) is then small. Likewise the effect at P is small if the screen S is not exactly circular. For, consider that the screen S is bounded by infinitely small circular arcs of varying radii drawn about M_0 as a centre. Let the angle subtended at the centre by the first arc be $d\phi_1$, the distance of this arc from the point P be b_1, and from Q, a_1. Then, by (11) and the above considerations, the effect of the entire opening which lies between the two radii vectores drawn from M_0 through the ends of this first arc is

$$ds_1' = \frac{k_1 \lambda A}{a_1 + b_1} \cdot \frac{d\phi_1}{2\pi} \sin 2\pi\left(\frac{t}{T} - \frac{a_1 + b_1}{\lambda}\right).$$

Similarly the effect of that part of the next angular opening $d\phi_2$ which is not covered by the screen is

$$ds_2' = \frac{k_2 \lambda A}{a_2 + b_2} \cdot \frac{d\phi_2}{2\pi} \sin 2\pi\left(\frac{t}{T} - \frac{a_2 + b_2}{\lambda}\right),$$

etc. All these effects must be summed in order to obtain the value of s' at P after the introduction of the irregular screen at M_0. If the screen is not too large, it is possible to set $k_1 = k_2 = k_3$, etc. Likewise the differences between the various a's and b's in the denominator may be neglected so that

$$s' = \frac{k_1 \lambda A}{(a + b)2\pi} \left\{ d\phi_1 \sin 2\pi\left(\frac{t}{T} - \frac{a_1 + b_1}{\lambda}\right) + d\phi_2 \sin 2\pi\left(\frac{t}{T} - \frac{a_2 + b_2}{\lambda}\right) + \ldots \right\}. \quad (11')$$

In the argument of the sin it is not permissible to set $a_1 + b_1 = a_2 + b_2$, etc., since these quantities are divided by the small quantity λ. For if the screen S is many wave lengths in diameter (it need be but a few mm.), the differences between the quantities $a + b$ amount to many wave lengths. Hence with an irregular screen the different terms of equation (11) are irregularly positive and negative so that in general the whole sum is small. Only when the screen has a regular form, for instance when all the a's and b's are exactly equal, is the sum s' finite. Hence it is possible to speak of rectilinear propagation of light, since the result of interposing a screen of sufficient size and irregular form upon the line QP is darkness at P.

If between Q and P a screen with a circular opening whose centre is at M_0 be introduced, then the effect at P varies greatly with the size of this opening. If the opening has the same size as half of the central zone, the effect at P is the same as though no screen were present, i.e. the light at P has the natural brightness. If the opening corresponds to the whole central zone, s' at P is twice as great as before, i.e. the intensity at P is four times the natural brightness. If the size of the opening be doubled, so that the first two central zones are free, then, according to (7), $s' = s_1 - s_2$, an expression whose value is nearly zero; etc. This conclusion also has been verified by experiment. Instead of using screens or apertures of various sizes, it is only necessary to move the point of observation along the line QM_0.

Although Fresnel's modification of Huygens' principle not only accounts for the straight-line propagation of light, showing this law to be but a limiting case,* but also explains the departures from this law shown in diffraction phenomena in a way which is in agreement with experiment, nevertheless his considerations are deficient in two respects. For, in the first place, according to his theory, light ought to spread out from any wave surface not only forward, but backward toward the source. This difficulty was contained in the original conception of the Huygens' principle (cf. page 161). In the second place, Fresnel's calculation gives the wrong phase to the light disturbance s' at P. For, according to equation (1) on page 163, in the case of direct propagation s' ought to be

$$s' = \frac{A}{a+b} \cos 2\pi\left(\frac{t}{T} - \frac{a+b}{\lambda}\right),$$

* That this is not true for sound is due to the fact that the sound-waves are so long that the obstacles interposed are not large in comparison.

while by (11) on page 166, s', as determined by the consideration of the elementary waves upon a wave surface, is

$$s' = \frac{k_1 \lambda A}{a+b} \sin 2\pi\left(\frac{t}{T} - \frac{a+b}{\lambda}\right).$$

In order to obtain agreement between the amplitudes in the two expressions for s', k_1 may be assumed equal to $\frac{1}{\lambda}$, but the phases in the two expressions cannot be made to agree. These difficulties disappear as soon as Huygens' principle is placed upon a more rigorous analytical basis. This was first done by Kirchhoff.* The simpler deduction which follows is due to Voigt.†

3. The Differential Equation of the Light Disturbance.— It would have been possible to find the analytical expression for the light disturbance s at any point P in space if all waves were either spherical or plane. But when light strikes an obstacle the wave surfaces often assume complicated forms. In order to obtain the analytical expression for s in such cases, it is necessary to base the argument upon more general considerations, i.e. to start with the differential equation which s satisfies.

Every theory of light, and, for that matter, every theory of the propagation of wave-like disturbances, leads to the differential equation

$$\frac{\partial^2 s}{\partial t^2} = V^2\left(\frac{\partial^2 s}{\partial x^2} + \frac{\partial^2 s}{\partial y^2} + \frac{\partial^2 s}{\partial z^2}\right) = V^2 \Delta s, \quad . \quad . \quad (12)$$

in which t represents the time, x, y, z the coordinates of a rectangular system, and V the velocity of propagation of the waves. This result of theory may for the present be assumed; a deduction of the equation from the standpoint of the electromagnetic theory will be given later (Section II, Chapter I).

* G. Kirchhoff, Ges. Abh. or Vorles. über math Optik.

† W. Voigt, Kompendium d. theor. Physik, II, p. 776. Leipzig. 1896.

It will first be shown how the analytical forms of s given above for plane and spherical waves are obtained from (12).

For *plane waves* let the x-axis be taken in the direction of the normal to the wave front, i.e. in the direction of propagation; then s can depend only upon x and t, since in every plane $x = const.$ which is a wave-front, the condition of vibration for a given value of t is everywhere the same. Equation (12) then reduces to

$$\frac{\partial^2 s}{\partial t^2} = V^2 \frac{\partial^2 s}{\partial x^2}. \quad . \quad . \quad . \quad . \quad . \quad . \qquad (13)$$

The general integral of this equation is

$$s = f_1\left(t - \frac{x}{V}\right) + f_2\left(t + \frac{x}{V}\right), \quad . \quad . \quad . \qquad (14)$$

in which f_1 is any function whatever of the argument $t - \frac{x}{V}$, and f_2 any function of the argument $t + \frac{x}{V}$. For if the first derivatives of the functions f_1 and f_2 with respect to their arguments be denoted by f_1' and f_2', the second derivatives by f_1'', f_2'', respectively, then

$$\frac{\partial s}{\partial t} = f_1' + f_2', \quad \frac{\partial^2 s}{\partial t^2} = f_1'' + f_2'',$$

$$\frac{\partial s}{\partial x} = -\frac{1}{V} f_1' + \frac{1}{V} f_2', \quad \frac{\partial^2 s}{\partial x^2} = + \frac{1}{V^2} f_1'' + \frac{1}{V^2} f_2'',$$

i.e. equation (13) is satisfied. If now the variation of s with the time is of the simple harmonic form, i.e. if it is proportional to $\cos 2\pi \frac{t}{T}$, as is the case for homogeneous light, then, by (14),

$$s = A_1 \cos 2\pi\left(\frac{t}{T} - \frac{x}{VT} + \delta_1\right) + A_2 \cos 2\pi\left(\frac{t}{T} + \frac{x}{VT} + \delta_2\right), \quad (15)$$

in which A_1, A_2, δ_1, δ_2 are constants. This corresponds to our former equation for a plane wave of wave length $\lambda = VT$. A_1 is the amplitude of the waves propagated in the positive direction of the x-axis, A_2 the amplitude of those propagated in the negative direction of the x-axis.

For *spherical waves* whose centre is at the origin, s can depend only upon t and the distance r from the origin. Hence

$$\frac{\partial s}{\partial x} = \frac{\partial s}{\partial r} \cdot \frac{\partial r}{\partial x} = \frac{\partial s}{\partial r} \cdot \frac{x}{r},$$

$$\frac{\partial s}{\partial y} = \frac{\partial s}{\partial r} \cdot \frac{\partial r}{\partial y} = \frac{\partial s}{\partial r} \cdot \frac{y}{r},$$

$$\frac{\partial s}{\partial z} = \frac{\partial s}{\partial r} \cdot \frac{\partial r}{\partial z} = \frac{\partial s}{\partial r} \cdot \frac{z}{r}.$$

For since $r^2 = x^2 + y^2 + z^2$, partial differentiation gives

$$r \cdot \partial r = x \cdot \partial x, \text{ i.e. } \frac{\partial r}{\partial x} = \frac{x}{r} = \cos (rx),$$

and similarly

$$\frac{\partial r}{\partial y} = \frac{y}{r}, \quad \frac{\partial r}{\partial z} = \frac{z}{r}.$$

Also,

$$\frac{\partial^2 s}{\partial x^2} = \frac{1}{r} \cdot \frac{\partial s}{\partial r} + \frac{x^2}{r} \cdot \frac{\partial}{\partial r}\left(\frac{1}{r} \cdot \frac{\partial s}{\partial r}\right) = \frac{x^2}{r^2} \cdot \frac{\partial^2 s}{\partial r^2} + \frac{\partial s}{\partial r}\left(\frac{1}{r} - \frac{x^2}{r^3}\right),$$

and similarly

$$\frac{\partial^2 s}{\partial y^2} = \frac{y^2}{r^2} \cdot \frac{\partial^2 s}{\partial r^2} + \frac{\partial s}{\partial r}\left(\frac{1}{r} - \frac{y^2}{r^3}\right),$$

$$\frac{\partial^2 s}{\partial z^2} = \frac{z^2}{r^2} \cdot \frac{\partial^2 s}{\partial r^2} + \frac{\partial s}{\partial r}\left(\frac{1}{r} - \frac{z^2}{r^3}\right).$$

Equation (12) becomes, therefore, for this case

$$\frac{\partial^2 s}{\partial t^2} = V^2\left(\frac{\partial^2 s}{\partial r^2} + \frac{2}{r}\frac{\partial s}{\partial r}\right), \quad . \quad . \quad . \quad . \quad (16)$$

which may also be written in the form

$$\frac{\partial^2 (rs)}{\partial t^2} = V^2 \frac{\partial^2 (rs)}{\partial r^2}. \quad . \quad . \quad . \quad . \quad . \quad . \quad (17)$$

This equation has the same form as (13) save that rs replaces s, and r replaces x. The integral of (17) is therefore, by (14),

$$rs = f_1\left(t - \frac{r}{V}\right) + f_2\left(t + \frac{r}{V}\right). \quad . \quad . \quad . \quad (18)$$

If, again, homogeneous light of period T be used, it follows that

$$s = \frac{A_1}{r} \cos 2\pi\left(\frac{t}{T} - \frac{r}{VT} + \delta_1\right) + \frac{A_2}{r} \cos 2\pi\left(\frac{t}{T} + \frac{r}{VT} + \delta_2\right). \quad (19)$$

This is our former equation for spherical waves. One train of waves moves from the origin, the other moves toward it. The amplitudes, for example $\frac{A_1}{r}$, are inversely proportional to r. This result, which was used above on page 126 in defining the measure of intensity, follows from equation (12).

Before deducing Huygens' principle from equation (12) the following principle must be presented.

4. A Mathematical Theorem.—Let $d\tau$ be an element of volume and F a function which is everywhere finite, continuous, and single-valued within a closed surface S. Consider the following integral, which is to be taken over the entire volume contained within S:

$$\int \frac{\partial F}{\partial x} d\tau = \int \frac{\partial F}{\partial x} dx\, dy\, dz.$$

First perform a partial integration with respect to x, i.e. make a summation of all the elements $\frac{\partial F}{\partial x} d\tau$ which lie upon any straight line $\mathfrak{G}$ parallel to the axis of x. The result is

$$dy\, dz \int \frac{\partial F}{\partial x} dx = dy\, dz(-F_1 + F_2 - F_3 + F_4 \text{ etc.}),$$

in which F_1, F_2, etc., represent the values of the function F at those points upon the surface S where the straight line $\mathfrak{G}$ intersects it. For the sake of generality it will be assumed that this line intersects the surface several times; since, however, S is a closed surface, the number of such intersections will always be even. In moving along the line 𝔊 in the direction of increasing x, F_1, F_3, etc., which have odd indices, represent the values of F at the points of entrance into the space enclosed by S; while F_2, F_4, etc., which have even indices, represent the values of F at the points of exit. Construct now upon the rectangular base $dy\ dz$ a column whose axis is parallel to the x-axis. This column will then cut from the surface S, at the points of entrance and exit, the elements dS_1, dS_2, etc., whose area is given by

$$dy\, dz = \pm\, dS \cdot \cos(nx),$$

in which (nx) represents the angle between the x-axis and the normal to the surface S at each particular point of intersection. The sign must be taken so that the right-hand side is positive, since the elements of surface dS are necessarily positive. *n will be taken positive toward the interior of the space enclosed by S.* Then, at the points of entrance,

$$dy\, dz = +\, dS_1 \cdot \cos\,(n_1x) = +\, dS_3 \cdot \cos\,(n_3x), \text{ etc.},$$

and at the points of exit

$$dy\, dz = -\, dS_2 \cdot \cos\,(n_2x) = -\, dS_4 \cdot \cos\,(n_4x), \text{ etc.}$$

Hence

$$dy\, dz \int \frac{\partial F}{\partial x} d\tau = -\, F_1 \cos\,(n_1x) \cdot dS_1 - F_2 \cos\,(n_2x) \cdot dS_2 - \text{etc.}$$

If now the integration be performed with respect to y and z in order to obtain the total space integral, i.e. if the summation of the products $F \cos\,(nx) dS$ over the whole surface be made, there results

$$\int \frac{\partial F}{\partial x} d\tau = - \int F \cos\,(nx) \cdot dS, \quad . \quad . \quad . \quad (20)$$

in which on the right-hand side F represents the value of the function at the surface element dS.

Thus by means of this theorem the original integral, which

was to be extended over the whole volume, is transformed into one which is taken over the surface which encloses the volume. From the method of proof it is evident that F must be finite, continuous, and single-valued within the space considered, since otherwise in the partial integration not only would there appear values F_1, F_2, etc., of F corresponding to points on the surface, but also values for points inside.

5. Two General Equations.—Let U be a function which contains explicitly x, y, z, and r. Let r represent the distance from the origin, i.e. $r^2 = x^2 + y^2 + z^2$. Let $\frac{\partial U}{\partial x}$ represent a differentiation with respect to the variable x as it explicitly appears, so that y, z, and r are in this differentiation considered constants. On the other hand let $\frac{dU}{dx}$ represent the differential coefficient of U, which arises from a motion dx along the x-axis; in which it is to be remembered that in this case r varies with x. Then

$$\frac{dU}{dx} = \frac{\partial U}{\partial x} + \frac{\partial U}{\partial r} \cdot \frac{\partial r}{\partial x} = \frac{\partial U}{\partial x} + \frac{\partial U}{\partial r} \cos (rx). \quad . \quad (21)$$

But (cf. page 171) $\frac{\partial r}{\partial x} = \frac{x}{r} = \cos (rx)$. Hence

$$\frac{d}{dx}\left(\frac{1}{r}\frac{\partial U}{\partial x}\right) = \frac{\partial}{\partial x}\left(\frac{1}{r}\frac{\partial U}{\partial x}\right) + \frac{\partial}{\partial r}\left(\frac{1}{r}\frac{\partial U}{\partial x}\right) \cdot \cos (rx),$$

or, since in the differentiation $\frac{\partial}{\partial x}$ the radius r is constant,

$$\left.\begin{aligned}
\frac{d}{dx}\left(\frac{1}{r}\frac{\partial U}{\partial x}\right) &= \frac{1}{r} \cdot \frac{\partial^2 U}{\partial x^2} - \frac{1}{r^2}\frac{\partial U}{\partial x}\cos (rx) + \frac{1}{r}\frac{\partial^2 U}{\partial r \partial x} \cos (rx), \\
\frac{d}{dy}\left(\frac{1}{r}\frac{\partial U}{\partial y}\right) &= \frac{1}{r} \cdot \frac{\partial^2 U}{\partial y^2} - \frac{1}{r^2}\frac{\partial U}{\partial y}\cos (ry) + \frac{1}{r}\frac{\partial^2 U}{\partial r \partial y} \cos (ry), \\
\frac{d}{dz}\left(\frac{1}{r}\frac{\partial U}{\partial z}\right) &= \frac{1}{r} \cdot \frac{\partial^2 U}{\partial z^2} - \frac{1}{r^2}\frac{\partial U}{\partial z}\cos (rz) + \frac{1}{r}\frac{\partial^2 U}{\partial r \partial z} \cos (rz).
\end{aligned}\right\} \quad (22)$$

Now let $\frac{dU}{dr}$ represent the ratio of the total change in U to a change in r, which arises from a motion dr along the fixed direction r. This change in U is a combination of several partial changes: First, U varies with r as it explicitly occurs, the amount of this variation being $\frac{\partial U}{\partial r}$. Second, it varies because x, y, z, which occur explicitly in U, are functions of r. Further a simple geometrical consideration shows that $dx = dr \cos(rx)$, $dy = dr \cos(ry)$, $dz = dr \cos(rz)$, hence

$$\frac{dU}{dr} = \frac{\partial U}{\partial r} + \frac{\partial U}{\partial x}\cos(rx) + \frac{\partial U}{\partial y}\cos(ry) + \frac{\partial U}{\partial z}\cos(rz). \quad (23)$$

If in this equation U be replaced by $\frac{\partial U}{\partial r}$, the result is

$$\frac{d}{dr}\left(\frac{\partial U}{\partial r}\right) = \frac{\partial^2 U}{\partial r^2} + \frac{\partial^2 U}{\partial r \partial x}\cos(rx) + \frac{\partial^2 U}{\partial r \partial y}\cos(ry) + \frac{\partial^2 U}{\partial r \partial z}\cos(rz). \quad (24)$$

Addition of the three equations (22) gives, in consideration of (23) and (24),

$$\frac{d}{dx}\left(\frac{1}{r}\frac{\partial U}{\partial x}\right) + \frac{d}{dy}\left(\frac{1}{r}\frac{\partial U}{\partial y}\right) + \frac{d}{dz}\left(\frac{1}{r}\frac{\partial U}{\partial z}\right) =$$

$$\frac{1}{r}\left(\frac{\partial^2 U}{\partial x^2} + \frac{\partial^2 U}{\partial y^2} + \frac{\partial^2 U}{\partial z^2} - \frac{\partial^2 U}{\partial r^2}\right) + \frac{1}{r}\frac{d}{dr}\left(\frac{\partial U}{\partial r}\right) - \frac{1}{r^2}\left(\frac{dU}{dr} - \frac{\partial U}{\partial r}\right). \quad (25)$$

But

$$\frac{1}{r}\frac{d}{dr}\left(\frac{\partial U}{\partial r}\right) + \frac{1}{r^2}\frac{\partial U}{\partial r} = \frac{1}{r^2}\frac{d}{dr}\left(r\frac{\partial U}{\partial r}\right). \quad . \quad . \quad (26)$$

If equation (25) be multiplied by the volume element $d\tau = dx\,dy\,dz$ and integrated over a space within which $\frac{1}{r}\frac{\partial U}{\partial x}$, $\frac{1}{r}\frac{\partial U}{\partial y}$, $\frac{1}{r}\frac{\partial U}{\partial z}$ are finite, continuous, and single-valued, and if theorem

(20) on page 173 be applied three times,* there results, in consideration of (26),

$$-\int \frac{1}{r}\left\{\frac{\partial U}{\partial x}\cos(nx)+\frac{\partial U}{\partial y}\cos(ny)+\frac{\partial U}{\partial z}\cos(nz)\right\}dS=$$

$$\int \frac{1}{r}\left(\frac{\partial^2 U}{\partial x^2}+\frac{\partial^2 U}{\partial y^2}+\frac{\partial^2 U}{\partial z^2}-\frac{\partial^2 U}{\partial r^2}\right)d\tau+\int \frac{1}{r^2}\frac{d}{dr}\left(r\frac{\partial U}{\partial r}-U\right)d\tau. \quad (27)$$

The space over which the integration is extended evidently cannot contain the origin, since there $\frac{1}{r}$ becomes infinite. Now two cases are to be distinguished: I. The space over which the integration is extended is bounded by a surface S which does not include the origin; II. The outer surface S of that space does include the origin.

CASE II. In this case, which will be first considered, conceive the origin to be excluded from the space over which the integration is extended by means of a sphere K of small radius ρ about the origin as a centre. The region of integration has then two boundaries, the outer one the surface S, the inner one the surface K of the sphere. The surface integral of equation (27) is therefore to be extended over both these surfaces. The value of the integral over the surface K is, however, not finite when ρ is infinitely small, since this surface is an infinitesimal of the second order with respect to ρ, and r appears in the denominator of the left-hand side of (27) in the first power only. Further,

$$\frac{\partial U}{\partial x}\cos(nx)+\frac{\partial U}{\partial y}\cos(ny)+\frac{\partial U}{dz}\cos(nz)=\frac{\partial U}{\partial n}, \quad (28)$$

in which $\partial U:\partial n$ is the differential coefficient which arises from a motion ∂n in the positive direction along the normal n to S

* The symbol $\frac{\partial}{\partial x}$ which appears in equation (20) has the same meaning as $\frac{d}{dx}$ here. That equation is also to be applied in this case when the differentiation is taken with respect to y and z.

when r is treated as a constant. Hence the left-hand side of equation (27) becomes

$$-\int \frac{1}{r}\frac{\partial U}{\partial n}dS,$$

and this integral is to be taken over the outer surface only, not over the small spherical surface K.

The last term on the right-hand side of (27) will now be transformed by writing

$$d\tau = r^2 d\phi\, dr, \quad . \quad . \quad . \quad . \quad . \quad (29)$$

i.e. the volume element is now conceived as the section cut by an elementary cone of solid angle $d\phi$ from a spherical shell whose inner and outer radii are r and $r + dr$ respectively. Then

$$\int \frac{1}{r^2}\frac{d}{dr}\left(r\frac{\partial U}{\partial r} - U\right)d\tau = \int d\phi \int_\rho^{\bar{r}} dr \cdot \frac{d}{dr}\left(r\frac{\partial U}{\partial r} - U\right) =$$

$$\int d\phi\left\{\left(r\frac{\partial U}{\partial r} - U\right)_{r=\bar{r}} - \left(r\frac{\partial U}{\partial r} - U\right)_{r=\rho}\right\}. \quad . \quad (30)$$

$\bar{r}$ denotes the value of r upon the outer surface S of the region of integration. If now ρ is infinitely small, the quantity $r\frac{\partial U}{\partial r}$ has no finite value for $r = \rho$. Furthermore, in the limit ($\rho = 0$)

$$\int d\phi \cdot (U)_{r=\rho} = 4\pi U_0, \quad . \quad . \quad . \quad . \quad (31)$$

in which U_0 represents the value of U at the origin. Again, since

$$\bar{r}^2 d\phi = -\,dS \cos(nr), \quad . \quad . \quad . \quad . \quad (32)$$

if the positive direction of r be away from the origin, then

$$\int d\phi\left(r\frac{\partial U}{\partial r} - U\right)_{r=\bar{r}} = -\int dS \cdot \cos(nr)\left(\frac{1}{r}\frac{\partial U}{\partial r} - \frac{U}{r^2}\right)$$

$$= -\int dS \cdot \cos(nr)\,\frac{\partial}{\partial r}\left(\frac{U}{r}\right), \quad (33)$$

which integral is to be extended over the outer surface S. It follows therefore from (27), in consideration of (30), (31), and (33), that

$$-\int \left\{ \frac{1}{r}\frac{\partial U}{\partial n} - \cos (nr) \frac{\partial}{\partial r}\left(\frac{U}{r}\right) \right\} dS =$$
$$\int \frac{1}{r}\left(\frac{\partial^2 U}{\partial x^2} + \frac{\partial^2 U}{\partial y^2} + \frac{\partial^2 U}{\partial z^2} - \frac{\partial^2 U}{\partial r^2}\right) d\tau + 4\pi U_0. \quad . \quad (34)$$

In this equation the volume integral may be extended over the whole space included within the surface S, since the infinitely small sphere K whose volume is proportional to ρ^3 adds when $\rho = 0$ an infinitely small amount to the integral, because r appears in the denominator in the first power only.

CASE I. If the surface does not enclose the origin, the discussion is exactly the same, save that it is unnecessary to construct the sphere K. In order to integrate the last term of the right-hand side of (27), assume as before

$$d\tau = r^2 d\phi \, dr;$$

but now the limits of integration are not ρ and $\bar{r}$, but r_1 and r_2, which represent the two distances from the origin at which the axis of the elementary cone of solid angle $d\phi$ intercepts the surface S. Hence

$$\int \frac{1}{r^2}\frac{d}{dr}\left(r\frac{\partial U}{\partial r} - U\right) d\tau =$$
$$\int d\phi \left\{ \left(r\frac{\partial U}{\partial r} - U\right)_{r = r_2} - \left(r\frac{\partial U}{\partial r} - U\right)_{r = r_1} \right\}. \quad (30')$$

If now dS represent a surface element which the elementary cone cuts from the surface S, then, at the point of entrance of the elementary cone into the enclosed space, since n, the normal to S, is drawn inward,

$$r_1^2 d\phi = + dS \cdot \cos (nr),$$

while at the point of exit

$$r_2^2 d\phi = - dS \cdot \cos (nr).$$

Hence the volume integral (30′) may be written as the surface integral

$$=-\int dS\cdot\cos(nr)\left(\frac{1}{r}\frac{\partial U}{\partial r}-\frac{U}{r^2}\right)=-\int dS\cdot\cos(nr)\frac{\partial}{\partial r}\left(\frac{U}{r}\right)\cdot(30')$$

Hence for this case (27) becomes

$$-\int\left\{\frac{1}{r}\frac{\partial U}{\partial n}-\cos(nr)\frac{\partial}{\partial r}\left(\frac{U}{r}\right)\right\}dS=$$

$$\int\frac{1}{r}\left(\frac{\partial^2 U}{\partial x^2}+\frac{\partial^2 U}{\partial y^2}+\frac{\partial^2 U}{\partial z^2}-\frac{\partial^2 U}{\partial r^2}\right)d\tau. \quad . \quad . \quad (34')$$

6. Rigorous Formulation of Huygens' Principle.—The following application will be made of (34) and (34′): Let s be the light disturbance at any point, s_0 the value of s at the origin. s satisfies the differential equation (12) on page 169. U will now be understood to be that function which is obtained by replacing in s the argument t (time) by $t-{}^r/_V$. This will be expressed by

$$U=s(t-{}^r/_V).$$

It is then evident that $U_0=s_0$, since at the origin $r=0$. Furthermore, from (12),

$$\frac{\partial^2 U}{\partial t^2}=V^2\left(\frac{\partial^2 U}{\partial x^2}+\frac{\partial^2 U}{\partial y^2}+\frac{\partial^2 U}{\partial z^2}\right),$$

but since U is a function of $t-{}^r/_V$, (cf. equations (17) and (18), page 171) the following relation also holds:

$$\frac{\partial^2 U}{\partial t^2}=V^2\frac{\partial^2 U}{\partial r^2}.$$

Hence, from the last two equations,

$$\frac{\partial^2 U}{\partial x^2}+\frac{\partial^2 U}{\partial y^2}+\frac{\partial^2 U}{\partial z^2}=\frac{\partial^2 U}{\partial r^2}.$$

Hence (34) gives, for *the case in which the origin lies within the surface S*,

$$4\pi s_0=\int\left\{\frac{\partial\dfrac{s(t-{}^r/_V)}{r}}{\partial r}\cos(nr)-\frac{1}{r}\frac{\partial s(t-{}^r/_V)}{\partial n}\right\}dS. \quad (35)$$

This equation may be interpreted in the following way: *The light disturbance* s_0 *at any point* P_0 (which has been taken as origin) *may be looked upon as the superposition of disturbances which are propagated with a velocity V toward* P_0 *from the surface elements dS of any closed surface which includes the point* P_0. For, since the elements of the surface integral (35) are functions of the argument $t - {}^r/_V$, any given phase of the elementary disturbance will exist at P_0, ${}^r/_V$ seconds after it has existed at dS.

In this interpretation of (35) it is easy to recognize the foundation of the original Huygens' principle, but the condition of vibration of the separate sources dS is much more complicated than was required by the earlier conceptions, according to which the elements of the integration were simply proportional to $s(t - {}^{r'}/_V)$ (cf. (4) on page 163).

Further, it is possible to calculate from equation (35) the disturbance s_0 at the point P_0 if the disturbances s and $\frac{\partial s}{\partial n}$ are known over any closed surface S. In certain cases these are known, as, for instance, when the source is a point and the spreading of the light is not disturbed by screens or changes in the homogeneity of the space. In this case, to be sure, s^0 can be determined directly; nevertheless, for the sake of what follows, it will be useful to calculate it from (35).

Let the source Q lie outside of the closed surface S. Let the disturbance at any point P which lies upon S and is distant r_1 from the source Q be represented by

$$s = \frac{A}{r_1} \cos 2\pi\left(\frac{t}{T} - \frac{r_1}{\lambda}\right). \quad . \quad . \quad . \quad . \qquad (36)$$

Then

$$\frac{\partial s}{\partial n} = \frac{\partial s}{\partial r_1} \cos (nr_1),$$

or

$$\frac{\partial s}{\partial n} = \cos (nr_1)\left\{-\frac{A}{r_1^{\,2}} \cos 2\pi\left(\frac{t}{T} - \frac{r_1}{\lambda}\right) + \frac{2\pi A}{\lambda r_1} \sin 2\pi\left(\frac{t}{T} - \frac{r_1}{\lambda}\right)\right\}. \qquad (37)$$

Now r_1 must be large in comparison with λ, hence the first term is negligible in comparison with the second, so that

$$\frac{\partial s(t-{}^{r}/_{v})}{\partial n}=\cos(nr_1)\cdot\frac{2\pi A}{\lambda r_1}\sin 2\pi\left(\frac{t}{T}-\frac{r+r_1}{\lambda}\right). \quad . \quad (38)$$

Further, from (36),

$$\frac{s(t-{}^{r}/_{v})}{r}=\frac{A}{rr_1}\cos 2\pi\left(\frac{t}{T}-\frac{r+r_1}{\lambda}\right).$$

If this expression be differentiated with respect to r, a term may again be neglected as in (37), since r also is large in comparison with λ; hence

$$\frac{\partial\dfrac{s(t-{}^{r}/_{v})}{r}}{\partial r}=\frac{2\pi A}{\lambda rr_1}\sin 2\pi\left(\frac{t}{T}-\frac{r+r_1}{\lambda}\right). \quad . \quad . \quad (39)$$

Substitution of the values (38) and (39) in (35) gives

$$s_0=\frac{A}{2\lambda}\int\frac{1}{rr_1}\sin 2\pi\left(\frac{t}{T}-\frac{r+r_1}{\lambda}\right)[\cos(nr)-\cos(nr_1)]dS. \quad (40)$$

This equation contains the principle of Fresnel stated above on page 163, but with the following improvements:

1. Fresnel's factor k is here determined directly from the differential equation for s, which constitutes the basis of the theory. Consider, for example, an element dS which lies at the point M_0 (Fig. 61) along the line QP_0; then for this ele-

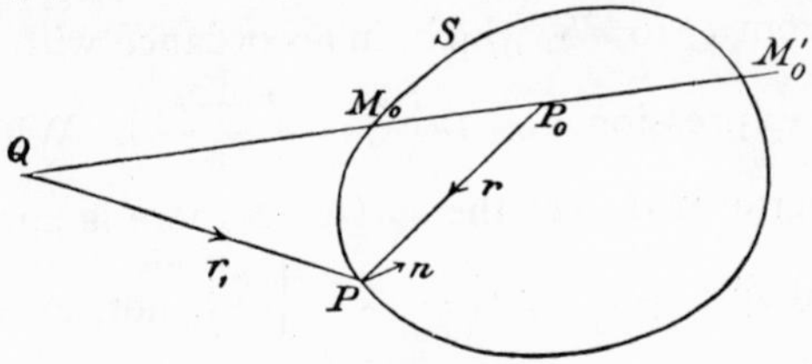

FIG. 61.

ment $\cos(nr)=-\cos(nr_1)$, since the positive directions of r and r_1 are opposite. Hence Fresnel's radiation factor k is

$$k=\frac{\cos(nr)}{\lambda}.$$

If dS is perpendicular to QP_0, then $\cos(nr) = -1$, and, save for the sign, the factor k_1 (cf. page 169) of the central zone has been deduced in an indirect way.

2. For an element dS, which lies at M_0' (Fig. 61), the positive directions of r and r_1 are the same, i.e.

$$\cos(nr) - \cos(nr_1) = 0.$$

Hence the influence of this element upon the value of s_0 disappears, i.e. the elementary waves are not propagated backward as they should be according to Huygens' and Fresnel's conceptions of the principle. It is at once evident that this disappearance of the waves which travel backward is a consequence of the fact that in (35) every elementary effect appears as the difference of two quantities.

3. The phase at P_0 is determined correctly, being the same as that due to the direct propagation from Q to P_0. For surface elements dS which lie at M_0 perpendicular to QP_0 are multiplied in (40) by the factor

$$-\sin 2\pi\left(\frac{t}{T} - \frac{r+r_1}{\lambda}\right),$$

and hence the effect is the same as though these surface elements vibrated in a phase which is $\frac{\pi}{2}$ ahead * of that of the direct wave from Q to dS, which, in accordance with (36), would lead to the expression $\cos 2\pi\left(\frac{t}{T} - \frac{r+r_1}{\lambda}\right)$. When the integration is performed over the surface S there is again obtained for the point P_0: $+\cos 2\pi\left(\frac{t}{T} - \frac{a+b}{\lambda}\right)$, not, as in Fresnel's

* If the light disturbance be assumed to exist not as a convex, but as a concave, spherical wave, which travels toward a point Q outside of S, the considerations are somewhat modified, as may be seen from (35). (In Mascart, Traité d'Optique, I, p. 260, Paris, 1889, this case is worked out.) Under some circumstances this case is of great importance for interference phenomena. Cf. Gouy, C. R. 110, p. 1251; 111, p. 33, 1890. Also Wied. Beibl. 14, p. 969.

calculation, $\sin 2\pi\left(\frac{t}{T} - \frac{a+b}{\lambda}\right)$ (cf. page 169). Thus this contradiction in Fresnel's theory is also removed.

Now if any screen be introduced, the problem of rigorously determining s_0 is extremely complicated, since, on account of the presence of the screen, the light disturbance s at a given point P is different from the disturbance $\bar{s}$ which would be produced by the sources alone if the screen were absent. In order to obtain an approximate solution of the problem, the assumption may be made that, if the screen is perfectly opaque and does not reflect light, both s and $\frac{\partial s}{\partial n}$ vanish at points which lie close to that side of the screen which is turned away from the source; while, for points which are not protected from the sources by the screen, the disturbance s has the value $\bar{s}$ which it would have in free space.

In fact this was the method of procedure in the above presentation of Fresnel's theory. Then, starting from equation (40), by constructing the surface S so that as much as possible lies on the side of the screen remote from the source, a very approximate calculation of the disturbance s_0 at any point P_0 may be made. Only the unprotected elements appear in (40). It is immaterial what particular form be given to this unprotected surface, provided only that it be bounded by the openings in the screen. This result can be deduced from equation (34′) on page 179, which shows that the right-hand side of (40) becomes zero for this case, if the closed surface S excludes the point P_0 (and also the source Q), for which s_0 is to be calculated. Hence if the integral s_0 of equation (40) be taken over an unclosed surface S which is bounded by a curve C, and if another surface S' be constructed which is likewise bounded by C, then $S + S'$ may be looked upon as one single closed surface which does not include the origin P_0. (34′) shows that the sum $s_0 + s_0'$ of the two integrals extended over S and S' vanishes. But in this n is always drawn toward the interior of the closed surface formed by S and S', so that, if the positive direction of the normal to S points toward the side upon which P_0 lies, then the positive direction of the normal to S' points away from this side. If then the positive direction of the normal to S' be taken toward the side upon which P_0 lies, the sign of the integral s_0' becomes reversed. Hence it follows that $s_0 - s_0' = 0$, or $s_0 = s_0'$, or, expressed in words: *The integral* s_0, *defined by equation (40), has the same value for all unclosed surfaces S of any form which are bounded by a curve C, provided the normal be always reckoned positive in the same direction (from the side upon which the source lies to that upon which* P_0 *lies), and provided these different surfaces S do not enclose either the source Q or the point* P_0 *for which* s_0 *is to be calculated.*

How, now, from equation (40) the rectilinear propagation of light, and certain departures from the same, may be deduced has already been shown in § 2 with the aid of Fresnel's zones. In the following chapter these departures from the law of rectilinear propagation, the so-called diffraction phenomena, will be more completely treated.

CHAPTER IV

DIFFRACTION OF LIGHT

As is evident from the discussion in § 2 of the preceding chapter, diffraction phenomena always appear when the screens or the apertures are not too large in comparison with the wave length. But, as will be seen later, diffraction phenomena may appear under certain circumstances even if the screen is large, for example at the edge of the geometrical shadow cast by a large object. If now, starting with equation (40), the diffraction phenomena be calculated in accordance with the considerations on page 182, it must not be forgotten that the theoretical results thus obtained are *only approximate;* since, on the one hand, when screens are present, the value of s is not exactly the same at unprotected points as it would be with undisturbed propagation, and, on the other hand, at protected points s and $\frac{\partial s}{\partial n}$ do not entirely vanish. The approximation is more and more close as the size of the apertures in the screens is increased; in fact the approximate results obtained from theory agree well with experiment if the apertures are not unusually small. The *rigorous theory* of diffraction will be presented in § 7 of this chapter.

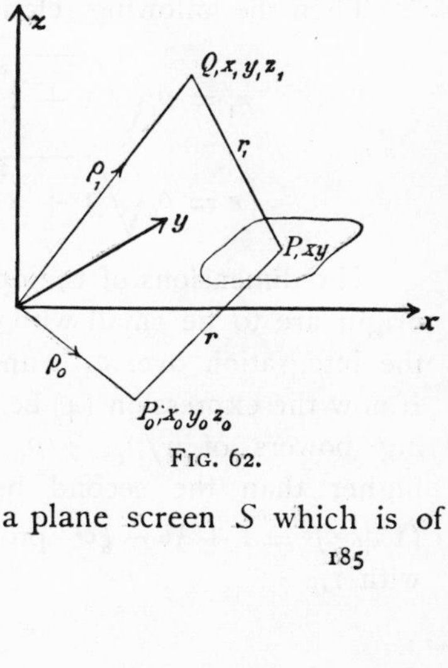

FIG. 62.

1. General Treatment of Diffraction Phenomena.—Assume that between the source Q and the point P_0 there is introduced a plane screen S which is of infinite extent and contains an opening σ of any form. Let this opening be small in comparison with its distance r_1 from the source Q, and also in comparison with its distance r from the point P_0 at which the disturbance s_0 is to be calculated by equation (40) of the preceding chapter. In performing the integration over σ the angles (nr) and (nr_1) are, on account of the smallness of σ, to be considered constant; likewise the quantities r and r_1 whenever they are not divided by λ; hence

$$s_0 = \frac{A}{2\lambda} \cdot \frac{\cos(nr) - \cos(nr_1)}{rr_1} \int \sin 2\pi\left(\frac{t}{T} - \frac{r + r_1}{\lambda}\right) d\sigma. \quad (1)$$

Assume now a rectangular coordinate system x, y, z. Let the xy-plane coincide with the screen S, and let some point P in the opening σ have the coordinates x and y. Let x_1, y_1, z_1 be the coordinates of the source, z_1 being positive; and x_0, y_0, z_0 those of P_0. z_0 is then negative. Then

$$r_1^2 = (x_1 - x)^2 + (y_1 - y)^2 + z_1^2, \quad r^2 = (x_0 - x)^2 + (y_0 - y)^2 + z_0^2. \quad (2)$$

Let the distances of Q and P_0 from the origin be ρ_1 and ρ_0 respectively; then

$$\rho_1^2 = x_1^2 + y_1^2 + z_1^2, \quad \rho_0^2 = x_0^2 + y_0^2 + z_0^2. \quad . \quad (3)$$

Then the following relations hold:

$$\left.\begin{aligned} r_1 &= \rho_1\sqrt{1 + \frac{x^2 + y^2 - 2(xx_1 + yy_1)}{\rho_1^2}}, \\ r &= \rho_0\sqrt{1 + \frac{x^2 + y^2 - 2(xx_0 + yy_0)}{\rho_0^2}}. \end{aligned}\right\} \quad . \quad . \quad (4)$$

The dimensions of the opening σ and its distance from the origin are to be small with respect to ρ_1 and ρ_0. Hence, in the integration over σ, x and y are small with respect to ρ. If now the expression (4) be expanded in a series with increasing powers of x/ρ_1, y/ρ_1 and x/ρ_0, y/ρ_0, and if powers higher than the second be neglected, there results, since $(1 + \epsilon)^{\frac{1}{2}} = 1 + \frac{1}{2}\epsilon - \frac{1}{8}\epsilon^2$ provided ϵ is small in comparison with 1,

$$r_1 = \rho_1 \left\{ 1 + \frac{x^2+y^2}{2\rho_1^2} - \frac{xx_1+yy_1}{\rho_1^2} - \frac{(xx_1+yy_1)^2}{2\rho_1^4} \right\}, \quad . \quad (5)$$

$$r = \rho_0 \left\{ 1 + \frac{x^2+y^2}{2\rho_0^2} - \frac{xx_0+yy_0}{\rho_0^2} - \frac{(xx_0+yy_0)^2}{2\rho_0^4} \right\}. \quad . \quad (6)$$

Denoting the direction cosines of ρ_1 and ρ_0 by α_1, β_1, γ_1 and α_0, β_0, γ_0, respectively, in which the positive directions of ρ_1 and ρ_0 point away from the origin, then

$$\alpha_1 = \frac{x_1}{\rho_1}, \quad \beta_1 = \frac{y_1}{\rho_1}; \quad \alpha_0 = \frac{x_0}{\rho_0}, \quad \beta_0 = \frac{y_0}{\rho_0}. \quad . \quad . \quad (7)$$

Hence the addition of (5) and (6) gives

$$r_1 + r = \rho_1 + \rho_0 - x(\alpha_1+\alpha_0) - y(\beta_1+\beta_0) + \frac{x^2+y^2}{2}\left(\frac{1}{\rho_1}+\frac{1}{\rho_0}\right)$$
$$- \frac{(x\alpha_1+y\beta_1)^2}{2\rho_1} - \frac{(x\alpha_0+y\beta_0)^2}{2\rho_0}. \quad . \quad . \quad . \quad (8)$$

Substituting this value in (1) and writing for brevity

$$\left.\begin{aligned} r_1 + r &= \rho_1 + \rho_0 + f(x, y)\cdot\frac{\lambda}{2\pi}, \\ \frac{t}{T} - \frac{\rho_1+\rho_0}{\lambda} &= \frac{t'}{T}{}^{*}, \\ \frac{A}{2\lambda}\,\frac{\cos(nr) - \cos(nr_1)}{rr_1} &= A', \end{aligned}\right\} \quad . \quad . \quad . \quad (9)$$

(1) becomes

$$s_0 = A' \left\{ \sin 2\pi\frac{t'}{T}\int \cos[f(x, y)]d\sigma \right.$$
$$\left. - \cos 2\pi\frac{t'}{T}\int \sin[f(x, y)]d\sigma \right\}. \quad (10)$$

s_0 may therefore be conceived as due to the superposition of two waves whose amplitudes are proportional to

$$C = \int \cos[f(x, y)]d\sigma,$$
$$S = \int \sin[f(x, y)]d\sigma, \quad . \quad . \quad . \quad . \quad . \quad (11)$$

* This change displaces the origin of time.

and whose difference of phase is $\frac{\pi}{2}$. Hence, from the law on page 131 [cf. equation (11)], the intensity of illumination of the light at the point P_0 is

$$J = A'^2(C^2 + S^2). \quad . \quad . \quad . \quad . \quad . \quad (12)$$

Now two cases are to be distinguished: 1. That in which both the source and the point P_0 lie at finite distances (*Fresnel's diffraction phenomena*); and 2. That in which the source and P_0 are infinitely far apart (*Fraunhofer's diffraction phenomena*).

2. Fresnel's Diffraction Phenomena.—Let the origin lie upon the line QP_0 and in the plane of the screen. Then ρ_1 and ρ_0 lie in the same straight line, but have opposite signs, hence

$$\alpha_1 = -\alpha_0, \quad \beta_1 = -\beta_0.$$

A comparison of equations (8) with equations (9), which define $f(x, y)$, gives

$$f(x, y) = \frac{\pi}{\lambda}\left(\frac{1}{\rho_1} + \frac{1}{\rho_0}\right)[x^2 + y^2 - (x\alpha_1 + y\beta_1)^2]. \quad . \quad (13)$$

This equation may be still further simplified by choosing as the x-axis the projection of QP_0 upon the screen. Then $\beta_1 = 0$. Also if the angle which ρ_1 makes with the z-axis be represented by ϕ, then

$$f(x, y) = \frac{\pi}{\lambda}\left(\frac{1}{\rho_1} + \frac{1}{\rho_0}\right)[x^2 \cdot \cos^2\phi + y^2]. \quad . \quad . \quad (14)$$

In order to avoid the necessity of interrupting the discussion later by lengthy calculations, a few mathematical considerations will be introduced here.

3. Fresnel's Integrals.—The characteristics of the functions which are known as Fresnel's integrals will here be discussed geometrically.* There are two of these integrals, namely,

$$\xi = \int_0^v \cos\frac{\pi v^2}{2}dv, \quad \eta = \int_0^v \sin\frac{\pi v^2}{2}dv. \quad . \quad . \quad . \quad (15)$$

---

* This method was proposed by Cornu in Jour. de Phys. 3, 1874.

The ξ and η which correspond to each particular value of the parameter v may be thought of as the rectangular coordinates of a point E. Then, as v changes continuously, E describes a curve whose form will be here determined.

Since, when $v = 0$, $\xi = \eta = 0$, the curve passes through the origin. When v changes to $-v$, the expression under the integral is not altered, but the upper limit of the integral, and hence also ξ and η, change sign. Hence the origin is a centre of symmetry for the curve, for to every point $+\xi$, $+\eta$, there corresponds a point $-\xi$, $-\eta$. The projections of an element of arc ds of the curve upon the axes are, by (15),

$$d\xi = dv \cdot \cos\frac{\pi v^2}{2}, \quad d\eta = dv \cdot \sin\frac{\pi v^2}{2}. \quad . \quad . \quad (16)$$

Hence

$$ds = \sqrt{d\xi^2 + d\eta^2} = dv,$$

or, if the length s be measured from the origin,

$$s = v. \quad . \quad . \quad . \quad . \quad . \quad . \quad . \quad (17)$$

The angle τ which is included between the tangent to the curve at any point E and the ξ-axis is given by

$$\tan\tau = \frac{d\eta}{d\xi} = \tan\frac{\pi v^2}{2}, \text{ i.e. } \tau = \frac{\pi}{2}v^2. \quad . \quad . \quad (18)$$

Hence at the origin the curve is parallel to the ξ-axis; when $v = 1$, i.e. when the arc $s = 1$, it is parallel to the η-axis; when $s^2 = 2$ it is parallel to the ξ-axis; when $s^2 = 3$ it is parallel to the η-axis; etc.

The radius of curvature ρ of the curve at any point E is given by [cf. (17) and (18)]

$$\rho = \frac{ds}{d\tau} = \frac{1}{\pi v} = \frac{1}{\pi s}. \quad . \quad . \quad . \quad . \quad . \quad (19)$$

Hence at the origin, where $v = 0$, there is a point of inflection. As v increases, i.e. as the arc increases, ρ continually diminishes. Hence the curve is a double spiral, without double points, which winds itself about the two asymptotic points F and F', whose position is determined by $v = +\infty$ and $v = -\infty$. The coordinates of these points will now be calculated. For F,

$$\xi_F = \int_0^\infty \cos\frac{\pi v^2}{2}dv, \quad \eta_F = \int_0^\infty \sin\frac{\pi v^2}{2}dv. \quad . \quad (20)$$

To obtain the value of this definite integral set

$$\int_0^\infty e^{-x^2}dx = M. \quad . \quad . \quad . \quad . \quad . \quad . \quad (21)$$

If y is the variable, then also

$$\int_0^\infty e^{-y^2}dy = M.$$

The product of these two definite integrals is

$$\int_0^\infty \int_0^\infty e^{-(x^2+y^2)}\,dx\,dy = M^2. \quad . \quad . \quad . \quad . \quad (22)$$

If now x and y be conceived as the rectangular coordinates of a point P, then $x^2 + y^2 = r^2$, in which r is the distance of P from the origin. Furthermore $dx\,dy$ may be looked upon as a surface element in the xy-plane. But if a surface element be bounded by two infinitely small arcs which have the origin as centre, subtend the angle $d\phi$ at the centre, and are at a distance dr apart, then its area do is

$$do = r\,dr\,d\phi. \quad . \quad . \quad . \quad . \quad . \quad . \quad (23)$$

Hence, since the integration is to be taken over one quadrant of the coordinate plane, (22) may be written

$$M^2 = \int_0^{\pi/2} d\phi \int_0^\infty e^{-r^2} r\,dr. \quad . \quad . \quad . \quad . \quad (24)$$

But now

$$\int e^{-r^2} r\,dr = -\frac{1}{2}e^{-r^2},$$

Hence

$$M^2 = \frac{\pi}{4}, \quad M = \frac{1}{2}\sqrt{\pi}. \quad . \quad . \quad . \quad . \quad (25)$$

Writing in (21) for x

$$x^2 = -i\frac{\pi v^2}{2}, \text{ i.e. } x = v\sqrt{\frac{-i\pi}{2}}, \quad . \quad . \quad . \quad (26)$$

in which i represents the imaginary, there results from (21) and (25)

$$\sqrt{\frac{-i\pi}{2}}\int_0^\infty e^{i\frac{\pi v^2}{2}}dv = \frac{1}{2}\sqrt{\pi},$$

or, because

$$\frac{1}{\sqrt{-i}} = \sqrt{i} = \frac{1+i}{\sqrt{2}},$$

$$\int_0^\infty e^{i\frac{\pi v^2}{2}}dv = \frac{1+i}{2}. \quad . \quad . \quad . \quad . \quad . \quad (27)$$

But since

$$e^{i\frac{\pi v^2}{2}} = \cos\frac{\pi v^2}{2} + i\sin\frac{\pi v^2}{2}, \quad . \quad . \quad . \quad (28)$$

it follows, by equating the real and the imaginary parts of (27), that

$$\int_0^\infty \cos\frac{\pi v^2}{2}dv = \frac{1}{2}, \quad \int_0^\infty \sin\frac{\pi v^2}{2}dv = \frac{1}{2}. \quad . \quad (29)$$

Hence, in accordance with (20), the asymptotic point F has the coordinates $\xi_F = \eta_F = \frac{1}{2}$. The form of the curve is therefore that given in Fig. 63. The curve may be constructed in the following way: Move from o along the ξ-axis a distance $s = 0.1$. Construct a circle of radius $\rho = \frac{1}{\pi s} = \frac{10}{\pi}$ which passes through the point o and whose centre lies upon a line which passes through the point $s = 0.1$ and makes with the η-axis the angle $\tau = \frac{\pi s^2}{2} = 0.01\frac{\pi}{2}$ [cf. (18)]. On the circle thus constructed lay off from o the arc $s = 0.1$. Through its end point draw another circular arc of radius $\rho = \frac{1}{\pi s} = \frac{1}{\pi \cdot 0.2} = \frac{5}{\pi}$ whose centre lies upon a line which passes through the point

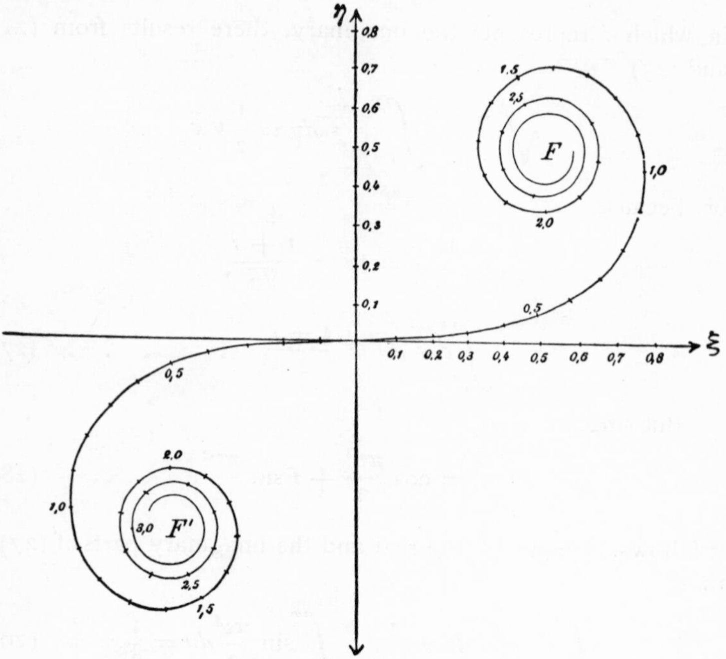

FIG. 63.

$s = 0.1$ on the curve and which makes with the η-axis an angle $\tau = \frac{\pi s^2}{2} = 0.04 \frac{\pi}{2}$. Proceeding in this way, the entire curve may be constructed.

4. Diffraction by a Straight Edge.—Resume the notation of § 2. Let the y-axis be parallel to the edge of the screen, and let the screen extend from $x = +\infty$ to $x = x'$ (the edge of the screen, cf. Fig. 64). In the figure x' is positive, i.e. P_0 lies outside of the geometrical shadow of the screen. Consider the intensity of the light in a plane which passes through the source Q and is perpendicular to the edge of the screen. QP_0 then lies in the xz-plane. Equation (14) is here applicable, and gives, in combination with (11), the following expressions to be evaluated:

$$\left.\begin{aligned} C &= \int_{-\infty}^{x'}\int_{-\infty}^{+\infty} dx\,dy \cos\left[\frac{\pi}{\lambda}\left(\frac{1}{\rho_1}+\frac{1}{\rho_0}\right)(x^2\cos^2\phi+y^2)\right], \\ S &= \int_{-\infty}^{x'}\int_{-\infty}^{+\infty} dx\,dy \sin\left[\frac{\pi}{\lambda}\left(\frac{1}{\rho_1}+\frac{1}{\rho_0}\right)(x^2\cos^2\phi+y^2)\right]. \end{aligned}\right\} \quad (30)$$

It is necessary first to justify the extension in this case of the integration over the whole portion of the xy-plane not covered by the screen, for it will be remembered that in the preceding discussion (cf. page 186) the integral was extended only over an opening all of whose points lay at distances from the origin which were small in comparison with ρ_1 and ρ_0. As a matter

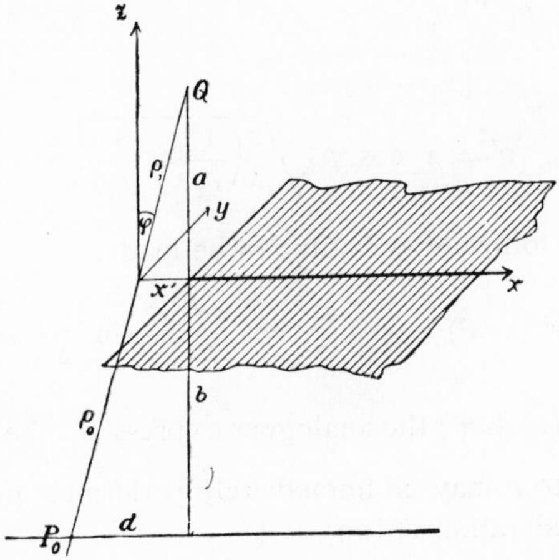

FIG. 64.

of fact such a limited region of integration is in itself determinative of the intensity J of the light at the point P_0, since it includes the central zones, and indeed a large number of them. An extension of the integration over a larger region adds nothing to J, since, as was previously shown, the edge of the screen exerts no further influence upon the intensity at the point P_0 when it is many zones distant from the line connecting P_0 and Q. Hence in (30) the result is not altered when the integration is taken over the entire portion of the xy-plane not covered by the screen.

Substitution in (30) of

$$\frac{\pi}{\lambda}\left(\frac{1}{\rho_1}+\frac{1}{\rho_0}\right)x^2\cos^2\phi=\frac{\pi v^2}{2},\quad \frac{\pi}{\lambda}\left(\frac{1}{\rho_1}+\frac{1}{\rho_0}\right)y^2=\frac{\pi u^2}{2} \quad . \quad (31)$$

gives

$$\left.\begin{aligned} C&=\frac{1}{\cos\phi\cdot\frac{2}{\lambda}\left(\frac{1}{\rho_1}+\frac{1}{\rho_0}\right)}\cdot\int_{-\infty}^{v'}\int_{-\infty}^{+\infty}dv\,du\cos\frac{\pi}{2}(v^2+u^2),\\ S&=\frac{1}{\cos\phi\cdot\frac{2}{\lambda}\left(\frac{1}{\rho_1}+\frac{1}{\rho_0}\right)}\cdot\int_{-\infty}^{v'}\int_{-\infty}^{+\infty}dv\,du\sin\frac{\pi}{2}(v^2+u^2),\end{aligned}\right\} \quad (32)$$

in which

$$v'=x'\cos\phi\sqrt{\frac{2}{\lambda}\left(\frac{1}{\rho_1}+\frac{1}{\rho_0}\right)}. \quad . \quad . \quad . \quad (33)$$

If in (32) the following substitution be made,

$$\cos\frac{\pi}{2}(v^2+u^2)=\cos\frac{\pi v^2}{2}\cos\frac{\pi u^2}{2}-\sin\frac{\pi v^2}{2}\sin\frac{\pi u^2}{2},$$

and for $\sin\frac{\pi}{2}(v^2+u^2)$ the analogous expression, the integration with respect to u may be immediately performed and there results, in consideration of (29),

$$\left.\begin{aligned} C&=f\cdot\left\{\int_{-\infty}^{v'}\cos\frac{\pi v^2}{2}dv-\int_{-\infty}^{v'}\sin\frac{\pi v^2}{2}dv\right\},\\ S&=f\cdot\left\{\int_{-\infty}^{v'}\sin\frac{\pi v^2}{2}dv+\int_{-\infty}^{v'}\cos\frac{\pi v^2}{2}dv\right\},\end{aligned}\right\}, \quad . \quad (34)$$

$$f=\frac{\lambda}{2\cos\phi\left(\frac{1}{\rho_1}+\frac{1}{\rho_0}\right)}. \quad . \quad . \quad . \quad . \quad (35)$$

Hence it follows from (12) that

$$J = 2A'^2 \cdot f^2 \cdot \left\{ \left(\int_{-\infty}^{v'} \cos \frac{\pi v^2}{2} dv \right)^2 + \left(\int_{-\infty}^{v'} \sin \frac{\pi v^2}{2} dv \right)^2 \right\} \quad . \quad . \quad (36)$$

The value of A' is given in (9), page 187. Since, according to the observations on the preceding page, only those portions of the xy-plane which lie near the origin are in the integration determinative of the intensity J at the point P_0, it is possible to set in the expression for A'

$$r = \rho_0, \quad r_1 = \rho_1, \quad \cos(nr) = -\cos(nr_1) = \cos\phi.$$

Hence

$$A' \cdot f = \frac{A}{2(\rho_0 + \rho_1)}. \quad . \quad . \quad . \quad . \quad . \quad (37)$$

The two Fresnel integrals which occur in (36) will be interpreted geometrically as in § 3. If the coordinates of a point E of the curve of Fig. 63 be represented by the above equations (15), i.e. by

$$\xi = \int_0^v \cos \frac{\pi v^2}{2} dv, \qquad \eta = \int_0^v \sin \frac{\pi v^2}{2} dv,$$

and the coordinates of another point E' on the curve, corresponding to the parameter v', by

$$\xi' = \int_0^{v'} \cos \frac{\pi v^2}{2} dv, \quad \eta' = \int_0^{v'} \sin \frac{\pi v^2}{2} dv,$$

then evidently

$$\int_v^{v'} \cos \frac{\pi v^2}{2} dv = \xi' - \xi, \quad \int_v^{v'} \sin \frac{\pi v^2}{2} dv = \eta' - \eta.$$

The sum of the squares of these two integrals is then equal to the square of the distance between the two points E and E′ of the curve in Fig. 63. The point $E = F'$ corresponds to the parameter $v = -\infty$. Hence if the distance of the point F'

from a point E', which corresponds to a parameter v', be represented by $(-\infty, v')$, then, by (36) and (37),

$$J = \frac{A^2}{2(\rho_0 + \rho_1)^2} \cdot (-\infty, v')^2. \quad . \quad . \quad . \quad (38)$$

From the form of the curve in Fig. 63 it is evident *that J has maxima and minima for positive values of v', i.e. for cases in which P_0 lies outside the geometrical shadow of the screen. But when P_0 lies inside the shadow, the intensity of the light decreases continuously as P_0 moves back into the shadow;* for in this case v' is negative and the point E' continuously approaches the point F'.

If $v' = +\infty$, then $(-\infty, +\infty)^2 = 2$, since each of the points F and F' has the coordinates $\xi = \eta = \frac{1}{2}$. In this case P_0 lies far outside of the geometrical shadow, and by (38) the intensity is the same as though no screen were present. For $v' = 0$, P_0 lies at the edge of the geometrical shadow, in which case $(-\infty, 0)^2 = \frac{1}{2}$, and, by (38), the intensity is one fourth the natural intensity.

The rigorous calculation of the maxima and minima of intensity when P_0 lies outside the shadow will not be given here.* It is evident from Fig. 63 that these maxima and minima lie approximately at the intersections of the line FF' with the curve. Since this line cuts the curve nearly at right angles, it is evident that at the maxima the angle of inclination τ of the curve with the ξ-axis is $(\frac{3}{4} + 2h)\pi$, at the minima $\tau = (\frac{7}{4} + 2h)\pi$, in which $h = 0, 1, 2$, etc. Hence at the maxima, cf. equation (18) on page 189, $v' = \sqrt{\frac{3}{2} + 4h}$, at the minima, $v' = \sqrt{\frac{7}{2} + 4h}$. Now in order to determine the position of the diffraction fringes, conceive the screen so

* Cf. Fresnel, Œuvr. compl. I, p. 322. For a development in series of Fresnel's integrals, cf. F. Neumann, Vorles. ü. theor. Optik. herausgeg. von Dorn, Leipzig, 1885, p. 62. Lommel in the Abhandl. d. bayr. Akad., Vol. 15, p. 229, 529, treats very fully, both theoretically and experimentally, the diffraction produced by circles and straight edges.

rotated* about its edge that it stands perpendicular to the shortest line a which can be drawn from Q to the edge (cf. Fig. 64). Then $\rho_1 = a : \cos\phi$. Further, draw through P_0 a line parallel to the x-axis, and let the distance of P_0 from the geometrical shadow of the screen measured along this line be represented by d. Then $x' : d = a : a + b$. Hence d denotes the distance of the point P_0 from the geometrical shadow, in a plane which lies a distance b behind the screen. Introducing now in (33) the quantity d in place of x', and setting $\rho_1 = a$, $\rho_0 = b$, which is allowable since $\cos\phi$ does not differ appreciably from 1 provided P_0 be taken in the neighborhood of the shadow, there results

$$v' = d\sqrt{\frac{2a}{\lambda b(a+b)}} = d : p, \quad . \quad . \quad . \quad (39)$$

in which p is an abbreviation for

$$p = \sqrt{\frac{\lambda b(a+b)}{2a}}. \quad . \quad . \quad . \quad . \quad . \quad . \quad (40)$$

There are therefore maxima of intensity when $d = p\sqrt{\frac{3}{2} + 4h}$, i.e. when

$$d_1 = p \cdot 1.225; \quad d_2 = p \cdot 2.345; \quad d_3 = p \cdot 3.082, \text{ etc.},$$

minima when $d = p\sqrt{\frac{7}{2} + 4h}$, i.e. when

$$d_1' = p \cdot 1.871; \quad d_2' = p \cdot 2.739; \quad d_3' = p \cdot 3.391, \text{ etc.}$$

The exact values differ only slightly from the approximate ones, which are also in agreement with observation.†

According to (38) the intensity of the light at these maxima and minima may be determined by measuring the successive sections which the line FF' cuts from the curve. Thus, if the free intensity be 1, the maxima are

$$J_1 = 1.34; \quad J_2 = 1.20; \quad J_3 = 1.16;$$

* Such a rotation of the screen and corresponding rotation of the free surface over which the integration is extended produces no change in the result (cf. proposition on page 184).

† The diffraction fringes may be observed either by means of a suitably placed screen or a lens with a micrometer (cf. p. 133, note).

the minima,

$$J_1' = 0.78; \quad J_2' = 0.84; \quad J_3' = 0.87.$$

From a more exact evaluation of his integrals Fresnel obtained values differing but little from these.

5. Diffraction through a Narrow Slit.—Using the same coordinate system and the same notation as in the preceding paragraph, the intensity of the light will be investigated in a plane which passes through the source Q and is perpendicular to the edges of the slit. This plane is the xz-plane (cf. Fig. 65). Let the x coordinates of the edges of the slit be x_1 and x_2. If the point P_0, at which the intensity is to be calculated, lies in the geometrical shadow of one of the screens which bound the slit on either side, then x_1 and x_2 are either both positive or both negative. But if the line connecting Q with P_0 passes through the open slit, then the signs of x_1 and x_2 are opposite.

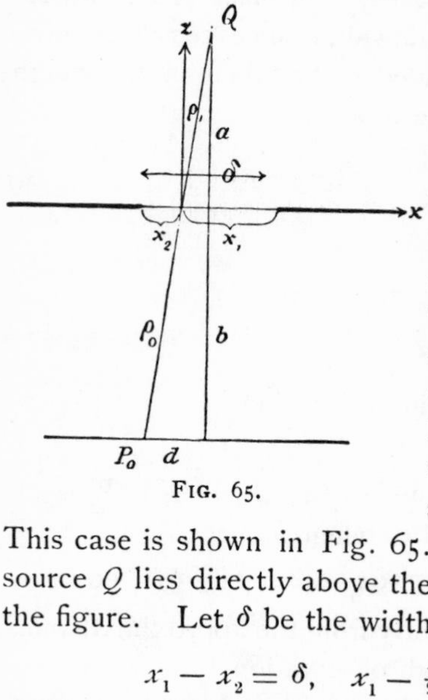

FIG. 65.

This case is shown in Fig. 65. It will be assumed that the source Q lies directly above the middle of the slit, as shown in the figure. Let δ be the width of the slit. Then

$$x_1 - x_2 = \delta, \quad x_1 - \tfrac{1}{2}\delta : d = a : a + b. \quad . \quad . \quad (41)$$

a and b may without appreciable error be replaced by ρ_1 and ρ_0, since when δ is small the inclination of ρ_1 to a is also small.

Introducing again the quantity v which is defined by (31) on page 194, and calling v_1 and v_2 the values of v which correspond to the limits of integration x_1 and x_2, the intensity of light at P_0 is, as in (38),

$$J = \frac{A_2}{2(\rho_0 + \rho_1)^2}(v_1, v_2)^2, \quad . \quad . \quad . \quad . \quad (42)$$

in which (v_1, v_2) represents the distance between the two points of the curve in Fig. 63 which correspond to the parameters v_1 and v_2. But now, by (41) and (31),

$$v_1 - v_2 = \delta\sqrt{\frac{2}{\lambda}\left(\frac{1}{a}+\frac{1}{b}\right)}, \quad \frac{v_1 + v_2}{2} = d : p, \quad . \quad (43)$$

in which p has the same meaning as in (40). If now it is desired to investigate the distribution of light in a plane which lies a distance b behind the screen, the dependence of equation (42) upon d must be discussed. According to (43) the difference between the parameters is constant. Hence the question is, how does the distance vary between the two points v_1 and v_2 whose distance apart, when measured along the arc of the curve in Fig. 63, has the constant value $s = v_1 - v_2$? Assume first a slit so small that the length of the constant arc s is about 0.1,* then the curve shows that the intensity remains constant from $d = 0$ up to a large value of v_1, i.e. of d, and then gradually decreases when v_1 and v_2 both attain very large positive or negative values, i.e. when P_0 lies very far within the geometrical shadow. Hence when the slit is narrow the geometrical shadow cannot be even approximately located, for the light is distributed almost evenly (diffused †) over a large region, and there is nowhere a sharp shadow formed.

If the width of the slit is somewhat larger (though still but a small fraction of a mm.), so that the constant arc length s amounts to 0.5, then the curve of Fig. 63 shows that here too the light extends far into the geometrical shadow, and that maxima and minima of intensity occur only when v_1 and v_2 have like signs, i.e. diffraction fringes are formed only within the geometrical shadow. Sharp minima exist (cf. Fig. 66) when the tangents to the two points v_1 and v_2 of the curve are parallel so that their

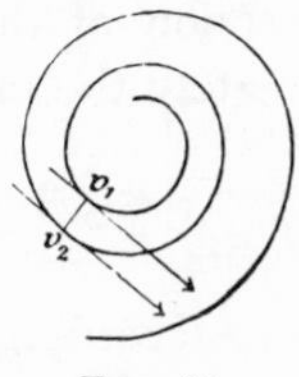

FIG. 66.

* For $a = b = 20$ cm., δ must be about 30λ to attain this.

† Diffusion of light must always occur, as can be shown from the construction of the Fresnel zones, if the width of the slit $\delta < \frac{1}{2}\lambda$.

angles (cf. page 189) differ from each other by a whole multiple of 2π. Since now, by (18) on page 189, $\tau = \frac{\pi}{2}v^2$, the positions of the diffraction fringes must be given by

$$\frac{\pi}{2}(v_1^2 - v_2^2) = \pm 2h\pi, \text{ i.e. } (v_1 - v_2)(v_1 + v_2) = \pm 4h,$$

or, in consideration of (43), by

$$d \cdot \delta = \pm h\lambda b, \quad h = 1, 2, 3 \ldots \quad . \quad . \quad (44)$$

These fringes are then equidistant and independent of a, i.e. of the distance of the source from the screen.

If the slit is made broader, or if a and b are reduced, the width of the slit remaining unchanged, so that the difference $v_1 - v_2$ is essentially increased, then diffraction fringes may also appear, as is shown by Fig. 63, when v_1 and v_2 have opposite signs, i.e. outside of the geometrical shadow. For a given value of $v_1 - v_2$ the numerical value of J corresponding to any particular value of d may be determined from the curve with a close degree of approximation. When the slit becomes very broad, i.e. when $v_1 - v_2$ is very large, the case approaches that treated in § 4 above.

At the mid-point where $d = 0$, J never vanishes. But for given values of a and δ, the value of b determines whether J is a maximum or a minimum. Since when $d = 0$, v_1 and v_2 are equal and of opposite sign, the line connecting them passes through the origin (cf. Fig. 63). Hence the points of intersection of the curve with the line FF' determine approximately the maxima and minima, i.e. (cf. page 196) there are

$$\text{Maxima when } v_1 = \sqrt{\tfrac{3}{2} + 4h},$$

$$\text{Minima when } v_1 = \sqrt{\tfrac{7}{2} + 4h},$$

or, according to (43), since $v_2 = -v_1$,

$$\left.\begin{aligned} &\text{Maxima when } \frac{\delta^2}{2\lambda}\left(\frac{1}{a} + \frac{1}{b}\right) = \frac{3}{2} + 4h, \\ &\text{Minima when } \frac{\delta^2}{2\lambda}\left(\frac{1}{a} + \frac{1}{b}\right) = \frac{7}{2} + 4h, \end{aligned}\right\} \quad . \quad . \quad (45)$$

$$h = 0, 1, 2, 3 \ldots$$

6. Diffraction by a Narrow Screen.*—Let the screen have the width δ, and let the source Q lie at a distance a directly over its mid-point. Consider the intensity of the light in a plane (the xz-plane) which passes through Q and is perpendicular to the parallel edges of the screen. Use the preceding notation (cf. Fig. 65), and let x_1 and x_2 be the x-coordinates of the edges of the screen, v_1 and v_2 the corresponding values of the parameter v. v_1 and v_2 then satisfy equation (43). The intensity of the light J is proportional to the sum of the square of the integrals (cf. page 195)

$$M = \int_{-\infty}^{v_1} \cos \frac{\pi v^2}{2} dv + \int_{v_2}^{+\infty} \cos \frac{\pi v^2}{2} dv,$$

$$N = \int_{-\infty}^{v_1} \sin \frac{\pi v^2}{2} dv + \int_{v_2}^{+\infty} \sin \frac{\pi v^2}{2} dv.$$

Now the first term of M is equal (cf. the analogous development on page 195) to the ξ-component of the line which connects F' and the point E_1 which corresponds to the parameter v_1 (cf. Fig. 67). The second term of M is equal to the ξ-

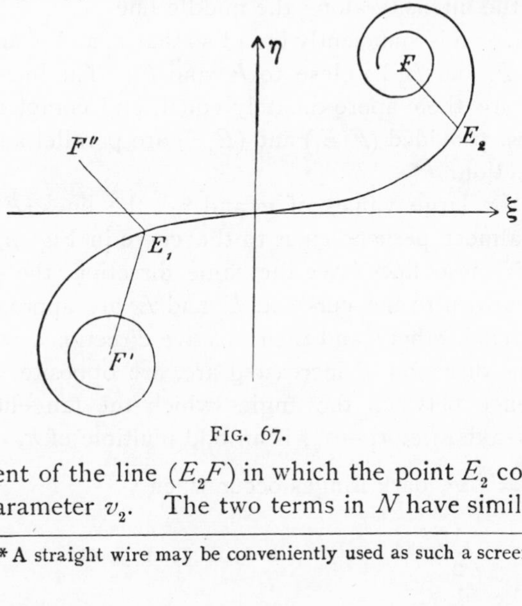

FIG. 67.

component of the line (E_2F) in which the point E_2 corresponds to the parameter v_2. The two terms in N have similar signifi-

* A straight wire may be conveniently used as such a screen.

cations. If the ξ and η components of the lines $(F'E_1)$ and (E_2F) be denoted by ξ_1, ξ_2, η_1, η_2, then

$$M^2 + N^2 = (\xi_1 + \xi_2)^2 + (\eta_1 + \eta_2)^2.$$

If at the end of the line $(F'E_1)$ the line (E_1F''), having the same length and direction as the line (E_2F), be drawn, then the line $(F'F'')$ has the components $\xi_1 + \xi_2$, $\eta_1 + \eta_2$. The intensity J at the point P_0 is then proportional to the square of the line $(F'F'')$, which is the geometrical sum of the two lines $(F'E_1)$ and (E_2F), i.e.

$$J = \frac{A^2}{2(\rho_0 + \rho_1)^2}\cdot(F'F'')^2. \quad . \quad . \quad . \quad . \quad (46)$$

From this it appears that the central line ($d = 0$) is always bright, although it lies farthest inside the geometrical shadow; for along it the values of v_1 and v_2 are equal and of opposite sign, so that the two points E_1 and E_2 in Fig. 67 are symmetrically placed with respect to the origin, and hence the lines $F'E_1$ and E_2F are equal and have the same direction, so that their sum can never be zero. The broader the screen, the smaller is the intensity along the middle line.

If the screen is sufficiently broad so that v_1 and v_2 are large, the points E_1 and E_2 lie close to F' and F. The lines $(F'E_1)$ and (E_2F) are then approximately equal, and complete darkness results, provided $(F'E_1)$ and (E_2F) are parallel and opposite in direction.

Since, for large values of v_1 and v_2, the lines $(F'E_1)$ and (FE_2) are almost perpendicular to the curve in Fig. 67, it follows that if these lines have the same direction, the tangents which are drawn to the curve at E_1 and E_2 are approximately parallel to each other; and their positive directions, which are taken in the direction of increasing arc, are opposite. Hence the difference between the angles which the tangents make with the ξ-axis, i.e. $\tau_1 - \tau_2$, is an odd multiple of π, or since, by (18), $\tau = \frac{\pi}{2}v^2$, dark fringes occur when

$$\frac{1}{2}(v_1^2 - v_2^2) = \pm 1, \pm 3, \pm 5, \text{ etc.}$$

This becomes, in consideration of (43),

$$2d\delta = \pm h\lambda b, \ h = 1, 3, 5, \text{ etc.} \quad . \quad . \quad . \quad . \quad (47)$$

These fringes become less black as d increases. They are equidistant and independent of the distance a of the source from the screen. These results hold only inside the geometrical shadow, i.e. only so long as $d < \frac{1}{2}\delta\frac{a+b}{a}$, and only then with close approximation provided the values of v_1 and v_2 which correspond to the edges of the screen are sufficiently large, i.e. provided the screen is broad enough and the point P_0 is sufficiently near to it and to the middle line of the shadow.

As P_0 moves toward the edge of the geometrical shadow or passes outside of it, maxima and minima occur at different positions of P_0 which can be determined for every special case by the construction given in Fig. 67. The law determining the positions of these fringes is, however, not a simple one.

These examples will suffice to show the utility of the geometrical method used by Cornu.* Observation verifies all the consequences here deduced.

7. Rigorous Treatment of Diffraction by a Straight Edge.—As was remarked at the beginning of this chapter (page 185), the foregoing treatment of diffraction phenomena, based upon Huygens' principle, is only approximately correct. Now it is important to notice that in at least one case, namely, that of diffraction by a straight edge, the problem can be solved rigorously, as has been shown by Sommerfeld.† This solution both furnishes a test of the accuracy of the approximate solution, and also makes it possible to discuss theoretically the phenomena when the angle of diffraction is large, i.e. when P_0 lies far within the limits of the geometrical shadow,—a discussion which was not possible with the other method, at least without making important extensions.

---

* Complicated cases are treated by this method by Mascart, Traité d'Optique, Paris, 1889, Vol. I, p. 283.

† A. Sommerfeld, Math. Annalen, Vol. XLVII, p. 317, 1895.

In the rigorous treatment of the diffraction phenomena the differential equation (12) on page 159,

$$\frac{\partial^2 s}{\partial t^2} = V^2\left(\frac{\partial^2 s}{\partial x^2} + \frac{\partial^2 s}{\partial y^2} + \frac{\partial^2 s}{\partial z^2}\right),$$

for the light disturbance must be integrated so as to satisfy certain boundary conditions which must be fulfilled at the surface of the diffraction screen. The form of these conditions will be deduced in Section II, Chapters, I, II, and IV; here the results of that deduction will be assumed. In the first place, to simplify the discussion, assume that the source is an infinitely long line parallel to the y-axis. Also let the edge of the screen be chosen as the y-axis, and let the x-axis be positive on the side of the screen, and the z-axis positive toward the source (cf. Fig. 68). In this case it is evident that

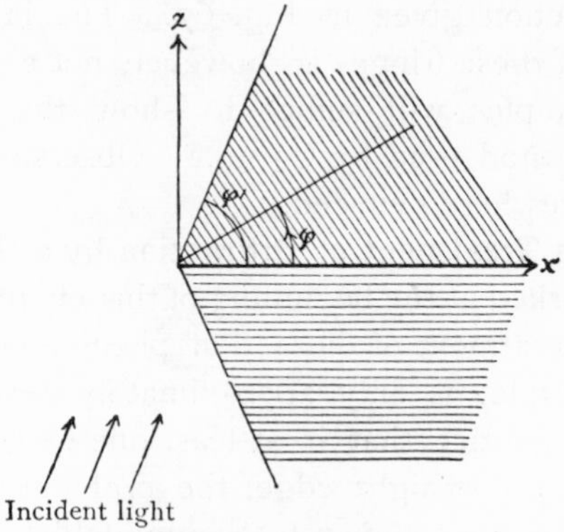

FIG. 68.

s cannot depend upon the coordinate y, so that the above equation reduces to

$$\frac{\partial^2 s}{\partial t^2} = V^2\left(\frac{\partial^2 s}{\partial x^2} + \frac{\partial^2 s}{\partial z^2}\right). \quad . \quad . \quad . \quad . \quad (48)$$

Let the screen be infinitely thin and have an infinite absorption coefficient. It can then transmit no light, but can reflect perfectly, as will be shown in Section II. A very thin, highly polished film of silver may constitute such a screen. It is then not a "perfectly black" screen, but rather one "perfectly white." * The boundary conditions at such a screen are:

(49) $s = 0$, if the incident light is polarized in a plane perpendicular to the edge of the screen,

(50) $\frac{\partial s}{\partial z} = 0$, if the light is polarized in a plane parallel to the edge of the screen.†

The meaning of these symbols and of the word polarized will not be explained until the next chapter. Here it is sufficient to know that the solution of the differential equation (48) must satisfy either (49) or (50). The boundary conditions hold upon the surface of the screen, i.e. for $z = 0$, $x > 0$; or if polar coordinates are introduced by means of the equations

$$x = r \cos \phi, \quad z = r \sin \phi, \quad . \quad . \quad . \quad . \quad (51)$$

for $\phi = 0$ or $\phi = 2\pi$.

If these polar coordinates be introduced into the differential equation (48), there results

$$\frac{\partial^2 s}{\partial t^2} = V^2\left(\frac{\partial^2 s}{\partial r^2} + \frac{1}{r}\frac{\partial s}{\partial r} + \frac{1}{r^2}\frac{\partial^2 s}{\partial \phi^2}\right). \quad . \quad . \quad . \quad (52)$$

Now a solution of this differential equation, which satisfies the boundary condition (49) or (50), gives for the particular

---

* A perfectly black screen, i.e. one which neither transmits nor reflects light, is realized when the index of refraction of the substance constituting it changes gradually at the surface to that of the surrounding medium, and the coefficient of absorption at the surface changes gradually to the value zero. Every discontinuity in the properties of an optical medium produces necessarily reflection of light. Hence an ideal black screen, consisting of a thin body, with sharp boundaries, at which definite boundary conditions can be set up, is inconceivable.

† As will be seen later in the discussion of the electro-magnetic theory, s has not the same meaning in the two equations. In (49) s represents the electric force vibrating parallel to the edge of the screen, in (50) the magnetic force vibrating parallel to the edge of the screen. The intensity is calculated in both cases in the same way, at least for the side of the screen which is turned away from the source.

case in which the source lies at infinity and the incident rays make an angle ϕ' with the x-axis

$$s=A\cdot\frac{1+i}{2}\cdot e^{i2\pi\frac{t}{T}}\left\{e^{-i\gamma}\int_{-\infty}^{\sigma}e^{-i\frac{\pi v^2}{2}}dv \mp e^{-i\gamma'}\int_{-\infty}^{\sigma'}e^{-i\frac{\pi v^2}{2}}dv\right\}, \quad (53)$$

in which

$$\gamma=\frac{2\pi r}{\lambda}\cos(\phi-\phi'),\quad \gamma'=\frac{2\pi r}{\lambda}\cos(\phi+\phi'), \quad . \quad (54)$$

$$\sigma=\sqrt{\frac{8r}{\lambda}}\sin\frac{1}{2}(\phi-\phi'),\quad \sigma'=-\sqrt{\frac{8r}{\lambda}}\sin\frac{1}{2}(\phi+\phi'). \quad . \quad (55)$$

In (53) the sign is minus or plus according as it is the condition (49) or (50) which must be fulfilled. The letter i denotes the imaginary $\sqrt{-1}$. Thus the solution of s appears as a complex quantity. In order to obtain its physical significance, it is only necessary to take into account the real part of this quantity. Thus setting

$$s=(A+Bi)e^{i2\pi\frac{t}{T}}, \quad . \quad . \quad . \quad . \quad . \quad (56)$$

the physical meaning of s is the real part, i.e.

$$s=A\cos 2\pi\frac{t}{T}-B\sin 2\pi\frac{t}{T}. \quad . \quad . \quad . \quad (57)$$

The intensity of the light would in this case be (cf. similar conclusion on page 188)

$$J=A^2+B^2. \quad . \quad . \quad . \quad . \quad . \quad . \quad . \quad (58)$$

This result could have been obtained from (56) directly by multiplying s by the conjugate complex quantity, i.e. by that quantity which differs from the right-hand side of (56) only in the sign of i, namely, by $(A-Bi)e^{-i2\pi\frac{t}{T}}$. For the sake of later use this result may be here stated in the following form: *When the expression for the light disturbance s is a complex quantity* (in which s signifies physically only the real part of this complex quantity), *the intensity of the light is obtained by multiplication by the conjugate complex quantity.*

That equations (53), (54), and (55) are a real solution of the differential equation (52) can be shown by taking the differential coefficients with respect to r and ϕ.* Also the boundary condition (49) is fulfilled when the minus sign is used in (53), since for $\phi = 0$ and $\phi = 2\pi$, $\gamma = \gamma'$, $\sigma = \sigma'$. The boundary condition (50) is fulfilled when the plus sign is used in (53), since $\frac{\partial s}{\partial z} = \frac{1}{r}\frac{\partial s}{\partial \phi}$ for $\phi = 0$, and since the differential coefficient with respect to ϕ of the two terms in the brackets of (53) take opposite signs for $\phi = 0$ or $\phi = 2\pi$. Furthermore, that (53) is a solution corresponding to the assumed case of a plane wave from an infinitely distant source lying in the given direction will be seen from a more detailed discussion. But it is first necessary to consider a very important point. If the point P_0, for which s is to be calculated, be made to execute a complete revolution in the xz-plane about the edge of the screen and at a fixed distance r from it, then ϕ increases an amount 2π. s does not regain its original value, because, on account of the factor $\sin \frac{1}{2}(\phi \mp \phi')$, σ and σ', in the change from ϕ to $\phi + 2\pi$, have changed their signs. s is therefore not a single-valued function of the coordinates. But the physical meaning of s demands that it be single-valued. This demand can at once be satisfied if, in the change of ϕ, P_0 be never allowed to pass through the screen. This restriction will be made, so that ϕ is allowed to vary only between 0 (the shadow side of the screen) and 2π (its light side).

Three regions are to be distinguished within which s must be treated differently:

1. *The region of the shadow:* $0 < \phi < \phi'$. From (55), σ and σ' are negative. Hence, for an infinitely large value of r, s is zero.

---

* The way in which Sommerfeld reached this solution cannot here be presented, as it would require too long a mathematical deduction.

2. *The region of no shadow:* $\phi' < \phi < 2\pi - \phi'$. σ is positive, σ' negative. Since, from (27) on page 191,

$$\int_{-\infty}^{+\infty} e^{-i\frac{\pi v^2}{2}} dv = 2\int_0^{\infty} e^{-i\frac{\pi v^2}{2}} dv = 1 - i, \quad . \quad . \quad (59)$$

it follows that, for infinitely large values of r,

$$s = Ae^{i2\pi\left(\frac{t}{T} - \frac{r}{\lambda}\cos(\phi - \phi')\right)}.$$

The real part of this expression corresponds to plane waves which have amplitude A, and whose direction of propagation makes the angle ϕ' with the x-axis. The solution actually corresponds then, for large values of r, to the incident light from an infinitely distant source Q which lies in the direction ϕ'.

3. *The region of reflection:* $2\pi - \phi' < \phi < 2\pi$. σ and σ' are positive. Hence, for infinitely large values of r,

$$s = A \cdot e^{i2\pi\frac{t}{T}} \left\{ e^{-i\frac{2\pi r}{\lambda}\cos(\phi - \phi')} \mp e^{-i\frac{2\pi r}{\lambda}\cos(\phi + \phi')} \right\}.$$

The real part of this expression corresponds to the superposition of the incident plane wave and the plane wave reflected at the screen in accordance with the laws of reflection. The reflected amplitude is in numerical value equal to the incident amplitude.

Equation (53) may be made more intelligible by again making use of the curve of Fig. 63. For, from page 195,

$$\int_{-\infty}^{\sigma} e^{-i\frac{\pi v^2}{2}} dv = \xi - i\eta, \quad . \quad . \quad . \quad . \quad (60)$$

in which ξ and η are the projections of the line $(F'E)$ upon the ξ and η axes respectively, and E represents the point of the curve corresponding to the parameter σ. Similarly

$$\int_{-\infty}^{\sigma'} e^{-i\frac{\pi v^2}{2}} dv = \xi' - i\eta', \quad . \quad . \quad . \quad . \quad (61)$$

in which ξ' and η' are the projections of the line $(F'E')$, and E' is a point of the curve which corresponds to the parameter σ'.

Now upon the side of the screen turned away from the source, $0 < \phi < \pi$, and it is to be noticed that, on account of the small denominator λ (wave length), σ' is always very large and negative, provided r be not taken very small. Hence, for large values of r, it is possible by equation (61) to write approximately $\xi' = \eta' = 0$, and there results from (53) and (60)

$$s = A\frac{1+i}{2}e^{i2\pi\frac{t}{T}}e^{-i\gamma}(\xi - i\eta),$$

and by theorem (58), for the intensity of the light,

$$J = \frac{A^2}{2}\cdot(F'E)^2. \quad . \quad . \quad . \quad . \quad . \quad . \quad (62)$$

Almost the same equation would have been obtained from the approximate method of § 4 above. For, when the source is infinitely distant, equation (38) there given would lead to

$$J = \frac{A^2}{2}(-\infty\,,\ v')^2, \quad . \quad . \quad . \quad . \quad . \quad (63)$$

and by (39),

$$v' = d\sqrt{\frac{2}{\lambda b}}.$$

The meaning of d may be obtained from Fig. 64. If the distance r of the point P_0 from the edge of the screen be introduced, then $d = r\sin(\phi - \phi')$, if $\phi - \phi'$ be the angle of diffraction, i.e. the angle between the incident and the diffracted rays. Since in the neighborhood of the edge of the shadow it is permissible to write $b = r$, it follows that $v' = \sin(\phi - \phi')\sqrt{\frac{2r}{\lambda}}$; but [cf. (55)] this expression is also the value of σ when the angle of diffraction is small, i.e. the point E in equation (62) corresponds to the parameter v' of equation (63).

Hence both equations lead to the same value of J in the neighborhood of the edge of the shadow. At greater distances from it the more rigorous equation (62) differs from that obtained by the above approximate method. The previous conclusion that diffraction fringes occur only outside the region of shadow is confirmed by this more rigorous discussion.

Upon the side of the screen turned toward the source $(\pi < \phi < 2\pi)$ within the region of reflection $(\phi > 2\pi - \phi')$ equation (61) assumes values of considerable size.

Hence if it is desired to deduce a general rigorous equation for the intensity of the light, integral (61) cannot be neglected in comparison with (60). This is true, both for the region of reflection and for the other regions, when r is very small or when the angle of diffraction $\phi - \phi'$ is large.

This rigorous equation for the intensity J is obtained by multiplying the right-hand side of (53) by the conjugate complex expression. Using the notation of (60) and (61), the following is thus obtained:

$$J = \frac{A^2}{2}\left\{\xi^2 + \eta^2 + \xi'^2 + \eta'^2 \mp 2\cos(\gamma - \gamma')\cdot(\xi\xi' + \eta\eta') \right.$$
$$\left. \pm 2\sin(\gamma - \gamma')\cdot(\eta\xi' - \eta'\xi)\right\},$$

or

$$J = \frac{A^2}{2}\left\{(F'E)^2 + (F'E')^2 \mp 2(F'E)(F'E')\cos(\gamma - \gamma' + \chi)\right\}, \quad (64)$$

in which χ denotes the angle included between the lines $(F'E)$ and $(F'E')$. χ is taken positive when the rotation which leads most directly from $F'E$ to $F'E'$ takes place in the same direction as a rotation from the η- to the ξ-axis. By (54),

$$\gamma - \gamma' = \frac{4\pi r}{\lambda}\sin\phi\sin\phi'. \quad . \quad . \quad . \quad (65)$$

By (64) J is proportional to the square of the geometrical difference or sum of the two lines of length $(F'E)$ and $(F'E')$ which include the angle $\chi + \gamma - \gamma'$. The geometrical difference is to be taken when the incident light is polarized in a plane perpendicular to the edge of the screen, the geometrical sum when it is polarized in the plane parallel to that edge.

The expression (64) may still be much simplified when the intensity J is reckoned for points which are not in the neighborhood of the edge of the shadow, i.e. when the difference between ϕ and ϕ' is large.

For then in the region of the shadow σ and σ' have large negative values, and hence, as is evident from the discussion of the form of the curve of Fig. 63 given in § 3, $F'E$ becomes equal to the radius of curvature ρ of the curve at the point E, $F'E'$ to its radius of curvature at the point E', and the angle χ, which the two lines make with each other, equal to the angle included between the tangents drawn to the curve at the points E and E'. Hence, from equations (18) and (19) on page 189,

$$F'E = \frac{1}{\pi\sigma}, \quad F'E' = \frac{1}{\pi\sigma'}, \quad \chi = \frac{\pi}{2}(\sigma^2 - \sigma'^2).$$

Now, from (55) and (65), $\gamma - \gamma' + \chi = 0$, and hence, from (64),

$$J = \frac{A^2}{2\pi^2}\left(\frac{1}{\sigma} \mp \frac{1}{\sigma'}\right)^2. \quad . \quad . \quad . \quad . \quad . \quad (66)$$

If the values of σ and σ' given in (55) be introduced here, then, when the sign is negative, i.e. when the incident light is polarized in a plane perpendicular to the edge of the screen,

$$(\perp)\ J = \frac{A^2}{\pi^2}\cdot\frac{\lambda}{r}\cdot\frac{\sin^2\frac{1}{2}\phi\cdot\cos^2\frac{1}{2}\phi'}{(\cos\phi - \cos\phi')^2}, \quad . \quad . \quad . \quad (67)$$

while when the sign is positive, i.e. when the incident light is polarized in a plane parallel to the edge of the screen,

$$(\parallel)\ J = \frac{A^2}{\pi^2}\cdot\frac{\lambda}{r}\cdot\frac{\cos^2\frac{1}{2}\phi\cdot\sin^2\frac{1}{2}\phi'}{(\cos\phi - \cos\phi')^2}. \quad . \quad . \quad . \quad (68)$$

These equations for the region of the shadow hold only so long as $\frac{\lambda}{r}$ is very small and the difference between ϕ and ϕ' is large. Thus they do not hold at the edge of the shadow. The equations show that, at the screen itself ($\phi = 0$), the light is completely polarized in a plane parallel to the edge of the screen; also that, as ϕ increases, the intensity J in both equations continually increases, and that the intensity (67) of the light polarized in the plane perpendicular to the edge of the screen is always smaller than the intensity (68) of the light polarized in the plane parallel to the edge of the screen. The difference between the two intensities continually decreases as the edge of the shadow is approached.

Gouy * has made observations upon the diffraction of light by a straight edge when the angle of diffraction is very large. When the edge of the screen was rounded, colors were produced which depended upon the nature of the screen. The theory here given requires that, independent of the nature of the screen, the colors of long wave-length predominate in light diffracted at a large angle. If there is to be a dependence of the color upon the nature of the screen, the boundary conditions (49) and (50) must contain the optical constants of the screen. Thus far no integration of the differential equation (48) which involves such complicated boundary conditions has been made.

Outside of the region of the shadow, and also outside of the region of reflection, and at a sufficient distance from the limits of these two regions, σ has a large positive and σ' a large negative value. Hence $F'E'$ is very small and, disregarding the sign, has the value $1 : \pi\sigma'$, while $F'E$ is approximately equal to $\sqrt{2}$. Further, since the angle included between $F'E$ and the ξ-axis is approximately $\frac{1}{4}\pi$, $\chi = -\frac{1}{4}\pi - \frac{1}{2}\pi\sigma'^2$, so that

$$\chi + \gamma - \gamma' = -\tfrac{1}{4}\pi - \frac{4\pi r}{\lambda}\sin^2 \tfrac{1}{2}(\phi - \phi').$$

* Gouy, Ann. d. Phys. et de Chim. (6), 8, p. 145, 1886.

Hence, neglecting $(F'E')^2$, there results from (64)

$$J = A^2 \left\{ 1 \pm \frac{1}{\pi}\sqrt{\frac{\lambda}{4r}} \cdot \frac{\cos\left[\frac{1}{4}\pi + \frac{4\pi r}{\lambda}\sin^2\frac{1}{2}(\phi - \phi')\right]}{\sin\frac{1}{2}(\phi + \phi')} \right\}. \qquad (69)$$

Thus, as ϕ varies, diffraction fringes appear which are, to be sure, very indistinct. The fringes become clearer the nearer ϕ approaches $2\pi - \phi'$. But then equation (69) no longer holds, and for points close to the boundary of the region of reflection the result must be obtained from (64) and the curve of Fig. 63, since in this case $F'E'$ is larger.

In the region of reflection, at a sufficient distance from its boundary $\phi = 2\pi - \phi'$, both $F'E$ and $F'E'$ are approximately equal to $\sqrt{2}$ and $\chi = 0$. Hence, from (64) and (65), the intensity changes periodically from perfect darkness to four times the intensity of the incident light according as $\frac{2r}{\lambda}\sin\phi\sin\phi'$ is a whole number or half of an odd number. Hence the phenomenon of stationary waves, discussed above on page 155, is again encountered. Such stationary waves always occur when the incident and the reflected light are superposed. But it is important to remark that the significance of s depends upon the condition of polarization of the incident light (cf. foot-note, p. 205). This matter will be discussed in a later chapter.

8. Fraunhofer's Diffraction Phenomena.—As was remarked on page 188, Fraunhofer's diffraction phenomena are those in which the source Q lies at an infinite distance from the point P_0 of observation. These phenomena may be observed by placing a point source Q at the focus of a convergent lens, so as to render the emergent rays parallel, and observing by means of a telescope placed behind the diffraction screen and focussed for parallel rays.

The discussion will be based, as in § 1, on Huygens' principle; and hence the treatment will not be altogether rigorous. But, as has already been seen, this principle gives a very close approximation when the angle of diffraction is not too large. In accordance with equations (8) and (9) on page 187, when $\rho_1 = \rho_0 = \infty$,

$$f(x, y) = -\frac{2\pi}{\lambda}\left\{x(\alpha_1 + \alpha_0) + y(\beta_1 + \beta_0)\right\}, \quad (70)$$

in which α_1, β_1, α_0, β_0 denote the direction cosines with respect to the x- and y-axes of the lines drawn from the origin to the source Q and the point of observation P_0 respectively. (Cf. Fig. 62, page 185.)

Hence, from equations (11) and (12) on pages 187 and 188, using the abbreviations

$$\frac{2\pi}{\lambda}(\alpha_1 + \alpha_0) = \mu, \quad \frac{2\pi}{\lambda}(\beta_1 + \beta_0) = \nu, \quad . \quad . \quad . \quad (71)$$

there results for the intensity of the light at the point P_0,

$$J = A'^2(C^2 + S^2), \quad . \quad . \quad . \quad . \quad . \quad . \quad (72)$$

in which

$$C = \int \cos(\mu x + \nu y)d\sigma, \quad S = \int \sin(\mu x + \nu y)d\sigma, \quad . \quad (73)$$

and the integration is to be extended over the opening in the screen.

The meaning of the constant A' may be brought out by introducing the intensity J' which is observed behind the diffraction screen when the telescope is pointed in the direction of the incident light. For then, at all points of the screen which are not infinitely distant from the origin, $\mu = \nu = 0$, so that the relation holds

$$J' = A'^2 \cdot \sigma^2,$$

where σ denotes the area of the entire opening. Hence for any direction of the telescope it follows that

$$J = \frac{J'}{\sigma^2}(C^2 + S^2). \quad . \quad . \quad . \quad . \quad . \quad . \quad (74)$$

9. Diffraction through a Rectangular Opening. — The integral of (73) may be most easily obtained when the opening is a rectangle. Take the middle of the rectangle as the origin, and let the axes be parallel to its sides and let the lengths of these sides be a (parallel to the x-axis) and b (parallel to the y-axis) respectively, then

$$C = \frac{4}{\mu\nu} \sin\frac{\mu a}{2} \sin\frac{\nu b}{2}, \quad S = 0.$$

Hence, from (74), since $\sigma = ab$,

$$J = J' \cdot \left[\frac{\sin\frac{\mu a}{2}}{\frac{\mu a}{2}}\right]^2 \cdot \left[\frac{\sin\frac{\nu b}{2}}{\frac{\nu b}{2}}\right]^2 \quad . \quad . \quad . \quad . \quad (75)$$

Therefore complete darkness occurs in directions for which μa or νb is an exact multiple of 2π.

If the light from Q falls perpendicularly upon the screen, $\alpha_1 = \beta_1 = 0$. Let the optical axis of the observing telescope be parallel to the incident light, i.e. perpendicular to the screen. The intensity J in the direction determined by α_0, β_0 is then observed at a point P of the focal plane of the telescope objective which has the coordinates

$$x' = f\alpha_0, \quad y' = f\beta_0 \quad . \quad . \quad . \quad . \quad . \quad (76)$$

in a coordinate system $x'y'$ whose origin lies at the focus F of the objective, and whose axes are parallel to the sides of the rectangle. f represents the focal length of the objective. In (76) it is assumed that α_0, β_0 are small quantities, i.e. the angle of diffraction is small.

Now, from (71),

$$\mu = \frac{2\pi x'}{\lambda f}, \quad \nu = \frac{2\pi y'}{\lambda f}. \quad . \quad . \quad . \quad . \quad (77)$$

Hence complete darkness occurs when

$$\mu a = \pm 2h\pi, \quad \text{i.e. } x' = \pm h\frac{\lambda f}{a}, \quad h = 1, 2, 3 \ldots$$

and when

$$\nu b = \pm 2h\pi, \quad \text{i.e. } y' = \pm k\frac{\lambda f}{b}, \quad k = 1, 2, 3 \ldots$$

Hence in the focal plane of the objective there is produced, when monochromatic light is used, a pattern crossed by dark lines as shown in Fig. 69. The lines are a constant distance

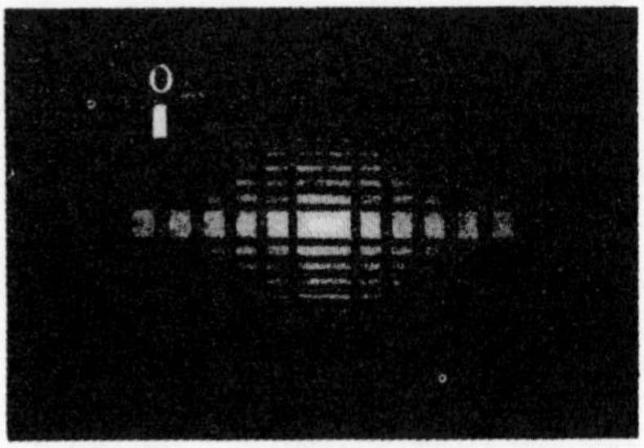

FIG. 69.

apart save in the middle of the pattern, where their distance is twice as great. The aperture which produced this pattern is shown in the upper left-hand corner of the figure. Hence the fringes are rectangles which are similar to the aperture but lie inversely to it.

At the focus of the objective the intensity reaches its greatest value $J = J'$; for when $\mu = 0$, the limiting value of the quotient $\sin \frac{\mu a}{2} : \frac{\mu a}{2} = 1$. J has other but weaker maxima approximately in the middle points of the rectangles bounded by the diffraction fringes in Fig. 69. For these points

$$\mu a = \pi(2h + 1), \quad \nu b = \pi(2k + 1), \quad h, k = 1, 2, 3 \ldots$$

But for the middle points of those rectangles upon the x'-axis

$$\mu a = \pi(2h + 1), \quad \nu = 0, \quad h = 1, 2, 3 \ldots$$

Hence the intensities in the maxima upon the x'-axis (or the y'-axis) are

$$J_1 = J' \frac{4}{\pi^2(2h + 1)^2},$$

while the intensities at the middle points of other rectangles for which neither x' nor y' vanish are

$$J_2 = J' \frac{16 : \pi^4}{(2h+1)^2(2k+1)^2}.$$

Thus the intensities J_2 are much smaller than the intensities J_1; so that the figure viewed as a whole gives the impression of a cross which grows brighter toward the centre and whose arms lie parallel to the sides of the rectangle. In Fig. 69 the distribution of the light is indicated by the shading.

10. Diffraction through a Rhomboid.—This case may be immediately deduced from the former by noting that in (73) the integrals C and S, and consequently the intensity J, remain unchanged if the coordinates x, y of the diffraction aperture are multiplied by the factors p, q, while at the same time the μ, ν, i.e. the cordinates x', y' of the diffraction pattern, are divided by the same factors p, q. Thus a rectangular parallelogram whose sides are not parallel to the coordinate axes x, y may be reduced to a rhomboid by the use of two factors p, q, and in this case the diffraction fringes will also be rhomboids whose sides are perpendicular to the sides of the diffracting opening.

11. Diffraction through a Slit.—A slit may be looked upon as a rectangle one of whose sides b is very large. Hence the diffraction pattern reduces to a narrow strip of light along the x'-axis. This is crossed by dark spots corresponding to the equation

$$J = J' \left[\frac{\sin \frac{\mu a}{2}}{\frac{\mu a}{2}} \right]^2, \quad . \quad . \quad . \quad . \quad . \quad (78)$$

in which, when the incident light is perpendicular to the plane of the slit,

$$\mu = \frac{2\pi}{\lambda} \sin \phi, \quad . \quad . \quad . \quad . \quad . \quad (78')$$

where ϕ denotes the angle of diffraction, i.e. the angle included between the diffracted and the incident rays. If Q is a line source which is parallel to the slit, the diffraction pattern becomes a broad band of light which is crossed by parallel fringes at the places determined by $\mu a = 2h\pi$. Between the limits $\mu a = \pm 2\pi$ the intensity is much greater than elsewhere. The position of the dark fringes can also be determined directly from the following considerations:

In order to find the intensity for a given angle of diffraction (cf. Fig. 70) conceive the slit AB divided into such portions AA_1, A_1A_2, A_2A_3, etc., that the distances from A, A_1, A_2, . . . to the infinitely distant point P_0 differ from each other successively by $\frac{1}{2}\lambda$. The combined effect of any two neighboring zones is zero. Hence there is darkness if AB can be divided into an even number of such zones, i.e. if the side BC of the right-angled triangle ACB is equal to $h . \lambda$, where $h = 1, 2, 3$, etc. Since now $BC = a \sin \phi$, in which a is the width of the slit, there is darkness when the angle of diffraction is such that

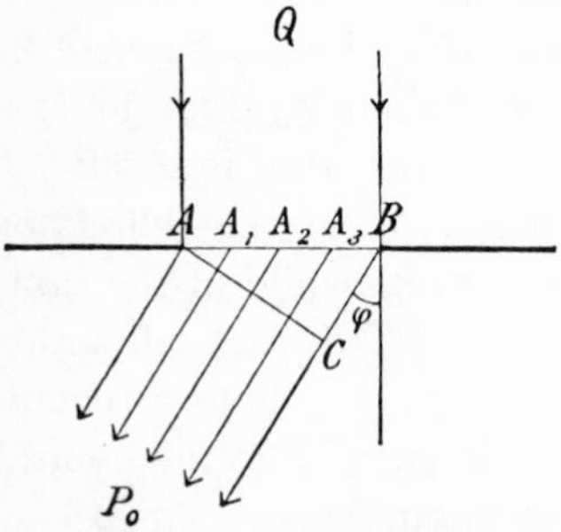

FIG. 70.

$$\sin \phi = \pm h \cdot \frac{\lambda}{a}. \quad . \quad . \quad . \quad . \quad . \quad (79)$$

But from (78′) this is identical with the condition $\mu a = 2h\pi$. Hence it follows that when $a < \lambda$ there is darkness for no angle of diffraction, i.e. *diffusion* takes place (cf. page 199).

If the incident light is white, and if the intensity J' which corresponds to a given color, i.e. a given wave-length λ, be denoted by J'_λ, and if the abbreviation $\pi a \sin \phi = a'$ be introduced, then for a given value of a' the whole intensity is

$$J = \Sigma J_\lambda' \cdot \frac{\sin^2 a'/\lambda}{(a'/\lambda)^2}. \quad . \quad . \quad . \quad . \quad . \quad . \quad (79)$$

If a' is not very small, e.g. if it is about $3\pi\lambda$, then in (79′) $\sin \frac{a'}{\lambda}$ varies much more rapidly with λ than does $\frac{a'}{\lambda}$. If $\frac{a'}{\lambda}$ be considered approximately constant, (79′) assumes the form given for the intensity of light reflected from a thin plate (cf. Section II, Chapter II, § 1). Hence at some distance from the centre of the field of view colors appear which resemble closely those of Newton's rings.

12. Diffraction Openings of any Form.—With any sort of unsymmetrical opening, the integrals C and S have in general a value different from zero. At positions of zero intensity in the diffraction pattern the two conditions $C = 0$ and $S = 0$ must be simultaneously fulfilled. Hence in general such positions are discrete points, not, as with a rectangular opening, continuous lines. For the theoretical discussion of special forms of diffraction apertures cf. Schwerd, "Die Beugungserscheinungen," Mannheim, 1835.

13. Several Diffraction Openings of like Form and Orientation.—Let the coordinates of any point of a diffraction opening referred to a point A lying within that opening be ξ and η, and let the point A in all the openings be similarly placed. Let the coordinates of the points A referred to any arbitrary coordinate system xy lying in the diffraction screen be x_1y_1, x_2y_2, x_3y_3, etc. Then for any point in any opening, for instance the third,

$$x = x_3 + \xi, \quad y = y_3 + \eta,$$

and, from (73),

$$\left.\begin{aligned} C &= \sum_i \int \cos\,[\mu(x_i + \xi) + \nu(y_i + \eta)]d\xi d\eta, \\ S &= \sum_i \int \sin\,[\mu(x_i + \xi) + \nu(y_i + \eta)]d\xi d\eta. \end{aligned}\right\} \quad . \qquad (80)$$

The ξ and η vary in all the openings within the same limits. Hence denoting the integrals C and S when they are extended over a single opening by c and s, that is, setting

$$c = \int \cos\,(\mu\xi + \nu\eta)d\xi d\eta, \quad s = \int \sin\,(\mu\xi + \nu\eta)d\xi d\eta, \qquad (81)$$

and, for the sake of brevity, writing

$$c' = \sum_i \cos(\mu x_i + \nu y_i), \quad s' = \sum_i \sin(\mu x_i + \nu y_i), \quad . \quad (82)$$

then, from (80),

$$C = c'\cdot c - s'\cdot s, \quad S = s'\cdot c + c'\cdot s,$$

and hence, from (72),

$$J = A'^2(c'^2 + s'^2)(c^2 + s^2). \quad . \quad . \quad . \quad (83)$$

From this equation it appears that *those places in the diffraction pattern which in the case of a single opening are dark remain dark in the case of several similar openings.* The intensity at any point is $c'^2 + s'^2$ times that due to a single opening. This quantity $c'^2 + s'^2$ may have various values. It may be written in the form

$$c'^2 + s'^2 = \sum_i \cos^2(\mu x_i + \nu y_i) + 2\sum_{i,k} \cos(\mu x_i + \nu y_i)\cos(\mu x_k + \nu y_k)$$
$$+ \sum_i \sin^2(\mu x_i + \nu y_i) + 2\sum_{i,k} \sin(\mu x_i + \nu y_i)\sin(\mu x_k + \nu y_k),$$

or $$c'^2 + s'^2 = m + 2\sum_{i,k} \cos[\mu(x_i - x_k) + \nu(y_i - y_k)], \quad . \quad (84)$$

in which m denotes the number of openings. In the case of a large number of openings *irregularly arranged*, the second term of the right-hand side of (84) may be neglected in comparison with the first, because the values of the separate terms under the sign Σ vary irregularly between -1 and $+1$. *Hence the intensity in the diffraction pattern is everywhere m times greater than when there is but one opening.* This phenomenon may be studied by using as a diffraction screen a piece of tin-foil in which holes of equal size have been pierced at random by a needle. The diffraction pattern consists of a system of concentric rings which differ from those produced by a single hole only in that they are more intense.

The result is entirely different when the holes are regularly arranged or are few in number. Consider, for example, the case of *two openings*, and set

$$x_1 = 0, \quad x_2 = d, \quad y_1 = y_2 = 0,$$

then

$$c'^2 + s'^2 = 4 \cos^2 \frac{\mu d}{2}.$$

The diffraction pattern which is produced by a single opening is now crossed by dark fringes corresponding to the equation $\mu d = (2h + 1)\pi$, i.e. by fringes which are perpendicular to the line connecting two corresponding points of the openings and which are, in the focal plane of the objective, a distance $\lambda f : d$ apart.

14. Babinet's Theorem.—Before passing to the discussion of the grating, which consists of a large number of regularly arranged diffraction openings, the case of *two complementary diffraction screens* will be considered. If a diffraction screen σ_1 has any openings whatever, while a second screen σ_2 has exactly those places covered which are open in σ_1, while the places in σ_2 are open which are covered in σ_1, then σ_1 and σ_2 are called complementary screens. The intensity J_1 when the screen σ_1 is used is proportional to $C_1^2 + S_1^2$, in which C_1 and S_1 are integrals which are extended over the openings in σ_1. The intensity J_2 when the screen σ_2 is used is proportional to $C_2^2 + S_2^2$, in which C_2 and S_2 are extended over the openings in σ_2. The intensity J_0 when no screen is used is therefore proportional to $(C_1 + C_2)^2 + (S_1 + S_2)^2$. But, in this latter case, at a point in the field of observation which corresponds to a diffraction angle greater than zero, $J_0 = 0$, i.e. $C_1 = - C_2$, $S_1 = - S_2$, and hence $J_1 = J_2$. Or in other words: *The diffraction patterns which are produced by two complementary screens are identical excepting the central spot, which corresponds to the diffraction angle zero.* This is Babinet's theorem.

Application of this theorem will be made to the diffraction pattern produced by irregularly placed circular screens of equal size. This pattern must be the same as that produced by irregularly arranged openings of the same size. Hence it consists of a system of concentric rings. The phenomenon may be produced by scattering lycopodium powder upon a glass plate. Similarly the halos about the sun and moon may be explained as the diffraction effects of water drops of equal size.*

15. The Diffraction Grating.—A diffraction grating consists of a large number of parallel slits a constant distance apart. As in § 13, set

$$x_1 = 0, \quad x_2 = d, \quad x_3 = 2d, \quad x_4 = 3d, \text{ etc.},$$
$$y_1 = y_2 = y_3 \ldots = 0,$$

in which d denotes the distance between two corresponding points in adjacent slits, the so-called *constant of the grating*. Then, from (82),

$$c' = 1 + \cos \mu d + \cos 2\mu d + \cos 3\mu d + \ldots$$
$$s' = \sin \mu d + \sin 2\mu d + \sin 3\mu d + \ldots$$

In order to obtain the value of $c'^2 + s'^2$, it is convenient to introduce imaginary quantities by writing, assuming that there are m openings,

$$c' + is' = 1 + e^{i\mu d} + e^{2i\mu d} + e^{3i\mu d} + \ldots + e^{i(m-1)\mu d}.$$

This summation gives at once

$$c' + is' = \frac{e^{im\mu d} - 1}{e^{i\mu d} - 1}.$$

A multiplication of each side of this equation by its complementary complex expression gives

$$c'^2 + s'^2 = \frac{1 - \cos m\mu d}{1 - \cos \mu d} = \frac{\sin^2 \frac{m\mu d}{2}}{\sin^2 \frac{\mu d}{2}},$$

so that there follows, from (83) and (78),

$$J = J_1' \frac{\sin^2 \frac{\mu a}{2}}{\left(\frac{\mu a}{2}\right)^2} \cdot \frac{\sin^2 \frac{m\mu d}{2}}{\sin^2 \frac{\mu d}{2}}. \quad \ldots \quad (85)$$

* For a calculation of the size of the drops from the diameter of the halo cf. F. Neumann, Vorles. über theor. Optik, Leipzig, 1885, p. 105.

In this J_1' denotes the intensity which would be produced by a single slit for the diffraction angle zero ($\mu = 0$). From this equation it appears that the diffraction pattern is the same as that of a single slit (which is represented by the first two factors) save that it is crossed by a series of dark fringes which are very close together and correspond to the equation $\frac{m\mu d}{2} = h\pi$. These fringes are closer together the greater the number m of the slits. Between the fringes the intensity J reaches maxima which are, however, at most equal to the intensities produced at the same points by a single slit. But much stronger maxima occur when $\sin \frac{\mu d}{2}$ vanishes, i.e. when

$$\mu = \frac{2h\pi}{d}, \text{ i.e. } \sin \phi = h\frac{\lambda}{d}, \quad . \quad . \quad . \quad . \quad (86)$$

in which ϕ denotes the angle of diffraction. (The light is assumed to fall perpendicularly upon the grating.)

For the diffraction angles ϕ thus determined

$$\frac{\sin^2 \frac{m\mu d}{2}}{\sin^2 \frac{\mu d}{2}} = m^2,$$

so that the intensity is m^2 times as great as it is at the same point when there is but one slit. When m is very great, it is these maxima only which are perceptible.* One of these maxima may be wanting if a minimum of the diffraction pattern due to a single slit falls at the same place, i.e. if both (86) and

$$\mu = \frac{2k\pi}{a}$$

are at the same time fulfilled.

---

* If the constant of the grating is less than λ, no maxima appear, since, by (86), $\sin \phi > 1$. Hence transparent bodies may be conceived as made up of ponderable opaque particles embedded in transparent ether. If the distance between the particles is less than a wave length, only the undiffracted light passes through.

This is only possible if the width of the slit a is an exact multiple of the constant of the grating d. Close-line gratings are produced by scratching fine lines upon glass or metal by means of a diamond. The furrows made by the diamond act as opaque or non-reflecting places. According to Babinet's theorem the width of the furrow may also be looked upon as the width a of the slit. This latter then is much smaller than the constant d of the grating, so that, in any case, the first maxima, which in (86) correspond to small values of h, do not vanish. These maxima have a nearly constant intensity, since for small values of the width a of the slit the diffraction figure which is produced by a single slit illuminates the larger portion of the field with a nearly constant intensity.

Hence, when the number m of the slits is sufficiently large, the diffraction pattern in monochromatic light, which proceeds from a line source Q, consists of a series of fine bright lines which appear at the diffraction angles ϕ_0, ϕ_1, ϕ_2, etc., determined by

$$\phi_0 = 0, \quad \sin\phi_1 = \pm\frac{\lambda}{d}, \quad \sin\phi_2 = \pm\frac{2\lambda}{d}, \quad \sin\phi_3 = \pm\frac{3\lambda}{d}, \text{ etc.}$$

If the grating is illuminated by white light from a line source Q, pure spectra must be produced, since the different colors appear at different angles. *These grating spectra are called normal spectra*, to distinguish them from the *dispersion spectra* produced by prisms, because the deviation of each color from the direction of the incident light is proportional to its wave length,—at least so long as ϕ is so small that it is permissible to write $\sin\phi = \phi$. Since each color corresponding to the different values of h in (86) appears many times, many spectra are also produced. The spectrum corresponding to $h = 1$ is called that of the first order; that to $h = 2$, the spectrum of the second order, etc. In the first spectrum the violet is deviated least; the other colors follow in order to the red. After an interval of darkness the violet of the second order follows. But the red of the second spectrum and the blue of the third overlap, since $3\lambda_v < 2\lambda_r$, in which λ_v and λ_r

denote the wave lengths of the visible violet and red rays contained in white light. This overlapping of several colors increases rapidly with the angle of diffraction.

That pure spectral colors are produced by a grating and not by a slit, which gives approximately the colors of Newton's rings (cf. page 219), is due to the fact that in the case of the grating it is the positions of the maxima, while in the case of a slit it is the positions of the minima, which are sharply defined.

The grating furnishes the best means of measuring wave lengths. The measurement consists in a determination of d and ϕ and is more accurate the smaller d is, since then the diffraction angles are large. Rutherford made gratings upon glass which have as many as 700 lines to the millimetre. The quality of a grating depends primarily upon the ruling engine which makes the scratches. The lines must be exactly parallel and a constant distance apart. Rowland now produces faultless gratings with a machine which is able to rule 1700 lines to the millimetre.

16. The Concave Grating.—A further advance was made by Rowland in that he ruled gratings upon concave spherical mirrors of speculum metal, the distance between the lines measured along a chord being equal. These gratings produce a real image P of a line source Q without the help of lenses; the diffraction maxima P_1, P_2, etc., are also real images. In order to locate these images, construct a circle tangent to the grating (Fig. 71) upon the radius of curvature of the grating as its diameter. If the line source Q lies upon the

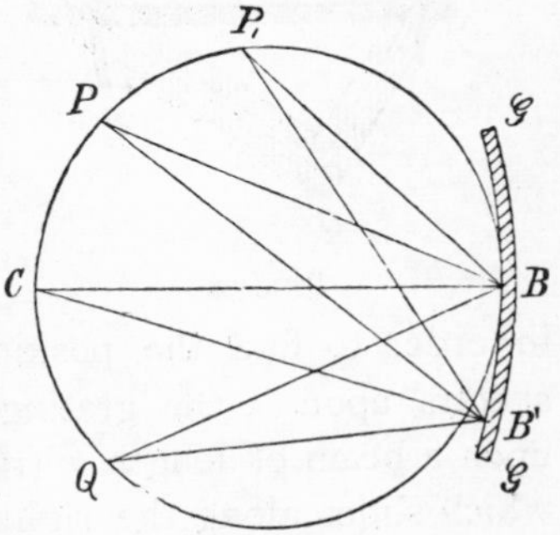

FIG. 71.

circle, an undiffracted image is produced upon the same circle at P by direct reflection, in such a way that P and Q are symmetrical to C, C being the centre of curvature of the grating

GG. For the line *CB* is the normal to the mirror at the point *B*, hence the angle of incidence *QBC* is equal to the angle of reflection *PBC*. But a ray reflected from any point *B′* of the mirror must also pass through *P* because *CB′* is the normal to the mirror at *B′*, since *C* is the centre of curvature of the mirror and since approximately $\sphericalangle QB'C = \sphericalangle PB'C$, and therefore *B′P* is the direction of the reflected ray. The angles *QB′C* and *PB′C* would be rigorously equal if *B′* lay upon the circle itself, since then they would be inscribed angles subtended by equal arcs. *P* is then the position of the undiffracted image which is formed by reflection by the mirror of the light from *Q*.*

The position of the diffraction image P_1 is at the intersection of two rays BP_1 and $B'P_1$ which make equal angles with *BP* and *B′P*. Hence it is evident that P_1 also lies upon the circle passing through *PCQB*, since the angles $PB'P_1$ and PBP_1 would be rigorously equal if *B′* lay upon the circle.

If the real diffraction spectrum at P_1 were to be received upon a screen *S*, it would be necessary to place the screen very obliquely to the rays. Since it is better that the rays fall perpendicularly upon the screen *S*, the latter is placed at the point *C* parallel to the grating. The source *Q* must also lie upon the circle whose diameter is *CB*, i.e. the angle *CQB* must always be a right angle. In practice, in order to find the positions of *Q* which throw diffraction spectra upon *S*, the grating *G* and the screen *S* are mounted upon a beam of length *r* (radius of curvature of the grating) which slides along the right-angled ways *QM*, *QN*, as shown

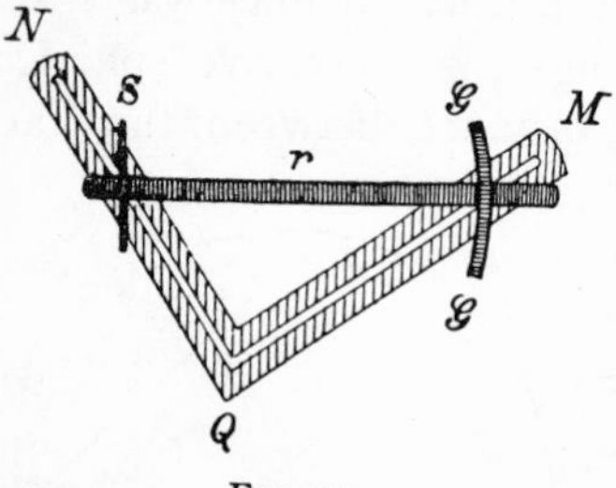

FIG. 72.

* This would follow from the second of equations (34), page 51, which apply to the formation of astigmatic images by reflection. For this case $\sphericalangle CBQ = \phi$, $CB = r$, and hence $QB = s = -r \cos \phi$. Hence $s_1 = -s$, i.e. the point *P*, symmetrical to *Q* with respect to *C*, must be the image of *Q* upon the circle.

in Fig. 72. The source is placed at Q. As S is moved away from Q the spectra of higher order fall successively upon the screen.

17. Focal Properties of a Plane Grating.—If the distance d between the lines of a grating is not constant, then the diffraction angle ϕ which corresponds to a maximum, for instance the first which is given by $\sin\phi = \lambda : d$, is different for different parts of the grating. d may be made to vary in such a way that these directions which correspond to a maximum all intersect in a point F. This point is then a focal point of the grating, since it has the same properties as the focus of a lens.*

18. Resolving Power of a Grating.—The power of a grating to separate two adjacent spectral lines must be proportional to its number of lines m, since it has been already shown that the diffraction maxima which correspond to a given wave length λ become narrower as m increases. By equation (86) on page 223, the maximum of the order h is determined by

$$\mu = 2h\pi : d, \text{ i.e. } \sin\phi = h\lambda : d.$$

If μ rises above or falls below this value, then, by (85), the first position of zero intensity occurs when μ has changed in such a way that $m\mu d/2$ has altered its value by π, i.e. when the change in μ amounts to

$$d\mu = 2\pi : md.$$

Hence the corresponding change in the diffraction angle ϕ, whose dependence upon μ is given in equation (78′), is

$$d\phi = \lambda : m\,d\cos\phi. \quad . \quad . \quad . \quad . \quad . \quad (87)$$

Hence this quantity $d\phi$ is half the angular width of the diffraction image.

* For the law of distribution of the lines cf. Cornu, C. R. 80, p. 645, 1875; Pogg. Ann. 156, p. 114, 1875; Soret, Arch. d. Scienc. Phys. 52, p. 320, 1875; Pogg. Ann. 156, p. 99, 1875; Winkelmann's Handbuch, II, p. 622.

For an adjacent spectral line of wave length $\lambda + d\lambda$ the position of the diffraction maximum of order h is given by

$$\sin (\phi + d\phi') = h(\lambda + d\lambda) : d,$$

i.e. the angle $d\phi'$ between the diffraction maxima corresponding to the lines λ and $\lambda + d\lambda$ is

$$d\phi' = h \cdot d\lambda : d \cos \phi.$$

In order that the grating may separate these two lines, this angle $d\phi'$ must be greater than half the breadth of the diffraction image of one of the lines. i.e.

$$d\phi' > d\phi, \quad h \cdot d\lambda > \lambda : m, \quad \frac{d\lambda}{\lambda} > \frac{1}{hm}. \quad . \quad . \quad (88)$$

Thus the *resolving power of a grating is proportional to the total number of lines m and to the order h of the spectrum, but is independent of the constant d of the grating.* To be sure, if d is too large, it may be necessary to use a special magnifying device in order to separate the lines, but the separation may always be effected if only the resolving power defined by (88) has not been exceeded.

In order to separate the double D line of sodium for which $d\lambda : \lambda = 0.001$, a grating must have at least 500 lines if the observation is made in the second spectrum.

19. Michelson's Echelon.*—From the above it is evident that the resolving power may be increased by using a spectrum of high order. With the gratings thus far considered it is not practicable to use an order of spectrum higher than the third, on account of the lack of intensity of the light in the higher orders. But even when the angle of diffraction is very small, if the light be made to pass through different thicknesses of glass, a large difference of phase may be introduced between the interfering rays, i.e. the same effect may be obtained as with an ordinary grating if the spectra of higher orders could be used. Consider, for instance, two parallel slits, and let a

* A. A. Michelson, Astrophysical Journal, 1898, Vol. 8, p. 37.

glass plate several millimetres thick be placed in front of one of the slits; then at very small angles of diffraction rays come to interference which have a difference of path of several thousand wave lengths. This is the fundamental idea in Michelson's echelon spectroscope. m plates of thickness δ are arranged in steps as in Fig. 73. Let the width of the

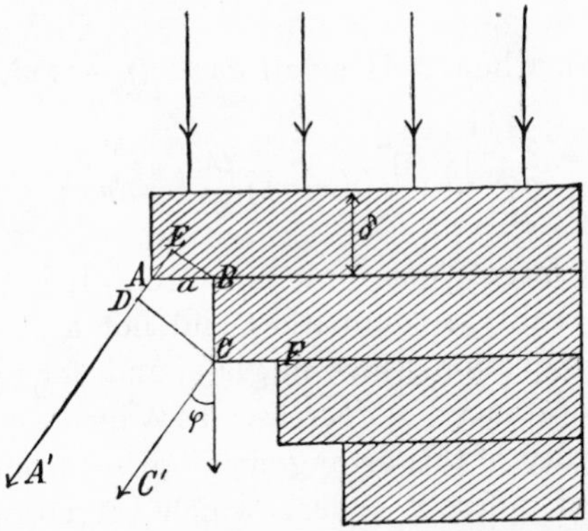

FIG. 73.

steps be a, and let the light fall from above perpendicularly upon the plates. The difference in path between the two parallel rays AA' and CC', which make an angle ϕ with the incident light, is, if CD is $\perp AA'$ and if n denote the index of refraction of the glass plates,

$$n \cdot BC - AD = n\delta - \delta \cos \phi + a \sin \phi,$$

since $AD = DE - AE$ and $DE = \delta \cos \phi$, $AE = a \sin \phi$. If this difference of path is an exact multiple of a wave length, i.e. if

$$h \cdot \lambda = n\delta - \delta \cos \phi + a \sin \phi, \quad . \quad . \quad . \quad (89)$$

then a maximum effect must take place in the direction ϕ, since all the rays emerging from AB are reinforced by the parallel rays emerging from CF. Hence equation (89) gives the directions ϕ of the diffraction maxima.

The change $d\phi$ in the position of the diffraction maxima corresponding to a small change $d\lambda$ in λ is large, since it follows from (89) by differentiation that

$$hd\lambda = \delta \cdot dn + (\delta \sin \phi + a \cos \phi)d\phi',$$

i.e. if ϕ be taken small,

$$d\phi' = \frac{h \cdot d\lambda - \delta \cdot dn}{a}. \quad . \quad . \quad . \quad . \quad (90)$$

Since, by (89), when ϕ is small $h\lambda = (n - 1)\delta$, (90) may be written

$$d\phi' = \frac{\delta}{a}\left[(n - 1)\frac{d\lambda}{\lambda} - dn\right]; \quad . \quad . \quad . \quad (90')$$

Hence $d\phi'$ is large when $\delta : a$ is large. It is to be observed that it is in reality a summation and not a difference which occurs in this equation, since in glass, and, for that matter, all transparent substances, n decreases as λ increases.

One difficulty of this arrangement arises from the fact that the maxima of different orders, which yet correspond to the same λ, lie very close together. For, by (89), the following relation exists between the diffraction angle $\phi + d\phi''$ of order $h + 1$ and the wave-length λ:

$$\lambda = (\delta \sin \phi + a \cos \phi)d\phi'',$$

i.e. when ϕ is small,

$$d\phi'' = \lambda : a. \quad . \quad . \quad . \quad . \quad . \quad . \quad . \quad (91)$$

Thus, for example, with flint-glass plates 5 mm. thick the two sodium lines D_1 and D_2 are separated ten times farther than are the two adjacent spectra of order h and $h + 1$ of one of the sodium lines. In consequence of this the source must consist of very narrow, i.e. homogeneous, lines, if the spectra of different order are not to overlap, i.e. if $d\phi'' > d\phi'$. Thus, for example, Michelson constructed an instrument of twenty plates, each 18 mm. thick, with $a = 1$ mm., which requires a source the spectral line of which cannot be broader than $\frac{1}{15}$ the distance between the two sodium lines.

In order to determine the *resolving power of the echelon* it is necessary to calculate the breadth of the diffraction maximum of order h, i.e. those angles of diffraction ($\phi \pm d\phi$) corresponding to those zero positions which are immediately adjacent to the maxima determined by (89). In order to find these positions of zero intensity, consider the m plates of the echelon divided into two equal portions I and II. Darkness occurs for those angles of diffraction $\phi + d\phi$ for which the difference of path of any two rays, one of which passes through any point of portion I, the other through the corresponding point of portion II, is an odd multiple of $\frac{1}{2}\lambda$. Just as the right side of (89) gives the difference of path of two rays, one of which has passed through one more plate than the other, so the difference of path in this case, in which one wave has passed through $\frac{m}{2}$ more plates than the other, may be obtained by multiplying the right-hand side of (89) by $\frac{m}{2}$.

Hence, at a position of zero intensity which corresponds to the angle of diffraction $\phi + d\phi$,

$$(k \pm \tfrac{1}{2})\lambda = \frac{m}{2}[n\delta - \delta \cos (\phi \pm d\phi) + a \sin (\phi \pm d\phi)].$$

In order that $d\phi$ may be as small as possible, i.e. in order to obtain the two positions of zero intensity which are closest to the maxima determined by (89), it is necessary, as a comparison with (89) shows, to make in this equation $k = h\frac{m}{2}$. Hence from these two equations

$$\pm \tfrac{1}{2}\lambda = \frac{m}{2}(\delta \sin \phi + a \cos \phi)d\phi,$$

or, when ϕ is small,

$$d\phi = \pm \frac{\lambda}{ma} \quad . \quad . \quad . \quad . \quad . \quad . \quad (92)$$

Thus this angle $d\phi$ is half the angular width of the diffraction image of the spectral line of wave length λ. That a double line whose components have the wave lengths λ and $\lambda + d\lambda$ may be resolved, the angle of dispersion $d\phi'$, corresponding to equation (90), must be greater than $d\phi.$, i.e.

$$\frac{d\lambda}{\lambda} > \frac{1}{m\delta\left(\frac{n-1}{\lambda} - \frac{dn}{d\lambda}\right)}. \quad . \quad . \quad . \quad . \quad (93)$$

Thus *the resolving power of the echelon depends only upon its total length $m\delta$ no matter whether it consists of many thin plates or of a smaller number of thicker ones.* But for the sake of a greater separation $d\phi''$ of the spectra of different orders, and for the sake of increasing the angle $d\phi'$ of dispersion, it is advisable to use a large number of plates so that a may be made small [cf. equations (90) and (91)].

For flint glass $-\frac{dn}{d\lambda}$ has about the value 100 if λ is expressed in mm. For a thickness δ of 18 mm. and a number of plates $m = 20$ the resolving power is, by (93),

$$m\delta\left(\frac{n-1}{\lambda} - \frac{dn}{d\lambda}\right) = 0.46 . 10^6,$$

which, according to (88), can only be attained with a line grating of half a million lines.

Although, as was seen above, the diffraction maxima of different orders lie close together, there are never more than two of them visible. For it is to be remembered that, in the expression for the intensity in the diffraction pattern produced by a grating, the intensity due to a single slit enters as a factor (cf. page 222). In the echelon the uncovered portion of width a of each plate corresponds to a single slit, so that (cf. page 218) the intensity differs appreciably from zero only between the angles $\phi = \pm \frac{\lambda}{a}$, which correspond to the first positions of zero intensity in the diffraction pattern due to one slit. Thus the intensity is practically zero outside of the angular region $2\lambda : a$. Since, by (91), the angular distance between two successive maxima of different order has the value $\frac{\lambda}{a}$, only two such maxima can be visible.

In order that the echelon may give good results, the separate plates must have exactly the same thickness δ throughout. The plates are tested by means of the interference curves of equal inclination (cf. page 149, note 1) and polished until correct.

20. The Resolving Power of a Prism.—In connection with the above considerations it is of interest to ask whether the resolving power of a prism exceeds that of a grating or not. The resolving power of a prism depends not only upon its dispersion, but also upon its width (measured perpendicular to the refracting edge). For if this width be small, each separate spectral line is broadened by diffraction.

The joint effect of dispersion and cross-section of the beam upon the resolving power of a prism, or of a system of prisms, has been calculated by Rayleigh in the following way: * If, by means of refraction in the system P (Fig. 74), the plane wave

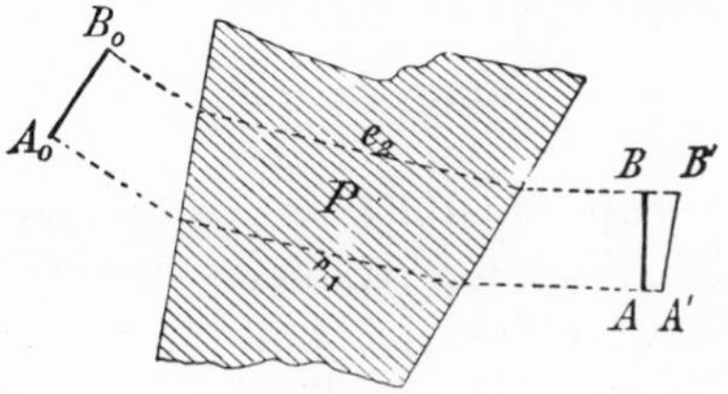

FIG. 74.

A_0B_0 of incident light of wave length λ is brought into the position AB, the optical paths from A_0 to A and B_0 to B are equal (cf. page 6). A wave of other wave length $\lambda + d\lambda$ is brought in the same time into some other position $A'B'$. The difference between the optical paths A_0A' and A_0A, i.e. the distance AA', can be expressed as follows:

$$(A_0A') - (A_0A) = A'A = dn \cdot e_1,$$

* Rayleigh, Phil. Mag. (5), 9, p. 271, 1879; Winkelmann's Handb. Optik, p. 166.

in which dn denotes the difference between the indices of refraction of the prism for the two wave lengths λ and $\lambda + d\lambda$,* and e_1 the path traversed in the prism by the limiting rays (cf. Fig. 74). This path is assumed to be the same for the different colors, an assumption which is permissible since AA' contains the small factor dn.

Likewise the difference between the optical paths B_0B' and B_0B, i.e. the line BB', is

$$(B_0B') - (B_0B) = B'B = dn \cdot e_2,$$

in which e_2 denotes the path traversed in the prism by the other limiting rays of the beam. Now the angle di which the plane wave $A'B'$ makes with the wave AB, i.e. the dispersion of the prism, is evidently

$$di = \frac{BB' - AA'}{b} = dn\frac{e_2 - e_1}{b},$$

in which b denotes the width of the emergent beam, i.e. the line AB. If the limiting rays A_0A pass through the edge of the prism, $e_1 = 0$, and

$$di = dn \cdot \frac{e}{b}, \quad . \quad . \quad . \quad . \quad . \quad . \quad . \quad (94)$$

in which e represents the thickness of the prism at its base, provided the prism is set for minimum deviation, i.e. the rays within it are parallel to the base, and the incident beam covers the entire face of the prism. The same considerations hold for a train of prisms; if all the prisms are in the position of minimum deviation, e represents the sum of all the thicknesses of the prisms at their bases.

In order that such a train of prisms may be able to resolve in the spectrum a doublet whose angular separation is di, the central images in the diffraction patterns, which are produced by each spectral line in consequence of the limited area b of the beam, must be sufficiently separated. For an opening of

* The dispersion of the air is neglected.

breadth b the first minimum in the diffraction image lies, by (79) on page 218, at the angle $\phi = \lambda : b$.* If then two spectral lines are to be separated, their dispersion di must at least be greater than this angle ϕ, which is half the angular width of the central band in the diffraction image of a spectral line; i.e. by (94) the following must hold:

$$dn \cdot \frac{e}{b} > \frac{\lambda}{b},$$

$$e > \frac{\lambda}{dn}. \quad \ldots \ldots \quad (95)$$

Hence *the resolving power of a prism depends only upon the thickness of the prism at the base, and is independent of the angle of the prism.* Thus for the resolution of the two sodium lines a prism of flint glass ($n = 1.650$, $dn = 0.000055$, $\lambda = 0.000589$ mm.) at least 1 cm. thick is required. But for the resolution of two lines for which $d\lambda : \lambda = 2 : 10^6$, which may be accomplished with the Michelson echelon or with a grating of half a million lines, the thickness of the prism would need to be $e = 5 \cdot 10^2$ cm., i.e. 5 m., a thickness which is evidently unattainable because of the great absorption of light by glass of such thickness. *A grating device permits, therefore, of higher resolving power than a train of prisms.*

21. Limit of Resolution of a Telescope.—If a telescope is focussed upon a fixed star, then, on account of the diffraction at the rim of the objective, the image in the focal plane is a luminous disc which is larger the smaller the diameter of the objective. The diffraction caused by a circular screen of radius h gives rise to concentric dark rings. The first minimum occurs when the angle of diffraction is such that $\sin \phi = 0.61 \frac{\lambda}{h}$.† Assume that a second star would be distinguished from the first if its central image fell upon the first minimum of the first star; then the limiting value of the angle which the two stars

* Since b is large in comparison to λ, ϕ is substituted for $\sin \phi$.

† For the deduction of this number cf. F. Neumann, Vorles. ü. Optik, p. 89.

must subtend at the objective if they are to be separated by the telescope, provided with a suitable eyepiece, is *

$$\phi > 0.61 \cdot \frac{\lambda}{h}.$$

If λ be assumed to be 0.00056 mm., and if ϕ be expressed in minutes of arc, then

$$\phi > \frac{1.17'}{h}, \quad \ldots \ldots \quad (96)$$

in which h must be expressed in mm. A telescope whose objective is 20 cm. in diameter is then able to resolve two stars whose angular distance apart is $\phi = 0.0117' = 0.7''$.

22. The Limit of Resolution of the Human Eye.—The above considerations may be applied to the human eye with the single difference that the wave length λ of the light in the lens of the eye, whose index is 1.4, is 1 : 1.4 times smaller than in air. The radius of the pupil takes the place of h. If h be assumed to be 2 mm., then the smallest visual angle which two luminous points can subtend if they are to be resolved by the eye is

$$\phi = 0.42'.$$

The actual limit is about $\phi = 1'$.

23. The Limit of Resolution of the Microscope.—The images formed by microscopes are of illuminated, not of self-luminous, objects.† The importance of this distinction was first pointed out by Abbe. From the standpoint of pure geometrical optics, which deals with rays, the exact similarity of object and image follows from the principles laid down in the first part of this book. From the standpoint of physical optics, which does not deal with rays of light as independent geometrical directions, since this is not rigorously permissible, but which is based upon deformations of the wave front, the similarity of

---

* On account of the smallness of ϕ, ϕ may be written for sin ϕ.

† Objects which are visible by diffusely reflected light may be approximately treated as self-luminous objects.

object and image is not only not self-evident, but is, strictly speaking, unattainable. For the incident light, assumed in the first case to be parallel, will, after passing through the object which it illuminates, form a diffraction pattern in that focal plane $\mathfrak{F}'$ of the objective which is nearest the eyepiece. The question now is, what light effect will this diffraction figure produce in the plane $\mathfrak{P}'$ which is conjugate with respect to the objective to the object plane $\mathfrak{P}$? The image formed in this plane is the one observed by the eyepiece. The formation of the image of an illuminated object is therefore not *direct* (primary) but *indirect* (secondary), since it depends upon the effect of the diffraction pattern formed by the object.

It is at once clear that a given diffraction pattern in the focal plane $\mathfrak{F}'$ gives rise always to the same image in the plane $\mathfrak{P}'$ upon which the eyepiece is focussed. Now in general different objects produce different diffraction patterns in the plane $\mathfrak{F}'$.* But if the aperture of the objective of the microscope is very small, so that only the small and nearly uniformly illuminated spot of the diffraction pattern produced by two different objects is operative, then these objects must give rise to the same light effects in the plane $\mathfrak{P}'$, i.e. they look alike when seen in the microscope. Now in this case there is seen in the microscope only a uniformly illuminated field, and no evidence of the structure of the object. In order to bring out the structure, the numerical aperture of the microscope must be so great that not only the effect of the central bright spot of the diffraction pattern appears, but also that of at least one of the other maxima. When this is so, the distribution of light in the plane $\mathfrak{P}'$ is no longer uniform, i.e. some sort of an image appears

---

*By the introduction of suitable stops in the plane $\mathfrak{F}'$ the same diffraction pattern may be produced by different objects. In this case the same image is also seen at the eyepiece in the plane $\mathfrak{P}'$, although the objects are quite different. Thus if the object is a grating whose constant is d, and if all the diffraction images of odd order be cut out by the stop, then the object seems in the image to have a grating constant $\frac{d}{2}$. Cf. Müller-Pouillet (Lummer), Optik, p. 713. The house of C. Zeiss in Jena constructs apparatus to verify these conclusions.

which has a rough similarity to the object. As more maxima of the diffraction pattern are admitted to the microscope tube, i.e. as more of the diffraction pattern is utilized, the image in the microscope becomes more and more similar to the object. But perfect similarity can only be attained when all the rays diffracted by the object, which are of sufficient intensity to be able to produce appreciable effects in the focal plane $\mathfrak{F}'$ of the objective, are received by the objective, i.e. are not cut off by stops. This shows the great importance of using an objective of large numerical aperture. The greater the aperture the sooner will an image be formed which approximately reproduces the fine detail in the object. Perfect similarity is an impossibility even theoretically. A microscope reproduces the detail of an object up to a certain limit only.

To illustrate this by an example, assume that the object P is a grating whose constant is d, and that the incident beam is parallel and falls perpendicularly upon the grating. The first maximum from the centre of the field lies in a direction determined by $\sin \phi = \lambda : d$. Let the real image of this maximum in the focal plane $\mathfrak{F}'$ of the objective be C_1, while C_0 is that of the centre of the field (Fig. 75). Let the distance between

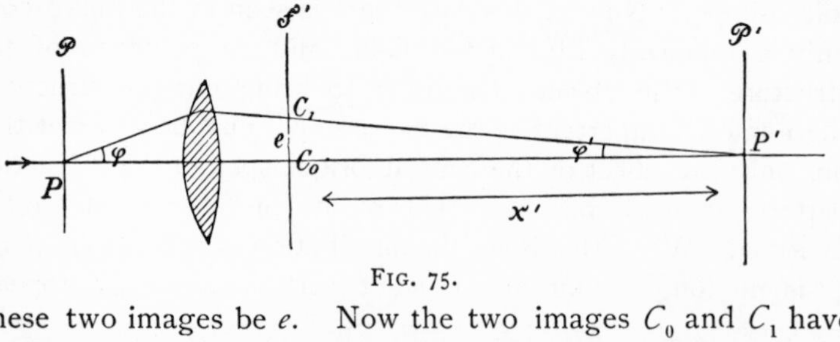

FIG. 75.

these two images be e. Now the two images C_0 and C_1 have approximately the same intensity and send out coherent waves, i.e. waves capable of producing interference. Hence there is formed at a distance x' behind the focal plane $\mathfrak{F}'$ a system of fringes whose distance apart is $d' = x'\lambda : e$. If now the objective is aplanatic, i.e. fulfils the sine law (cf. page 58), then

$$\sin \phi = \epsilon \cdot \sin \phi',$$

in which ϵ denotes a constant. Setting $\sin \phi' = e : x'$, which is permissible since ϕ' is always small (while ϕ may be large), and remembering that $\sin \phi = \lambda : d$, it follows that

$$\frac{\lambda}{d} = \epsilon \frac{e}{x'},$$

i.e. the distance d' between the fringes is

$$d' = \frac{x'\lambda}{e} = \epsilon d,$$

or, the distance between the fringes is proportional to the constant of the grating and independent of the color of the light used.

Hence in order that the grating lines may be perceptible in the image, the objective must receive rays whose inclination is at least as great as that determined by $\sin \phi = \lambda : d$. In the case of an immersion system λ denotes the wave length in the immersion fluid, i.e. it is equal to $\lambda : n$ when λ denotes the wave length in air and n the index of the fluid with respect to air. Hence

$$n \sin \phi = \lambda : d.$$

Now $n \sin U = a$ is the numerical aperture of the microscope (cf. equation (80) on page 86), provided U is the angle included between the limiting ray and the axis. Hence the smallest distance d which can be resolved by a microscope of aperture a is

$$d = \lambda : a. \quad \ldots \ldots \quad (97)$$

This equation holds for perpendicular illumination of the object. With oblique illumination the resolving power may be increased, for, if the central spot of the diffraction pattern does not lie in the middle but is displaced to one side, the first diffraction maximum appears at a smaller angle of inclination to the axis. The conditions are most favorable when the incident light has the same inclination to the axis as the diffracted light of the first maximum, and both just get in to the objective.

If the incident and the diffracted light make the same angle U with the normal to the grating, then, by (71) on page 214, $\mu = \frac{2\pi}{\lambda} \cdot 2 \sin U$. Since, further, by (86) on page 223, the first diffraction maximum appears when $\mu = \frac{2\pi}{d}$, it follows that in this case

$$\sin U = \frac{\lambda}{2d}.$$

Hence the smallest distance d which the microscope objective is able to resolve with the *most favorable illumination* is

$$d = \frac{\lambda}{2a}, \qquad . \quad . \quad . \quad . \quad . \quad . \quad . \quad (98)$$

in which a is the numerical aperture of the microscope and λ the wave length of light in air. This is the equation given on page 92 for the limit of resolution of the microscope.

In order to increase the amount of light in the microscope, the object is illuminated with strongly convergent light (with the aid of an Abbé condenser, cf. page 102). The above considerations hold in this case for each direction of the incident light; but in the resolution of the object only those directions are actually useful for which not only the central image but also at least the first maximum of the diffraction pattern falls within the field of view of the eyepiece. The diffraction maxima corresponding to the different directions of the incident light lie at different places in the focal plane of the objective, but they exert no influence whatever upon one another, since they correspond to incoherent rays; for the light in each direction comes from a different point of the source, for example the sky.

If, instead of a grating, a single slit of width d were used, no detail whatever would be recognizable unless the diffraction pattern were effective at least to the first minimum. Since, according to equation (79) on page 218, for perpendicularly incident light this first minimum lies at the diffraction angle determined by $\sin \phi = \lambda : d$,* the result for one slit is the same as for a grating. Only in this case a real similarity between the image and the slit, i.e. a correct recognition of the width of the slit, is not obtained if the diffraction pattern is effective only up to the first minimum.

If only an approximate similarity between object and image is sufficient, for example if it is only desired to detect the *existence* of a small opaque body, its dimensions may lie considerably within the limit of resolution d as here deduced; for so long as the diffraction pattern formed by the object causes an appreciable variation in the uniform illumination in the image plane which is conjugate to the object, its existence may be detected.

From the above considerations it is evident that the limit of resolution d is smaller the shorter the wave length of the light used. Hence microphotography, in which ultraviolet light is used, is advantageous, although no very great increase in the resolving power is in this way obtained. But the advantages of an immersion system become in this case very marked, since by an immersion fluid of high index the wave length is considerably shortened. This result appears at once from equations (97) and (98), since the numerical aperture a is proportional to the index of refraction of the immersion fluid.

* d here has the same signification as a there.

CHAPTER V

POLARIZATION

1. Polarization by Double Refraction.—A ray of light is said to be polarized when its properties are not symmetrical with respect to its direction of propagation. This lack of symmetry is proved by the fact that a rotation of the ray about the direction of propagation as axis produces a change in the observed optical phenomena. This was first observed by Huygens * in the passage of light through Iceland spar. Polarization is always present when there is double refraction. Those crystals which do not belong to the regular system always show double refraction, i.e. an incident ray is divided within the crystal into two rays which have different directions.

The phenomenon is especially easy to observe in calc-spar, which belongs to the hexagonal system and cleaves beautifully in planes corresponding to the three faces of a rhombohedron. In six of the corners of the rhombohedron the three intersecting edges include one obtuse and two acute angles, but in the two remaining corners A, A', which lie opposite one another (cf. Fig. 76), the three intersecting edges enclose three equal obtuse angles of 101° 53′. A line drawn through the obtuse corner A so as to make equal angles with the edges intersecting at A lies in the direction of *the principal crystallographic axis*.† If a rhombohedron be so split out that all of its edges are equal, this principal axis lies in the direction of the line connecting the two obtuse angles A, A'. Fig. 76 represents such a crystal.

---

* Huygens, Traité de la Lumière, Leyden, 1690.

† The principal axis, like the normal to a surface, is merely a direction, not a definite line.

If now a ray of light *LL* be incident perpendicularly upon the upper surface of the rhombohedron, it splits up into two rays *LO* and *LE* of equal intensity which emerge from the crystal as parallel rays *OL'* and *EL''* perpendicular to the lower face. Of these rays *LO* is the direct prolongation of the incident ray and hence follows the ordinary law of refraction in isotropic bodies, in accordance with which no change in direction occurs when the incidence is normal. This ray *LO* together with its prolongation *L'O* is therefore called the *ordinary* ray. But the second ray *LE*, with its prolongation *L''E*, which follows a law of refraction altogther different from that of isotropic bodies, is called the *extraordinary* ray. Also the plane defined by the two rays is parallel to the direction of the crystallographic axis. A section of the crystal by a plane which includes the normal to the surface and the axis is called a principal section. *Hence the extraordinary ray lies in the principal section;* it rotates about the ordinary ray as the crystal is turned about *LL* as an axis.

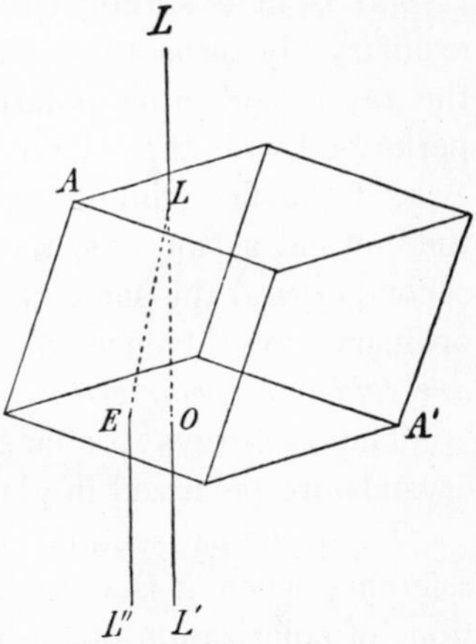

FIG. 76.

The intensities of the ordinary and extraordinary rays are equal. But if one of these rays, for instance the extraordinary, is cut off, and the ordinary ray is allowed to fall upon a second crystal of calc-spar, it undergoes in general a second division into two rays, *which have not, however, in general the same intensity.* These intensities depend upon the orientation of the two rhombohedrons with respect to each other, i.e. upon the angle included between their principal sections. If this angle is 0 or 180°, there appears in the second crystal an ordinary but no extraordinary ray; but if it is 90°, there appears only an extraordinary ray. Two rays of equal intensity are produced if the angle between the principal sections is 45°. Hence the appearance continually changes when the second crystal is held stationary and the first rotated, i.e. when the ordinary ray turns about its own direction as an axis. Hence the ray is said to be polarized. This experiment can also be performed with the extraordinary ray, i.e. it too is polarized. Also if the first rhombohedron is rotated through 90° about the normal as an axis, the extraordinary ray produces in the second crystal the same effects as were before produced by the ordinary ray. Hence *the ordinary and extraordinary rays are said to be polarized in planes at right angles to each other.*

The two rays produced by all other doubly refracting crystals are polarized in planes at right angles to each other.

The principal section is conveniently chosen as a plane of reference when it is desired to distinguish between the directions of polarization of the two rays. Since these phenomena produced by two crystals of calc-spar depend only upon the absolute size of the angle included between their principal sections and not upon its sign, the properties of the ordinary and extraordinary rays must be symmetrical with respect to the principal section.

The principal section is called the plane of polarization of the ordinary ray,—an expression which asserts nothing save that this ray is not symmetrical with respect to the direction of propagation, but that the variations in symmetry in different directions are symmetrical with respect to this plane of polarization, the principal section.

Since, as was observed above, the ordinary ray is polarized at right angles to the extraordinary ray, it is necessary to call the plane which is perpendicular to the principal section the plane of polarization of the extraordinary ray. These relations may also be expressed as follows: *The ordinary ray is polarized in the principal section, the extraordinary perpendicular to the principal section.*

2. The Nicol Prism.—In order to obtain light polarized in but one plane, it is necessary to cut off or remove one of the two rays produced by double refraction. In the year 1828 Nicol devised the following method of accomplishing this end: By suitable cleavage a crystal of calc-spar is obtained which is fully three times as long as broad. The end surfaces, which make an angle of 72° with the edges of the side, are ground off until this angle (*ABA'* in Fig. 77) is 68°. The crystal is

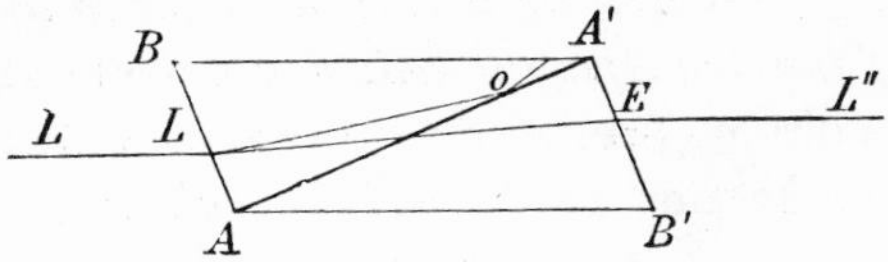

FIG. 77.

then sawed in two along a plane *AA'*, which passes through the corners *AA'* and is perpendicular both to the end faces and to a plane defined by the crystallographic axis and the long axis of the rhombohedron. These two cut faces of the two halves of the prism are then cemented together with Canada balsam. This balsam has an index of refraction which is smaller than that of the ordinary but larger than that of the extraordinary ray. If now a ray of light *LL* enters parallel to the long axis of the rhombohedron, the ordinary ray *LO* is totally reflected at the surface of the Canada balsam and absorbed by the blackened surface *BA'*, while the extraordinary ray alone passes through the prism. The plane of polarization of the emergent light *EL''* is then perpendicular to the principal section, i.e. parallel to the long diagonal of the surfaces *AB* or *A'B'*.

The angle of aperture of the cone of rays which can enter the prism in such a way that the ordinary ray is totally reflected amounts to about 30°. Furthermore a convergent incident beam is not rigorously polarized in one plane, since the plane of polarization varies somewhat with the inclination of the incident ray; for the plane of polarization of the extraordinary ray is always perpendicular to the plane defined by the ray and the crystallographic axis (principal plane). The principal plane and the principal section are identical for normal incidence.

3. Other Means of Producing Polarized Light.—Apart from polarization prisms* constructed in other ways, tourmaline plates may be used for obtaining light polarized in one plane, provided they are cut parallel to the crystallographic axis and are from one to two millimetres thick. For under these conditions the ordinary ray is completely absorbed within the crystal. *Also, polarized light may be obtained by reflection at the surface of any transparent body* if the angle of reflection ϕ fulfils the condition (Brewster's law) $\tan \phi = n$, in which n is the index of refraction of the body. *This angle ϕ is called the polarizing angle.* For crown glass it is 57°. *The reflected light is polarized in the plane of incidence*, as may be shown by passing the reflected light through a crystal of calc-spar.

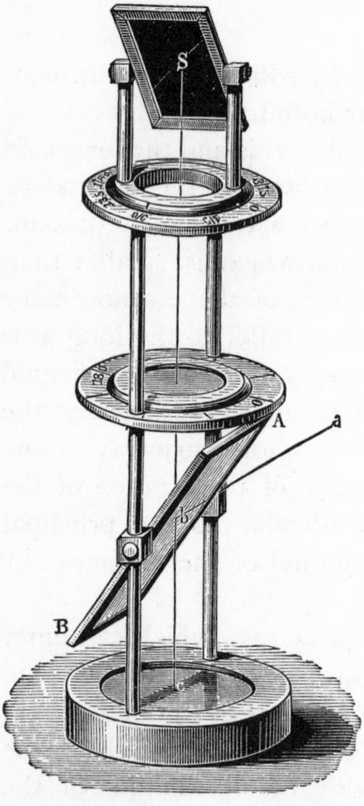

FIG. 78.

If light reflected at the polarizing angle from a glass plate be allowed to fall at the same angle upon a second glass plate, the final intensity depends upon the angle α included between the planes of incidence upon the two surfaces and is proportional to $\cos^2 \alpha$. This case can be studied by means of the Nörrenberg polariscope. The ray a is polarized by reflection upon the glass plate A and then falls perpendicularly upon a silvered mirror at c. This mirror reflects it to the black glass mirror S which turns upon a vertical axis. The ray cb falls also at the polarizing angle upon S and, after reflection upon

* Cf. W. Grosse, Die gebräuchlichen Polarisationsprismen, etc., Klaustahl, 1889; Winkelmann's Handbuch d. Physik, Optik, p. 629.

S, has an intensity which varies as S is turned about a vertical axis. Between A and S a movable glass stage is introduced in order to make it convenient to study transparent objects at different orientations in polarized light. But since the intensity of light after but one reflection is comparatively small, this means of producing polarized light is little used; the same difficulty is met with in the use of tourmaline plates (not to mention a color effect).

A somewhat imperfect polarization is also produced by the oblique passage of light through a bundle of parallel glass plates. This case will be treated in Section II, Chapter II. That polarization is also produced by diffraction was mentioned on page 212.

4. Interference of Polarized Light.—The interference phenomena described above *may all be produced by light polarized in one plane.* But *two rays which are polarized at right angles never interfere.* This can be proved by placing a tourmaline plate before each of the openings of a pair of slits. The diffraction fringes which are produced by the slits are seen when the axes of the plates are parallel, but they vanish completely when one of the plates is turned through 90°.

Fresnel and Arago investigated completely the conditions of interference of two rays polarized at right angles to each other after they had been brought back to the same plane of polarization by passing them through a crystal of calc-spar whose principal section made an angle of 45° with the planes of polarization of each of the two rays. They found the following laws:

1. Two rays polarized at right angles to each other, which have come from an unpolarized ray, do not interfere even when they are brought into the same plane of polarization.

2. Two rays polarized at right angles, which have come from a polarized ray, interfere when they are brought back to the same plane of polarization.

5. Mathematical Discussion of Polarized Light.—It has been already shown that the phenomena of interference lead to the wave theory of light, in accordance with which the light disturbance at a given point in space is represented by

$$s = A \sin\left(2\pi\frac{t}{T} + \delta\right). \quad . \quad . \quad . \quad . \quad (1)$$

It is now possible to make further assertions concerning the properties of this disturbance. For in polarized light these properties must be directed quantities, i.e. vectors, as are lines, velocities, forces, etc. Undirected quantities like density and temperature are called scalars to distinguish them from vectors. If the properties of polarized light were not vectors, they could not exhibit differences in different azimuths. For the same reason these vectors cannot be parallel to the direction of propagation of the light. Hence s will now be called a *light vector*. Now a vector may be resolved into three components along the rectangular axes x, y, z. These components of s will be denoted by u, v, w. Hence the most general representation of the light disturbance at a point P is

$$\left.\begin{array}{c} u = A \sin\left(2\pi\frac{t}{T} + p\right), \quad v = B \sin\left(2\pi\frac{t}{T} + q\right), \\ w = C \sin\left(2\pi\frac{t}{T} + r\right). \end{array}\right\} \quad . \quad (2)$$

The meaning of these equations can be brought out by representing by a straight line through the origin the magnitude and direction of the light vector at any time. The end $\mathfrak{E}$ of this line can be located by considering u, v, w, as its rectangular coordinates. The path which this point $\mathfrak{E}$ describes as the time changes is called the *vibration form* and is obtained from equations (2) by elimination of t. (2) may be written

$$\left.\begin{array}{l} \frac{u}{A} = \sin 2\pi\frac{t}{T}\cdot\cos p + \cos 2\pi\frac{t}{T}\cdot\sin p, \\ \frac{v}{B} = \sin 2\pi\frac{t}{T}\cdot\cos q + \cos 2\pi\frac{t}{T}\cdot\sin q, \\ \frac{w}{C} = \sin 2\pi\frac{t}{T}\cdot\cos r + \cos 2\pi\frac{t}{T}\cdot\sin r. \end{array}\right\} \quad . \quad . \quad . \quad (3)$$

Multiplying these equations by sin $(q - r)$, sin $(r - p)$, and sin $(p - q)$ respectively, and adding them, there results

$$\frac{u}{A}\sin(q-r)+\frac{v}{B}\sin(r-p)+\frac{w}{C}\sin(p-q)=0, \quad (4)$$

i.e. since a linear equation connects the quantities u, v, w, the vibration form is always a plane curve.

The equations of its projections upon the coordinate planes may be obtained by eliminating t from any two of equations (3). Thus, for instance, from the first two of these equations

$$\sin 2\pi\frac{t}{T}(\cos p\sin q-\cos q\sin p)=\frac{u}{A}\sin q-\frac{v}{B}\sin p,$$

$$\cos 2\pi\frac{t}{T}(\cos p\sin q-\cos q\sin p)=-\frac{u}{A}\cos q+\frac{v}{B}\cos p.$$

Squaring and adding these two equations gives

$$\sin^2(p-q)=\frac{u^2}{A^2}+\frac{v^2}{B^2}-\frac{2uv}{AB}\cos(p-q). \quad . \quad . \quad (5)$$

But this is the equation of an ellipse whose principal axes coincide with the coordinate axes when $p - q = \frac{\pi}{2}$. Hence, *in the most general case, the vibration form is a plane elliptical curve.* This corresponds to so-called *elliptically polarized light.* When the vibration form becomes a circle, the light is said to be circularly polarized. This occurs, for instance, when $w = 0$, $A = B$, and $p - q = \pm\frac{\pi}{2}$, so that either the relation

$$u = A\sin 2\pi\frac{t}{T}, \quad v = A\cos 2\pi\frac{t}{T}, \quad . \quad . \quad . \quad (6)$$

or the relation

$$u = A\sin 2\pi\frac{t}{T}, \quad v = -A\cos 2\pi\frac{t}{T} \quad . \quad . \quad (6')$$

holds. These two cases are distinguished as *right-handed* and *left-handed circular polarization.* The polarization is right-handed when, to an observer looking in a direction opposite to that of propagation, the rotation corresponds to that of the hands of a watch. When the vibration ellipse becomes a straight line, the *light is said to be plane-polarized.* This occurs when $w = 0$, and $p - q = 0$ or π. The equation of the path is then, by (5),

$$\frac{u}{A} \pm \frac{v}{B} = 0. \qquad (7)$$

The intensity of the disturbance has already been set equal to the square of the amplitude A of the light vector. This point of view must now be maintained, and it must be remembered that the square of the amplitude is equal to the sum of the squares of the amplitudes of the three components. The intensity J is then, in accordance with the notation in (2),

$$J \sim A^2 + B^2 + C^2. \qquad (8)$$

An investigation will now be made of the vibration form which corresponds to the light which in the previous paragraph was merely said to be polarized, i.e. the light which has suffered double refraction or reflection at the polarizing angle. The principal characteristic of this light is that two rays which are polarized at right angles never interfere, but give always an intensity equal to the sum of the intensities of the separate rays.

If there be superposed upon ray (2), which is assumed to be travelling along the z-axis, a ray of equal intensity, which is polarized at right angles to it and whose components are u', v', w', and which differs from it in phase by any arbitrary amount δ, then

$$\left.\begin{aligned} u' = B \sin\left(2\pi\frac{t}{T} + q + \delta\right), \quad v' = -A \sin\left(2\pi\frac{t}{T} + p + \delta\right), \\ w' = C \sin\left(2\pi\frac{t}{T} + r + \delta\right). \end{aligned}\right\} \qquad (9)$$

For, save for the difference in phase δ, these equations become equations (2) if the coordinate system be rotated through 90° about the z-axis.

By superposition of the two rays (2) and (9), i.e. by taking the sums $u + u'$, $v + v'$, $w + w'$, there results, according to the rule given above [equation (11) page 131], for the squares of the amplitudes of the three components

$$A'^2 = A^2 + B^2 + 2AB \cos(\delta + q - p),$$
$$B'^2 = A^2 + B^2 - 2AB \cos(\delta + p - q),$$
$$C'^2 = 2C^2 (1 + \cos\delta).$$

Addition of these three equations gives, in consideration of (8),

$$J' = 2J + 2C^2 \cos\delta - 4AB \sin\delta \sin(q - p).$$

Since now experiment shows that J' is equal simply to the sum of the intensities of the separate rays and is wholly independent of δ, it follows that $C = 0$, i.e. the light vector is perpendicular to the direction of propagation, or the *wave is transverse;* it also follows that $\sin(p - q) = 0$, i.e., from (5) or (7), *the vibration form is a straight line.*

Hence rays which have suffered double refraction or reflection at the polarizing angle are plane-polarized transverse waves.

Since, as was shown on page 244, the properties of a polarized ray must be symmetrical with respect to its plane of polarization, it follows that *the light vector must lie either in the plane of polarization or in the plane perpendicular to it.* Whether it lies in the first or the second of these planes is a question upon which light is thrown by the following experiment.

6. Stationary Waves produced by Obliquely Incident Polarized Light.—Wiener investigated the formation of stationary waves by polarized light which was incident at an angle of 45° (cf. page 155), and found that such waves were distinctly formed when the plane of polarization coincided with the plane of incidence, but that they vanished completely when the plane of polarization was at right angles to the plane of incidence. The conclusion is inevitable that *the light vector which produces the photographic effect* is perpendicular to the*

* The same holds for the fluorescent effect produced by stationary waves. Cf. foot-note, p. 156 above.

plane of polarization; for stationary waves can be formed only when the light vectors of the incident and reflected rays are parallel. When they are perpendicular to each other every trace of interference vanishes.

It will be seen later that, from the standpoint of the electromagnetic theory, *the above question has no meaning if merely the direction of the vector be taken into account.* For in that theory, and in fact in any other, two vectors which are at right angles to each other (the electric and the magnetic force) are necessarily involved. However, the question may well be asked, which of these two vectors is determinative of the light phenomena, or whether, in fact, both are. If both were determinative of the photographic effect, then in Wiener's experiment no stationary waves could have been obtained even with perpendicular incidence, since the nodes of one vector coincide with the loops of the other, and inversely, as will be proved in the later development of the theory of light. But the fact that stationary waves are actually observed proves that, for the photo-chemical as well as for the fluorescent effects, only one light vector is determinative; and indeed that it is the one which is perpendicular to the plane of polarization is shown by the experiments in polarized light mentioned above.

The phenomena shown by pleochroic crystals like tourmaline lead also to the same conclusions.

7. Position of the Determinative Vector in Crystals.—In crystals the velocity depends upon the direction of the wave normal and upon the plane of polarization. Similarly in the pleochroic crystals the absorption of the light depends upon the same quantities. Now it appears * that these relations *are most easily understood upon the assumption that the light vector is perpendicular to the plane of polarization.* For then the velocity and the absorption † of the wave depend only upon the

* This is more fully treated in Section II, Chap. II, § 7.

† The fluorescence phenomena in crystals lead also to the same conclusion. Cf. Lommel, Wied. Ann. 44, p. 311.

direction of the light vector with respect to the optical axis of the crystal. The following example will illustrate: A plate of tourmaline cut parallel to the principal axis does not change color or brightness when rotated about that axis, i.e. when the light is made to pass through obliquely, but its direction is kept perpendicular to the axis. But the brightness of the plate changes markedly if it be rotated about an axis perpendicular to the principal axis of the crystal. The plane of polarization of the emergent ray is in the first case perpendicular to the principal axis, i.e. to the axis of rotation of the plate; in the second case it is parallel to this axis. The vector which is perpendicular to the plane of polarization is, therefore, in the first case continually parallel to the principal axis of the plate, but in the second it changes its position with respect to this axis.

Thus far no case has been observed in which a light vector which lies in the plane of polarization is alone determinative of the effects, i.e. furnishes the simplest explanation of the phenomena. Hence in view of what precedes it may be said: *The light vector is perpendicular to the plane of polarization.**

8. Natural and Partially Polarized Light.—It has been shown above that two plane-polarized beams may be obtained by double refraction from a single beam of natural light. Superposition of two plane-polarized rays which have the same direction but different phases and azimuths produces, as is shown by equation (5), elliptically polarized light. The vibration in such a ray is, however, wholly transverse, since the plane of the ellipse is perpendicular to the direction of propagation.

As will be fully shown later, elliptically polarized light is produced by the passage of a plane-polarized beam through a doubly refracting crystal whenever the two beams produced by the double refraction are not separated from each other.

---

* At least this assumption gives a simpler presentation of optical phenomena than the other (which is also possible) which makes the light vector parallel to the plane of polarization.

Also the most general case, represented by equations (2), of *elliptically polarized light which is not transverse can be realized by means of total reflection or absorption*, as will be shown later.

The question now arises, What is the nature of natural light? Since it does not show different properties in different azimuths, and yet is not identical with circularly polarized light, because, unlike circularly polarized light, it shows no one-sidedness after passing through a thin doubly refracting crystal, the only assumption which can be made is that natural light is plane or elliptically polarized for a small interval of time δt, but that, in the course of a longer interval, the vibration form changes in such a way that the mean effect is that of a ray which is perfectly symmetrical about the direction of propagation.

Since Michelson has observed interference in natural light for a difference of path of $540{,}000\lambda$ (cf. page 150), it is evident that in this case light must execute 540,000 vibrations at least before it changes its vibration form. But since a million vibrations are performed in a very short time, namely, in 20.10^{-10} seconds, the human eye could never recognize a ray of natural light as polarized even though several million vibrations were performed before a change occurred in the vibration form. For, in the shortest interval which is necessary to give the impression of light, the vibration form would have changed several thousand times.

As regards the two laws announced by Fresnel and Arago (cf. page 247), the second, namely, that two rays polarized at right angles interfere when they are brought into the same plane of polarization provided they originated in a polarized ray, is easily understood; for in this case the original ray has but one vibration form, hence the two reuniting rays must be in the same condition of polarization, i.e. must be capable of interfering. This is the case also when the original ray is natural light so long as the vibration form does not change, i.e. within the above-mentioned interval δt. But for another interval $\delta t'$, although interference fringes must be produced, the position of these fringes is not the same as that of the fringes corresponding to the first interval δt. For a change in the vibration form of the original ray is equivalent to a change of phase. Hence the mean intensity, taken over a large number of elements δt, is equivalent to a uniform intensity, i.e. two rays polarized at right angles to each other, which originated in natural light, do not interfere even though they are brought together in the same azimuth. This is the first of the Fresnel-Arago laws.

The term *partially polarized light* is used to denote the effect produced by a superposition of natural light and light polarized in some particular way. Partially polarized light has different properties in different directions, yet it can never be reduced to plane polarized light, as can be done with light which has a fixed vibration form (cf. below).

9. Experimental Investigation of Elliptically Polarized Light.—In order to obtain the vibration form of an elliptically polarized ray, it is changed into a plane-polarized ray by means of a doubly refracting crystalline plate. For, as was remarked upon page 242, the passage of plane-polarized light through a doubly refracting crystal decomposes it into two waves polarized at right angles to each other. The directions of the light vectors in the two waves are called the *principal directions of vibration.* These have fixed positions within the crystal and are perpendicular to each other. Since now the two rays are propagated with different velocities within the crystal, they acquire a difference of phase which depends upon the nature and thickness of the plate. An incident light vector which is parallel to one of these two principal directions of vibration within the crystal is not decomposed into two waves.

Two methods of procedure are now possible: first, the plate of crystal may be of such thickness that it introduces a difference of phase of $\frac{\pi}{2}$ (difference of path $\frac{1}{4}\lambda$) between the two waves propagated through it. This is called a quarter-wave plate (*Senarmont's compensator*). If the quarter-wave plate is rotated until its principal directions are parallel to the principal axes of the elliptical vibration form of the incident light, the emergent light must evidently be plane-polarized, and the position of its plane of polarization must depend upon the ratio of the principal axes of the incident ellipse. For the two light vectors which lie in the directions of the principal axes of this ellipse have, after passage through the plate, a difference of phase of 0 or π, and in this case there results (cf. page 250) plane-polarized light in which the direction of the light vector is given by equation (7). Hence if the emergent light is observed through a nicol, entire darkness is obtained when the nicol is in the proper azimuth. Hence this method of investigation requires a rotation both of the crystalline plate about its normal and of the nicol about its axis until complete darkness is obtained. The position of the crystal then gives the position of the principal axes of the incident ellipse; that of the nicol, the ratio of these axes.

Second, a fixed plate of variable thickness, such as a quartz wedge, may be used in order to give those two components of the incident light which are in the principal directions of vibration of the plate such a difference of phase that, after passage through the crystal, they combine to form plane-polarized light. A nicol is used to test whether or not this has been accomplished. The position of the nicol gives the ratio of the components u, v, of the incident light, while their original difference of phase is calculated from the thickness of the plate which has been used to change the incident light into plane-polarized light.

In order that the crystal may produce a difference of phase zero, it is convenient to so combine two quartz wedges, whose optical axes lie in different directions, that they produce differences of phase of different sign. Thus, for example, in Fig. 79, A is a wedge of quartz whose crystallographic axis is parallel to the edge of the wedge, while B is another plate

FIG. 79.

whose principal axis is perpendicular to the edge but parallel to the surface (*Babinet's compensator*). Only the difference in the thickness of the two wedges is effective. Hence, if the incident light is homogeneous and elliptically polarized, a suitable setting of the analyzing nicol brings out dark bands which run parallel to the axis of the wedge. These bands move across the compensator if one wedge is displaced with reference to the other. A micrometer screw effects this displacement. After the instrument has been calibrated by means of plane-polarized light, it is easy from the reading on the micrometer when a given band has been brought into a definite position to calculate the difference of phase of those two components u, v, which are parallel to the two principal axes of the quartz wedges.

The construction must be somewhat altered if it is desired to obtain a large uniform field of plane-polarized light. Then, in place of a quartz wedge, a plane parallel plate of quartz must be used as a compensator. Such a plate is produced by combining two adjustable quartz wedges whose axes lie in the same direction (Fig. 80). In order to make

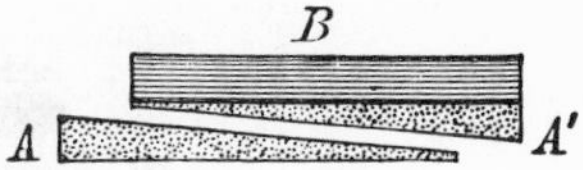

FIG. 80.

it possible to introduce a difference of phase zero, the two wedges are again combined with a plane parallel plate of quartz B whose principal axis is at right angles to the axes of A and A'; so that the effective thickness is the difference between the thickness of B and the sum of the thicknesses of the wedges A and A'. This construction, that of the Soleil-Babinet compensator, is shown in Fig. 80. In the wedges A, A' the principal axis is parallel to the edges of the wedges; in the plate B the principal axis is perpendicular to the edge and parallel to the surface. It is convenient to have one plate, for example A', cemented to B, while A is micrometrically adjustable. For a suitable setting of the micrometer and the analyzing nicol the whole field is dark.

This construction of the compensator is particularly convenient for studying the modifications which plane-polarized light undergoes upon reflection or refraction. In a spectrometer (Fig. 81) the collimator K and the telescope F are furnished with nicol prisms whose orientations may be read off on the graduated circles p, p'. The Soleil-Babinet compen-

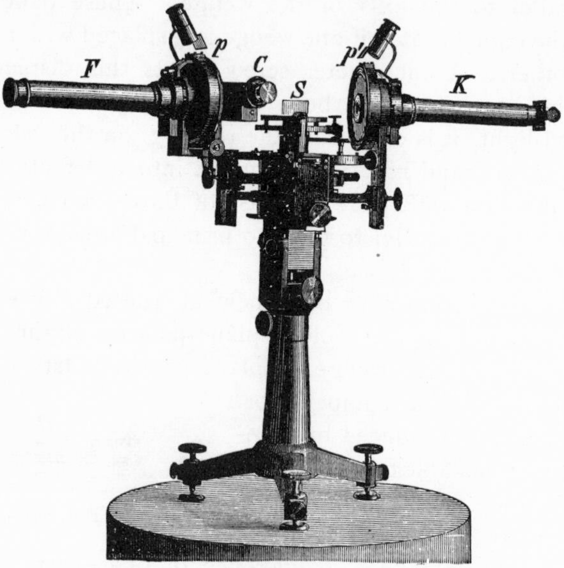

FIG. 81.

sator C is attached to the telescope. Its principal directions of vibration (the principal axes) are parallel and perpendicular to the plane of incidence of the light. S is the reflecting or refracting body. Thus the light is parallel in passing through the nicols and the compensator.*

* Since the telescope must be focussed for infinity, the simple Babinet compensator cannot be used.

SECTION II

OPTICAL PROPERTIES OF BODIES

CHAPTER I

THEORY OF LIGHT

1. Mechanical Theory.—The aim of a theory of light is to deduce mathematically from some particular hypothesis the differential equation which the light vector satisfies, and the boundary conditions which must be fulfilled when light crosses the boundary between two different media. Now the differential equation (12) on page 169 of the light vector is also the general equation of motion in an elastic medium, and hence it was natural at first to base a theory of light upon the theory of elasticity. According to this mechanical conception, *a light vector must be a displacement of the ether particles from their positions of equilibrium*, and the ether, i.e. the medium in which the light vibrations are able to be propagated, must be an elastic material of very small density.

But a difficulty arises at once from the fact that light-waves are transverse. In general both transverse and longitudinal vibrations are propagated in an elastic medium; but fluids which have no rigidity are capable of transmitting longitudinal vibrations only, while solids which are perfectly incompressible can transmit transverse vibrations only. The fact that the heavenly bodies move without friction through free space would point strongly to the conclusion that the ether is a fluid, not an incompressible solid. Nevertheless this difficulty may be met by the consideration that, with respect to such slowly acting forces as are manifested in the motions of the heavenly bodies, the ether acts like a frictionless fluid; while, with respect to the rapidly changing forces such as are present in the vibrations of light, a slight trace of friction causes it to act like a rigid body.

But a second difficulty arises in setting up the boundary conditions for the light vector. The theory of elasticity furnishes six conditions for the passage of a motion through the bounding surface between two elastic media, namely, the equality on both sides of the boundary of the components of the displacements of the particles, and the equality of the components of the elastic forces. But in order to satisfy these six conditions both transverse and longitudinal waves must be present. How the various mechanical theories attempt to meet this difficulty will not be considered here: * suffice it to say that most of these theories retain only four of the boundary conditions.

In order to bring theory into agreement with the observations upon the properties of reflected light, for instance to deduce Brewster's law as to the polarizing angle (cf. page 246), it is necessary to assume either that the density or that the elasticity of the ether is the same in all bodies. The former standpoint was taken by F. Neumann, the latter by Fresnel. Neumann's assumption leads to the conclusion that the displacement of the ether particles in a plane-polarized ray lies in the plane of polarization, while Fresnel's makes it perpendicular to this plane.

2. **Electromagnetic Theory.**—The fundamental hypothesis of this theory, first announced by Faraday, and afterwards mathematically developed by Maxwell, is that *the velocity of light* in a non-absorbing medium is identical with *the velocity of*

---

* For complete presentation cf. Winkelmann's Handbuch, Optik, pp. 641–674.

an electromagnetic wave in the same medium. Either the electric or the magnetic force may be looked upon as the light vector; both are continually vibrating and, in a plane-polarized ray, are perpendicular to each other. This two-sidedness of the theory leaves open the question as to the position of the light vector with respect to the plane of polarization; nevertheless, for the reasons stated on page 252, it is simpler to interpret the electric force, which lies perpendicular to the plane of polarization, as the light vector. This leads to the results of Fresnel's mechanical theory, while Neumann's results are obtained when the magnetic force is interpreted as the light vector.

The following are the essential advantages of the electromagnetic theory:

1. That the waves are transverse follows at once from Maxwell's simple conception of electromagnetic action, according to which there exist only closed electrical circuits.

2. The boundary conditions hold for every electromagnetic field. It is not necessary, as in the case of the mechanical theories, to make special assumptions for the light vibrations.

3. *The velocity of light in space, and in many cases in ponderable bodies also, can be determined from pure electromagnetic experiments. This latter is an especial advantage of this theory over the mechanical theory*, and it was this point which immediately gained adherents for the electromagnetic conception of the nature of light. In fact it is an epoch-making advance in natural science when in this way two originally distinct fields of investigation, like optics and electricity, are brought into relations which can be made the subject of quantitative measurements.

Henceforth *the electromagnetic point of view will be maintained.* But it may be remarked that the conclusions reached in the preceding chapters are altogether independent of any particular theory, i.e. independent of what is understood by a light vector.

3. The Definition of the Electric and of the Magnetic Force.—Two very long thin magnets exert forces upon each other which appear to emanate from the ends or poles of the magnets. *The strengths of two magnet-poles* m and m_1 are defined by the fact that in a vacuum, at a distance apart r, they exert upon each other a mechanical force (which can be measured in C. G. S. units)

$$K = \frac{m \cdot m_1}{r^2}. \quad . \quad . \quad . \quad . \quad . \quad . \quad . \quad (1)$$

In accordance with this equation *a unit magnetic pole* ($m = 1$) is defined as one which, placed at unit distance from a like pole, exerts upon it unit force.

The strength $\mathfrak{H}$ *of a magnetic field* in any medium * is the force which the field exerts upon unit magnetic pole. The components of $\mathfrak{H}$ along the rectangular axes x, y, z will be denoted by α, β, γ.

The direction of *the magnetic lines of force* determines the direction of the magnetic field; the density of the lines, the strength of the field, since in a vacuum the strength of field is represented by the number of lines of force which pass perpendicularly through unit surface. A correct conception of the law of force (1) is obtained if a pole of strength m be conceived as the origin of $4\pi m$ lines of force. For then the density of the lines upon a sphere of radius r described about the pole as centre is equal to $m : r^2$, i.e. is equal to the strength of field $\mathfrak{H}$, according to law (1).

Similar definitions hold in *the electrostatic system for the electric field.*

The quantities of two electric charges e and e_1 are defined by the fact that in a vacuum, at a distance apart r, they exert upon each other a measurable mechanical force

$$K = \frac{e \cdot e_1}{r^2}. \quad . \quad . \quad . \quad . \quad . \quad . \quad . \quad . \quad (2)$$

The definition of *unit charge* is then similar to that of unit pole above.

* This medium can be filled with matter or be totally devoid of it.

The strength $\mathfrak{F}$ *of any electric field* in any medium is the force which it exerts upon unit charge. The components of $\mathfrak{F}$ along the three rectangular axes will be denoted by X, Y, Z.

The direction of *the electric lines of force* determines the direction of the electric field, and the number of lines which intersect perpendicularly unit surface in a vacuum determines the strength $\mathfrak{F}$ of the field. Hence, since law (2) holds, $4\pi e$ lines of force originate in a charge whose quantity is e.

4. Definition of the Electric Current in the Electrostatic and in the Electromagnetic Systems.—*In the electrostatic system the electric current* i which is passing through any cross-section q is defined as the number of electrostatic units of quantity which pass through q in unit time. Thus if, in the element of time dt, the quantity de passes through q, the current is

$$i = \frac{de}{dt}. \quad . \quad . \quad . \quad . \quad . \quad . \quad . \quad (3)$$

If the cross-section q is unity, i is equal to the current density j. The components of the current density, namely, j_x, j_y, j_z, are obtained by choosing q perpendicular to the x-, y-, or z-axis respectively.

In the electromagnetic system, the current i' is defined by means of its magnetic effect. A continuous current is obtained in a wire when the ends of the wire are connected to the poles of a galvanic cell. In this case also definite quantities of electricity are driven along the wire, for the isolated poles of the cell are actually electrically charged bodies. A magnetic pole placed in the neighborhood of an electric current is acted upon by a magnetic force. *In the electromagnetic system the current* i' *is defined by the fact that it requires* $4\pi i' = \mathfrak{A}$ *units of work to carry unit magnetic pole once around the current.**

Take, for example, a rectangle whose sides are dx, dy (Fig. 82), and through which a current $i' = j'_z \cdot dx\,dy$ flows in a

* The work $\mathfrak{A}$ is independent of both the path of the magnet pole and the nature of the medium surrounding the current. Cf. Drude, Physik des Aethers, pp. 77, 83.

direction perpendicular to its plane. j'_z is the z-component of the current density in the electromagnetic system. *If the current flows toward the reader (Fig. 82), and the positive direction of the coordinates is that shown in the figure*, then, according to Ampère's rule, a positive magnetic pole is deflected in the direction of the arrow. The whole work $\mathfrak{A}$ done in moving a magnet pole $m = +1$ around the circuit from A through B, C, D, and back to A is

$$\mathfrak{A} = \alpha \cdot dx + \beta' \cdot dy - \alpha' \cdot dx - \beta \cdot dy, \quad . \quad . \quad . \quad (4)$$

if α and β denote the components of the magnetic force which act along AB and AD, while α' and β' denote the components which act along DC and BC. α' differs from α only in that it acts along a line whose y-coordinate is dy greater than the y-coordinate of the line AB along which α acts When dy is sufficiently small $(\alpha' - \alpha) : dy$ is the differential coefficient $\partial\alpha : \partial y$, so that

$$\alpha' = \alpha + \frac{\partial \alpha}{\partial y} dy.$$

Similarly

$$\beta' = \beta + \frac{\partial \beta}{\partial x} dx,$$

so that, from (4),

$$\mathfrak{A} = \left(\frac{\partial \beta}{\partial x} - \frac{\partial \alpha}{\partial y}\right) dx\, dy. \quad . \quad . \quad . \quad . \quad . \quad (4')$$

Since now by the definition of the current i' this work is equal to $4\pi i' = 4\pi j'_z \cdot dx\, dy$, it follows that

$$4\pi j'_z = \frac{\partial \beta}{\partial x} - \frac{\partial \alpha}{\partial y},$$

and in the same way the two other differential equations may be deduced, namely,

$$\left.\begin{aligned} 4\pi j'_x &= \frac{\partial \gamma}{\partial y} - \frac{\partial \beta}{\partial z}, \\ 4\pi j_y &= \frac{\partial \alpha}{\partial z} - \frac{\partial \gamma}{\partial x}. \end{aligned}\right\} \quad . \quad . \quad . \quad . \quad . \quad (5)$$

These are Maxwell's differential equations of the electromagnetic field. In order to use them with the signs given in (5), the coordinate system must be chosen in accordance with Fig. 82. In these equations the current density j' defined electromagnetically may be replaced by the current density j defined electrostatically by introducing c, the ratio of the electromagnetic to the electrostatic unit. Thus

$$i : i' = c, \quad j_x : j'_x = c, \text{ etc.} \quad . \quad . \quad . \quad . \quad . \qquad (6)$$

Hence, by (5),

$$\frac{4\pi}{c} j_x = \frac{\partial \gamma}{\partial y} - \frac{\partial \beta}{\partial z}, \quad \frac{4\pi}{c} j_y = \frac{\partial \alpha}{\partial z} - \frac{\partial \gamma}{\partial x}, \quad \frac{4\pi}{c} j_z = \frac{\partial \beta}{\partial x} - \frac{\partial \alpha}{\partial y}. \qquad (7)$$

These equations are independent of the nature of the medium in which the electromagnetic phenomena occur (cf. note 1, page 263), *and hence they hold also in non-homogeneous and crystalline media.*

The value of the ratio c can be obtained by observing the magnetic effect which is produced by the discharge of a quantity e of electricity measured in electrostatic units. It may be shown that c has the dimensions of a velocity. Its value is

$$c = 3 \cdot 10^{10} \text{ cm./sec.}$$

5. Definition of the Magnetic Current.—Following the analogy of the electric current, the magnetic current which passes through any cross-section q is defined as the number of units of magnetism which pass through q in unit time. The magnetic current divided by the area of the surface q is called the density of the current, and its components are represented by s_x, s_y, s_z.

Equations (7) express the fact that an electric current is always surrounded by circular lines of magnetic force. But on the other hand a magnetic current must always be surrounded by circular lines of electric force. This follows at once from an application of the principle of energy.

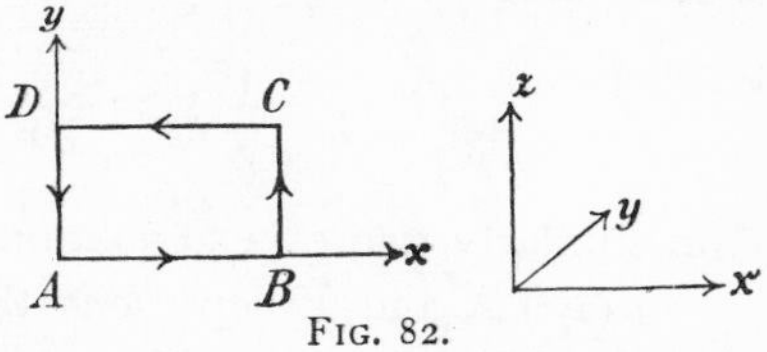

FIG. 82.

Imagine the rectangle $ABCD$ of Fig. 82 traversed by an electric current of intensity i (measured in electrostatic units) flowing in the direction of the arrows. Then a positive magnetic pole would be driven through the rectangle toward the reader, i.e. in the positive direction of the z-axis, and would continually revolve about one side of the rectangle. *The work thus performed must be done at the expense of the amount of energy which is required to maintain the current at the constant intensity i* while it is doing the work; or, in other words, *the motion of the pole must create a certain counter-electromotive force which must be overcome if the current is to remain constant.* The expression for the work done when a unit charge is carried once about the rectangle in the direction of the arrows is analogous to that given in (4) and (4′), i.e.

$$\mathfrak{A} = \left(\frac{\partial Y}{\partial x} - \frac{\partial X}{\partial y}\right) dx\, dy. \quad . \quad . \quad . \quad . \quad . \quad (8)$$

In order to maintain the current at intensity i during the time t, this work must be multiplied by the number of unit charges which traverse the circuit in the time t, i.e. by $i \cdot t$. The principle of energy requires that this work $\mathfrak{A}it$ be equal to the work which is done upon a magnet pole of strength m in carrying it once around a side of the rectangle in the time t. Since (cf. page 263) this work is equal to $4\pi m i' = 4\pi m i : c$, it follows that

$$\mathfrak{A} \cdot i \cdot t = 4\pi m i : c, \quad \text{i.e. } \mathfrak{A} = 4\pi m : ct. \quad . \quad . \quad (9)$$

But $m : t$ is the strength of the magnetic current which passes through the rectangle, and $m/t \cdot dx\, dy$ is equal to the z-component of the magnetic density. Hence from (8) and (9) it follows that

$$\frac{4\pi}{c} s_z = \frac{\partial Y}{\partial x} - \frac{\partial X}{\partial y}. \quad . \quad . \quad . \quad . \quad . \quad (10)$$

And similarly two other equations for s_x and s_y are obtained.

In (10) X and Y represent the electric forces which must be called into play in order to keep the current constant. But if X and Y denote the opposite forces produced by the magnetic current by induction, they are of the same magnitude but opposite in sign. Hence

$$\frac{4\pi}{c}s_x = \frac{\partial Y}{\partial z} - \frac{\partial Z}{\partial y}, \quad \frac{4\pi}{c}s_y = \frac{\partial Z}{\partial x} - \frac{\partial X}{\partial z}, \quad \frac{4\pi}{c}s_z = \frac{\partial X}{\partial y} - \frac{\partial Y}{\partial x}. \quad (11)$$

These equations are perfectly general and hold in all media, even in those which are non-homogeneous and crystalline.

The general equations (7) and (11) may be called *the fundamental equations of Maxwell's theory.* In all extensions of the original theory of Maxwell to bodies possessing peculiar optical properties, such as dispersion, absorption, natural and magnetic rotation of the plane of polarization, these fundamental equations remain unchanged. But the equations which connect j_x and s_x, etc., with the electric and magnetic forces have different forms for particular cases.

6. The Ether.—Constant electric currents can only be produced in conductors like the metals, not in dielectrics. Nevertheless a change in an electric charge produces in the latter currents which are called *displacement currents* to distinguish them from the *conduction currents*, and the cornerstone of Maxwell's theory is the assumption that these displacement currents have the same magnetic effects as the conduction currents. This assumption gives to Maxwell's theory the greatest simplicity in comparison with the other electrical theories. Constant magnetic currents cannot be produced, since there are no magnetic conductors.

It is first necessary to determine how the electric and magnetic current densities in the free ether depend upon the electric and magnetic forces. In the free ether there are no charges e or poles m concentrated at given points, but there are lines of force. Now, in accordance with the convention adopted on pages 262 and 263, namely, that every charge e or pole m sends out $4\pi e$ or $4\pi m$ lines of force, it may be said that 4π multiplied by the current density is equal to the change in the density of the lines of force in unit time, i.e.

$$\left.\begin{aligned} 4\pi j_x &= \frac{\partial N_x}{\partial t}, \quad 4\pi j_y = \frac{\partial N_y}{\partial t}, \quad 4\pi j_z = \frac{\partial N_z}{\partial t}, \\ 4\pi s_x &= \frac{\partial M_x}{\partial t}, \quad 4\pi s_y = \frac{\partial M_y}{\partial t}, \quad 4\pi s_z = \frac{\partial M_z}{\partial t}, \end{aligned}\right\} \quad . \quad (12)$$

in which N_x, N_y, N_z, M_x, M_y, M_z are the components of the densities of the electric and magnetic lines of force. But now, in accordance with the definitions on pages 262 and 263, in a vacuum the density of the electric or magnetic lines of force is numerically equal to the electric or magnetic force, so that, for a vacuum, equations (12) become

$$\left.\begin{aligned} 4\pi j_x &= \frac{\partial X}{\partial t}, \quad 4\pi j_y = \frac{\partial Y}{\partial t}, \quad 4\pi j_z = \frac{\partial Z}{\partial t}, \\ 4\pi s_x &= \frac{\partial \alpha}{\partial t}, \quad 4\pi s_y = \frac{\partial \beta}{\partial t}, \quad 4\pi s_z = \frac{\partial \gamma}{\partial t}. \end{aligned}\right\} \quad . \quad (13)$$

Hence for the free ether the equations (7) and (11) of the electromagnetic field take the form

$$\left.\begin{aligned} \frac{1}{c}\frac{\partial X}{\partial t} &= \frac{\partial \gamma}{\partial y} - \frac{\partial \beta}{\partial z}, \quad \frac{1}{c}\frac{\partial Y}{\partial t} = \frac{\partial \alpha}{\partial z} - \frac{\partial \gamma}{\partial x}, \quad \frac{1}{c}\frac{\partial Z}{\partial t} = \frac{\partial \beta}{\partial x} - \frac{\partial \alpha}{\partial y}, \\ \frac{1}{c}\frac{\partial \alpha}{\partial t} &= \frac{\partial Y}{\partial z} - \frac{\partial Z}{\partial y}, \quad \frac{1}{c}\frac{\partial \beta}{\partial t} = \frac{\partial Z}{\partial x} - \frac{\partial X}{\partial z}, \quad \frac{1}{c}\frac{\partial \gamma}{\partial t} = \frac{\partial X}{\partial y} - \frac{\partial Y}{\partial x}. \end{aligned}\right\} (14)$$

7. Isotropic Dielectrics.—For a space filled with insulating matter laws (1) and (2) must be modified. For if the electric charges e and e_1 are brought from empty space into a dielectric, for example a fluid, they exert a weaker influence upon each other than in empty space, so that it is necessary to write

$$K = \frac{1}{\epsilon}\frac{ee_1}{r^2}. \quad . \quad . \quad . \quad . \quad . \quad . \quad (15)$$

The constant ϵ is called the *dielectric constant.* The definition holds also for solid bodies, only in them the attracting or repelling forces cannot be observed so conveniently as in fluids. But there are other methods of determining the dielectric constant of solid bodies for which the reader is referred to texts upon electricity. The dielectric constant of all material bodies is greater than 1.

Similarly the forces between magnetic poles are altered somewhat when the poles are brought from a vacuum into a material substance, so that it is necessary to write

$$K = \frac{1}{\mu}\frac{mm_1}{r^2}. \quad . \quad . \quad . \quad . \quad . \quad . \quad (16)$$

The constant μ is called the *permeability* of the substance. It is sometimes greater than 1 (*paramagnetic* bodies), sometimes less than 1 (*diamagnetic* bodies). It differs appreciably from 1 only in the paramagnetic metals iron, nickel, and cobalt. At present dielectrics only are important since it is desired to consider first perfectly *transparent* substances, namely, those which transmit the energy of the electromagnetic waves without absorption, i.e. without becoming heated. In dielectrics μ differs so little from 1 (generally only a few thousandths of 1 per cent) that *in what follows it will always be considered equal to 1.**

Because of the change of the law (2) into (15) a change must also be made in equations (13), since with the same currents the electric force in the dielectric is $\frac{1}{\epsilon}$ weaker than in the free ether. Hence (13) become

$$4\pi j_x = \epsilon\frac{\partial X}{\partial t}, \text{ etc.,} \quad 4\pi s_x = \mu\frac{\partial \alpha}{\partial t}, \text{ etc.} \quad . \quad . \quad (17)$$

For an isotropic dielectric, since equations (7) and (11) are applicable to this case also, the following equations hold when $\mu = 1$:

$$\left.\begin{aligned}
\frac{\epsilon}{c}\frac{\partial X}{\partial t} &= \frac{\partial \gamma}{\partial y} - \frac{\partial \beta}{\partial z}, & \frac{\epsilon}{c}\frac{\partial Y}{\partial t} &= \frac{\partial \alpha}{\partial z} - \frac{\partial \gamma}{\partial x}, & \frac{\epsilon}{c}\frac{\partial Z}{\partial t} &= \frac{\partial \beta}{\partial x} - \frac{\partial \alpha}{\partial y},\\
\frac{1}{c}\frac{\partial \alpha}{\partial t} &= \frac{\partial Y}{\partial z} - \frac{\partial Z}{\partial y}, & \frac{1}{c}\frac{\partial \beta}{\partial t} &= \frac{\partial Z}{\partial x} - \frac{\partial X}{\partial z}, & \frac{1}{c}\frac{\partial \gamma}{\partial t} &= \frac{\partial X}{\partial y} - \frac{\partial Y}{\partial x}.
\end{aligned}\right\} (18)$$

* In the discussion of the optical properties of magnetized bodies it will be shown why it is justifiable to assume for light vibrations $\mu = 1$ for all bodies. The reason for this is not that the magnetization of a body cannot follow the rapid changes of field which occur in light vibrations, but is far more complicated.

These equations completely determine all the properties of the electromagnetic field in a dielectric.

If equations (12) be considered general, i.e. if the number of lines of force which originate in a charge be considered independent of the nature of the medium, then a comparison of (17) with (12) shows that within the body

$$\left.\begin{matrix} N_x = \epsilon X, & N_y = \epsilon Y, & N_z = \epsilon Z, \\ M_x = \mu\alpha, & M_y = \mu\beta, & M_z = \mu\gamma, \end{matrix}\right\} \quad . \quad . \quad (19)$$

i.e. *only in the ether* ($\epsilon = 1$, $\mu = 1$) *is the density of the lines of force numerically equal to the electric, or the magnetic, force.*

$4\pi e$ lines of force must be sent out from the entire surface of an elementary cube which contains the charge e and has the dimensions $dx\,dy\,dz$. But the number of emitted lines can also be calculated from the surface of the cube; thus the two sides which lie perpendicular to the x-axis emit the number $-(N_x)_1 dy\,dz + (N_x)_2 dy\,dz$, in which the indices 1 and 2 relate to the opposite faces which are dx apart. Now evidently, from the definition of a derivative,

$$(N_x)_2 = (N_x)_1 + \frac{\partial N_x}{\partial x} dx,$$

so in this way the whole number of lines passing out of the surface is found to be

$$\left(\frac{\partial N_x}{\partial x} + \frac{\partial N_y}{\partial y} + \frac{\partial N_z}{\partial z}\right) dx\,dy\,dz.$$

If this expression be placed equal to $4\pi e$, then it follows, in consideration of (19), if $e : dx\,dy\,dz = \rho$ be called the density of the charge (charge of unit volume),

$$4\pi\rho = \frac{\partial(\epsilon X)}{\partial x} + \frac{\partial(\epsilon Y)}{\partial y} + \frac{\partial(\epsilon Z)}{\partial z}. \quad . \quad . \quad . \quad (20)$$

It is evident from its derivation that *this equation holds also for isotropic non-homogeneous bodies*, i.e. for bodies in which ϵ varies with x, y, z. An analogous equation may be deduced for the density of the magnetization.

8. The Boundary Conditions.—If two different media are in contact, there are certain conditions which the electric and magnetic forces must fulfil in passing from one medium into the other. These conditions may be obtained from the equations (18) by the following consideration: In the passage from a medium of dielectric constant ϵ_1 to one of dielectric constant ϵ_2 the change in the electric and magnetic forces is not abrupt, as would be the case if the *surface of separation* were a mathematical plane, but gradual, so that within the transition layer the dielectric constant varies continuously from the value ϵ_1 to the value ϵ_2. Also within this *transition layer* the equations (7), (11), and (17), and hence also (18), must hold, i.e. all the differential coefficients which appear in them must remain finite. Assume now, for example, that the plane of contact between the two media is the xy-plane. Since the differential coefficients $\frac{\partial Y}{\partial z}$, $\frac{\partial X}{\partial z}$, $\frac{\partial \beta}{\partial z}$, $\frac{\partial \alpha}{\partial z}$ must remain finite within the transition layer, it follows that, if the thickness of this layer, i.e. dz, is infinitely small, the changes in Y, X, β, α in the transition layer are infinitely small. In other words, *the components of the electric and magnetic forces parallel to the surface must vary continuously in passing through the transition layer*, assumed to be infinitely thin. That is,

$$X_1 = X_2, \quad Y_1 = Y_2, \quad \alpha_1 = \alpha_2, \quad \beta_1 = \beta_2 \text{ for } z = 0, \qquad (21)$$

in which the subscripts refer to the two different media.

Since in equations (18) the differential coefficients $\frac{\partial Z}{\partial z}$ and $\frac{\partial \gamma}{\partial z}$ do not appear, the same conclusions do not hold for Z and γ which held for X, Y, β, α. Nevertheless it is evident from the last of equations (18) that $\frac{\partial \gamma}{\partial t}$, and hence also γ, has the same value on both sides of the transition layer, because, for all values of x and y, X and Y have the same values on both sides of that layer. *Hence there is no discontinuity in γ in passing through the infinitely thin boundary layer.* In the same way the conclusion may be drawn from the third of equations (18) that *the product* ϵZ *is continuous and hence that* Z *is discontinuous.* To the boundary conditions (21) there are then also to be added

$$\epsilon_1 Z_1 = \epsilon_2 Z_2, \quad \gamma_1 = \gamma_2 \text{ for } z = 0. \quad . \quad . \quad (21')$$

But on account of the existence of the principal equations (18) *only four of the six equations (21) and (21′) are independent of one another.*

Equation (19) in connection with (21) shows that *the lines of force do not have free ends at the boundary between two media.* (N.B in (21′) μ is assumed equal to 1, otherwise it would be necessary to write $\mu_1\gamma_1 = \mu_2\gamma_2$.

9. The Energy of the Electromagnetic Field.—If equations (18) be multiplied by the factors $Xd\tau$, $Yd\tau$, $Zd\tau$, $\alpha d\tau$, $\beta d\tau$, $\gamma d\tau$, in which $d\tau$ represents an element of volume, and then integrated over any region, there results, after adding and setting

$$\mathfrak{E} = \frac{\epsilon}{8\pi}(X^2 + Y^2 + Z^2) + \frac{1}{8\pi}(\alpha^2 + \beta^2 + \gamma^2), \quad . \quad (22)$$

$$\left.\begin{aligned} \frac{4\pi}{c}\frac{\partial}{\partial t}\int \mathfrak{E}d\tau &= \int\left(\frac{\partial \gamma}{\partial y} - \frac{\partial \beta}{\partial z}\right)Xd\tau + \ldots \\ &+ \int\left(\frac{\partial Y}{\partial z} - \frac{\partial Z}{\partial y}\right)\alpha d\tau + \ldots \end{aligned}\right\}. \quad (23)$$

The application of theorem (20) on page 173 gives

$$\int \frac{\partial \gamma}{\partial y} X d\tau = -\int \gamma X \cos(ny)\, dS - \int \gamma \frac{\partial X}{\partial y} d\tau,$$

in which dS denotes an element of the surface which bounds the region over which the integration is taken, and n the inner normal to dS. When this transformation is applied to the first three integrals which appear on the right-hand side of (23) the volume integrals disappear, and there results

$$\frac{\partial}{\partial t}\int \mathfrak{E}d\tau = \frac{c}{4\pi}\int\Big[(\gamma Y - \beta Z)\cos(nx) + (\alpha Z - \gamma X)\cos(ny)$$
$$+ (\beta X - \alpha Y)\cos(nz)\Big]dS. \quad (24)$$

If the region of integration be taken so large that at its limits the electric and magnetic forces are vanishingly small, then equation (24) asserts that the quantity $\mathfrak{E}$ for this region does not vary with the time. $\mathfrak{E}$ *signifies the energy of the electromagnetic field in unit volume.* This can be shown to be the meaning of $\mathfrak{E}$ by a calculation of the work done in moving the electric or the magnetic charges. (Cf. Drude, Physik des Aethers, pages 127, 272.)

10. The Rays of Light as the Lines of Energy Flow.—If at the boundary of the region of integration X, Y, Z, α, β, γ, do not vanish, equation (24) can be interpreted to mean that the change of electromagnetic energy in any region is due to an inflow or outflow of energy through the boundary. According to (24), the components of this energy flow, represented by f_x, f_y, f_z, may be regarded as the following:

$$f_x = \frac{c}{4\pi}(\gamma Y - \beta Z), \quad f_y = \frac{c}{4\pi}(\alpha Z - \gamma X), \quad f_z = \frac{c}{4\pi}(\beta X - \alpha Y). \quad (25)$$

From this it follows that

$$\alpha \cdot f_x + \beta \cdot f_y + \gamma \cdot f_z = 0,$$
$$X \cdot f_x + Y \cdot f_y + Z \cdot f_z = 0,$$

and hence the direction of the flow of energy is always perpendicular to the electric and magnetic forces.

This theory, due to Poynting, of the flow of energy in the electromagnetic field, is of great importance in the theory of light in that the rays of light must be considered as the lines of energy flow. For on page 2 a light-ray which passes from a source Q to a point P was defined as the locus of those points at which an obstacle, i.e. an opaque body, must be placed in order to cut off the light effect at P. Now evidently the energy cannot be propagated from Q to P if the lines of energy flow from Q to P are intercepted by an obstacle.

Hence, by (25), the direction of the rays of light must be perpendicular to the electric and magnetic forces.

CHAPTER II

TRANSPARENT ISOTROPIC MEDIA

1. Velocity of Light.—From the standpoint of the electric theory a plane electromagnetic wave may be conceived to originate as follows: Imagine that at a certain instant an electric current parallel to the x-axis is excited in a thin layer which is parallel to the xy-plane. This current gives rise to magnetic forces at the surface of the layer, which are parallel to the y-axis. The growth of the magnetic field induces electric forces which within the layer are parallel to the negative x-axis, without the layer parallel to the positive x-axis. Hence within the layer the electric current disappears, because the induced currents neutralize the original current; but in its place there arises outside the layer electric currents which run along the positive direction of the x-axis. In this way an electric impulse is propagated in the form of a wave along both the positive and negative directions of the z-axis.

In order to find the velocity of propagation, it is necessary to return to equations (18) of the previous chapter.

If the first three of these equations be differentiated with respect to the time, and if the values of $\frac{\partial \alpha}{\partial t}, \frac{\partial \beta}{\partial t}, \frac{\partial \gamma}{\partial t}$ given in the last three of these equations be introduced, there results

$$\frac{\epsilon}{c^2}\frac{\partial^2 X}{\partial t^2} = \frac{\partial}{\partial y}\left(\frac{\partial X}{\partial y} - \frac{\partial Y}{\partial x}\right) - \frac{\partial}{\partial z}\left(\frac{\partial Z}{\partial x} - \frac{\partial X}{\partial z}\right),$$

and similarly two other equations are obtained. Now this equation may be written in the form

$$\frac{\epsilon}{c^2}\frac{\partial^2 X}{\partial t^2} = \frac{\partial^2 X}{\partial x^2} + \frac{\partial^2 X}{\partial y^2} + \frac{\partial^2 X}{\partial z^2} - \frac{\partial}{\partial x}\left(\frac{\partial X}{\partial x} + \frac{\partial Y}{\partial y} + \frac{\partial Z}{\partial z}\right). \quad (1)$$

Also differentiation of the first three of the equations (18) with respect to x, y, z, and addition of them gives

$$\frac{\partial}{\partial t}\left(\frac{\partial X}{\partial x} + \frac{\partial Y}{\partial y} + \frac{\partial Z}{\partial z}\right) = 0.$$

Since in what follows we are only concerned with periodic changes in the electric and magnetic forces, and since for these the differential coefficient with respect to the time is proportional to the changes themselves (when the phase $\frac{\pi}{2}$ has been added), the conclusion may be drawn from the last equation that

$$\frac{\partial X}{\partial x} + \frac{\partial Y}{\partial y} + \frac{\partial Z}{\partial z} = 0. \quad . \quad . \quad . \quad . \quad (2)$$

Hence equation (1) becomes

$$\frac{\epsilon}{c^2}\frac{\partial^2 X}{\partial t^2} = \frac{\partial^2 X}{\partial x^2} + \frac{\partial^2 X}{\partial y^2} + \frac{\partial^2 X}{\partial z^2} = \Delta X.$$

Similar equations hold for Y and Z, so that the following system of equations is obtained:

$$\frac{\epsilon}{c^2}\frac{\partial^2 X}{\partial t^2} = \Delta X, \quad \frac{\epsilon}{c^2}\frac{\partial^2 Y}{\partial t^2} = \Delta Y, \quad \frac{\epsilon}{c^2}\frac{\partial^2 Z}{\partial t^2} = \Delta Z. \quad . \quad (3)$$

For the components of the magnetic force similar equations hold, thus

$$\frac{\partial \alpha}{\partial x} + \frac{\partial \beta}{\partial y} + \frac{\partial \gamma}{\partial z} = 0, \quad . \quad . \quad . \quad . \quad . \quad (2')$$

$$\frac{\epsilon}{c^2}\frac{\partial^2 \alpha}{\partial t^2} = \Delta \alpha, \quad \frac{\epsilon}{c^2}\frac{\partial^2 \beta}{\partial t^2} = \Delta \beta, \quad \frac{\epsilon}{c^2}\frac{\partial^2 \gamma}{\partial t^2} = \Delta \gamma. \quad . \quad (3')$$

Now it has been shown on page 170 that differential equations of the form of (3) and (3′) represent waves which are propagated with a velocity

$$V = \frac{c}{\sqrt{\epsilon}}. \quad . \quad . \quad . \quad . \quad . \quad . \quad . \quad (4)$$

This is then, according to the electromagnetic view of the nature of light, the velocity of light, and it is immaterial whether the electric or the magnetic force be interpreted as the light vector, for the two are inseparably connected and have the same velocity.

Applying equation (4) to the case of the free ether, it follows *that the velocity of light in ether is equal to the ratio of the electromagnetic to the electrostatic units.* This conclusion has actually been strikingly verified, for (cf. page 119) the mean of the best determinations of the velocity of light was seen to be $V = 2.9989 \cdot 10^{10}$ cm./sec., a number which agrees within the observational error with that given for the ratio of the units, namely, $c = 3 \cdot 10^{10}$ cm./sec.

This is the first brilliant success of the electromagnetic theory.

According to (4) the velocity in ponderable bodies must be $1 \cdot \sqrt{\epsilon}$ smaller than in the free ether, or, since the index of refraction n_0 of a body with respect to the ether is the ratio of the velocities in ether and in the body,

$$n_0 = \sqrt{\epsilon}, \quad n_0^2 = \epsilon, \quad . \quad . \quad . \quad . \quad . \quad . \quad (5)$$

i.e. *the square of the index of refraction is equal to the dielectric constant.*

Evidently this relation cannot be rigorously fulfilled, for the reason that the index depends for all bodies upon the color, i.e. upon the period of oscillation, while from its definition ϵ is independent of the period of oscillation.

But in case of the gases, in which the dependence of the index upon the color is small, the relation (5) is well satisfied, as is shown by the following table, in which the values of the dielectric constants are due to Boltzmann,* while the indices are those for yellow light:

	n_0	$\sqrt{\epsilon}$
Air	1.000 294	1.000 295
Hydrogen	1.000 138	1.000 132
Carbon dioxide	1.000 449	1.000 473
Carbon monoxide	1.000 346	1.000 345
Nitrous oxide	1.000 503	1.000 497

Relation (5) also holds well for the liquid hydrocarbons; for example, for benzole n_0 (yellow) $= 1.482$, $\sqrt{\epsilon} = 1.49$.

On the other hand many of the solid bodies, such as the glasses, as well as some liquids, like water and alcohol, show a marked departure from equation (5). For these substances ϵ is always larger than n_0^2, as the following table shows:

	n_0	$\sqrt{\epsilon}$
Water	1.33	9.0
Methyl alcohol	1.34	5.7
Ethyl alcohol	1.36	5.0

In order to explain these departures, the fundamental equations of the electric theory must be extended. This extension will be made in Chapter V of this section. In this extension the quantity ϵ which is here considered as constant will be found to depend upon the period of oscillation.

But first an investigation will be made from the standpoint of the electric theory of those optical properties of bodies which do not depend upon dispersion. *In what follows it will be assumed that the light is monochromatic, and that the extension to be given in Chapter V has already been made, so that the constant* ϵ *appearing in the fundamental equations is equal to the square of the index of refraction for the given color.*

* L. Boltzmann, Wien. Ber. 69, p. 795, 1874. Pogg. Ann. 155, p. 407, 1873.

2. The Transverse Nature of Plane Waves.—A plane wave is represented by the equations

$$\left.\begin{aligned} X &= A_x\cdot\cos\frac{2\pi}{T}\left(t - \frac{mx + ny + pz}{V}\right), \\ Y &= A_y\cdot\cos\frac{2\pi}{T}\left(t - \frac{mx + ny + pz}{V}\right), \\ Z &= A_z\cdot\cos\frac{2\pi}{T}\left(t - \frac{mx + ny + pz}{V}\right). \end{aligned}\right\} \quad . \quad . \quad (6)$$

For the phase is the same in the planes

$$mx + ny + pz = \text{const.}, \quad . \quad . \quad . \quad . \quad (7)$$

which is then the equation of the wave fronts. m, n, and p are the direction cosines of the normal to the wave front, provided the further condition be imposed that

$$m^2 + n^2 + p^2 = 1. \quad . \quad . \quad . \quad . \quad . \quad (8)$$

A_x, A_y, A_z are the components of the amplitude of the resultant electrical force. They are then proportional to the direction cosines of the amplitude A. In consequence of equation (2) on page 275,

$$A_x\cdot m + A_y\cdot n + A_z\cdot p = 0, \quad . \quad . \quad . \quad . \quad (9)$$

an equation which expresses the fact that the resulting amplitude A is perpendicular to the normal to the wave front, i.e. to the direction of propagation; or in other words, *that the wave is transverse*. This conclusion holds for the magnetic force also. That plane waves are transverse follows from equations (2) or (2′), i.e. from the form of the fundamental equations of the theory.

3. Reflection and Refraction at the Boundary between two Transparent Isotropic Media.—Let two media 1 and 2 having the dielectric constants ϵ_1 and ϵ_2 meet in a plane which will be taken as the xy-plane. Let the positive z-axis extend from medium 1 to medium 2 (Fig. 83). Let a plane wave fall from the former upon the latter at an angle of incidence ϕ, and let the xz-plane be the plane of incidence. The direction cosines of the direction of propagation of the incident wave are then

$$m = \sin\phi, \quad n = 0, \quad p = \cos\phi. \quad . \quad . \quad . \quad (10)$$

Let the incident electric force be resolved into two components, one perpendicular to the plane of incidence and of amplitude E_s, and one in the plane of incidence and of amplitude E_p. The first component is parallel to the y-axis so that, in consideration of (6) and (10), the y-component of the incident force may be written

$$Y_e = E_s \cdot \cos \frac{2\pi}{T}\left(t - \frac{x \sin \phi + z \cos \phi}{V_1}\right), \quad . \quad (11)$$

in which V_1 is the velocity of light in the first medium. By (4),

$$V_1 = c : \sqrt{\epsilon_1}. \quad . \quad . \quad . \quad . \quad . \quad . \quad (12)$$

Since the wave is transverse, the component E_p of the electrical force, which lies in the plane of incidence, is perpendicular to the ray, i.e. the components A_x and A_z, along the x- and z-axes, of the amplitude E_p must have the values

$$A_x = E_p \cdot \cos \phi, \quad A_z = - E_p \cdot \sin \phi,$$

if, as shown in Fig. 83, the positive direction of E_p is taken downward, i.e. into the second medium.

The x- and z-components of the electric force of the incident wave are, therefore,

$$\left. \begin{aligned} X_e &= E_p \cdot \cos \phi \cdot \cos \frac{2\pi}{T}\left(t - \frac{x \sin \phi + z \cos \phi}{V_1}\right), \\ Z_e &= - E_p \cdot \sin \phi \cdot \cos \frac{2\pi}{T}\left(t - \frac{x \sin \phi + z \cos \phi}{V_1}\right). \end{aligned} \right\} \quad (13)$$

Now a magnetic force is necessarily connected with the electric force in the incident wave, and from the fundamental equations (18) on page 269, and (12) above, the components of this force are found to be

$$\left. \begin{aligned} \alpha_e &= -E_s \cdot \cos \phi \sqrt{\epsilon_1} \cos \frac{2\pi}{T}\left(t - \frac{x \sin \phi + z \cos \phi}{V_1}\right), \\ \beta_e &= +E_p \cdot \sqrt{\epsilon_1} \cos \frac{2\pi}{T}\left(t - \frac{x \sin \phi + z \cos \phi}{V_1}\right), \\ \gamma_e &= +E_s \cdot \sin \phi \sqrt{\epsilon_1} \cos \frac{2\pi}{T}\left(t - \frac{x \sin \phi + z \cos \phi}{V_1}\right). \end{aligned} \right\} \quad (14)$$

If $E_s = 0$, $E_p > 0$, then $\alpha_e = \gamma_e = 0$, and β_e differs from zero, i.e. the amplitude E_p of the electric force, which lies in the plane of incidence, gives rise to a component β_e of the magnetic force which is perpendicular to the plane of incidence. Conversely, the component E_s of the electric force, which is perpendicular to the plane of incidence, gives rise to a magnetic force which lies in the plane of incidence. This conclusion that the electric and magnetic forces which are inseparably connected are always perpendicular to each other follows from the considerations already given on page 274.

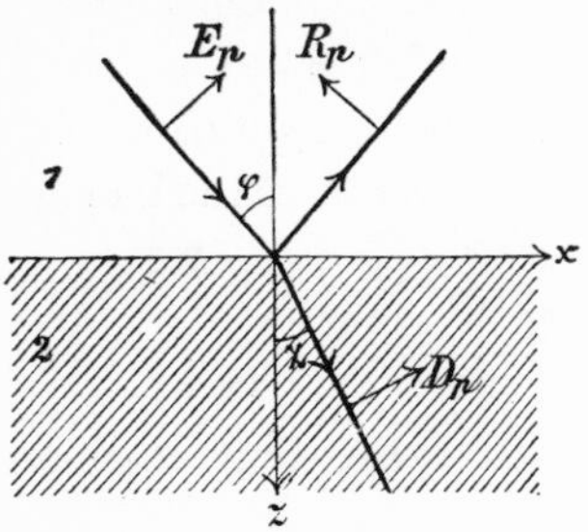

FIG. 83.

When the incident electromagnetic wave reaches the boundary it is divided into a reflected and a refracted wave. The electric forces in the reflected wave can be represented by expressions analogous to those in (11) and (13), namely, by

$$\left.\begin{aligned} X_r &= R_p \cdot \cos\phi' \cdot \cos\frac{2\pi}{T}\left(t - \frac{x\sin\phi' + z\cos\phi'}{V_1}\right), \\ Y_r &= R_s \cdot \cos\frac{2\pi}{T}\left(t - \frac{x\sin\phi' + z\cos\phi'}{V_1}\right), \\ Z_r &= -R_p \cdot \sin\phi' \cos\frac{2\pi}{T}\left(t - \frac{x\sin\phi' + z\cos\phi'}{V_1}\right). \end{aligned}\right\} \quad (15)$$

The corresponding equations for the refracted wave are

$$\left.\begin{aligned} X_2 &= D_p \cdot \cos\chi \cdot \cos\frac{2\pi}{T}\left(t - \frac{x\sin\chi + z\cos\chi}{V_2}\right), \\ Y_2 &= D_s \cdot \cos\frac{2\pi}{T}\left(t - \frac{x\sin\chi + z\cos\chi}{V_2}\right), \\ Z_2 &= -D_p \cdot \sin\chi \cdot \cos\frac{2\pi}{T}\left(t - \frac{x\sin\chi + z\cos\chi}{V_2}\right). \end{aligned}\right\} \quad (16)$$

In these equations R_p, R_s, D_p, D_s denote amplitudes, ϕ' the angle of reflection, i.e. the angle between the $+ z$-axis and the direction of propagation of the reflected wave, χ the angle of refraction.

The corresponding magnetic forces are, cf. (14),

$$\left.\begin{aligned}\alpha_r &= -R_s\cdot\cos\phi'\cdot\sqrt{\epsilon_1}\cdot\cos\frac{2\pi}{T}\left(t-\frac{x\sin\phi'+z\cos\phi'}{V_1}\right),\\ \beta_r &= +R_p\cdot\sqrt{\epsilon_1}\cdot\cos\frac{2\pi}{T}\left(t\ \ldots\ \right),\\ \gamma_r &= +R_s\cdot\sin\phi'\sqrt{\epsilon_1}\cdot\cos\frac{2\pi}{T}\left(t\ \ldots\ \right).\end{aligned}\right\}\quad(17)$$

$$\left.\begin{aligned}\alpha_2 &= -D_s\cdot\cos\chi\cdot\sqrt{\epsilon_2}\cdot\cos\frac{2\pi}{T}\left(t-\frac{x\sin\chi+z\cos\chi}{V_2}\right),\\ \beta_2 &= +D_p\cdot\sqrt{\epsilon_2}\cdot\cos\frac{2\pi}{T}\left(t\ \ldots\ \right),\\ \gamma_2 &= +D_s\cdot\sin\chi\cdot\sqrt{\epsilon_2}\cdot\cos\frac{2\pi}{T}\left(t\ \ldots\ \right).\end{aligned}\right\}\quad(18)$$

On account of the boundary conditions (21) of the previous chapter, there must exist between the electric (or the magnetic) forces certain relations for all values of the time and of the coordinates x and y. Such conditions can only be fulfilled if, for $z = 0$, all forces become proportional to the same function of t, x, y, i.e. the following relations must hold:

$$\frac{\sin\phi}{V_1} = \frac{\sin\phi'}{V_1} = \frac{\sin\chi}{V_2}. \quad . \quad . \quad . \quad . \quad (19)$$

From the first of these equations it follows immediately that $\sin\phi = \sin\phi'$; i.e., since the direction of the reflected ray cannot coincide with that of the incident ray,

$$\cos\phi = -\cos\phi',\ \text{i e.}\ \phi' = \pi - \phi. \quad . \quad . \quad (20)$$

This is the law of reflection, in accordance with which the incident and reflected rays lie symmetrically with respect to the normal at the point of incidence.

The second of equations (19) contains the law of refraction, since from this equation

$$\sin\phi : \sin\chi = V_1 : V_2 = n, \quad . \quad . \quad . \quad . \quad (21)$$

in which n is the index of refraction of medium 2 with respect to medium 1.

The laws of reflection and refraction follow, then, from the fact of the existence of boundary conditions and are altogether independent of the particular form of these conditions.

As to the form of these conditions it is to be noted that here $X_1 = X_e + X_r$, with similar expressions for the other components, since the electric force in medium 1 is due to a superposition of the incident and reflected forces. Hence the boundary conditions (21) on page 272 give, in connection with (20),

$$\left.\begin{aligned} (E_p - R_p)\cos\phi &= D_p \cos\chi, \\ E_s + R_s &= D_s, \\ (E_s - R_s)\sqrt{\epsilon_1}\cos\phi &= D_s\sqrt{\epsilon_2}\cos\chi, \\ (E_p + R_p)\sqrt{\epsilon_1} &= D_p\sqrt{\epsilon_2}. \end{aligned}\right\} \quad . \quad . \quad (22)$$

From this the reflected and refracted amplitudes can be calculated in terms of the incident amplitude. Thus:

$$\left.\begin{aligned} 2E_s &= D_s\left(1 + \frac{\sqrt{\epsilon_2}\cos\chi}{\sqrt{\epsilon_1}\cos\phi}\right), \\ E_s\left(\frac{\sqrt{\epsilon_1}\cos\phi}{\sqrt{\epsilon_2}\cos\chi} - 1\right) &= R_s\left(\frac{\sqrt{\epsilon_1}\cos\phi}{\sqrt{\epsilon_2}\cos\chi} + 1\right), \\ 2E_p &= D_p\left(\frac{\cos\chi}{\cos\phi} + \frac{\sqrt{\epsilon_2}}{\sqrt{\epsilon_1}}\right), \\ E_p\left(\frac{\cos\phi}{\cos\chi} - \frac{\sqrt{\epsilon_1}}{\sqrt{\epsilon_2}}\right) &= R_p\left(\frac{\cos\phi}{\cos\chi} + \frac{\sqrt{\epsilon_1}}{\sqrt{\epsilon_2}}\right). \end{aligned}\right\} \quad . \quad (23)$$

If the ratio $\sqrt{\epsilon_2} : \sqrt{\epsilon_1}$, which, according to (4), is the index of refraction n of medium 2 with respect to 1, be replaced by $\sin\phi : \sin\chi$ [cf. (21)], then (23) may be written in the form

$$\left.\begin{aligned} R_s &= -E_s\frac{\sin(\phi-\chi)}{\sin(\phi+\chi)}, & R_p &= E_p\frac{\tan(\phi-\chi)}{\tan(\phi+\chi)}, \\ D_s &= E_s\frac{2\sin\chi\cos\phi}{\sin(\phi+\chi)}, & D_p &= E_p\frac{2\sin\chi\cos\phi}{\sin(\phi+\chi)\cos(\phi-\chi)}. \end{aligned}\right\} (24)$$

These are Fresnel's reflection equations, from which the phase and the intensity of the reflected light can be calculated in terms of the characteristics of the incident light.

It is seen from (24) that R_s never vanishes, but that R_p becomes zero when

$$\tan(\phi + \chi) = \infty, \quad \phi + \chi = \frac{\pi}{2}, \quad . \quad . \quad . \quad (25)$$

i.e. when the reflected ray is perpendicular to the refracted ray.

In this case it follows from (25) that

$$\sin \chi = \sin\left(\frac{\pi}{2} - \phi\right) = \cos \phi, \text{ or, cf. (21),}$$

$$\tan \phi = n. \quad . \quad . \quad . \quad . \quad . \quad . \quad (25')$$

When, then, the angle of incidence has this value, the electric amplitude in the reflected wave has no component which lies in the plane of incidence, no matter what the nature of the incident light, i.e. no matter what ratio exists between E_s and E_p. Thus if natural light is incident at an angle ϕ which corresponds to (25′), the electric force in the reflected wave has but one component, namely, that perpendicular to the plane of incidence; in other words, it is *plane-polarized*. Now this angle ϕ actually corresponds to Brewster's law given above on page 246. At the same time it now appears, since the plane of incidence was called the plane of polarization, that *in a plane-polarized wave the light vector is perpendicular to the plane of polarization, provided this vector be identified with the electric force.*

On the other hand the light vector would *lie in the plane of polarization if it were identified with the magnetic force*, since, by equation (17) (cf. also page 280), R_p signifies the amplitude of the component of the magnetic force which is perpendicular to the plane of incidence. *Neumann's reflection equations* would follow from the assumption that the magnetic force is the light vector.

The intensities of the reflected electric and magnetic waves are equal. For, given incident light polarized in the plane of incidence, in order to calculate the reflected intensity it is necessary to apply only the first of equations (24), no matter whether the electric or the magnetic force be interpreted as the light vector. For, by (14) on page 279, E_s is in every case the amplitude of the incident light.

On the other hand the signs of the reflected electric and magnetic amplitudes are opposite. This difference does not affect the intensity, which depends upon the square of the amplitude only, but it does affect the phase of the wave. This will be more fully discussed for a particular case.

4. Perpendicular Incidence. Stationary Waves.—Equations (24) become indeterminate when $\phi = 0$, because then χ is also zero. However, in this case, since $\sqrt{\epsilon_1} : \sqrt{\epsilon_2} = n$ and $\cos \phi = \cos \chi = 1$, (23) gives

$$R_s = - E_s \frac{n - 1}{n + 1}, \quad R_p = E_p \frac{n - 1}{n + 1}. \quad . \quad . \quad (26)$$

The first of these equations asserts that, if $n > 1$, *the reflected electric amplitude is of opposite sign to the incident amplitude.* But the second equation asserts the same thing, for, when $\phi = 0$, like signs of R_p and E_p actually denote opposite directions of these amplitudes, as appears from the way in which R_p and E_p are taken positive in Fig. 83 on page 280. The stationary waves (cf. page 155) produced by the interference of the incident and reflected waves must have a node at the reflecting surface, which, to be sure, would be a point of complete rest only if R_s were exactly as large as E_s, i.e. if $n = \infty$. For finite n only a minimum occurs at the mirror, since the reflected amplitude only partially neutralizes the effect of the incident amplitude.

For the magnetic forces, however, E_p and R_p represent the components of the amplitude which are perpendicular to the plane of incidence, i.e. parallel to the y-axis. Like signs of these amplitudes represent actually like directions, so that it follows from the second of equations (26) (also from the first, if the proper interpretation be put upon the direction of the amplitudes in space) that the *reflected magnetic amplitude has the same direction as the incident magnetic amplitude*. Hence stationary magnetic waves have a loop at the mirror itself if $n > 1$.

Wiener's photographic investigation showed that at the bounding surface between glass and metal a node was formed at the surface of the mirror. This indicates that the electric force is the determinative vector for photographic effects, as was even more convincingly proved by the investigation of stationary waves formed in polarized light at oblique incidence (cf. page 251).

5. Polarization of Natural Light by Passage through a Pile of Plates.—From equation (24) it is seen that $R_s : E_s$ continually increases as ϕ increases from zero to $\frac{\pi}{2}$. On the other hand $R_p : E_p$ first decreases, until it reaches a zero value at the polarizing angle, and then increases to the maximum value 1 when $\phi = \frac{\pi}{2}$ (grazing incidence). But for all angles of incidence if $E_s = E_p$, $R_s > R_p$. For, from (24),

$$\frac{R_p}{R_s} = -\frac{E_p}{E_s} \cdot \frac{\cos(\phi + \chi)}{\cos(\phi - \chi)}. \quad . \quad . \quad . \quad . \quad (27)$$

Hence at every angle of incidence natural light is partially (or completely) polarized in the plane of incidence. And since by assumption no light is lost, the refracted light must be partially polarized in a plane perpendicular to the plane of incidence. This explains the polarizing effect of a pile of plates.

Also an application of the last two of equations (24) to the two surfaces of a glass plate gives directly, for the passage of the light through the plate,

$$\frac{D'_s}{D_p} = \frac{E_s}{E_p} \cos^2(\phi - \chi), \quad . \quad . \quad . \quad . \quad (28)$$

in which D'_s, D'_p denote the amplitudes of the ray emerging from the plate. Hence when $E_s = E_p$, it follows from (28) that $D'_s < D'_p$, i.e. incident natural light becomes by passage through the plate partially polarized in a plane perpendicular to the plane of incidence. To be sure, there is no angle ϕ at which this polarization is complete, as is the case for reflection; it is more complete the larger the value of ϕ. If ϕ is equal to the polarizing angle* $\left(\tan \phi = n,\ \phi + \chi = \frac{\pi}{2}\right)$, then, by (28), when $E_s = E_p$,

$$\frac{D'_s}{D'_p} = \sin^2 2\phi = \frac{4n^2}{(1 + n^2)^2}.$$

Hence when $n = 1.5$, $D'_s : D'_p = 0.85$, and the ratio of the intensities $D'^2_s : D'^2_p = 0.73$. After passage through five plates this ratio sinks to $0.73^5 = 0.20$, i.e. the light would still differ considerably from plane-polarized light.

6. Experimental Verification of the Theory.—Equations (24) may be experimentally verified either by comparing the intensities of the reflected and incident light, or more conveniently by measuring the *rotation which the plane of polarization of the incident light undergoes at reflection or refraction.* The amount of this rotation may be calculated from equations (27) or (28).

If the incident light is plane-polarized, the quantity α contained in the expression for the ratio of the components, namely, $E_p : E_s = \tan \alpha$, is the *azimuth of the plane of polarization* of the incident light. The reflected and refracted light is likewise plane-polarized and the azimuth ψ of its plane of polarization is determined by (27) and (28). Thus $\tan \psi = R_p : R_s$. For the measurement of this angle it is convenient to use the apparatus shown on page 258 without the Babinet compensator. The incident light is polarized by means of the Nicol p (*the polarizer*), and the Nicol p' (*the analyzer*) is then turned until the light is extinguished. The value of ψ which corresponds to any particular α can thus be observed.

---

* At this angle the transmitted light is by no means completely polarized.

Both methods furnish satisfactory verification of the laws of reflection; but Jamin found by very careful investigation that, in the neighborhood of the polarizing angle, there is always a departure from those laws, in that the polarization of the reflected light is not strictly plane but somewhat elliptical. Hence it cannot be entirely extinguished by the analyzer unless the compensator is used. The explanation of this phenomenon follows.

7. Elliptic Polarization of the Reflected Light and the Surface or Transition Layer.—The above developments make application of the boundary conditions (21) on page 271 and rest upon the assumption that when light passes from medium 1 to medium 2 there is a discontinuity at the bounding surface. But strictly speaking there is no discontinuity in Nature. Between two media 1 and 2 there must always exist a transition layer within which the dielectric constant varies continuously from ϵ_1 to ϵ_2. This transition layer is indeed very thin, but whether its thickness may be neglected, as has hitherto been done, when so short electromagnetic waves as are the light-waves are under consideration, is very doubtful. Furthermore the thickness of this transition layer between two media is generally increased by polishing the surface.

In any case the actual relations can be better represented if a transition layer be taken into account.

Nevertheless, in order not to unnecessarily complicate the calculation, it may be assumed that the thickness l of this transition layer is so small that all terms of higher order than the first in l may be neglected.

First the boundary conditions which hold for the electric and magnetic forces at the two boundaries of the transition layer will be deduced. These boundaries are defined as the loci of those points at which the dielectric constant first attains the values ϵ_1 and ϵ_2 respectively.

According to the remark of page 267 equations (18) on page 269 hold within the transition layer also.

If the fourth and fifth of these equations (18) be multiplied by an element dz of the thickness of the transition layer, and integrated between the two boundaries 1 and 2, there results, since the quantities involved do not depend upon y, provided y be taken perpendicular to the plane of incidence,

$$\left.\begin{aligned} \frac{1}{c}\frac{\partial}{\partial t}\int_1^2 \alpha \cdot dz &= Y_2 - Y_1, \\ \frac{1}{c}\frac{\partial}{\partial t}\int_1^2 \beta dz &= \int_1^2 \frac{\partial Z}{\partial x} dz - (X_2 - X_1). \end{aligned}\right\} \quad . \quad (29)$$

Now, by (21) and (21′) on pages 271 and 272, α, β, and ϵZ are approximately constant within the transition layer, so that α, β, and ϵZ may be placed before the sign of integration in the above equations and replaced by α_2, β_2, $\epsilon_2 Z_2$ (or by α_1, β_1, $\epsilon_1 Z_1$). Thus

$$\int \alpha \cdot dz = \alpha \int dz, \quad \int_1^2 \frac{\partial Z}{\partial x} dz = \epsilon_2 \frac{\partial Z_2}{\partial x} \int_1^2 \frac{dz}{\epsilon}.$$

Introducing the abbreviation

$$\int_1^2 dz = l, \quad \int_1^2 \epsilon dz = p, \quad \int_1^2 \frac{dz}{\epsilon} = q, \quad . \quad . \quad (30)$$

in which l denotes the thickness of the transition layer and ϵ its dielectric constant at the point corresponding to the element dz of the thickncss, equations (29) become

$$X_1 = X_2 + \frac{l}{c}\frac{\partial \beta_2}{\partial t} - \epsilon_2 \frac{\partial Z_2}{\partial x} q, \quad Y_1 = Y_2 - \frac{l}{c}\frac{\partial \alpha_2}{\partial t}. \quad (31)$$

Likewise the first two of equations (18) give, after multiplication by dz, integration, and treatment as above,

$$\alpha_1 = \alpha_2 - l\frac{\partial \gamma_2}{\partial x} - \frac{p}{c}\frac{\partial Y_2}{\partial t}, \quad \beta_1 = \beta_2 + \frac{p}{c}\frac{\partial X_2}{\partial t}. \quad . \quad (32)$$

Equations (31) and (32) take the place of the previous boundary conditions (21) on page 271.

To determine the electric and magnetic forces in media 1 and 2, equations (11), (13), (14), (15), (16), (17), (18) of this chapter may be used, but with the limitation that the forces in the reflected and refracted wave must differ in phase from the incident wave by an amount which must be deduced from equations (31) and (32). Without such a difference of phase these equations cannot be satisfied.

Now these differences of phase may be most simply taken into account in the following way: Write, for instance [cf. equations (15), page 280],

$$Y_r = R_s \cos\left[\frac{2\pi}{T}\left(t - \frac{x \sin\phi' + z\cos\phi'}{V_1}\right) + \delta\right],$$

then Y_r is the real part of the complex quantity

$$R_s \cdot e^{i\left[\frac{2\pi}{T}\left(t - \frac{x\sin\phi' + z\cos\phi'}{V_1}\right) + \delta\right]}.$$

Writing now

$$R_s \cdot e^{i\delta} = \mathrm{R}_s, \quad . \quad . \quad . \quad . \quad . \quad . \quad (33)$$

then

$$Y_r = \Re\left\{\mathrm{R}_s \cdot e^{i\frac{2\pi}{T}\left(t - \frac{x\sin\phi' + z\cos\phi'}{V_1}\right)}\right\}, \quad . \quad . \quad (34)$$

in which the symbol $\Re$ means that the real part of the complex quantity which follows it is to be taken. This complex quantity within the brackets contains the amplitude R_s which is also complex, *so that an advance in phase δ which occurs in Y_r may be represented by setting Y_r equal to the real part of an exponential function containing a complex factor* (*complex amplitude*). The other electric and magnetic forces may be treated in the same way.

Instead of performing the calculations with the real parts only of the complex quantities, it is possible, when only linear equations (or linear differential equations) are involved, to first set the electric and magnetic forces equal to the complex quantities and, at the end of the calculation, to take the real parts only into consideration in determining the physical meaning.

Thus in the previous equations (11), (13), (14), (15), (16), (17), (18) for the electric and magnetic forces, the real amplitudes E_s, E_p, R_s, R_p, etc., will be replaced by the complex amplitudes E_s, E_p, R_s, R_p, etc., and the cosines by the exponential expression (cf. equation (34)). Then the boundary conditions (31) and (32) give, since they are to hold for $z = 0$, and since $X_1 = X_e + X_r$, $\alpha_1 = \alpha_e + \alpha_r$, etc.,

$$\left.\begin{aligned}
(E_p - R_p)\cos\phi &= D_p\left[\cos\chi + i\frac{2\pi}{T}\left(\sqrt{\epsilon_2}\frac{l}{c} - \frac{\sin^2\chi}{V_2}\epsilon_2 q\right)\right],\\
E_s + R_s &= D_s\left[1 + i\frac{2\pi}{T}\cos\chi\sqrt{\epsilon_2}\frac{l}{c}\right],\\
(E_s - R_s)\sqrt{\epsilon_1}\cos\phi &= D_s\left[\sqrt{\epsilon_2}\cos\chi - i\frac{2\pi}{T}\left(\frac{\sin^2\chi}{V_2}\sqrt{\epsilon_2}\,l - \frac{p}{c}\right)\right],\\
(E_p + R_p)\sqrt{\epsilon_1} &= D_p\left[\sqrt{\epsilon^2} + i\frac{2\pi}{T}\cos\chi\frac{p}{c}\right].
\end{aligned}\right\} \quad (35)$$

From these equations R_s, R_p, D_s, D_p may be calculated in terms of E_s and E_p. It is the reflected light only which is here of interest. If the product Tc be replaced by λ, the wave length in vacuo of the light considered, and if V_2 be replaced by $c : \sqrt{\epsilon_2}$, then, from (35),

$$\left.\begin{aligned}
\frac{R_p}{E_p} &= \frac{\cos\phi\sqrt{\epsilon_2} - \cos\chi\sqrt{\epsilon_1} + i\frac{2\pi}{\lambda}\left[p\cos\phi\cos\chi - (l - q\epsilon_2\sin^2\chi)\sqrt{\epsilon_1\epsilon_2}\right]}{\cos\phi\sqrt{\epsilon_2} + \cos\chi\sqrt{\epsilon_1} + i\frac{2\pi}{\lambda}\left[p\cos\phi\cos\chi + (l - q\epsilon_2\sin^2\chi)\sqrt{\epsilon_1\epsilon_2}\right]},\\
\frac{R_s}{E_s} &= \frac{\cos\phi\sqrt{\epsilon_1} - \cos\chi\sqrt{\epsilon_2} + i\frac{2\pi}{\lambda}\left[l\cos\phi\cos\chi\sqrt{\epsilon_1\epsilon_2} - p + l\epsilon_2\sin^2\chi\right]}{\cos\phi\sqrt{\epsilon_1} + \cos\chi\sqrt{\epsilon_2} + i\frac{2\pi}{\lambda}\left[l\cos\phi\cos\chi\sqrt{\epsilon_1\epsilon_2} + p - l\epsilon_2\sin^2\chi\right]}.
\end{aligned}\right\} \quad (36)$$

Now it is to be remembered that the terms which contain the factor $i\frac{2\pi}{\lambda}$ are very small correction terms, since they are proportional to the thickness l of the transition layer. Hence if the expressions (36) be developed to terms of the first power only of the ratio $l : \lambda$, there results

$$\left.\begin{aligned}
\frac{R_p}{E_p} &= \frac{\cos\phi\sqrt{\epsilon_2} - \cos\chi\sqrt{\epsilon_1}}{\cos\phi\sqrt{\epsilon_2} + \cos\chi\sqrt{\epsilon_1}}\left\{1 + i\frac{4\pi}{\lambda}\cos\phi\sqrt{\epsilon_1}\frac{p\cos^2\chi - l\epsilon_2 + q\epsilon_2^2\sin^2\chi}{\epsilon_2\cos^2\phi - \epsilon_1\cos^2\chi}\right\},\\
\frac{R_s}{E_s} &= \frac{\cos\phi\sqrt{\epsilon_1} - \cos\chi\sqrt{\epsilon_2}}{\cos\phi\sqrt{\epsilon_1} + \cos\chi\sqrt{\epsilon_2}}\left\{1 + i\frac{4\pi}{\lambda}\cos\phi\sqrt{\epsilon_1}\frac{l\epsilon_2 - p}{\epsilon_1\cos^2\phi - \epsilon_2\cos^2\chi}\right\}.
\end{aligned}\right\} \quad (37)$$

The denominator of the correction term which appears in the second of these equations can never vanish, i.e. $\epsilon_1 \cos^2 \phi$ can never be equal to $\epsilon_2 \cos^2 \chi$, for if $\epsilon_2 > \epsilon_1$, then always $\phi > \chi$, and hence $\cos \phi < \cos \chi$. But the denominator of the correction term of the first of equations (37) does vanish if

$$\cos \phi \sqrt{\epsilon_2} = \cos \chi \sqrt{\epsilon_1}. \quad . \quad . \quad . \quad . \quad (38)$$

A simple transformation of (38) shows, since $\sqrt{\epsilon_2} : \sqrt{\epsilon_1} = n$, that this condition is fulfilled for the polarizing angle $\bar{\phi}$, which, according to Brewster's law, is determined by $\tan \bar{\phi} = n$. Hence for this angle of incidence it follows from (37), or also directly from (36), that

$$\frac{R_p}{E_p} = i\frac{4\pi}{\lambda} \cos \phi \sqrt{\epsilon_1} \frac{p \cos^2 \chi - l\epsilon_2 + g\epsilon_2^2 \sin^2 \chi}{(\cos \phi \sqrt{\epsilon_2} + \cos \chi \sqrt{\epsilon_1})^2}. \quad (39)$$

Equations (37) can be further simplified by consideration of the law of refraction, namely,

$$\sin \phi : \sin \chi = n = \sqrt{\epsilon_2} : \sqrt{\epsilon_1}. \quad . \quad . \quad . \quad (40)$$

For from this it follows that

$$\left.\begin{aligned} \epsilon_1 \cos^2 \phi - \epsilon_2 \cos^2 \chi &= \epsilon_1 - \epsilon_2, \\ \epsilon_2 \cos^2 \phi - \epsilon_1 \cos^2 \chi &= \frac{\epsilon_1 - \epsilon_2}{\epsilon_2} (\epsilon_1 \sin^2 \phi - \epsilon_2 \cos^2 \phi) \end{aligned}\right\} . \quad (41)$$

Now the nature of the reflected light is completely determined by the ratio $R_p : R_s$. Assume that the incident light is plane-polarized at an azimuth of 45° to the plane of incidence (cf. page 286). Then $E_p = E_s$, and from (37) it follows, in consideration of (40) and (41), that

$$\frac{R_p}{R_s} = -\frac{\cos(\phi+\chi)}{\cos(\phi-\chi)} \left\{ 1 + i\frac{4\pi}{\lambda} \cdot \frac{\epsilon_2 \sqrt{\epsilon_1}}{\epsilon_1 - \epsilon_2} \cdot \frac{\cos \phi \sin^2 \phi}{\epsilon_1 \sin^2 \phi - \epsilon_2 \cos^2 \phi} \eta \right\}, \quad (42)$$

in which η is an abbreviation for

$$\eta = p - l(\epsilon_1 + \epsilon_2) + q\epsilon_1\epsilon_2. \quad . \quad . \quad . \quad (43)$$

At the polarizing angle ($\tan \bar{\phi} = n$) (42) assumes the value

$$\frac{R_p}{R_s} = i\frac{\pi}{\lambda} \frac{\sqrt{\epsilon_1 + \epsilon_2}}{\epsilon_1 - \epsilon_2} \eta, \quad . \quad . \quad . \quad . \quad . \quad (44)$$

as is seen most easily from (39) by dividing it by the second of equations (37) and retaining terms of the first order only in $\eta : \lambda$.

In order now to recognize the physical significance of (42) and (44) it must be borne in mind that, according to (33),

$$\mathrm{R_p} = R_p \cdot e^{i\delta_p}, \quad \mathrm{R_s} = R_s \cdot e^{i\delta_s}, \quad . \quad . \quad . \quad (45)$$

in which R_p and R_s are the components which are respectively parallel and perpendicular to the plane of incidence of the amplitude of the reflected electric force, and δ_p and δ_s are the advances in phase of these components with respect to the incident wave. Hence

$$\frac{\mathrm{R_p}}{\mathrm{R_s}} = \frac{R_p}{R_s} e^{i(\delta_p - \delta_s)} = \rho \cdot e^{i\Delta}, \quad . \quad . \quad . \quad . \quad (46)$$

in which ρ *is the ratio of the amplitudes and* Δ *the difference in phase of the two components.* Hence, from (44), it follows that at the polarizing angle $\bar{\phi}$

$$\bar{\rho} = \frac{\pi}{\lambda} \eta \frac{\sqrt{\epsilon_1 + \epsilon_2}}{\epsilon_1 - \epsilon_2}, \quad \Delta = \pi/2, \quad . \quad . \quad . \quad (47)$$

i.e. the reflected light is not plane-polarized in the plane of incidence as it was above shown to be when the transition layer was not considered, but it is *elliptically polarized.* The principal axes of the ellipse are parallel and perpendicular to the plane of incidence (cf. page 249) and their ratio is $\bar{\rho}$. $\bar{\rho}$ will be called the *coefficient of ellipticity.* By (43), (47), and (30) this may be written

$$\bar{\rho} = \frac{\pi}{\lambda} \frac{\sqrt{\epsilon_1 + \epsilon_2}}{\epsilon_1 - \epsilon_2} \cdot \int \frac{(\epsilon - \epsilon_1)(\epsilon - \epsilon_2)}{\epsilon} dz, \quad . \quad (48)$$

in which the integration is to be extended through the transition layer between the two media.

According to (48) $\bar{\rho}$ is positive if the value of the dielectric constant ϵ of the transition layer varies continuously between the limiting values ϵ_1 and ϵ_2, and if $\epsilon_2 > \epsilon_1$. But if at any point within the transition layer $\epsilon > \epsilon_1$ and also $\epsilon > \epsilon_2$, then $\bar{\rho}$

is negative when $\epsilon_2 > \epsilon_1$. The relations are inverted when $\epsilon_1 > \epsilon_2$, i.e. when the medium producing the reflection has the smaller refractive index. In consideration of the way in which the amplitude R_p is taken positive (cf. Fig. 83, page 280), it is evident that, if the coefficient of ellipticity $\bar{\rho}$ is positive, the direction of rotation of the reflected light in its elliptical vibration form is counter-clockwise to an observer standing in the plane of incidence and looking toward the reflecting surface, provided the incident electrical force makes an angle of 45° with the plane of incidence and is directed from upper left to lower right. But if $\bar{\rho}$ is negative, then when the same conditions exist for the incident electrical force, the direction of rotation of the reflected electrical force is clockwise.

Also for any other angle of incidence the reflected light is always elliptically polarized, even though the incident light is plane-polarized, for there is always a difference of phase Δ between the *p*- and *s*-components, which, according to (42) and (46), has the value

$$\tan \Delta = 4\frac{\pi}{\lambda}\eta\frac{\epsilon_2\sqrt{\epsilon_1}}{\epsilon_1 - \epsilon_2}\frac{\cos\phi\sin^2\phi}{\epsilon_1\sin^2\phi - \epsilon_2\cos^2\phi}, \quad . \quad (49)$$

while the ratio ρ of the amplitudes does not depart appreciably from the normal value

$$\rho = -\frac{\cos(\phi+\chi)}{\cos(\phi-\chi)}, \quad . \quad . \quad . \quad . \quad . \quad (50)$$

which is obtained without the consideration of a surface layer. In consideration of (47), (49) may be written

$$\tan \Delta = 4\bar{\rho}\frac{n^2}{\sqrt{1+n^2}}\frac{\sin\phi\tan\phi}{\tan^2\phi - n^2}. \quad . \quad . \quad (51)$$

On account of the smallness of $\bar{\rho}$ the difference of phase is appreciable only in the neighborhood of the polarizing angle, for which $\tan\phi = n$.

These theoretical conclusions have been completely verified by experiment. For, in the first place, it is observed that when the angle of incidence is that determined by Brewster's law, the reflected light is not completely (though very nearly) plane-polarized, since it is not possible to entirely extinguish it with an analyzing Nicol. The results of the investigation of the elliptic polarization of reflected light by means of the analyzer and compensator (cf. page 255) are in good agreement with equations (50) and (51).

It is further found that the coefficient of ellipticity is smaller the less the reflecting surface has been contaminated by contact with foreign substances. Thus, for example, it is very small at the fresh surfaces of cleavage of crystals, and at the surfaces of liquids which are continually renewed by allowing the liquid to overflow. For polished mirrors $\bar{\rho}$ is considerable. The change in the sign of $\bar{\rho}$ when the relations of the two media are interchanged is in accord with the theory. The theory is also confirmed by the fact that, in the case of reflection from polished surfaces, $\bar{\rho}$ is in general positive. Only in the case of media which have relatively small indices of refraction, like fluor-spar ($n = 1.44$) and hyalite ($n = 1.42$), has $\bar{\rho}$ been observed to be negative. This also might be expected from the theory, provided the index of refraction of the polished transition layer were greater than that of the medium.

For well-cleaned polished glass surfaces, when the reflection takes place in air, the value of $\bar{\rho}$ lies between 0.03 (for heavy flint glass of index $n = 1.75$) and 0.007.

For liquids in contact with air the value of $\bar{\rho}$ does not exceed 0.01. Water has a negative coefficient of ellipticity which, when the surface is thoroughly cleaned, may be as small as 0.00035. There are also so-called neutral liquids like glycerine which produce no elliptic polarization by reflection. According to the theoretical equation given above for the coefficient of ellipticity it is not necessary that these liquids have no transition layer, i.e. that an actual discontinuity occur in the dielectric constants in passing from the air to the liquid. Rather, layers which have intermediate values of the dielectric constant may exist, provided only other layers whose dielectric constant is greater than that of the liquid are also present.

When the coefficient of ellipticity is positive (for reflection in air) *it is possible to determine a lower limit for the thickness of the transition layer.* For evidently, for a given positive value of $\bar{\rho}$, the smallest thickness which the transition layer can have is attained when its dielectric constant is assumed to be a constant whose value is determined by making the factor $\frac{(\epsilon - \epsilon_1)(\epsilon - \epsilon_2)}{\epsilon}$ in equation (48) a maximum. This is the case when $\epsilon = \sqrt{\epsilon_1 \epsilon_2}$, i.e. when the dielectric constant of the transition layer is a geometrical mean of the dielectric constants of the two media. Hence, from (48), the lower limit $\bar{l}$ for the thickness of the transition layer is given by

$$\frac{\bar{l}}{\lambda} = \frac{\bar{\rho}}{\pi \sqrt{\epsilon_1 + \epsilon_2}} \cdot \frac{\sqrt{\epsilon_2} + \sqrt{\epsilon_1}}{\sqrt{\epsilon_2} - \sqrt{\epsilon_1}} = \frac{\bar{\rho}}{\pi \sqrt{1 + n^2}} \frac{n + 1}{n - 1}, \quad . \quad (52)$$

in which n denotes the index of refraction of the medium 2 with respect to the medium 1 (air). Thus for flint glass, for which $n = 1.75$, $\bar{\rho} = 0.03$ (cf. page 294), $\bar{l} : \lambda = 0.0175$. *Hence the assumption of a transition layer of very small thickness is sufficient to account for a very strong elliptic polarization in reflected light.*

8. Total Reflection.—Consider again the case in which the light incident in medium 1 is reflected from the surface of medium 2. If the index n of 2 with respect to 1 is less than 1, the angle of refraction χ which corresponds to the angle of incidence ϕ is not real if

$$\sin \chi = \frac{\sin \phi}{n} > 1. \quad . \quad . \quad . \quad . \quad . \quad . \quad (53)$$

At this angle of incidence ϕ there is then no refracted light, but all of the incident light is reflected (total reflection).

In order to determine in this case the relation between the nature of the reflected light and that of the incident light, the method used in § 3 of this chapter must be followed. The discussion and the conclusions there given are applicable. In order to avoid the use of the angle of refraction χ in equations (22), (23), and (24), $\sin\chi$ may be regarded as an abbreviation for $\sin\phi : n$, so that $\cos\chi$ may be replaced by

$$\cos\chi = \sqrt{1 - \frac{\sin^2\phi}{n^2}}.$$

If $\sin\phi > n$, this quantity is imaginary. In order to bring this out clearly the imaginary unit $\sqrt{-1} = i$ will be introduced, thus:

$$\cos\chi = -i\sqrt{\frac{\sin^2\phi}{n^2} - 1}.^* \quad . \quad . \quad . \quad (54)$$

Equations (23) must hold under all circumstances,† for they are deduced from the general boundary conditions for the passage of light through the surface between two isotropic media, and these conditions always hold, whether total reflection occurs or not. But when (54) is substituted in (23) the amplitudes in the reflected light become complex, even when those of the incident light are real. From the physical meaning of a complex amplitude which was brought out on page 289, it is evident that *in total reflection the reflected light has suffered a change of phase with respect to the incident light.*

In order to calculate this change of phase, write, in accordance with (45), for the reflected amplitudes which appear in (23) the complex quantities $R_p e^{i\delta_p}$, $R_s e^{i\delta_s}$, so that from (23) and (54), since $\sqrt{\epsilon_2} : \sqrt{\epsilon_1} = n$,

$$\left.\begin{aligned} E_s\left(\frac{i\cos\phi}{\sqrt{\sin^2\phi - n^2}} - 1\right) &= R_s \cdot e^{i\delta}\left(\frac{i\cos\phi}{\sqrt{\sin^2\phi - n^2}} + 1\right), \\ E_p\left(\frac{i\cos\phi \cdot n}{\sqrt{\sin^2\phi - n^2}} - \frac{1}{n}\right) &= R_p \cdot e^{\delta}\left(\frac{i\cos\phi \cdot n}{\sqrt{\sin^2\phi - n^2}} + \frac{1}{n}\right). \end{aligned}\right\} \quad (55)$$

* Cos χ must be an imaginary with a negative sign. According to the conditions which are to be fulfilled, either a positive or a negative value of $\cos\chi$ would be possible. This could be physically realized only if the medium 2 were a plate upon both sides of which light were incident at the same angle ϕ, which must also be greater than the critical angle. This appears from the considerations in § 9.

† The transition layers will here be neglected. They have but a small influence upon total reflection; cf. Drude, Wied. Ann. 43, p. 146, 1891.

In order to obtain the intensities of the reflected light, i.e. the values of R_s^2 and R_p^2, it is only necessary to multiply equations (55) by the conjugate complex equations, i.e. by those equations which are obtained from (55) by substituting $-i$ for i.* The result is

$$E_s^2 = R_s^2, \quad E_p^2 = R_p^2, \quad . \quad . \quad . \quad . \quad (56)$$

i.e. the intensity of the reflected light is equal to that of the incident light (total reflection). This holds also for each of the components (the s and p) separately.

The absolute differences of phase δ_s and δ_p will not be discussed, but the relative difference $\Delta = \delta_p - \delta_s$ is of interest because, according to page 292, the vibration form of the reflected light is obtained from it. Division of the first of equations (55) by the second gives, when $E_s = E_p$, i.e. when the incident light is plane-polarized at an azimuth of 45° with respect to the plane of incidence, since then, according to (56), $R_s = R_p$,

$$\left.\frac{i\cos\phi - \sqrt{\sin^2\phi - n^2}}{i\cos\phi\cdot n - \frac{1}{n}\sqrt{\sin^2\phi - n^2}} = e^{i(\delta_s - \delta_p)}\frac{i\cos\phi + \sqrt{\sin^2\phi - n^2}}{i\cos\phi\cdot n + \frac{1}{n}\sqrt{\sin^2\phi - n^2}}\right\} . \quad (57)$$

From this it follows that

$$e^{i\Delta} = e^{i(\delta_p - \delta_s)} = \frac{\sin^2\phi + i\cos\phi\sqrt{\sin^2\phi - n^2}}{\sin^2\phi - i\cos\phi\sqrt{\sin^2\phi - n^2}}.$$

Hence

$$\frac{1 - e^{i\Delta}}{1 + e^{i\Delta}} = \frac{-i\cos\phi\sqrt{\sin^2\phi - n^2}}{\sin^2\phi}.$$

If this equation be multiplied by the conjugate complex expression, there results, since $e^{i\Delta} + e^{-i\Delta} = 2\cos\Delta$,

$$\frac{1 - \cos\Delta}{1 + \cos\Delta} = \left\{\frac{\cos\phi\sqrt{\sin^2\phi - n^2}}{\sin^2\phi}\right\}^2,$$

* Every equation between complex quantities can be replaced by the conjugate complex equation; for the real and the imaginary parts of both sides of such equations are separately equal to each other.

i.e.

$$\tan \tfrac{1}{2}\Delta = \frac{\cos \phi \sqrt{\sin^2 \phi - n^2}}{\sin^2 \phi}. \quad . \quad . \quad . \quad (58)$$

From this it appears that the relative difference of phase Δ is zero for grazing incidence $\phi = \frac{1}{2}\pi$, as well as for the critical angle $\sin \phi = n$; but for intermediate values of the angle of incidence it is not zero, i.e. *the reflected light is elliptically polarized* when the incident light is plane-polarized. A differentiation of (58) with respect to ϕ gives

$$\frac{1}{2 \cos^2 \frac{1}{2}\Delta} \frac{\partial \Delta}{\partial \phi} = \frac{2n^2 - \sin^2 \phi(1 + n^2)}{\sin^3 \phi \sqrt{\sin^2 \phi - n^2}}.$$

Hence it follows that the relative difference of phase Δ is a maximum for that angle of incidence ϕ' which satisfies the equation

$$\sin^2 \phi' = \frac{2n^2}{1 + n^2}. \quad . \quad . \quad . \quad . \quad . \quad (59)$$

Hence the maximum value Δ' of the difference of phase is given, according to (58), by

$$\tan \tfrac{1}{2}\Delta' = \frac{1 - n^2}{2n}. \quad . \quad . \quad . \quad . \quad . \quad (60)$$

For glass whose index is 1.51, i.e. for the case in which $n = 1 : 1.51$ (since the reflection takes place in glass, not in air), it follows from (59) that $\phi' = 51° \, 20'$, and from (60) that $\Delta' = 45° \, 36'$. Δ has exactly the value 45° both for $\phi = 48° \, 37'$ and for $\phi = 54° \, 37'$. Two total reflections at either of these angles of incidence produce circularly polarized light, provided the incident light is plane-polarized in the azimuth 45° with respect to the plane of incidence, i.e. provided $E_s = E_p$ and $R_s = R_p$. Such a twofold double reflection can be produced by Fresnel's rhomb, which consists of a parallelopiped of glass of the form shown in Fig. 84. When the light falls normally upon one end of the rhomb

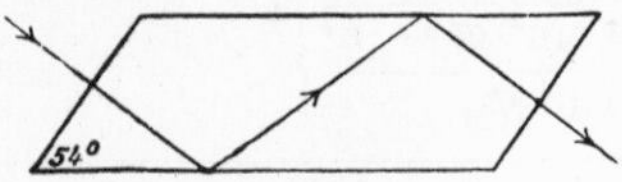

FIG. 84.

and is plane-polarized in the azimuth 45° with respect to the plane of incidence, the emergent light is circularly polarized.

Circular polarization can also be obtained by a threefold, fourfold, etc., total reflection at other angles of incidence. The glass parallelopipeds which must be used in these cases have other angles, for example 69° 12′, 74° 42′, etc., when the index of the glass is 1.51.

9. Penetration of the Light into the Second Medium in the Case of Total Reflection.—In the above discussion the reflected light only was considered. Nevertheless in the second medium the light vector is not zero, since equations (23) on page 282 give appreciable values for D_s and D_p. The amplitude decreases rapidly as z increases, i.e. as the distance from the surface increases, for by (16) and (18) on pages 280 and 281 the electric and magnetic forces in the second medium are proportional to the real parts of the complex quantities

$$e^{i\frac{2\pi}{T}\left(t-\frac{x\sin\chi+z\cos\chi}{V_2}\right)}, \quad . \quad . \quad . \quad . \quad . \quad (61)$$

which, when χ is eliminated by means of equations (53) and (54), takes the form

$$e^{-\frac{2\pi}{TV_2}\sqrt{\frac{\sin^2\phi}{n^2}-1}\cdot z}\cdot e^{i\frac{2\pi}{T}\left(t-\frac{x\sin\phi}{nV_2}\right)}. \quad . \quad . \quad . \quad (62)$$

Thus for values of z which are not infinitely large with respect to the wave length $TV_2=\lambda_2$ in the second medium, the amplitude is not strictly zero.

This appears at first sight to be a contradiction of the conclusion that the intensity of the reflected light is equal to the intensity of the incident light, for whence comes the energy of the refracted light?

This contradiction vanishes when the flow of energy through the bounding surface is considered. According to equation (24) on page 272 this flow is, since in this case $\cos(nx)=\cos(ny)=0$, $\cos(nz)=1$,

$$\frac{4\pi}{c}\cdot\frac{\partial\mathfrak{E}}{\partial t}dt=dt\int(\beta_2X_2-\alpha_2Y_2)dS. \quad . \quad . \quad (63)$$

If now the electric and magnetic forces be taken as the real parts of the complex quantities which are obtained from the right-hand sides of equations (16) and (18) on page 280 by replacing the factor $\cos \frac{2\pi}{T}(t\ .\ .\ .)$ by $e^{i\frac{2\pi}{T}(t\ .\ .\ .)}$, it is clear that, on account of the factor $\cos \chi$, which by (54) is purely imaginary, α_2 has a difference of phase $\frac{\pi}{2}$ with respect to Y_2, and β_2 a difference of phase $\frac{\pi}{2}$ with respect to X_2, so that by writing

$$Y_2 = a \cos\left(\frac{2\pi t}{T} + \delta\right),$$

in which a and δ no longer contain the time, the magnetic force α_2 takes the form

$$\alpha_2 = a' \cdot \sin\left(\frac{2\pi t}{T} + \delta\right).$$

Hence if $\alpha_2 Y_2 dt$, contained in the expression (63) for the energy flow, be integrated between the limits $t = 0$ and $t = T$, there results

$$\int_0^T \alpha_2 Y_2 dt = aa' \int_0^T \sin\left(\frac{2\pi t}{T} + \delta\right) \cdot \cos\left(\frac{2\pi t}{T} + \delta\right) \cdot dt$$
$$= \frac{aa' \cdot T}{4\pi}\left[\sin^2\left(\frac{2\pi t}{T} + \delta\right)\right]_0^T = 0.$$

In the same way the integral of $\beta_2 X_2 dt$ vanishes. Thus, on the whole, during a complete period, no energy passes from medium 1 to medium 2. Hence the reflected light contains the entire energy of the incident light.

That no energy passes through the xz-plane appears plausible from (62). For this equation represents waves which are propagated along the x-axis. But from equation (24) on page 272 there is an actual flow of energy into medium 2 when the direction of flow (i.e. the normal n) is parallel to the x-axis. There is then a passage of energy into medium 2 at one end of the incident wave, i.e. when x is negative, but this energy is carried back again into medium 1 by the waves of medium 2 at the other end of the wave, i.e. when x is positive.

These waves of variable amplitude possess still another peculiarity: *they are not transverse waves.* For it follows from (62) that they are propagated along the x-axis; hence if they were transverse, X_2 would of necessity be equal to zero. But this is not the case. This is no contradiction of the Fresnel-Arago experiments given on page 247 which were used as proof of the transverse nature of light; for those experiments relate to waves of constant amplitude. Quincke's investigation, showing that these waves of variable amplitude may be transformed into waves of constant amplitude when the thickness of medium 2 is small, i.e. when it is of the order of magnitude of the wave length of light, may be looked upon as proof that, in the case of total reflection, the light vector in the second medium is not zero. As a matter of fact, if medium 2 is a very thin film between two portions of medium 1, no total reflection takes place, for, in the limit, the thickness of this film is zero, so that the incident light must pass on undisturbed, since the homogeneity of the medium is not disturbed. As soon as the medium 2 becomes so thin as to appear transparent, then it is evident that, even at angles larger than the critical angle, the reflected light must lose something of its intensity. All the characteristics of this case can be theoretically deduced by simply applying upon both sides of film 2 the universally applicable boundary conditions (21) on page 271.*

10. Application of Total Reflection to the Determination of Index of Refraction.—When the incident beam lies in the more strongly refracting medium, if the angle of incidence be gradually increased, the occurrence of total reflection is made evident by a sudden increase in the intensity of the reflected light, and the complete disappearance of the refracted light. But it is to be remarked that the curves connecting the inten-

* Cf. Winkelmann's Handbuch, Optik, p. 780.

sities of the reflected and refracted light with the angle of incidence ϕ have no discontinuity at the point at which ϕ reaches the critical angle. Nevertheless these curves vary so rapidly with ϕ in this neighborhood that there is an apparent discontinuity which makes it possible to determine accurately the critical angle ϕ and hence the index of refraction.* Thus, for instance, for glass of index $n = 1.51$ the following relations exist between the intensity R_p^2 of the reflected light and the angle of incidence ϕ (E_p^2 is set equal to 1, ζ is the angle in minutes of arc by which ϕ is smaller than the critical angle):

ζ	0′	2′	4′	8′	15′	30′
R_p^2	1	0.74	0.64	0.53	0.43	0.25.

11. The Intensity of Light in Newton's Rings.—The intensities of the reflected and transmitted light will be calculated for the case of a plate of dielectric constant ϵ_2 and thickness d surrounded by a medium of dielectric constant ϵ_1. Let the first surface of the plate upon which the light falls be the xy-plane, the second surface the plane $z = d$.

For the sake of simplicity the incidence will be assumed to be normal and the incident light to satisfy the equations

$$X_e = 0, \quad Y_e = E \cdot e^{i\, 2\pi/T(t - z/V_1)}, \quad Z_e = 0. \quad . \quad (64)$$

Setting $X_e = 0$ places no limitation upon the generality of the conclusions, since, at perpendicular incidence, all results which hold for the y-component of the light vector hold without change for the x-component also.

According to equations (14) on page 279, if (64) represents the electric force, the incident magnetic force is represented by

$$\alpha_e = -E\sqrt{\epsilon_1} e^{i\, 2\pi/T(t - z/V_1)}, \quad \beta_e = 0, \quad \gamma_e = 0. \quad . \quad (65)$$

* For the construction of total refractometers and reflectometers for this purpose, cf. Winkelmann's Handbuch, Optik, p. 312.

By equations (15) and (17) on pages 280 and 281, the reflected electric and magnetic forces in medium 1 are represented by

$$\left.\begin{array}{l} X_r = 0, \quad Y_r = \mathrm{R}e^{i\,2\pi/T\,(t+z/V_1)}, \quad Z_r = 0, \\ \alpha_r = \mathrm{R}\sqrt{\epsilon_1}e^{i\,2\pi/T\,(t+z/V_1)}, \quad \beta_r = 0, \quad \gamma_r = 0; \end{array}\right\} . \qquad (66)$$

Now repeated reflections and refractions take place at the surfaces of the plate (cf. above, page 137); but it is not necessary to follow out each one of these separately, since their total effect can be easily brought into the calculation.* This effect consists in the propagation of waves within the plate along both the positive and the negative directions of the z-axis. For the former the following equations hold:

$$\left.\begin{array}{l} X' = 0, \quad Y' = D'e^{i\,2\pi/T\,(t-z/V_2)}, \quad Z' = 0; \\ \alpha' = -D'\sqrt{\epsilon_2}e^{i\,2\pi/T\,(t-z/V_2)}, \quad \beta' = 0, \quad \gamma' = 0; \end{array}\right\} \qquad (67)$$

while for the latter

$$\left.\begin{array}{l} X'' = 0, \quad Y'' = D''e^{i\,2\pi/T\,(t+z/V_2)}, \quad Z'' = 0; \\ \alpha'' = D''\sqrt{\epsilon_2}e^{i\,2\pi/T\,(t+z/V_2)}, \quad \beta'' = 0, \quad \gamma'' = 0. \end{array}\right\} \qquad (68)$$

Let the total effect of all the waves which have passed through the plate be

$$\left.\begin{array}{l} X_d = 0, \quad Y_d = De^{i\,2\pi/T\,(t-z/V_1)}, \quad Z_d = 0, \\ \alpha_d = -D\sqrt{\epsilon_1}e^{i\,2\pi/T\,(t-z/V_1)}, \quad \beta_d = 0, \quad \gamma_d = 0. \end{array}\right\} \qquad (69)$$

It is now necessary to apply at both sides of the plate ($z = 0$, $z = d$) the boundary conditions (21) on page 271, which here take the form

$$Y_e + Y_r = Y' + Y'', \quad \alpha_e + \alpha_r = \alpha' + \alpha'' \quad \text{for } z = 0, \quad . \quad (70)$$

$$Y' + Y'' = Y_d, \quad \alpha' + \alpha'' = \alpha_d \quad \text{for } z = d. \quad . \quad (71)$$

The conditions (70) give

$$E + \mathrm{R} = D' + D'', \quad (E - \mathrm{R})\sqrt{\epsilon_1} = (D' - D'')\sqrt{\epsilon_2}, \quad . \quad (70')$$

* Equations (66) are to represent the total effect of all the separate waves which are propagated in medium 1 along the negative z-axis.

and the conditions (71)

$$\left.\begin{aligned} D'e^{-ip} + D''e^{+ip} &= De^{-iq}, \\ (D'e^{-ip} - D''e^{+ip})\sqrt{\epsilon_2} &= De^{-iq}\sqrt{\epsilon_1}, \end{aligned}\right\} \quad . \quad . \quad (71')$$

in which p and q are abbreviations for

$$p = \frac{2\pi}{T}\cdot\frac{d}{V_2} = 2\pi\frac{d}{\lambda_2}, \quad q = \frac{2\pi}{T}\cdot\frac{d}{V_1} = 2\pi\frac{d}{\lambda_1}. \quad . \quad (72)$$

From (71′) follows at once

$$(D'e^{-ip} + D''e^{+ip})\sqrt{\epsilon_1} = (D'e^{-ip} - D''e^{+ip})\sqrt{\epsilon_2},$$

from which is deduced

$$D'e^{-ip}(\sqrt{\epsilon_2} - \sqrt{\epsilon_1}) = D''e^{+ip}(\sqrt{\epsilon_2} + \sqrt{\epsilon_1}). \quad . \quad . \quad (73)$$

From (70′),

$$\frac{E + R}{E - R} = \frac{D' + D''}{D' - D''}\cdot\frac{\sqrt{\epsilon_1}}{\sqrt{\epsilon_2}},$$

i.e.

$$\frac{R}{E} = \frac{D'(\sqrt{\epsilon_1} - \sqrt{\epsilon_2}) + D''(\sqrt{\epsilon_1} + \sqrt{\epsilon_2})}{D'(\sqrt{\epsilon_1} + \sqrt{\epsilon_2}) + D''(\sqrt{\epsilon_1} - \sqrt{\epsilon_2})}.$$

In consideration of (73) this last may be written

$$\frac{R}{E} = \frac{(e^{+ip} - e^{-ip})(\epsilon_1 - \epsilon_2)}{e^{+ip}(\sqrt{\epsilon_1} + \sqrt{\epsilon_2})^2 - e^{-ip}(\sqrt{\epsilon_1} - \sqrt{\epsilon_2})^2}$$

$$= \frac{i \sin p\cdot(\epsilon_1 - \epsilon_2)}{i \sin p\cdot(\epsilon_1 + \epsilon_2) + 2\sqrt{\epsilon_1\epsilon_2}\cdot\cos p}.$$

In order to obtain the intensity J_r of the reflected light, this equation must be multiplied by the conjugate complex equation (cf. page 297). Thus, when J_e denotes the intensity of the incident light, there results

$$J_r = J_e\frac{\sin^2 p\,(\epsilon_1 - \epsilon_2)^2}{\sin^2 p\,(\epsilon_1 - \epsilon_2)^2 + 4\epsilon_1\epsilon_2} = J_e\frac{\sin^2 p\,(1 - n^2)^2}{\sin^2 p\,(1 - n^2)^2 + 4n^2}, \quad (74)$$

provided $\epsilon_2 : \epsilon_1 = n^2$, so that n is the index of the plate 2 with respect to medium 1.

From (70′) and (71′) it is easy to deduce the equation

$$\frac{De^{-iq}}{E} = \frac{4\sqrt{\epsilon_1\epsilon_2}}{e^{ip}(\sqrt{\epsilon_1}+\sqrt{\epsilon_2})^2 - e^{-ip}(\sqrt{\epsilon_1}-\sqrt{\epsilon_2})^2}$$

$$= \frac{2\sqrt{\epsilon_1\epsilon_2}}{i \sin p(\epsilon_1+\epsilon_2) + 2\sqrt{\epsilon_1\epsilon_2}\cdot\cos p}.$$

So that the intensity J_d of the transmitted light is

$$J_d = J_e \frac{4\epsilon_1\epsilon_2}{\sin^2 p\,(\epsilon_1-\epsilon_2)^2 + 4\epsilon_1\epsilon_2}. \quad . \quad . \quad . \quad (75)$$

Hence the relation holds

$$J_d + J_r = J_e, \quad . \quad . \quad . \quad . \quad . \quad . \quad (76)$$

as was to be expected, since the plate absorbs no light

According to (74) the reflected light vanishes completely when $p = 0, \pi, 2\pi$, etc., i.e. when the thickness of the plate $d = 0, \frac{1}{2}\lambda_2, \lambda_2, \frac{3}{2}\lambda_2$, etc. This is in agreement with the results deduced from equation (17) on page 139. A maximum of intensity occurs when $\sin p = 1$. Then $J_r = J_e\left(\frac{1-n^2}{1+n^2}\right)^2$. [In the case of normal reflection at one surface only, equation (26) on page 284 gives $J_r = J_e\left(\frac{1-n}{1+n}\right)^2$.]

If media 1 and 2 are air and glass, $n = 1.5$. In the case of Newton's rings these media are glass and air, so that $n = 1 : 1.5$. In both cases equation (74) becomes

$$J_r = J_e \frac{\sin^2 p\cdot 1.56}{\sin^2 p\cdot 1.56 + 9}.$$

Hence, for an approximation, the term $\sin^2 p(1-n^2)^2$ in the denominator of (74) may be neglected in comparison with $4n^2$, so that at a point in the Newton ring apparatus at which the thickness of the air film is d,

$$J_r = J_e\left(\frac{1-n^2}{2n}\right)^2 \sin^2 2\pi\, {}^{d}/_{\lambda}. \quad . \quad . \quad . \quad . \quad (77)$$

λ denotes the wave length in air. If the incident light is white, and if J_λ denotes the intensity in the incident beam of light of wave length λ, then the intensity of the reflected light is, provided dispersion or the dependence of n upon λ be neglected,

$$J_r = \left(\frac{1 - n^2}{2n}\right)^2 \Sigma J_\lambda \sin^2 2\pi \, {}^d/_\lambda. \quad . \quad . \quad . \quad (78)$$

The colors of thin plates are then a mixture composed of pure colors in a manner easily evident from (78).

12. Non-Homogeneous Media: Curved Rays.—The optical properties of a non-homogeneous medium, in which the dielectric constant ϵ is a function of the coordinates x, y, z, will be briefly considered. The most logical way of doing this would be to integrate the differential equations (18) on page 269; for these hold for non-homogeneous media also. To do this ϵ must be given as a function of x, y, and z. This method would give both the paths of the rays and the intensities of the reflections necessarily taking place inside of a non-homogeneous medium. But even with the simplest possible assumption for ϵ this method is complicated and has never yet been carried out. Investigation has been limited to the determination of the form of the rays from Snell's law or Huygens' principle—a process which succeeds at once if the medium be conceived to be composed of thin homogeneous layers having different indices. When the index varies continuously, the ray must of course be curved. Heath * has deduced for its radius of curvature ρ at a point P the equation

$$\frac{1}{\rho} = \frac{d \log n}{d\nu}, \quad . \quad . \quad . \quad . \quad . \quad . \quad (79)$$

in which ν denotes the direction of most rapid change (decreasing) of the index n.

This equation explains the phenomenon of mirage, which is observed when the distribution of the density of the air over

* Heath, Geometrical Optics. Cambridge, 1897.

the earth's surface is abnormal, as is the case over heated deserts. At a certain height above the earth the index n of the air is then a maximum. But in this case, by (79), $\rho = \infty$, i.e. at this height the ray has a point of inflection. Hence two different rays can come from an object to the eye of an observer, who then sees two images of the object, one erect, the other inverted.*

An interesting application of the theory of curved rays has been made by A. Schmidt.† He explains the appearance of the sun by showing that a luminous sphere of gas of the dimensions of the sun, whose *density increases continuously* from without towards the interior, would have sharp limits, as the sun appears to have. For a ray of light which travels towards such a sphere of gas so as to make an angle less than a certain angle ϕ with the line drawn from the observer to the centre of the sphere is deflected toward the centre of the sphere and passes many times around that centre. It thus attains depths from which a continuous spectrum is emitted, for an incandescent gas emits such a spectrum when the pressure is sufficient. But a ray which makes an angle greater than ϕ with a line drawn to the centre of the sphere must again leave the sphere without having traversed intensely luminous layers. Although there is no discontinuity in the sun's density yet it appears as a sharply bounded disc which subtends a visual angle 2ϕ.

For the experimental presentation of curved rays cf. J. Macé de Lépinay and A. Perot (Ann. d. chim. et d. phys. (6) 27, page 94, 1892); also O. Wiener (Wied. Ann. 49, page 105, 1893). The latter has made use of the curved rays in investigations upon diffusion and upon the conduction of heat.

---

* A more complete discussion of these interesting phenomena with the references is given in Winkelmann's Handb., Optik, pp. 344–384.

† A. Schmidt, Die Strahlenbrechung auf der Sonne. Stuttgart, 1891.

CHAPTER III

OPTICAL PROPERTIES OF TRANSPARENT CRYSTALS

1. Differential Equations and Boundary Conditions.—A crystal differs from an isotropic substance in that its properties are different in different directions. Now in the electromagnetic theory the specific properties of a substance depend solely upon its dielectric constant, provided the standpoint taken on page 269, that the permeability of all substances is equal to unity, be maintained.

Now an inspection of the deduction of the differential equations for an isotropic body as given upon pages 269 sq. shows that equations (17) contain only the specific properties of the body, i.e. its dielectric constants. But equations (7) and (11) are also applicable to crystals, as has been already remarked. Hence only equations (17) need to be extended, since in a crystal the dielectric constant depends upon the direction of the electric lines of force. The most general equations for the extension of (17) are

$$\left.\begin{aligned} 4\pi j_x &= \epsilon_{11}\frac{\partial X}{\partial t} + \epsilon_{12}\frac{\partial Y}{\partial t} + \epsilon_{13}\frac{\partial Z}{\partial t}, \\ 4\pi j_y &= \epsilon_{21}\frac{\partial X}{\partial t} + \epsilon_{22}\frac{\partial Y}{\partial t} + \epsilon_{23}\frac{\partial Z}{\partial t}, \\ 4\pi j_z &= \epsilon_{31}\frac{\partial X}{\partial t} + \epsilon_{32}\frac{\partial Y}{\partial t} + \epsilon_{33}\frac{\partial Z}{\partial t}, \end{aligned}\right\} \quad . \quad . \quad (1)$$

since the components of the current must always remain linear functions of $\frac{\partial X}{\partial t}, \frac{\partial Y}{\partial t}, \frac{\partial Z}{\partial t}$. Equations (1) assert that in general in a crystal the direction of a line of current flow does not coincide with the direction of a line of force, since if, for example, Y and Z vanish while X remains finite, j and j_z do not vanish.

Equation (23) on page 272 for the flow of energy may be deduced by multiplying the general equations (9) and (11), namely,

$$\frac{4\pi}{c}j_x = \frac{\partial\gamma}{\partial y} - \frac{\partial\beta}{\partial z}, \ldots \quad \frac{4\pi}{c}s_x = \frac{\partial Y}{\partial z} - \frac{\partial Z}{\partial y}, \ldots$$

by $Xd\tau$, ... $\alpha d\tau$, and integrating with respect to τ. ($d\tau$ represents element of volume.) The result is

$$\frac{4\pi}{c}\int(j_xX + j_yY + j_zZ)d\tau$$

$$+ \frac{4\pi}{c}\int(s_x\alpha + s_y\beta + s_z\gamma)d\tau = \frac{4\pi}{c}\frac{\partial}{\partial t}\int\mathfrak{E}d\tau,$$

in which $\mathfrak{E}$ represents the energy in the volume element $d\tau$. This equation may also be applied to crystals, since the specific properties of the medium do not appear in it. Hence the change in the electromagnetic energy in unit volume with respect to the time is

$$\frac{\partial\mathfrak{E}}{\partial t} = j_xX + j_yY + j_zZ + s_x\alpha + s_y\beta + s_z\gamma.$$

Since the last three of equations (17) on page 269 hold in this case also (when $\mu = 1$) the last three terms of this equation are a differential coefficient with respect to the time, i.e.

$$s_x\alpha + s_y\beta + s_z\gamma = \frac{1}{8\pi}\frac{\partial}{\partial t}(\alpha^2 + \beta^2 + \gamma^2).$$

Consequently $j_xX + j_yY + j_zZ$ must also be a differential coefficient with respect to the time. In order that this may be possible in consideration of (1), the following conditions must be fulfilled:

$$\epsilon_{21} = \epsilon_{12}, \quad \epsilon_{31} = \epsilon_{13}, \quad \epsilon_{23} = \epsilon_{32}, \quad . \quad . \quad . \quad (2)$$

and in this case the part $\mathfrak{E}_1$ of the energy which depends upon the electric forces is

$$\left.\begin{aligned}\mathfrak{E}_1 = \frac{1}{8\pi}(\epsilon_{11}X^2 + \epsilon_{22}Y^2 + \epsilon_{33}Z^2 + 2\epsilon_{23}YZ \\ + 2\epsilon_{31}ZX + 2\epsilon_{12}XY).\end{aligned}\right\} \quad . \quad . \quad (3)$$

By means of a transformation of coordinates $\mathfrak{E}_1$ may always be reduced to the canonical form

$$\mathfrak{E}_1 = \frac{1}{8\pi}(\epsilon_1 X^2 + \epsilon_2 Y^2 + \epsilon_3 Z^2). \quad . \quad . \quad . \quad . \quad (4)$$

When the coordinates have been thus chosen the factors ϵ_h vanish and equations (1) take the simplified form

$$j_x = \frac{\epsilon_1}{4\pi}\frac{\partial X}{\partial t}, \quad j_y = \frac{\epsilon_2}{4\pi}\frac{\partial Y}{\partial t}, \quad j_z = \frac{\epsilon_3}{4\pi}\frac{\partial Z}{\partial t}. \quad . \quad (5)$$

These coordinate axes are characterized by the fact that along their direction the electric current coincides with the direction of the electric force. These rectangular axes will be called *axes of electric symmetry*, since the crystal is symmetrical in its electrical properties with respect to them, or also with respect to the three coordinate planes which they define. ϵ_1, ϵ_2, ϵ_3 signify the dielectric constants corresponding to the three axes of symmetry. They will be called the *principal dielectric constants*.

As was remarked above, the assumption will be made that the permeability of the crystal is the same in all directions. Although this is not rigorously true, as is evident from the tendency shown by a sphere of crystal when hung in a powerful magnetic field to set itself in a particular direction, yet experiment justifies the assumption in the case of light vibrations.*

Hence in the differential equations (18) on page 269, which apply to isotropic media, only such modifications are necessary

* The theoretical reason for setting $\mu = 1$ in the case of the light vibrations will be given later, in Chapter VII.

as are due to the fact that the dielectric constant has different values in different directions. The dielectric constant appears in only the first three of equations (18). These equations assert that the components of the current are proportional to the quantities $\frac{\partial \gamma}{\partial y} - \frac{\partial \beta}{\partial z}$, etc. Since the components of the current in a crystal are given by equations (1) and (5), the general differential equations (7) and (11) of the electromagnetic field on pages 265 and 267 become for a crystal, when its axes of electric symmetry have been chosen as coordinate axes,

$$\frac{\epsilon_1}{c}\frac{\partial X}{\partial t} = \frac{\partial \gamma}{\partial y} - \frac{\partial \beta}{\partial z}, \quad \frac{\epsilon_2}{c}\frac{\partial Y}{\partial t} = \frac{\partial \alpha}{\partial z} - \frac{\partial \gamma}{\partial x}, \quad \frac{\epsilon_3}{c}\frac{\partial Z}{\partial t} = \frac{\partial \beta}{\partial x} - \frac{\partial \alpha}{\partial z}, \qquad (6)$$

$$\frac{1}{c}\frac{\partial \alpha}{\partial t} = \frac{\partial Y}{\partial z} - \frac{\partial Z}{\partial y}, \quad \frac{1}{c}\frac{\partial \beta}{\partial t} = \frac{\partial Z}{\partial x} - \frac{\partial X}{\partial z}, \quad \frac{1}{c}\frac{\partial \gamma}{\partial t} = \frac{\partial X}{\partial y} - \frac{\partial Y}{\partial x}. \qquad (7)$$

When referred to any arbitrary system of coordinates, equations (6) must be replaced by

$$\frac{1}{c}\left(\epsilon_{11}\frac{\partial X}{\partial t} + \epsilon_{12}\frac{\partial Y}{\partial t} + \epsilon_{13}\frac{\partial Z}{\partial t}\right) = \frac{\partial \gamma}{\partial y} - \frac{\partial \beta}{\partial z}, \text{ etc. } . \qquad (6')$$

The conditions which must be fulfilled at the bounding surface between two crystals, or between a crystal and an isotropic medium, for example air, may be obtained from the considerations which were presented in § 8 of Chapter I, page 271. They demand *that, in passing through the boundary, the components of the electric and magnetic forces parallel to the boundary be continuous.*

2. Light-vectors and Light-rays.—In the discussion of isotropic media on page 283 it was shown that different interpretations of optical phenomena are obtained according as the light-vector is identified with the electric or with the magnetic force. Both courses accord with the results of experiment if the phenomena of stationary waves be left out of account. The case is similar in the optics of crystals, save that there is here a third possibility, namely, that of choosing the electric current as the light-vector. Its components are then proportional to $\epsilon_1 \frac{\partial X}{\partial t}$, $\epsilon_2 \frac{\partial Y}{\partial t}$, $\epsilon_3 \frac{\partial Z}{\partial t}$. Thus in the optics of crystals there are three possible theories which differ from one another both as regards the position of the light-vector with respect to the plane of polarization, and also as regards its position with respect to the wave normal in the case of plane waves. As to the latter difference it appears from page 278 that the light-vector is perpendicular to the wave normal in the case of plane waves (i.e. *plane waves are transverse*), if its components, which will here be represented by u, v, and w, satisfy the differential equation

$$\frac{\partial u}{\partial x} + \frac{\partial v}{\partial y} + \frac{\partial w}{\partial z} = 0. \quad . \quad . \quad . \quad . \quad . \quad . \quad (8)$$

Differentiation of equations (7) with respect to x, y, and z and addition of them gives, as above on page 275,

$$\frac{\partial}{\partial t}\left(\frac{\partial \alpha}{\partial x} + \frac{\partial \beta}{\partial y} + \frac{\partial \gamma}{\partial z}\right) = 0, \quad . \quad . \quad . \quad . \quad . \quad (9)$$

i.e. the waves are transverse if the magnetic force is taken as the light-vector.

If the same operation be performed upon the three equations (6), there results

$$\frac{\partial}{\partial x}\left(\epsilon_1 \frac{\partial X}{\partial t}\right) + \frac{\partial}{\partial y}\left(\epsilon_2 \frac{\partial Y}{\partial t}\right) + \frac{\partial}{\partial z}\left(\epsilon_3 \frac{\partial Z}{\partial t}\right) = 0, \quad . \quad . \quad (10)$$

i.e. the waves are likewise transverse if the electric current be interpreted as the light-vector.

But the waves are not transverse if the electric force is taken as the light-vector, since, in consequence of the last equation, because of the differences between ϵ_1, ϵ_2, and ϵ_3, the following inequality exists:

$$\frac{\partial X}{\partial x} + \frac{\partial Y}{\partial y} + \frac{\partial Z}{\partial z} \gtrless 0. \quad . \quad . \quad . \quad . \quad . \quad (11)$$

The plane of polarization is defined by the direction of the wave normal and the magnetic force, as was shown on page 283 to be the case for isotropic media.

Thus the characteristics of the three possible theories of the optics of crystals are the following:

1. *The magnetic force is the light-vector.* Plane waves are transverse; the light-vector lies in the plane of polarization. (Mechanical theory of F. Neumann, G. Kirchhoff, W. Voigt, and others.)

2. *The electric force is the light-vector.* Plane waves are not strictly transverse; the light-vector is almost perpendicular to the plane of polarization. (Mechanical theory of Ketteler, Boussinesq, Lord Rayleigh, and others.)

3. *The electric current is the light-vector.* Plane waves are transverse; the light-vector lies perpendicular to the plane of polarization. (Mechanical theory of Fresnel.)

These differences in the theory cannot lead to observable differences in phenomena so long as the observations of the final light effect are made in an isotropic medium upon advancing, not stationary, waves. No other kinds of observations are possible in the case of crystals. Hence nothing more can be done than to solve each particular problem rigorously, i.e. in consideration of its special boundary conditions.

The system of differential equations and boundary conditions to be treated are then completely determined, and there results one definite value for the electric force in the outer isotropic medium no matter what is interpreted as the light-vector in the crystal. The results which can be tested by experiment are the same whether the magnetic force or the electric force is taken as the light-vector in the outer medium. For, according to the fundamental equations, the intensity of the advancing magnetic wave is always the same as the intensity of the advancing electric wave.

The electromagnetic theory has then the advantage that it includes a number of analytically different theories and shows why they must lead to the same result.

A ray of light was defined on page 273 as the path of the energy flow. According to the equation given on page 310 for the electromagnetic energy in crystals, equation (23) on page 272 for the flow of energy holds for crystals also. The direction cosines of the ray of light are then also in the crystal proportional to the quantities f_x, f_y, f_z, defined in equation (25) on page 273.

The ray of light is then perpendicular both to the electric and to the magnetic force. In general it does not coincide with the *normal* to a plane wave, since from the inequality (11) this normal is not perpendicular to the electric force.

3. Fresnel's Law for the Velocity of Light.—In order to find the velocity of light in crystals, it is necessary to deduce from equations (6) and (7) such differential equations as contain either the electric force alone or the magnetic force alone. The former are obtained by differentiating the three equations (6) with respect to t and substituting for $\frac{\partial\alpha}{\partial t}, \frac{\partial\beta}{\partial t}, \frac{\partial\gamma}{\partial t}$, which appear upon the right-hand side, their values taken from (7). Thus from the first of equations (6)

$$\frac{\epsilon_1}{c^2}\frac{\partial^2 X}{\partial t^2} = \frac{\partial}{\partial y}\left(\frac{\partial X}{\partial y} - \frac{\partial Y}{\partial x}\right) - \frac{\partial}{\partial z}\left(\frac{\partial Z}{\partial x} - \frac{\partial X}{\partial z}\right).$$

The right-hand side of this equation can be written in the more symmetrical form

$$\frac{\epsilon_1}{c^2}\frac{\partial^2 X}{\partial t^2} = \Delta X - \frac{\partial}{\partial x}\left(\frac{\partial X}{\partial x} + \frac{\partial Y}{\partial y} + \frac{\partial Z}{\partial z}\right). \quad . \quad (12)$$

Similarly, from the two other equations of (6),

$$\left.\begin{aligned}\frac{\epsilon_2}{c^2}\frac{\partial^2 Y}{\partial t^2} &= \Delta Y - \frac{\partial}{\partial y}\left(\frac{\partial X}{\partial x} + \frac{\partial Y}{\partial y} + \frac{\partial Z}{\partial z}\right),\\ \frac{\epsilon_3}{c^2}\frac{\partial^2 Z}{\partial t^2} &= \Delta Z - \frac{\partial}{\partial z}\left(\frac{\partial X}{\partial x} + \frac{\partial Y}{\partial y} + \frac{\partial Z}{\partial z}\right).\end{aligned}\right\} \quad . \quad (12)$$

From the discussion of the preceding paragraph it appears that only analytical differences result from differences in the choice of the light-vector. In order to bring the discussion into accord with Fresnel's theory, the light-vector will be assumed to be proportional to the electric current. Let u, v,

w, be the components of the light-vector for plane waves, thus:

$$\left.\begin{aligned} u = \epsilon_1 X = A\mathfrak{M} \cos \frac{2\pi}{T}\left(t - \frac{mx + ny + pz}{V}\right), \\ v = \epsilon_2 Y = A\mathfrak{N} \cos \frac{2\pi}{T}\left(t - \frac{mx + ny + pz}{V}\right), \\ w = \epsilon_3 Z = A\mathfrak{P} \cos \frac{2\pi}{T}\left(t - \frac{mx + ny + pz}{V}\right), \end{aligned}\right\} \quad . \quad (13)$$

in which it is assumed that

$$\mathfrak{M}^2 + \mathfrak{N}^2 + \mathfrak{P}^2 = m^2 + n^2 + p^2 = 1 \quad . \quad . \quad . \quad (14)$$

A denotes then the amplitude of the light-vector, $\mathfrak{M}$, $\mathfrak{N}$, $\mathfrak{P}$ its direction cosines with respect to the axes of electric symmetry, m, n, p the direction cosines of the wave normal, V the velocity of light measured in the direction of the wave normal (the so-called velocity along the normal). On account of equation (10) the relation holds

$$\mathfrak{M}m + \mathfrak{N}n + \mathfrak{P}p = 0, \quad . \quad . \quad . \quad . \quad (15)$$

which signifies that the wave is transverse.

Substitution of the values (13) in (12) gives (C is written for c above)

$$\begin{aligned} \frac{\mathfrak{M}}{C^2} &= \frac{\mathfrak{M}}{\epsilon_1 V^2} - \frac{m}{V^2}\left(\frac{\mathfrak{M}m}{\epsilon_1} + \frac{\mathfrak{N}n}{\epsilon_2} + \frac{\mathfrak{P}p}{\epsilon_3}\right), \\ \frac{\mathfrak{N}}{C^2} &= \frac{\mathfrak{N}}{\epsilon_2 V^2} - \frac{n}{V^2}\left(\frac{\mathfrak{M}m}{\epsilon_1} + \frac{\mathfrak{N}n}{\epsilon_2} + \frac{\mathfrak{P}p}{\epsilon_3}\right), \\ \frac{\mathfrak{P}}{C^2} &= \frac{\mathfrak{P}}{\epsilon_3 V^2} - \frac{p}{V^2}\left(\frac{\mathfrak{M}m}{\epsilon_1} + \frac{\mathfrak{N}n}{\epsilon_2} + \frac{\mathfrak{P}p}{\epsilon_3}\right). \end{aligned}$$

A multiplication of these equations by C^2V^2 and a substitution, for brevity, of

$$C^2 : \epsilon_1 = a^2, \quad C^2 : \epsilon_2 = b^2, \quad C^2 : \epsilon_3 = c^2,^* \quad . \quad (16)$$

$$a^2\mathfrak{M}m + b^2\mathfrak{N}n + c^2\mathfrak{P}p = G^2, \quad . \quad . \quad . \quad (16')$$

---

* The letter c has two meanings in this book. In general c denotes the velocity of light in vacuo. In the section on optics of crystals C will be used to denote this velocity, and c will stand for $C : \sqrt{\epsilon_3}$.

gives

$$\mathfrak{M}(a^2 - V^2) = mG^2, \quad \mathfrak{N}(b^2 - V^2) = nG^2, \quad \mathfrak{P}(c^2 - V^2) = pG^2, \quad (17)$$

i.e.

$$\mathfrak{M} = G^2 \frac{m}{a^2 - V^2}, \quad \mathfrak{N} = G^2 \frac{n}{b^2 - V^2}, \quad \mathfrak{P} = G^2 \frac{p}{c^2 - V^2}. \quad (17')$$

If these last three equations be multiplied by m, n, p, respectively, and added, the left-hand side reduces to zero, because of (15), so that, by dropping the factor G^2, there results

$$\frac{m^2}{a^2 - V^2} + \frac{n^2}{b^2 - V^2} + \frac{p^2}{c^2 - V^2} = 0. \quad . \quad . \quad (18)$$

This equation, which expresses the functional relationship between V^2 and m, n, and p, is of the second degree in V^2. Hence *for every particular direction of the wave normal there are two different values for the velocity*. Equation (18) is called Fresnel's law.

When $m = 1$, $n = p = 0$, the two velocities are $V_1^2 = b^2$, $V_2^2 = c^2$. Thus when the wave normal coincides with one of the axes of electric symmetry of the crystal, two of the quantities a, b, and c represent velocities. Hence a, b, c are called the *principal velocities*.

The same law of velocity (18) results if either the electric or the magnetic force is taken as the light-vector.

4. The Directions of the Vibrations.—Two waves travelling with different velocities correspond to every wave normal. The position in these waves of the characteristic quantity, for example the electric current, is perfectly definite and different in the two waves. Thus if the indices 1 and 2 refer to the two waves respectively, then, from (17′), the position of the light-vector is obtained from

$$\left.\begin{aligned} \mathfrak{M}_1 : \mathfrak{N}_1 : \mathfrak{P}_1 &= \frac{m}{a^2 - V_1^2} : \frac{n}{b^2 - V_1^2} : \frac{p}{c^2 - V_1^2}, \\ \mathfrak{M}_2 : \mathfrak{N}_2 : \mathfrak{P}_2 &= \frac{m}{a^2 - V_2^2} : \frac{n}{b^2 - V_2^2} : \frac{p}{c^2 - V_2^2}. \end{aligned}\right\} \quad . \quad (19)$$

Thus in the direction of a given wave normal but two plane-polarized waves are able to be propagated, and these waves are polarized at right angles to each other. For, from (19),

$$\mathfrak{M}_1\mathfrak{M}_2 + \mathfrak{N}_1\mathfrak{N}_2 + \mathfrak{P}_1\mathfrak{P}_2 \sim \frac{m^2}{(a^2 - V_1^2)(a^2 - V_2^2)} + \text{etc.} \qquad (20)$$

But now

$$\frac{m^2}{(a^2 - V_1^2)(a^2 - V_2^2)} = \frac{m^2}{V_1^2 - V_2^2}\left(\frac{1}{a^2 - V_1^2} - \frac{1}{a^2 - V_2^2}\right),$$

so that the left-hand side of (20) is proportional to

$$\frac{1}{V_1^2 - V_2^2}\left\{\frac{m^2}{a^2 - V_1^2} + \frac{n^2}{b^2 - V_1^2} + \frac{p^2}{c^2 - V_1^2} - \frac{m^2}{a^2 - V_2^2} - \frac{n^2}{b^2 - V_2^2} - \frac{p^2}{c^2 - V_2^2}\right\}.$$

Now since both V_1 and V_2 satisfy equation (18), this entire expression is equal to zero. Consequently the light-vector $\mathfrak{M}_1$, $\mathfrak{N}_1$, $\mathfrak{P}_1$ is perpendicular to $\mathfrak{M}_2$, $\mathfrak{N}_2$, $\mathfrak{P}_2$.

The velocity is a single-valued function of the direction of vibration. For, in consideration of (19), Fresnel's law (18) may be written

$$(a^2 - V^2)\mathfrak{M}^2 + (b^2 - V^2)\mathfrak{N}^2 + (c^2 - V^2)\mathfrak{P}^2 = 0,$$

i.e., since $\mathfrak{M}^2 + \mathfrak{N}^2 + \mathfrak{P}^2 = 1$,

$$V^2 = a^2\mathfrak{M}^2 + b^2\mathfrak{N}^2 + c^2\mathfrak{P}^2. \quad . \quad . \quad . \quad . \qquad (18')$$

5. The Normal Surface.—In order to gain a conception of how the velocity varies with the direction of the wave normal, it is best to lay off from a given origin O, in all possible directions of the wave normals, the two velocities as radii vectores. In this way a surface consisting of two sheets is obtained,—the so-called *normal surface*. In a plane of electric symmetry, for example the yz-plane, the two values of the velocity are, by (18),

$$V_1^2 = a^2, \quad V_2^2 = b^2p^2 + c^2n^2, \quad . \quad . \quad . \qquad (21)$$

i.e. the section of the wave surface by a plane of electric symmetry consists of a circle and an oval. If $a > b > c$, the sections of the wave surface by the planes of symmetry are shown in Fig. 85. In the xz-plane, for two directions of the wave normal, which are denoted by A_1 and A_2, the two roots V_1 and V_2 of necessity coincide, since the two sheets of the normal surface intersect. It can be shown that *this occurs for*

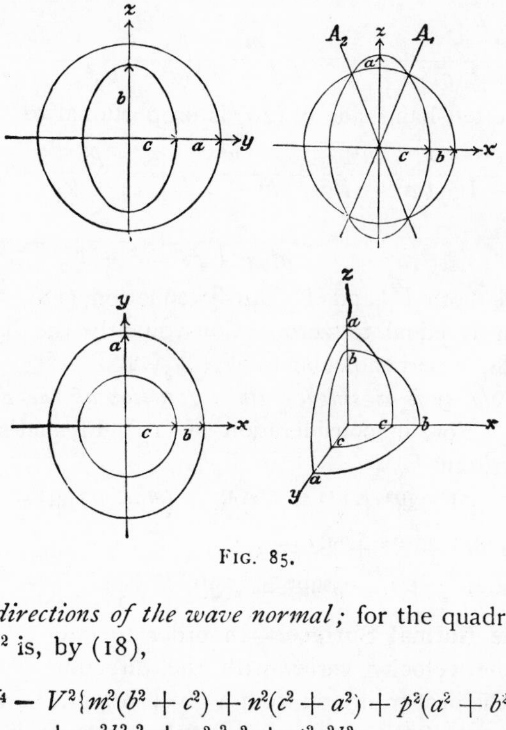

FIG. 85.

no other directions of the wave normal; for the quadratic equation in V^2 is, by (18),

$$V^4 - V^2\{m^2(b^2+c^2)+n^2(c^2+a^2)+p^2(a^2+b^2)\} + m^2b^2c^2 + n^2c^2a^2 + p^2a^2b^2 = 0. \quad . \quad . \quad . \quad (22)$$

If the following abbreviations be introduced:

$$M = m^2(b^2-c^2), \quad N = n^2(c^2-a^2), \quad P = p^2(a^2-b^2), \quad . \quad (23)$$

the solution of (22) is

$$\left.\begin{aligned} 2V^2 &= m^2(b^2+c^2)+n^2(c^2+a^2)+p^2(a^2+b^2) \\ &\pm \sqrt{M^2+N^2+P^2-2MN-2NP-2MP}. \end{aligned}\right\} \quad . \quad (24)$$

Now since $a > b > c$, M and P are positive, N negative. Since the quantity under the radical may be put in the form

$$(M + N - P)^2 - 4MN,$$

it is made up of two positive terms. Hence when the two roots in V^2 are equal, the two following conditions must be satisfied:

$$M + N - P = 0, \quad MN = 0.$$

Now M cannot be zero, since in that case $N = P$, which is impossible, for N is negative and P positive. Consequently the expression under the radical vanishes only when

$$N = 0, \quad M = P,$$

i.e. when

$$n = 0, \quad m^2(b^2 - c^2) = p^2(a^2 - b^2), \quad . \quad . \quad (25)$$

or since $m + n^2 + p^2 = 1$, when

$$m = \pm\sqrt{\frac{a^2 - b^2}{a^2 - c^2}}, \quad n = 0, \quad p = \pm\sqrt{\frac{b^2 - c^2}{a^2 - c^2}}. \quad (26)$$

These equations determine the two directions of the wave normals for which the two velocities are the same. These directions are called the *optic axes*. The axes of electric symmetry x and z which bisect the angles between the optic axes are called the *median lines of the crystal.*

The value of the common velocity of the two waves when the wave normal coincides with an optic axis is $V_1 = V_2 = b$. This is evident from Fig. 85 as well as from equation (24) taken in connection with (26). Hence, from (19), the direction of vibration of these waves is indeterminate, since an indeterminate expression, namely, $n : b^2 - V^2 = 0 : 0$, occurs in these equations. Hence along the optic axis any kind of light may be propagated, i.e. light polarized in any way, or even natural light.

The velocity V can be calculated more conveniently by introducing the angles g_1 and g_2 which the wave normal makes with the optic axes than by the use of (24). Let the positive direction of one of the optic axes A_1 be so taken that it makes acute angles with the positive directions of the x- and z-axes. The direction cosines of this axis are then, by (26),

$$m_1 = +\sqrt{\frac{a^2 - b^2}{a^2 - c^2}}, \quad n_1 = 0, \quad p_1 = +\sqrt{\frac{b^2 - c^2}{a^2 - c^2}}. \qquad (26')$$

Let the positive direction of the other optic axis A_2 be so taken that it makes an acute angle with the z-axis but an obtuse angle with the x-axis. Its direction cosines are then

$$m_2 = -\sqrt{\frac{a^2 - b^2}{a^2 - c^2}}, \quad n_2 = 0, \quad p_2 = +\sqrt{\frac{b^2 - c^2}{a^2 - c^2}}. \qquad (26'')$$

Hence the cosines of the angles g_1 and g_2 between the wave normal and the positive directions of A_1 and A_2 are

$$\cos g_1 = mm_1 + nn_1 + pp_1,$$

i.e.

$$\left.\begin{aligned} \cos g_1 &= m\sqrt{\frac{a^2 - b^2}{a^2 - c^2}} + p\sqrt{\frac{b^2 - c^2}{a^2 - c^2}}, \\ \cos g_2 &= -m\sqrt{\frac{a^2 - b^2}{a^2 - c^2}} + p\sqrt{\frac{b^2 - c^2}{a^2 - c^2}}. \end{aligned}\right\} \quad . \qquad (27)$$

In consequence of the relation $n^2 = 1 - m^2 - p^2$ it is easy to deduce the following:

$$m^2(b^2 + c^2) + n^2(c^2 + a^2) + p^2(a^2 + b^2)$$
$$= a^2 + c^2 + (a^2 - c^2)\cos g_1 \cos g_2, \qquad (28)$$

$$M^2 + N^2 + P^2 - 2MN - 2NP - 2MP$$
$$= (a^2 - c^2)^2 \sin^2 g_1 \sin^2 g_2.$$

Hence, from (24),

$$\left.\begin{aligned} 2V_1^2 &= a^2 + c^2 + (a^2 - c^2)\cos(g_1 - g_2), \\ 2V_2^2 &= a^2 + c^2 + (a^2 - c^2)\cos(g_1 + g_2). \end{aligned}\right\} \quad . \quad . \qquad (29)$$

6. Geometrical Construction of the Wave Surface and of the Direction of Vibration.—Fresnel gives the following geometrical construction for finding, with the aid of a surface called an *ovaloid*, the velocity and the direction of vibration: Let the direction cosines of the radius vector of the ovaloid be ϑ_1, ϑ_2, ϑ_3. The equation of the ovaloid is then

$$\rho^2 = a^2\vartheta_1^2 + b^2\vartheta_2^2 + c^2\vartheta_3^2, \quad . \quad . \quad . \quad . \quad . \quad (30)$$

a, b, and c being its principal axes. In order to obtain the velocity of propagation of a wave front, pass a plane through the centre of the ovaloid parallel to the wave front, and determine the largest and the smallest radii vectores ρ_1 and ρ_2 of the oval section thus obtained. These are equal to the velocities of the two waves, and the directions of ρ_1 and ρ_2 are the directions of vibration in the waves, the directions ρ_1 and ρ_2 corresponding to the velocities ρ_1 and ρ_2 respectively.

In order to prove that this construction is correct, account must be taken of the fact that ϑ_1, ϑ_2, ϑ_3 must also satisfy both of the conditions

$$1 = \vartheta_1^2 + \vartheta_2^2 + \vartheta_3^2, \quad . \quad . \quad . \quad . \quad . \quad (31)$$

$$0 = m\vartheta_1 + n\vartheta_2 + p\vartheta_3 \quad . \quad . \quad . \quad . \quad (32)$$

The last equation is an expression of the fact that the oval section is perpendicular to the wave normal. In order to determine those directions ϑ_1, ϑ_2, ϑ_3 for which ρ has a maximum or a minimum value, ϑ_1, ϑ_2, ϑ_3 may, in accordance with the rules of differential calculus, be regarded as independent variables provided equations (31) and (32) be multiplied by the indeterminate Lagrangian factors σ_1 and σ_2, and added to equation (30). By setting the separate differential coefficients of ρ^2 with respect to ϑ_1, ϑ_2, ϑ_3 equal to zero, there results

$$\left.\begin{aligned} 0 &= 2(a^2 + \sigma_1)\vartheta_1 + m\sigma_2, \\ 0 &= 2(b^2 + \sigma_1)\vartheta_2 + n\sigma_2, \\ 0 &= 2(c^2 + \sigma_1)\vartheta_3 + p\sigma_2. \end{aligned}\right\} \quad . \quad . \quad . \quad . \quad (33)$$

If these equations be multiplied by ϑ_1, ϑ_2, and ϑ_3 respectively and added, then, in consideration of (31) and (32),

$$a^2\vartheta_1^2 + b^2\vartheta_2^2 + c^2\vartheta_3^2 = -\sigma_1.$$

Hence, from (30), $\sigma_1 = -\rho^2$. If this value is substituted in (33), these three equations may be written in the form

$$\vartheta_1 = -\tfrac{1}{2}\sigma_2\frac{m}{a^2-\rho^2},\quad \vartheta_2 = -\tfrac{1}{2}\sigma_2\frac{n}{b^2-\rho^2},\quad \vartheta_3 = -\tfrac{1}{2}\sigma_2\frac{p}{c^2-\rho^2}. \quad (34)$$

If these equations be multiplied by m, n, and p respectively and added, then it follows from (32) that

$$\frac{m^2}{a^2-\rho^2}+\frac{n^2}{b^2-\rho^2}+\frac{p^2}{c^2-\rho^2}=0,$$

i.e. ρ actually satisfies the same equation as the velocity V [cf. equation (18), page 316].

From (34) it follows that ϑ_1, ϑ_2, ϑ_3 stand in the same ratio to one another as $\mathfrak{M}$, $\mathfrak{N}$, and $\mathfrak{P}$ in (19), i.e. the direction of the light-vector is that of the maximum or minimum radius vector of the oval section.

Since, by § 5, the direction of vibration is indeterminate in the case in which the wave normal coincides with one of the optic axes, the oval section has in this case no maximum or minimum radius vector, i.e. *the intersections with the ovaloid of planes which are perpendicular to the optic axes are circles.* The radii of these two circles are the same and equal to b. Any arbitrary oval section of a plane wave whose normal is N cuts the two circular sections of the ovaloid in two radii vectores r_1 and r_2 which have the same length b. These radii r_1 and r_2 are perpendicular to the planes which are defined by the wave normal N and the one or the other of the optic axes A_1 and A_2; since, e.g., r_1 is perpendicular to N as well as to A_1. Hence these planes (NA_1) or (NA_2) also cut the oval section of the ovaloid by the plane wave in two equal radii r_1' and r_2', since r_1' is perpendicular to r_1, and r_2' to r_2. Also, since $r_1 = r_2$, it follows, from the symmetry of the oval section, that $r_1' = r_2'$, and that the principal axes ρ_1 and ρ_2 of this section bisect the angles between r_1 and r_2, r_1' and r_2'. *The directions of vibration of the light-vectors* (which coincide with ρ_1 and ρ_2) *lie in the two planes which bisect the angles formed by the planes* (NA_1) *and* (NA_2). Thus the directions of the vibrations are determined, since they are also perpendicular to the wave normals N. The direction of vibration which corresponds to V_2 [defined by (29)] lies in the plane which bisects the angle (A_1, N, A_2), in which A_1 and A_2 denote the positive directions of the optic axes defined by (26'); the direction of vibration corresponding to V_1 is perpendicular to this plane, i.e. in the plane which bisects the angle $(A_1, N, -A_2)$.

7. Uniaxial Crystals.—When two of the principal velocities a, b, c are equal, for example when $a = b$, the equations become much simpler. From (26) on page 319 it follows that both optic axes coincide with the z-axis. Hence these crystals are called uniaxial. From (29) it follows, since $g_1 = g_2$, that

$$V_1^2 = a^2, \quad V_2^2 = a^2 \cos^2 g + c^2 \sin^2 g, \quad . \quad . \quad (35)$$

in which g denotes the angle included between the wave normal and the optic axis. One wave has then a constant velocity; it is called the *ordinary* wave. The direction of vibration of the *extraordinary* wave lies, according to the construction of the preceding page, in the principal plane of the crystal, i.e. in the plane defined by the principal axis and the normal to the wave. The direction of vibration of the ordinary wave is therefore perpendicular to the principal plane of the wave. Since the principal plane of the wave was defined above (page 244) as the plane of polarization of the ordinary wave, the direction of vibration is perpendicular to the plane of polarization, as is the case from Fresnel's standpoint for isotropic media. When the angle g which the wave normal makes with the optic axis varies, N remaining always in the same principal section, the direction of vibration of the ordinary wave remains fixed, while that of the extraordinary wave changes. Hence, as was mentioned on page 252, § 7, Fresnel's standpoint has the advantage of simplicity in that the direction of vibration is alone determinative of the characteristics of the wave. If this is unchanged, the velocity of the wave is unchanged even though the direction of the wave normal varies.

Uniaxial crystals belong to those crystallographic systems

which have one principal axis and perpendicular to it two or three secondary axes, i.e. to the tetragonal or hexagonal systems. The optic axis coincides with the principal crystallographic axis. The crystals of the regular system do not differ optically from isotropic substances, since from their crystallographic symmetry $a = b = c$.

Rhombic, monoclinic, and triclinic crystals can be optically biaxial. In the first the axes of crystallographic symmetry coincide necessarily with the axes of electric symmetry, since in all its physical properties a crystal has at least that symmetry which is peculiar to its crystalline form. In monoclinic crystals the crystalline form determines the position of but one of the axes of electric symmetry, since this latter is perpendicular to the one plane of crystallographic symmetry. In triclinic crystals the axes of electric symmetry have no fixed relation to the crystalline form.

In the case of uniaxial crystals ($a = b$) the ovaloid becomes, according to (30), the surface of revolution

$$\rho^2 = a^2 + (c^2 - a^2)\vartheta_3^{\,2}. \quad . \quad . \quad . \quad . \quad (36)$$

According as this surface is flattened or elongated in the direction of the axis, the crystal is said to be *positively* or *negatively* uniaxial. Thus in the former $a > c$, in the latter $a < c$. According to (35), in positive crystals the ordinary wave travels faster, i.e. is less refracted, while in negative crystals the ordinary wave is more strongly refracted than the extraordinary. Quartz is positively, calc-spar negatively, uniaxial.

8. Determination of the Direction of the Ray from the Direction of the Wave Normal.—Let the direction cosines of the ray be $\mathfrak{m}$, $\mathfrak{n}$, $\mathfrak{p}$. From the considerations presented on page 313 and equation (25) on page 273,

$$\mathfrak{m} : \mathfrak{n} : \mathfrak{p} = \gamma Y - \beta Z : \alpha Z - \gamma X : \beta X - \alpha Y. \quad . \quad (37)$$

But from equations (13) and (16) on page 315,

$$X : Y : Z = a^2\mathfrak{M} : b^2\mathfrak{N} : c^2\mathfrak{P}. \quad . \quad . \quad . \quad . \quad (38)$$

Also, from equations (7), page 311, and (13), it is easy to deduce

$$\alpha : \beta : \gamma = b^2p\mathfrak{N} - c^2n\mathfrak{P} : c^2m\mathfrak{P} - a^2p\mathfrak{M} : a^2n\mathfrak{M} - b^2m\mathfrak{N}. \quad (39)$$

Substitution of the values (38) and (39) in (37) gives

$$\mathfrak{m} : \mathfrak{n} : \mathfrak{p} = - m(a^4\mathfrak{M}^2 + b^4\mathfrak{N}^2 + c^4\mathfrak{P}^2) + \mathfrak{M}a^2(a^2m\mathfrak{M} + b^2n\mathfrak{N} + c^2p\mathfrak{P}) \ldots\ldots \quad (40)$$

The terms denoted thus . . . can be obtained from the written terms by a cyclical interchange of letters.

If now the abbreviation (16′) on page 315 be introduced, i.e. if

$$a^2m\mathfrak{M} + b^2n\mathfrak{N} + c^2p\mathfrak{P} = G^2, \quad \ldots \quad (41)$$

it follows from (17) that

$$a^2\mathfrak{M} = \mathfrak{M}V^2 + mG^2, \quad b^2\mathfrak{N} = \mathfrak{N}V^2 + nG^2, \quad c^2\mathfrak{P} = \mathfrak{P}V^2 + pG^2.$$

If these three equations be squared and added, then, since (cf. page 315)

$$\mathfrak{M}^2 + \mathfrak{N}^2 + \mathfrak{P}^2 = m^2 + n^2 + p^2 = 1,$$
$$\mathfrak{M}m + \mathfrak{N}n + \mathfrak{P}p = 0,$$

it follows that

$$a^4\mathfrak{M}^2 + b^4\mathfrak{N}^2 + c^4\mathfrak{P}^2 = V^4 + G^4. \quad \ldots \quad (42)$$

Squaring and adding equations (17′) gives

$$1 = G^4\left\{\left(\frac{m}{a^2 - V^2}\right)^2 + \left(\frac{n}{b^2 - V^2}\right)^2 + \left(\frac{p}{c^2 - V^2}\right)^2\right\}. \quad (43)$$

If now the value of $\mathfrak{M}a^2$ obtained from (17′) be introduced, namely,

$$\mathfrak{M}a^2 = G^2\frac{ma^2}{a^2 - V^2},$$

then, in consideration of (41) and (42), (40) becomes

$$\mathfrak{m} : \mathfrak{n} : \mathfrak{p} = - m(V^4 + G^4) + mG^4\frac{a^2}{a^2 - V^2} : \ldots\ldots,$$

or

$$\mathfrak{m} : \mathfrak{n} : \mathfrak{p} = m\left(V^2 + \frac{G^4}{V^2 - a^2}\right) : n\left(V^2 + \frac{G^4}{V^2 - b^2}\right)$$
$$: p\left(V^2 + \frac{G^4}{V^2 - c^2}\right). \quad . \quad (44)$$

This equation gives the direction of the ray in terms of the direction of the wave normal, for V^2 is expressed in terms of m, n, and p in Fresnel's law (18), and G^2 [cf. (43)] in terms of m, n, p, and V^2.

In order to determine the absolute values of $\mathfrak{m}$, $\mathfrak{n}$, $\mathfrak{p}$, not their ratios merely, it is possible to write

$$\left.\begin{aligned} \mathfrak{m} = m\sigma\left(V^2 + \frac{G^4}{V^2 - a^2}\right), \quad \mathfrak{n} = n\sigma\left(V^2 + \frac{G^4}{V^2 - b^2}\right), \\ \mathfrak{p} = p\sigma\left(V^2 + \frac{G^4}{V^2 - c^2}\right), \end{aligned}\right\} . \quad (45)$$

in which σ is a factor of proportionality which can be determined by squaring and adding these three equations. This gives, in consideration of (18) and (43),

$$1 = \sigma^2(V^4 + G^4). \quad . \quad . \quad . \quad . \quad . \quad (46)$$

9. The Ray Surface.—If a wave front has travelled parallel to itself in unit time a distance V, then V is called the velocity along the normal. The ray is oblique to the normal, making with it an angle which is given by

$$\cos \zeta = \mathfrak{m}m + \mathfrak{n}n + \mathfrak{p}p. \quad . \quad . \quad . \quad . \quad (47)$$

The ray has then in unit time travelled a distance $\mathfrak{V}$ such that

$$\mathfrak{V} \cos \zeta = V. \quad . \quad . \quad . \quad . \quad . \quad . \quad . \quad (48)$$

$\mathfrak{V}$ is called the *velocity of the ray:* it is larger than the velocity along the normal.

If the three equations (45) be multiplied by m, n, p, respectively, and added, it follows that $\cos \zeta = \sigma V^2$, or, in consideration of (48),

$$\sigma = 1 : V\mathfrak{V}. \quad . \quad . \quad . \quad . \quad . \quad . \quad . \quad (49)$$

Hence, from (46),

$$G^4 = V^2\mathfrak{V}^2 - V^4, \quad . \quad . \quad . \quad . \quad . \quad . \quad (50)$$

or, in consideration of (48),

$$G^2 = V^2 \tan \zeta. \quad . \quad . \quad . \quad . \quad . \quad . \quad . \quad (51)$$

If the value of G^4 from (50) be substituted in (45), then, in consideration of (49), there results, after a simple transformation,

$$\frac{\mathfrak{m}\mathfrak{V}}{\mathfrak{V}^2-a^2} = \frac{mV}{V^2-a^2}, \quad \frac{\mathfrak{n}\mathfrak{V}}{\mathfrak{V}^2-b^2} = \frac{nV}{V^2-b^2}, \quad \frac{\mathfrak{p}\mathfrak{V}}{\mathfrak{V}^2-c^2} = \frac{pV}{V^2-c^2}. \quad (52)$$

If these three equations be multiplied by $\mathfrak{m}a^2$, $\mathfrak{n}b^2$, $\mathfrak{p}c^2$, respectively, and added, then, in consideration of (17′),

$$\mathfrak{V}\left(\frac{\mathfrak{m}^2a^2}{\mathfrak{V}^2-a^2} + \frac{\mathfrak{n}^2b^2}{\mathfrak{V}^2-b^2} + \frac{\mathfrak{p}^2c^2}{\mathfrak{V}^2-c^2}\right) = -\frac{V}{G^2}(a^2\mathfrak{M}\mathfrak{m} + b^2\mathfrak{N}\mathfrak{n} + c^2\mathfrak{P}\mathfrak{p}).$$

But the light-ray is perpendicular to the electric force. Hence the right-hand side of the last equation vanishes, since the components of the electric force satisfy (38). Hence

$$\frac{\mathfrak{m}^2a^2}{\mathfrak{V}^2-a^2} + \frac{\mathfrak{n}^2b^2}{\mathfrak{V}^2-b^2} + \frac{\mathfrak{p}^2c^2}{\mathfrak{V}^2-c^2} = 0, \quad . \quad . \quad . \quad (53)$$

which may also be written in the form

$$\frac{\mathfrak{m}^2}{\frac{1}{a^2}-\frac{1}{\mathfrak{V}^2}} + \frac{\mathfrak{n}^2}{\frac{1}{b^2}-\frac{1}{\mathfrak{V}^2}} + \frac{\mathfrak{p}^2}{\frac{1}{c^2}-\frac{1}{\mathfrak{V}^2}} = 0. \quad . \quad . \quad (53')$$

The addition to (53) of $\mathfrak{m}^2 + \mathfrak{n}^2 + \mathfrak{p}^2 = 1$ gives

$$\frac{\mathfrak{m}^2\mathfrak{V}^2}{\mathfrak{V}^2-a^2} + \frac{\mathfrak{n}^2\mathfrak{V}^2}{\mathfrak{V}^2-b^2} + \frac{\mathfrak{p}^2\mathfrak{V}^2}{\mathfrak{V}^2-c^2} = 1. \quad . \quad . \quad (53'')$$

This equation expresses the velocity $\mathfrak{V}$ of the ray as a function of the direction of the ray. If in every direction $\mathfrak{m}$, $\mathfrak{n}$, $\mathfrak{p}$ the corresponding $\mathfrak{V}$ be laid off from a fixed point, the so-called *ray surface* is obtained. This surface, like the normal surface, consists of two sheets. These two surfaces are very similar to each other, since equation (53′) of the former is obtained from (18) of the latter by substituting for all lengths which appear in (18) their reciprocal values. Each of the planes of symmetry intersects the ray surface in a circle and an ellipse.

Hence, in order to apply the geometrical construction given in § 6 to this case, it is necessary to start from the surface [cf. (30)]

$$\frac{1}{\rho^2} = \frac{\vartheta_1^2}{a^2} + \frac{\vartheta_2^2}{b^2} + \frac{\vartheta_3^2}{c^2},$$

i.e. from an ellipsoid whose axes are a, b, c. The velocities $\mathfrak{V}$ of the ray in a direction $\mathfrak{m}$, $\mathfrak{n}$, $\mathfrak{p}$ are given by the principal axes ρ_1 and ρ_2 of that ellipse which is cut from the ellipsoid by a plane perpendicular to the ray.

In this case also there must be two directions, $\mathfrak{A}_1$ and $\mathfrak{A}_2$, for which the two roots $\mathfrak{V}^2$ of the quadratic equation (53′) are the same. These directions are obtained from the equations for the optic axes, namely, (26′) and (26″), by substituting in them for all lengths the reciprocal values. Thus

$$\mathfrak{m} = \pm\sqrt{\frac{\frac{1}{a^2} - \frac{1}{b^2}}{\frac{1}{a^2} - \frac{1}{c^2}}}, \quad \mathfrak{n} = 0, \quad \mathfrak{p} = \sqrt{\frac{\frac{1}{b^2} - \frac{1}{c}}{\frac{1}{a^2} - \frac{1}{c^2}}},$$

or

$$\mathfrak{m} = \pm\frac{c}{b}\sqrt{\frac{a^2 - b^2}{a^2 - c^2}}, \quad \mathfrak{n} = 0, \quad \mathfrak{p} = \frac{a}{b}\sqrt{\frac{b^2 - c^2}{a^2 - c^2}}. \quad . \quad (54)$$

These two directions are called the *ray axes*.

The ray surface can be looked upon as that surface at which the light disturbance originating in a point P has arrived at the end of unit time. For this reason it is commonly called the wave surface.

If, in accordance with Huygens' principle, the separate points P of a wave front are looked upon as centres of disturbance and if the wave surfaces are constructed about these points, the envelope of these surfaces represents the wave front at the end of unit time (cf. page 159). According to this construction *the wave front corresponding to a ray PS is a plane tangent to the wave surface at the point S.*

This result can also be deduced from the equations. If the rectangular coordinates of a point S of the wave surface are denoted by x, y, and z, then $m\mathfrak{V} = x$, etc., and $\mathfrak{V}^2 = x^2 + y^2 + z^2$, and, from $(53'')$,

$$\frac{x^2}{\mathfrak{V}^2 - a^2} + \frac{y^2}{\mathfrak{V}^2 - b^2} + \frac{z^2}{\mathfrak{V}^2 - c^2} - 1 = 0. \quad . \quad (55)$$

If this equation be written in the general form $F(x, y, z) = 0$, the direction cosines of the normal to the tangent plane at the point x, y, z are proportional to $\dfrac{\partial F}{\partial x}, \dfrac{\partial F}{\partial y}, \dfrac{\partial F}{\partial z}$. Hence it is necessary to prove that

$$\frac{\partial F}{\partial x} : \frac{\partial F}{\partial y} : \frac{\partial F}{\partial z} = m : n : p. \quad . \quad . \quad . \quad (56)$$

Now, from (55),

$$\frac{\partial F}{\partial x} = 2x\left(\frac{1}{\mathfrak{V}^2 - a^2} - \frac{x^2}{(\mathfrak{V}^2 - a^2)^2} - \frac{y^2}{(\mathfrak{V}^2 - b^2)^2} - \frac{z^2}{(\mathfrak{V}^2 - c^2)^2}\right).$$

From (52), $x : \mathfrak{V}^2 - a = mV : V^2 - a^2$, etc. Hence, in consideration of (43) and (50),

$$\frac{\partial F}{\partial x} = 2x\left(\frac{1}{\mathfrak{V}^2 - a^2} - \frac{V^2}{G^4}\right) = \frac{2xV^2}{G^4} \cdot \frac{a^2 - V^2}{\mathfrak{V}^2 - a^2},$$

i.e., in consideration of (52),

$$\frac{\partial F}{\partial x} = -2m\frac{V^3}{G^4}. \quad . \quad . \quad . \quad . \quad (57)$$

From this equation $\dfrac{\partial F}{\partial y}, \dfrac{\partial F}{\partial z}$ may be written out by a simple interchange of letters. Hence equation (56) immediately results, i.e. the construction found from Huygens' principle is verified.

From these considerations it is evident that the direction $\mathfrak{m}$, $\mathfrak{n}$, $\mathfrak{p}$ of the ray can be determined from the direction m, n,

p of the normal in the following way: Suppose a light disturbance to start at any instant from a point P; the ray surface is then tangent to all the wave fronts, i.e. it is the envelope of the wave fronts. Consider three elementary wave fronts the directions of whose normals are infinitely near to the direction of the line PN. Their intersection must then be infinitely near to the end point S of the ray PS which corresponds to the normal PN, since S is common to all three waves. The correctness of this construction will now be analytically proved. The equation of a wave front is

$$mx + ny + pz = V. \quad . \quad . \quad . \quad . \quad . \qquad (58)$$

If the point x, y, z is to lie upon an infinitely near wave front, the equation obtained by differentiating (58) with respect to m, n, and p will also hold. But these quantities are not independent of one another, since $m^2 + n^2 + p^2 = 1$. According to the theorem of Lagrange (cf. above, page 321) there can be added to (58) the identity

$$f(m^2 + n^2 + p^2) = f,$$

so that there results

$$mx + ny + pz + f(m^2 + n^2 + p^2) = V + f. \quad . \qquad (59)$$

f is an unknown constant. Since this constant has been introduced into the equation, m, n, and p in (59) may be looked upon as independent variables, and the partial differential coefficients of (59) with respect to m, n, and p may be formed, namely,

$$x + 2fm = \frac{\partial V}{\partial m}, \quad y + 2fn = \frac{\partial V}{\partial n}, \quad z + 2fp = \frac{\partial V}{\partial p}. \qquad (60)$$

But, from (18) and (43),

$$\frac{\partial V}{\partial m} = \frac{m}{V^2 - a^2} \cdot \frac{G^4}{V}. \quad . \quad . \quad . \quad . \quad . \qquad (61)$$

Similar expressions hold for $\frac{\partial V}{\partial n}$, $\frac{\partial V}{\partial p}$. If the three equations (60) be multiplied by m, n, and p, respectively, and added, it is evident from (18) and (61) that the right-hand side of the resulting equation reduces to zero, while the left-hand side is, by (58), $V + 2f$, so that the constant $2f$ is determined as $2f = - V$. Hence, in consideration of (61), the first of equations (60) becomes

$$x = m\left(V + \frac{1}{V^2 - a^2} \cdot \frac{G^4}{V}\right),$$

and similarly

$$y = n\left(V + \frac{1}{V^2 - b^2} \cdot \frac{G^4}{V}\right),$$

$$z = p\left(V + \frac{1}{V^2 - c^2} \cdot \frac{G^4}{V}\right).$$

Hence the radius vector drawn from the origin to the point of intersection x, y, z of the three infinitely near wave fronts coincides in fact with the direction of the ray as calculated on page 326, since $x : y : z = \mathfrak{m} : \mathfrak{n} : \mathfrak{p}$. Further, the velocity of the ray $\sqrt{x^2 + y^2 + z^2}$ is found to have the same value as that given above in (45) and (49).

For other geometrical relations between the ray, the wave normal, the optic axes, and the ray axes, cf. Winkelmann's Handbuch der Physik, Optik, p. 699.

10. Conical Refraction. — Corresponding to any given direction of a wave normal there are, in general, according to equation (44), two different rays, since for a given value of m, n, and p there are two different values of V^2. But it may happen that these equations assume the indeterminate form 0 : 0. Thus this occurs when one of the quantities m, n, or p is equal to zero. If, for example, $m = 0$, then, from (21) on page 317, $V_1^2 = a^2$. In this case, by (43) and (44),

$$G^4 = (V_1^2 - a^2)^2 : m^2,$$

$$\mathfrak{m} \sim m \frac{G^4}{V_1^2 - a^2} = m \cdot \frac{V_1^2 - a^2}{m^2}. \quad . \quad . \quad . \quad (62)$$

The value of this expression, which is of the form 0 : 0, is easily determined, since, by Fresnel's equation (18) on page 316, the expression $m^2 : V_1^2 - a^2$ has a finite, determinate value, namely,

$$\frac{m^2}{V_1^2 - a^2} = \frac{n^2}{b^2 - V_1^2} + \frac{p^2}{c^2 - V_1^2}. \quad . \quad . \quad . \quad (63)$$

The right-hand side of this equation can never be zero, since for $a > b > c$ and $V_1^2 = a^2$ both terms of the right-hand side are negative. Hence, by (62), $\mathfrak{m} = 0$ when $m = 0$, i.e. the light-ray is in the yz-plane when the wave normal is in the yz-plane. When $p = 0$ the conclusion is similar. But the case in which $n = 0$ requires special consideration. For then, when $V = b$, equations similar to (62) and (63) are obtained, namely,

$$\mathfrak{n} \sim n\frac{V^2 - b^2}{n^2}, \quad \frac{n^2}{V^2 - b^2} = \frac{m^2}{a^2 - V^2} + \frac{p^2}{c^2 - V^2}. \quad (64)$$

The right-hand side of this equation which corresponds to the case $V = b$ may become zero, namely, when

$$m^2(c^2 - b^2) + p^2(a^2 - b^2) = 0.$$

Now this relation is actually fulfilled when the wave normal coincides with an optic axis [cf. (25), page 319]. In this case, by (64), $\mathfrak{n}$ still retains the indeterminate form $0 : 0$, i.e. to this particular wave normal there correspond not two single determinate rays, but an infinite number of them, since $\mathfrak{n}$ always remains indeterminate. The locus of the rays in this case can be most simply determined from the equation

$$\frac{\mathfrak{m}m}{\mathfrak{V}^2 - a^2} + \frac{\mathfrak{n}n}{\mathfrak{V}^2 - b^2} + \frac{\mathfrak{p}p}{\mathfrak{V}^2 - c^2} = 0, \quad . \quad . \quad (65)$$

which is deduced from (52) by multiplying by m, n, and p, respectively, adding, and taking account of (18). If the wave normal coincides with an optic axis, then $n = 0$, but $\mathfrak{n}$ is not necessarily zero and $\mathfrak{V}$ is therefore in this case different from b. Hence

$$\frac{\mathfrak{m}m}{\mathfrak{V}^2 - a^2} + \frac{\mathfrak{p}p}{\mathfrak{V}^2 - c^2} = 0. \quad . \quad . \quad . \quad . \quad (66)$$

Further, from (47) and (48), since $V = b$,

$$\mathfrak{V}(\mathfrak{m}m + \mathfrak{p}p) = b. \quad . \quad . \quad . \quad . \quad . \quad (67)$$

Elimination of $\mathfrak{B}^2$ from these two equations gives

$$(\mathfrak{m}mc^2 + \mathfrak{p}pa^2)(\mathfrak{m}m + \mathfrak{p}p) = b^2. \quad . \quad . \quad . \quad (68)$$

If the coordinates of the end points of a ray are denoted by x, y, z, so that $\mathfrak{m} = x : \sqrt{x^2 + y^2 + z^2}$, etc., it follows that

$$(xmc^2 + zpa^2)(xm + zp) = b^2(x^2 + y^2 + z^2). \quad . \quad . \quad (69)$$

This equation of the second degree represents a cone whose vertex lies at the origin. Hence *when the wave normal coincides with the optic axis there are an infinite number of rays which lie upon the cone defined by equation (69).* This cone intersects the wave front

$$xm + zp = \text{const.} \quad . \quad . \quad . \quad . \quad . \quad (70)$$

in a circle, since when (70) is substituted in (69) the latter becomes

$$(xmc^2 + zpa^2)\cdot\text{const.} = b^2(x^2 + y^2 + z^2),$$

which is the equation of a sphere.

Hence from the discussion on page 328 it follows that the wave surface has two tangent planes which are perpendicular to the optic axis and tangent to the wave surface in a circle. The axis of the cone coincides with the optic axis; it is therefore perpendicular to the plane of the circle. The aperture χ of the cone is determined from (69) as

$$\tan \chi = \frac{\sqrt{(a^2 - b^2)(b^2 - c^2)}}{b^2}. \quad . \quad . \quad . \quad . \quad (71)$$

This phenomenon is known as *internal conical refraction*, for the following reason: If a ray of light is incident upon a crystal in such a direction that the refracted wave normal coincides with the optic axis of the crystal, then the light-rays within the crystal lie upon the surface of a cone. The rays which emerge from the plate lie therefore upon the surface of an elliptical cylinder whose axis is parallel to the incident light in case the plate of crystal is plane parallel.* Aragonite is

* For the direction of the rays in the outer medium depends only upon the position of the wave front within the crystal, not upon the direction of the internal rays. The law of refraction will be more fully discussed in the next paragraph.

especially suited for observation of this phenomenon, since in it
the angle of aperture of the cone is comparatively large

FIG. 86.

($\chi = 1° 52'$).* The arrangement
of the experiment is shown in
Fig. 86. A parallel beam *so* is
incident through a small opening
o upon one side of a plane-parallel
plate of aragonite which is cut
perpendicular to the line bisecting the acute angle between the
optic axes. When the plate is turned into the proper position
by rotating it about an axis perpendicular to the plane of the
optic axes, an elliptical ring appears upon the screen *SS*.

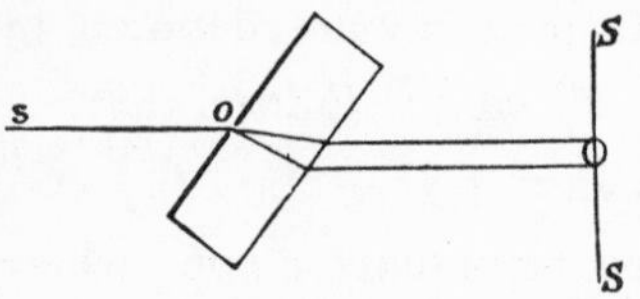

A microscope or a magnifying-glass focussed upon *o* may
be used instead of a screen for observation.

The equation representing the dependence of the direction
of the wave normal upon the direction of the ray may be easily
deduced from (52) taken in connection with (47) and (48).
The result shows that in general for each particular value of
$\mathfrak{m}$, $\mathfrak{n}$, $\mathfrak{p}$ there are two values of m, n, p. Only when $\mathfrak{n} = 0$
and $\mathfrak{V}^2 = b^2$, i.e. when the ray coincides with the ray axis,†
does *n* become indeterminate, as can be shown by a method
similar to that used above. Hence *when the ray coincides with
the ray axis, then at the point of exit of the ray the ray surface
does not have merely two definite tangent planes, but a cone of
tangent planes.* The corresponding wave normals lie upon a
cone of aperture ψ such that

$$\tan \psi = \sqrt{\frac{(a^2 - b^2)(b^2 - c^2)}{a^2 c^2}}. \quad \cdot \quad \cdot \quad \cdot \quad (72)$$

This equation is obtained from (71) by substituting in it
for all the lengths their reciprocal values.

---

* Sulphur is still better, since its angle of aperture is 7°; but its preparation is
much more difficult. The use of a sphere of sulphur for demonstrating conical
refraction is described by Schrauf, Wied. Ann. 37, p. 127.

† The ray axis is the axis of the cone of rays to which a single ray *SO* (Fig. 86)
gives rise when *SO* has the direction which corresponds to internal conical
refraction.—TR.

This phenomenon is called *external conical refraction*, for the reason that a ray which inside the crystal coincides with the ray axis becomes, upon emergence from the crystal, a cone of rays. For the rays after refraction into the outer medium have different directions corresponding to the different positions of the wave front in the crystal (cf. note, page 333).

Fig. 87 represents an arrangement for demonstrating experimentally external conical refraction. A beam of light is concentrated by a lens L upon a small opening o in front of

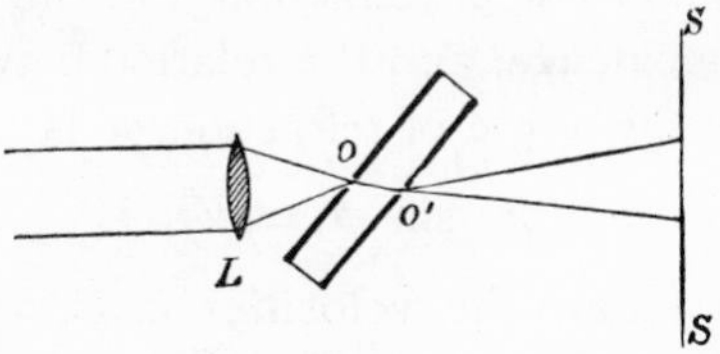

FIG. 87.

an aragonite plate. A second screen with an opening o' is placed on the other side of the plate. If the line oo' coïncides with the direction of a ray axis, a ring appears upon the screen SS. The diameter of this ring increases as the distance from o' to the screen increases. In this arrangement only those rays are effective which travel in the direction oo', the others are cut off by the second screen. The effective incident rays are parallel to the rays of the emergent cone.

The phenomena of conical refraction were not observed until after Hamilton had proved theoretically that they must exist.

11. Passage of Light through Plates and Prisms of Crystal.—The same analytical condition holds for the passage of light from air into a crystal as was shown on page 280 to hold for the refraction of light by an isotropic medium. If the incident wave is proportional to

$$\cos\frac{2\pi}{T}\left(t - \frac{mx + ny + pz}{V}\right),$$

while the refracted wave is proportional to

$$\cos\frac{2\pi}{T}\left(t - \frac{m'x + n'y + p'z}{V'}\right),$$

and if the boundary surface is the plane $z = 0$, then the fact that boundary conditions exist requires, without reference to their form, the equations

$$\frac{m}{V} = \frac{m'}{V'}, \quad \frac{n}{V} = \frac{n'}{V'}.$$

This is the common law of refraction, i.e. the refracted ray lies in the plane of incidence, and the relation between the angle of incidence ϕ and the angle of refraction ϕ' is

$$\sin\phi : \sin\phi' = V : V', \quad . \quad . \quad . \quad . \quad (73)$$

in which V and V' are the velocities in air and in the crystal respectively. But in the case of crystals this relation does not in general give the direct construction of the refracted wave normal, since in general V' depends upon the direction of this normal.

But the application of Huygens' principle, in accordance with the same fundamental laws which were stated on page 161 for isotropic bodies, does give directly not only the relation (73), but also the construction of both the refracted wave normal and the refracted ray. For let A_1B (Fig. 88) be the intersection of an incident wave front with the plane of incidence (plane of the paper), and let the angle $A_1BA_2 = \frac{\pi}{2}$, and $BA_2 = V$, and construct about A_1 the ray surface Σ within the crystal, this surface being the locus of the points to which the disturbance originating at A_1 has been propagated in unit time. Draw through A_2 a line perpendicular to the plane of incidence, and pass through it two planes A_2T_1 and A_2T_2 tangent respectively to the two sheets of the ray surface. According to Huygens' principle these tangent planes are the wave fronts of the refracted waves. The lines drawn from A_1 to the two points of tangency C_1 and C_2 of the planes with the ray surface give the directions of the refracted rays. In general these do not lie in the plane of incidence.

Hence for perpendicular incidence the wave normal is not doubly refracted, but there are two different rays whose directions may be determined by finding the points C_1 and C_2 in which the two sheets of the wave surface constructed about a point A of the bounding surface are tangent to two planes

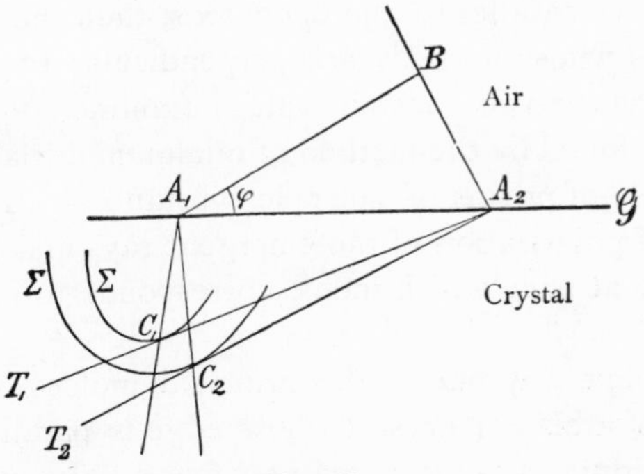

FIG. 88.

parallel to the bounding surface G. The directions of the rays are AC_1 and AC_2 respectively.

When the light passes from the crystal into air a similar construction is applicable. Hence in the passage of light through a plane-parallel plate of crystal there is never a double refraction of the wave normal, but only of the ray. In order to observe the phenomena of double refraction it is necessary to view a point on the remote side of the crystal. This point appears double, since its apparent position depends upon the paths of the rays.* But the introduction of a crystalline plate between collimator and telescope produces no displacement of the image, since in this case the wave normal is determinative of the position of the image. In order to detect double refraction in this case, which occurs in all observations

* The apparent position is displaced not only laterally but also vertically. Cf. Winkelmann's Handbuch d. Physik, Optik, p. 705.

with the spectrometer, it is necessary to introduce a prism of the crystal.

With the help of such a prism it is possible to find *the principal indices* of refraction, i.e. the quantities

$$n_1 = V : a, \quad n_2 = V : b, \quad n_3 = V : c. \quad . \quad . \quad (74)$$

If, for example, a prism of uniaxial crystal $(a = b)$ be used whose edge is parallel to the optic axis, then the velocity V' of the waves whose normals are perpendicular to the edge of the prism has the two constant values a and c. n_1 and n_3 can therefore be found by the method of minimum deviation exactly as in the case of prisms of isotropic substances. The different directions of polarization of the emergent rays make it possible to recognize at once which index corresponds to n_1 and which to n_3.

In the same way one of the principal indices of refraction of a prism of a biaxial crystal whose edge is parallel to one of the axes of optic symmetry may be found. In order to find the other two indices it is necessary to observe the deviation of a wave polarized parallel to the edge of the prism for at least two different angles of incidence.

From the meaning which the electromagnetic theory gives to the principal velocities a, b, c, it is evident from equations (16) on page 315 and (74) that

$$\epsilon_1 = n_1^2, \quad \epsilon_2 = n_2^2, \quad \epsilon_3 = n_3^2, \quad . \quad . \quad . \quad (75)$$

at least if C, the velocity in vacuo, be identified with V, the velocity in air. The error involved in this assumption may be neglected in view of the uncertainty which attends measurement of the dielectric constant.

The relation (75) cannot be rigorously fulfilled, if for no other reason, because the index depends upon the color, i.e. upon the period of the electric force, while the dielectric constant of a homogeneous dielectric is, at least within wide limits, independent of the period. It is, however, natural to test (75) under the assumption that n^2 is the index of infinitely long waves, i.e. the A of the Cauchy dispersion equation

$$n = A + \frac{B}{\lambda^2} \quad . \quad . \quad . \quad . \quad . \quad . \quad . \quad (76)$$

Relation (75) is approximately verified in the case of orthorhombic sulphur, whose dielectric constants have been determined by Boltzmann.* Its indices were measured by Schrauf.† In the following table n^2 denotes the index for yellow light and A the constant of (76):

$$n_1^2 = 3.80; \quad A_1^2 = 3.59; \quad \epsilon_1 = 3.81$$
$$n_2^2 = 4.16; \quad A_2^2 = 3.89; \quad \epsilon_2 = 3.97$$
$$n_3^2 = 5.02; \quad A_3^2 = 4.60; \quad \epsilon_3 = 4.77$$

Thus the dielectric constants have the same sequence as the principal indices of refraction when both are arranged in the order of their magnitudes, but are uniformly larger than the A's. With some other crystals this difference is even greater. The departure from the requirements of the electromagnetic theory is of the same kind as that shown by isotropic bodies (cf. page 277). Its explanation will be given in the treatment of the phenomena of dispersion.

Thus the electromagnetic theory is analytically in complete agreement with the phenomena, but the exact values of the optical constants cannot be obtained from electrical measurements. These constants depend in a way which cannot be foreseen upon the color of the light. In fact not only the principal velocities a, b, c, but also, in the case of monoclinic and triclinic crystals, the positions of the axes of optic symmetry depend upon the color.

12. Total Reflection at the Surface of Crystalline Plates. —The construction given on page 336 for the refracted wave front becomes impossible when the straight line 𝔊 which passes through A_2 and is perpendicular to the plane of incidence inter-

* Boltzmann, Wien. Ber. 70 (2), p. 342, 1874. Pogg. Ann. 153, p. 531, 1874.
† Schrauf, Wien. Ber. 41, p. 805, 1860.

sects one or both of the curves cut from the wave surface Σ by the bounding surface G. In this case there is no refracted wave front, but total reflection takes place. The limiting case, in which partial reflection becomes total, is reached for either one of the two refracted waves when the line $\mathfrak{G}$ is tangent to that sheet of the ray surface Σ which corresponds to the wave in question, i.e. is tangent to the section of the wave surface by the bounding plane G. In this case, since the point of tangency T of $\mathfrak{G}$ with Σ lies in the bounding plane G, the refracted ray is parallel to the boundary (cf. Fig. 89). This

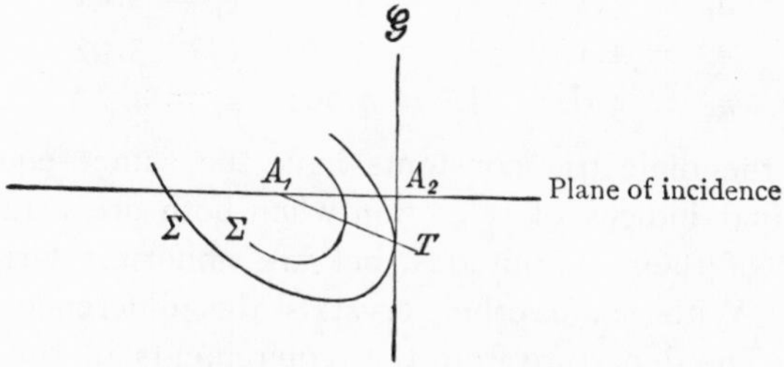

FIG. 89.

wave then can transfer no energy into the crystal, since the ray of light represents the path of energy flow (cf. page 313), and hence no energy passes through a plane parallel to the ray. Thus it appears from this consideration also that in this limiting case the reflected wave must contain the entire energy of the incident wave, i.e. total reflection must occur.

Hence if a plate of crystal be immersed in a more strongly refracting medium, and illuminated with diffuse homogeneous light, two curves which separate the regions of less intensity from those of greater appear in the field of the reflected light. If the observation is made, not upon the reflected light, but upon light which, entering the crystal at one side and then falling at grazing incidence upon the surface, passes out into a more strongly refractive medium, these limiting curves are much sharper since they separate brightness from complete darkness. From these curves the critical angles ϕ_1 and ϕ_2 may be determined. These curves are not in general perpendicular to the plane of reflection. Special instruments have been devised for their observation. Fig. 90 represents Abbe's crystal refractometer. The plate of crystal which is to be investigated is laid upon the flint-glass hemisphere K of index 1.89.

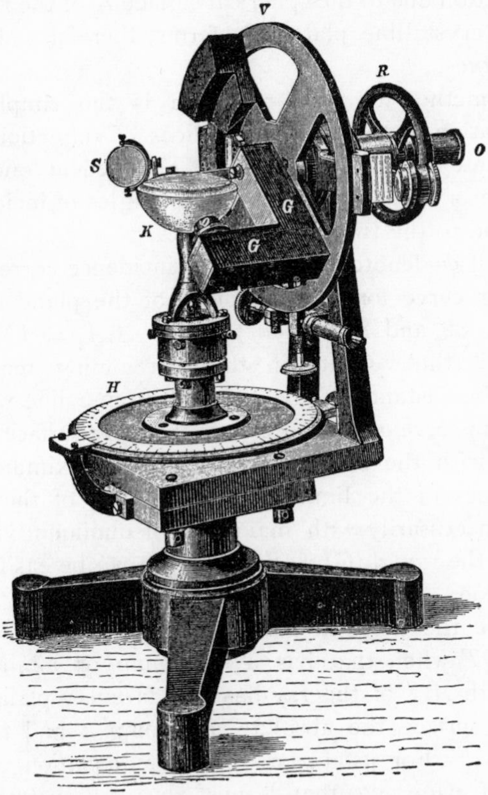

FIG. 90.

Between the crystal and the sphere a liquid of greater index than the latter is introduced. K can be rotated along with the azimuth circle H about a vertical axis. The movable mirror S makes it possible to illuminate the crystal plate either from below through K or from the side. The limiting curves of total reflection are observed through the telescope $OGGO$ which turns with the vertical circle V. For convenience of observation, the telescope is so shaped that the rays, after three total reflections within it, always emerge horizontally. The objective of the telescope is so arranged that it compensates the refraction due to the spherical surface K of the rays reflected from the crystalline plate. It forms, therefore, sharp images of the curves.

The method of total reflection is the simplest for the determination of the principal indices of refraction of a crystalline plate. These indices are obtained at once from the maximum or minimum values of the angles of incidence which correspond to the two limiting curves.

Thus if ϕ denotes the angle of incidence corresponding to a limiting curve for any azimuth ϑ of the plane of incidence (cf. Figs. 88 and 89), then the line $A_1 A_2 = V : \sin \phi$; for $BA_2 = V$ (the velocity in the surrounding medium), and $A_1 A_2$ is the distance of the point A_1 from a line which is tangent to the curve of intersection of the wave surface constructed about A_1 with the bounding surface G. Maximum and minimum values of the limiting angles ϕ, i.e. of the line $A_1 A_2$, coincide necessarily with maximum or minimum values of the length of the ray $A_1 T$ (cf. Fig. 89), as can be easily shown by construction. In fact in this case $A_1 A_2$ coincides with the ray $A_1 T$, since the tangents must be perpendicular to the radius vector $A_1 T$ when this has a maximum or minimum value. The length $A_1 T$ of the ray has now in every plane section of the wave surface the absolute maximum a and the absolute minimum c. For it appears from the equation of the wave surface (cf. page 327) that $\mathfrak{V}$ must always lie between a and c, since otherwise the three terms of equation (53) would have the same sign and their sum could not be zero. On the other hand it is also evident that in every plane section G of the wave surface $\mathfrak{V}$ reaches the limiting values a and c, for, from Fig. 85, $\mathfrak{V}$ attains the value a at least in the line of intersection of G with the yz-plane; since in the yz-plane one velocity has the constant value $\mathfrak{V} = a$, while in the line of intersection of G with the xy-plane $\mathfrak{V}$ must attain the value c. In the intersection of G with the xz-plane $\mathfrak{V} = b$; but it is uncertain, as can be shown from the last of Figs. 85, whether b belongs to the minimum of the outer or the maximum of the inner limiting curve. This can be decided by investigating the maxima or minima of the angle of incidence corresponding to the limiting curves for two plates of different orientations.* Four such measurements can be made upon each plate, and three of these must be common to the two plates. These three correspond to the three principal velocities a, b, c. Their respective values may be determined from

$$A_1 A_2 = V : \sin \phi = a, b, c, \qquad \cdot \quad \cdot \quad \cdot \quad (77)$$

where ϕ denotes the maximum or minimum value of the angle of incidence for the limiting curve which corresponds to the given azimuth ϑ of the plane of incidence. If the index of the medium (V) with respect to that of air (V_0) be denoted by n, i.e. if $V_0 : V = n$, then from (77) the principal indices of refraction of the crystal with respect to air are obtained from the equation, since $V_0 : a = n_1$, etc.,

$$n_1, n_2, n_3 = n \sin \phi. \quad \cdot \quad \cdot \quad \cdot \quad \cdot \quad (78)$$

For uniaxial crystals $(a = b)$ $\phi = $ const. along one of the limiting curves. This angle determines the principal velocity a. For the other limiting curve the angle of incidence varies. If γ denotes the angle which the optic axis makes with the bounding surface of the crystal, the ray velocity, when the plane of incidence passes through the optic axis, is

$$\mathfrak{V}^2 = \frac{a^2 c^2}{a^2 \sin^2 \gamma + c^2 \cos^2 \gamma}. \quad \cdot \quad \cdot \quad (79)$$

If the plane of incidence is perpendicular to the optic axis, then $\mathfrak{V}^2 = c^2$. For positive uniaxial crystals $(a > c)$ (79) gives

---

* If the polarization effects be also taken into account, one section of the crystal is enough. Cf. C. Viola, Wied. Beibl. 1899, p. 641.

the maximum value of $\mathfrak{B}$, i.e. it determines the minimum value of ϕ along the limiting curve which arises from a total reflection of the extraordinary ray. The maximum value of ϕ along this limiting curve determines, therefore, the value of c; from the minimum value of ϕ it is possible to calculate γ, i.e. the inclination of the face of the crystal to the optic axis. In the case of negative uniaxial crystals ($a < c$) the minimum value of ϕ determines the principal velocity c.

Likewise in the case of biaxial crystals the angle between the face and the axes of optic symmetry can be determined from observation of the limiting curves of total reflection. Nevertheless for the sake of greater accuracy it is advantageous to couple with this other methods, for example, the method which makes use of the interference phenomena in convergent polarized light (cf. below).

Conical refraction gives rise to peculiar phenomena in the limiting curves of total reflection. These may be observed if the bounding surface G coincides with the plane of the optic axes. For more complete discussion cf. Kohlrausch, Wied. Ann., 6, p. 86, 1879; Liebisch, Physik. Kryst., p. 423; Mascart, Traité d'Optique, vol. 2, p. 102, Paris, 1891.

13. Partial Reflection at the Surface of a Crystalline Plate.—In order to calculate the changes in amplitude which take place in partial reflection from a plate of crystal it is only necessary to apply equation (6′) and (7) on page 311 together with the boundary conditions there mentioned.

But since the calculation is complicated (cf. Winkelmann's Handbuch, Optik, p. 745) only the result will be here mentioned that there is an angle of complete polarization, i.e. an angle of incidence at which incident natural light is plane-polarized after reflection. But the plane of polarization does not in general coincide with the plane of incidence, as it does in the case of isotropic media.

14. Interference Phenomena Produced by Crystalline Plates in Polarized Light when the Incidence is Normal.—Let plane-polarized monochromatic light pass normally through a plate of crystal and then through a second polarizing arrangement. This case is realized when the crystalline plate is placed upon the stage of the Nörrenberg polarizing apparatus described on page 246. The upper mirror can be conveniently replaced by a Nicol prism, the analyzer. Let the plane of vibration of the electric force within the analyzer be A (Fig. 91), and that within the polarizer P. The incident polarized light, the amplitude of which will be denoted by E, is resolved after entrance into the doubly refracting crystal into two waves of amplitude $E \cos \phi$ and $E \sin \phi$ respectively, ϕ being the angle which P makes with the directions H_1 and H_2 of the vibrations of the two waves W_1 and W_2 within the crystal. The decrease in amplitude by reflection is neglected. It is very nearly the same for both waves. These two waves after passing through the crystal are brought into the same plane of polarization, and hence after passing through the analyzer have the amplitudes $E \cos \phi \cos (\phi - \chi)$, $E \sin \phi \sin (\phi - \chi)$. Now a difference in phase δ has been introduced between the two waves by their passage through the plate. This difference is

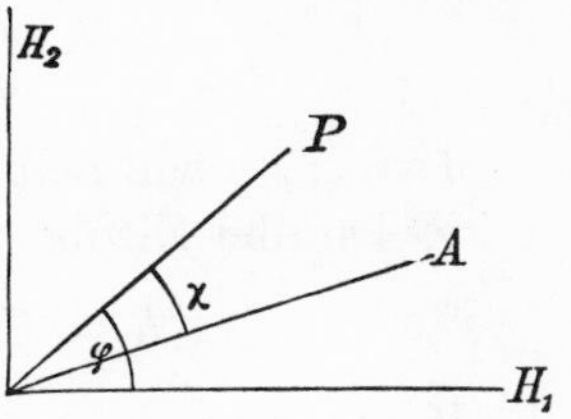

FIG. 91.

$$\delta = d\frac{2\pi}{T}\left(\frac{1}{V_1} - \frac{1}{V_2}\right) = 2\pi\frac{d}{\lambda}\left(\frac{V}{V_1} - \frac{V}{V_2}\right). \quad . \quad (80)$$

in which d denotes the thickness of the crystalline plate, V_1, V_2 the respective velocities of the two waves within it, V the velocity of light in air, and λ the wave length in air of the light used. Hence, according to page 131, the intensity of the light emerging from the analyzer is

$$J = E^2\{\cos^2 \phi \cos^2(\phi - \chi) + \sin^2 \phi \sin^2 (\phi - \chi)$$
$$+ 2 \sin \phi \cos \phi \sin (\phi - \chi) \cos (\phi - \chi) \cos \delta\}.$$

If $\cos \delta$ be replaced by $1 - 2 \sin^2 \frac{1}{2}\delta$, the equation becomes

$$J = E^2\{\cos^2 \chi - \sin 2\phi \sin 2(\phi - \chi) \sin^2 \tfrac{1}{2}\delta\}. \qquad (81)$$

The first term $E^2 \cos^2 \chi$ represents the intensity of the light which would have emerged from the analyzer in case the crystal had not been introduced. This intensity J_0 will be called the original intensity; thus

$$J_0 = E^2 \cos^2 \chi. \quad . \quad . \quad . \quad . \quad . \quad . \quad (82)$$

Two cases will be considered in greater detail:

1. Parallel Nicols: $\chi = 0$. Then

$$J_{\parallel} = J_0(1 - \sin^2 2\phi \sin^2 \tfrac{1}{2}\delta). \quad . \quad . \quad . \quad (83)$$

If the crystal be rotated, the original intensity will be attained in the four positions $\phi = 0$, $\phi = \frac{\pi}{2}$, $\phi = \pi$, $\phi = \frac{3\pi}{2}$, i.e. whenever one of the planes of vibration within the crystal coincides with that of the Nicols. In the positions midway between the above, i.e. $\phi = \frac{\pi}{4}$, etc.,

$$J_{\parallel} = J_0(1 - \sin^2 \tfrac{1}{2}\delta) = J_0 \cos^2 \tfrac{1}{2}\delta, \quad . \quad . \quad . \quad (84)$$

i.e. with the proper values of δ, i.e. of the thickness of the crystal, complete darkness may result.

2. Crossed Nicols: $\chi = \frac{\pi}{2}$. Here $J_0 = 0$ and

$$J_{\times} = E^2 \sin^2 2\phi \sin^2 \tfrac{1}{2}\delta \quad . \quad . \quad . \quad . \quad . \quad (85)$$

Thus, whatever its thickness, the plate appears dark when its planes of vibration coincide with those of the Nicols. If this is not the case, it is dark only when $\delta = 2h\pi$. In the positions $\phi = \frac{\pi}{4}$, etc.,

$$J_{\times} = E^2 \sin^2 \tfrac{1}{2}\delta. \quad . \quad . \quad . \quad . \quad . \quad . \quad . \quad (86)$$

Hence, unless it happens that $\delta = 2h\pi$, it is possible to find the direction of polarization or of vibration within the crystal by rotating it until the light is cut off.

Hence a crystalline wedge between crossed Nicols is traversed by dark bands which run parallel to the edge of the wedge, unless it is in the position in which the light is wholly cut off. These bands lie at those places at which the thickness of the wedge corresponds to the equation $\delta = \pm 2h\pi$. If the incident light is white, the bands must appear colored since δ varies with the color.

A plane-parallel plate of crystal between crossed Nicols must in general appear colored when the incident light is white. Not only does the amplitude E and the difference of phase δ depend upon the color, but also the angle ϕ, i.e. the position of the planes of vibration. However, this latter variation can in general be neglected on account of the small amount of the difference in the retardations for different colors. When the Nicols are crossed it appears from (86) that in white light for $\phi = \frac{\pi}{4}$

$$J_x = \Sigma E^2 \sin^2 \tfrac{1}{2}\delta,$$

in which Σ is to be extended over the values corresponding to the different colors. Thus

$$\Sigma E^2 = \text{white light.} \quad . \quad . \quad . \quad . \quad . \quad (87)$$

Now from (80) its evident that the dependence of δ upon λ is principally due to the appearance of λ in the denominator. Hence if the approximately correct assumption be made that $\frac{V}{V_1} - \frac{V}{V_2}$ is independent of the color, then

$$J_x = \Sigma E^2 \sin^2 \pi \frac{d'}{\lambda}, \quad . \quad . \quad . \quad . \quad . \quad (87')$$

in which

$$d' = d\left(\frac{V}{V_1} - \frac{V}{V_2}\right)$$

is approximately independent of λ. It appears from a comparison of (87′) with (78) on page 306 *that the plate of crystal shows approximately the same colors as those produced by the interference of the two waves reflected at the surfaces of a thin film of air of thickness* $\frac{d'}{2}$. (Newton's ring colors.) But the

Newton interference colors of thin plates differ widely from those produced by the crystal when the difference in the dispersion of the two waves within the crystal is large. Then d' is no longer independent of λ. This is, for example, the case with the hyposulphate of strontium, apophyllite (from the Faroe Islands), brucite, and vesuvian.

For a given angle ϕ the plate of crystal shows between parallel Nicols colors which are complementary to those which it shows between crossed Nicols. For from (83) and (85) the sum of the intensities in the two cases is always ΣE^2, which by (87) means white light.

In the case of Newton's interference colors there are certain values of δ which give what are called sensitive tints which change rapidly for a slight change in δ. For example, the violet of the first order, which appears when δ for the mean wave lengths has about the value π, is such a sensitive tint. For a slight increase in δ the color passes into blue, for a slight decrease into red. A plate of crystal $\mathfrak{P}$ which shows a sensitive tint—for example, a plate of quartz of suitable thickness cut parallel to the axis—may be used to detect traces of double refraction in another plate $\mathfrak{P}'$, since the latter produces at once a change in the color of $\mathfrak{P}$ when placed upon it and viewed between crossed Nicols. The arrangement is even more sensitive if the plate $\mathfrak{P}$ is cut in the direction of the line bisecting its planes of vibration, and the two parts cemented together along the plane of section after one of them has been rotated through 180° about the normal to that surface. A trace of double refraction in the plate $\mathfrak{P}'$ then produces in the two halves of $\mathfrak{P}$ changes of color in opposite senses. This arrangement has been called a Bravais bi-plate after its inventor. With such a plate it is easy to show that the pressure of the finger, for example, is sufficient to produce double refraction in a glass cube. Also, the directions in which the light is completely cut off by $\mathfrak{P}'$ can be accurately determined with the help of a Bravais biplate.

The application of the optical properties of crystals to the construction of Babinet's and Senarmont's compensators has been mentioned above on page 256.

15. Interference Phenomena in Crystalline Plates in Convergent Polarized Light.—Consider first the case in which the polarized light is incident upon the plate at an angle i. Let the angles of refraction be r_1 and r_2 (Fig. 92). It is evi-

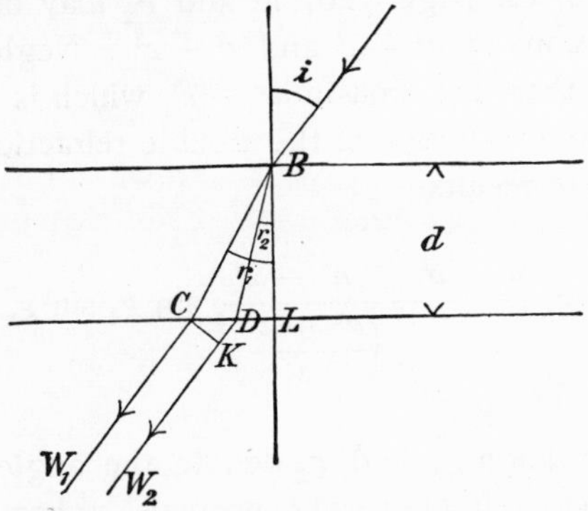

FIG. 92.

dent from the figure that the difference in phase between the two waves after propagation through the crystal is

$$\delta = \frac{2\pi}{T}\left(\frac{BD}{V_2} + \frac{DK}{V} - \frac{BC}{V_1}\right),$$

in which DK is the projection of CD upon the direction of propagation of the wave W_2. Now $BD = d : \cos r_2$, $BC = d : \cos r_1$, $DK = CD \sin i = (BC \sin r_1 - BD \sin r_2) \sin i$, hence

$$\delta = \frac{2\pi}{T}d\left\{\left(\frac{\sin i \sin r_1}{V} - \frac{1}{V_1}\right)\frac{1}{\cos r_1} - \left(\frac{\sin i \sin r_2}{V} - \frac{1}{V_2}\right)\frac{1}{\cos r_2}\right\}.$$

But from the law of refraction

$$\frac{\sin i}{V} = \frac{\sin r_1}{V_1} = \frac{\sin r_2}{V_2},$$

it follows that

$$\delta = \frac{2\pi}{T} d \left\{ \frac{\cos r_2}{V_2} - \frac{\cos r_1}{V_1} \right\} \quad . \quad . \quad . \quad (88)$$

If now the angles g_1 and g_2 which the wave normal makes with the optic axes within the crystal be introduced, then, from equations (29) on page 320, V_1 and V_2 may be expressed as rational functions of $a^2 + c^2$ and $a^2 - c^2$. Neglecting terms of higher order than the first in $a^2 - c^2$, which is permissible on account of the smallness of the double refraction in all known minerals, there results

$$\delta = \frac{\pi}{T} \cdot \frac{d}{\cos r} \frac{a^2 - c^2}{\left(\frac{a^2 + c^2}{2}\right)^{\frac{3}{2}}} \sin g_1 \sin g_2 . \quad . \quad . \quad (89)$$

In this equation g_1 and g_2 denote the angles which either one of the two refracted wave normals makes with the optic axes; r denotes the angle of refraction for one of the refracted wave normals. Hence $d : \cos r$ is the length of the path in the crystal. Since terms of the first order only in $a^2 - c^2$ have been retained, BD may be considered equal to BC.

If the principal indices n_1 and n_3 of the crystal be introduced, and if n denote their geometrical mean, then

$$a^2 = V^2 : n_1^2, \quad c^2 = V^2 : n_3^2,$$

and hence

$$\delta = \frac{\pi d}{\lambda \cos r} \frac{n_3^2 - n_1^2}{n} \sin g_1 \sin g_2 = \frac{2\pi d}{\lambda \cos r}(n_3 - n_1) \sin g_1 \sin g_2 . \quad (90)$$

If the plate of crystal be introduced between a polarizer and an analyzer, the resultant intensity is approximately expressed by (81), at least if the change in amplitude introduced by refraction at the surfaces of the crystal be neglected.

The case becomes of especial interest if the effects upon the intensity J corresponding to different angles of incidence i can be brought into the field at the same time and compared. This can be done by means of the polarizing apparatus shown in Figs. 93 and 94. The mirror A reflects light from the sky

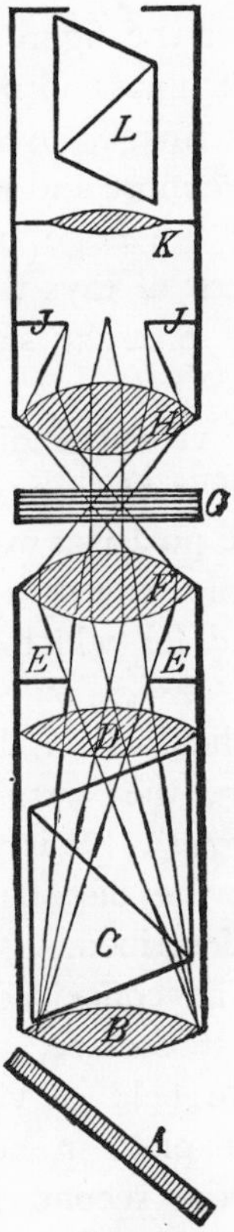

FIG. 93.

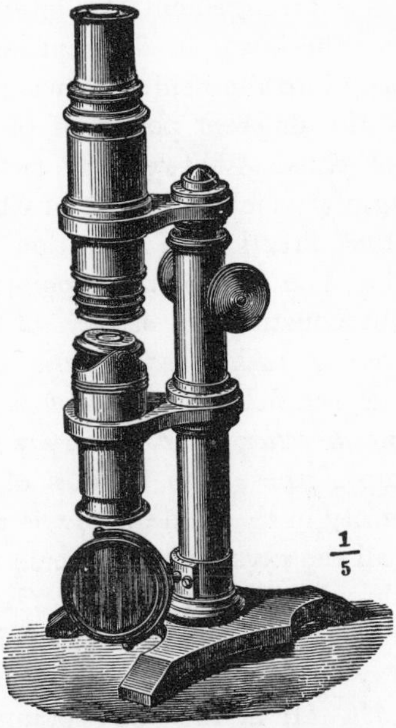

FIG. 94.

into the apparatus. This light is concentrated by means of two lenses B and D upon the aperture E. It is polarized by passage through the Nicol C. E lies at the principal focus of one or more convergent lenses F, which transform all the cones of rays which have their vertices at E into beams of parallel rays which pass through the crystal G in all possible directions. In the figure three such beams are shown. The rays then fall upon a convergent lens H which brings together in a point M at its principal focus, which lies in the aperture of the diaphragm J, each beam of parallel rays. The image formed at M is magnified by the eyepiece K, and the rays pass finally through the analyzer L. As is evident from the figure, the middle of the image at J is formed by rays which pass normally through the plate; the side portions of this image, by rays which traverse the plate in directions which are more and more oblique the nearer the point M approaches the edge of J. With this arrangement the interference effects of rays which traverse the plate in different directions are brought simultaneously into the field of view.

At the different points M of the field of view the difference of phase δ between the two waves is different, as is also the angle ϕ which the plane of vibration of the polarizer makes with the direction of vibration of one of the waves in the crystal. The loci of those points of the field for which δ is constant constitute a family of curves, *the curves of equal difference of path* (*isochromatic curves*). The loci of those points of the field for which ϕ is constant are the *curves of constant direction of polarization* (*isogyric curves*). It is with the help of these two families of curves that the distribution of intensity in the field of view is most easily described.

If all the rays which traverse the crystal be conceived to pass through a single point O upon its first surface, then only one ray comes to each point M in the field of view. This ray intersects the second surface of the plate in some point M'. If in this way points M' upon the second face of the crystal, corresponding to all the points M of the focal plane, be found, then the figures formed by these two sets of points are similar. Hence only the points M' will be considered. It appears from equation (89), in which $d : \cos r$ denotes the length of the path of the ray within the crystal, that the curves of equal difference of path are obtained from the intersection of the second surface of the crystal with the family of surfaces constructed about O whose equation is

$$\rho \sin g_1 \sin g_2 = \text{const.}, \quad . \quad . \quad . \quad . \quad . \quad (91)$$

in which ρ represents the radius vector of a point P with respect to the point O, while g_1 and g_2 are the angles included between the radius vector and the optic axes. Such a surface has a form like that shown in Fig. 95. It must be asymptotic to the optic axes, since for $g_1 = 0$ or $g_2 = 0$, $\rho = \infty$ [cf. (91)].

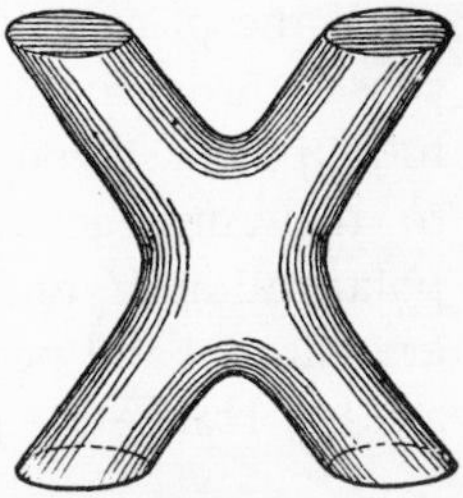

FIG. 95.

If the crystal be cut perpendicular to an optical median line, i.e. to an axis of optic symmetry lying in the plane of the optic axes, the curves of equal difference of path are lemniscates whose poles A_1 and A_2 are the optic axes. If the plate be observed between crossed Nicols, equation (85) is applicable. In homogeneous light the curves of equal difference of path for which $\delta = 2h\pi$ are black. In white light they are curves of like colors (hence called isochromatic), resembling closely the Newton interference colors. Nevertheless, for the reasons given on page 348, departures from this form are shown by some crystals,* and the entire phenomenon is complicated on account of the dispersion of the optic axes, i.e. on account of the fact that the trace of the optic axes upon the second surface of the crystal varies with the color.† In some crystals (brookite) the plane of the optic axes swings about through 90° if the color be changed. The form of the isochromatic curves in white light is greatly changed by the dispersion of the optic axes. The whole field of view is now,

* The rings shown by apophyllite from the Faroe Islands and from Peonah in the East Indies are especially remarkable. Each ring has the same color, and the alternate rings are dark violet and dull yellow. This apophyllite is positively doubly refracting for red light, negatively doubly refracting for blue light, and neutral for yellow light.

† Cf. Mascart, Traité d'Optique, vol. ii. pp. 173–190, Paris, 1891. In Rochelle salt the angle between the optic axes is for red 76°, for violet 56°.

in accordance with (85), traversed by a black curve, the so-called *principal isogyre*, for which $\sin 2\phi = 0$. If the plane of the optic axes coincides with the plane of polarization of the analyzer, or the polarizer (the so-called *principal position*), the principal isogyre is a black cross one of whose arms passes through the optic axes, while the other, perpendicular to it, passes through the middle of the field. For, according to the construction given upon page 322, the directions of polarization H_1 and H_2 corresponding to points on this cross are parallel and perpendicular to the line A_1A_2 joining the optic axes. Hence the interference figure is that shown in Fig. 96.

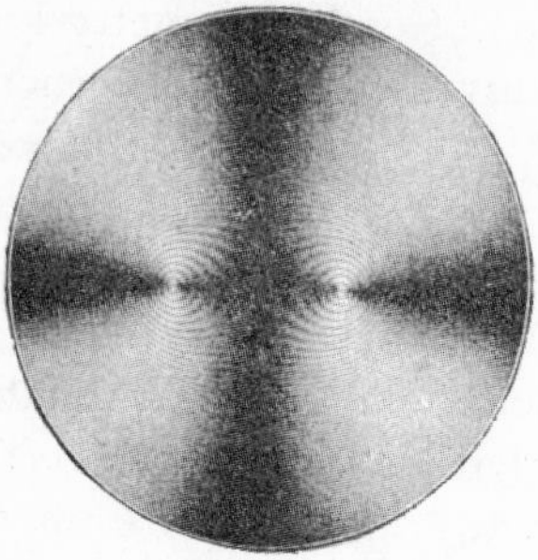

FIG. 96.

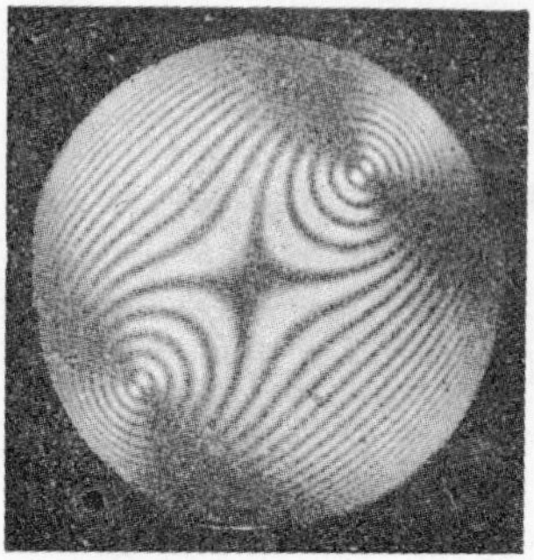

FIG. 97.

In the *second principal position* of the crystal, i.e. when the plane of the optic axes A_1 and A_2 makes an angle of 45° with the plane of the analyzer, the principal isogyres are hyperbolæ which pass through the optic axes. Hence the interference pattern is that shown in Fig. 97. The equation of the principal isogyre can be approximately obtained by taking the line PB, which bisects the angle A_1PA_2, as a direction of polarization H within the crystal,* P being any point upon the plate (cf. Fig. 98). Let the directions of the coordinates x and y

* From the rule given on page 322 it is evident that this is only approximately correct. The problem is more thoroughly discussed in Winkelmann's Handbuch der Physik, Optik, p. 726 sq.

lie in the planes of polarization of the analyzer and the polarizer respectively. Also, let $PA_1 = l_1$, $PA_2 = l_2$, $A_1A_2 = l$. Then

$$BA_1 : BA_2 = l_1 : l_2, \quad BA_1 + BA_2 = l,$$

i.e.

$$BA_1 = \frac{l_1}{l_1 + l_2} l. \quad . \quad . \quad . \quad . \quad . \quad (92)$$

Also, from the triangle A_1BP,

$$\sin \alpha : \sin \measuredangle A_1BP = BA_1 : l_1. \quad . \quad . \quad . \quad (93)$$

But now for the principal isogyre $\measuredangle A_1BP = 45°$, since the line A_1A_2 connecting the optic axes is to make an angle of 45°

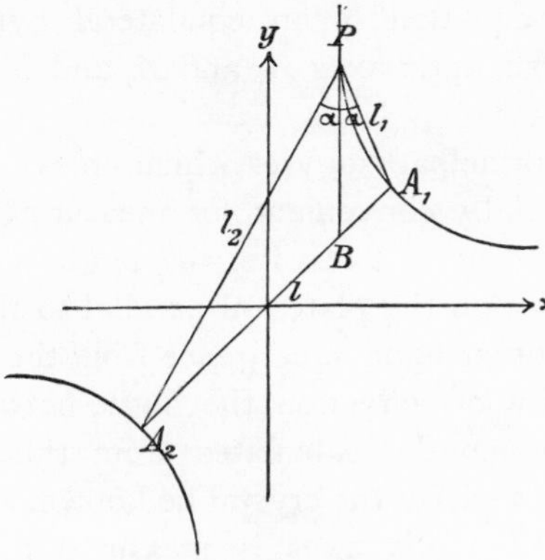

FIG. 98.

with the coordinate axes, and since, for the principal isogyre, the line PB is to be parallel to the y-axis. Hence, from (92) and (93),

$$\sin \alpha = \frac{1}{\sqrt{2}} \cdot \frac{l}{l_1 + l_2}. \quad . \quad . \quad . \quad . \quad . \quad (94)$$

Further, from the triangle A_1PA_2,

$$l^2 = l_1^2 + l_2^2 - 2l_1l_2 \cos \phi = (l_1 - l_2)^2 + 4l_1l_2 \sin^2 \alpha;$$

i.e., from (94),

$$l^2 = (l_1 - l_2)^2 + 2l^2 \frac{l_1 l_2}{(l_1 + l_2)^2},$$

or

$$l^2(l_1^2 + l_2^2) = (l_1^2 - l_2^2)^2. \quad . \quad . \quad . \quad . \quad (95)$$

If the coordinates of the points A_1 and A_2 of the optic axes are called $\pm p$, then

$$l_1^2 = (x - p)^2 + (y - p)^2, \quad l_2^2 = (x + p)^2 + (y + p)^2, \quad l^2 = 8p^2,$$

and (95) becomes

$$xy = p^2. \quad . \quad . \quad . \quad . \quad . \quad . \quad . \quad . \quad (96)$$

But this is the equation of an equilateral hyperbola which passes through the optic axes A_1 and A_2 and is asymptotic to the coordinate axes.

These black principal isogyres which cross the interference pattern are especially convenient for measuring the apparent angle between the optic axes, i.e. the angle which two wave normals, which within the plate are parallel to the optic axes, make with each other upon emergence from the plate. With the aid of the law of refraction the angle between the optic axes themselves may be calculated from this, if the mean principal velocity b within the crystal be known. The apparent angle between the optic axes is measured by rotating the crystal about an axis perpendicular to the plane of the optic axes, and thus bringing the traces of the optic axes successively into the middle of the field of view, i.e. under the cross-hairs. The angle through which the crystal is rotated is read off on a graduated circle. The apparatus constructed for measuring this angle is called a stauroscope.

In uniaxial crystals a surface of equal difference of path (δ = const.) has the form shown in Fig. 99. When the plate is cut perpendicular to the optic axis, the isochromatic curves are concentric circles about the optic axis. With crossed

Nicols the isogyre is a black right-angled cross. Hence the interference pattern is that shown in Fig. 100. From a measurement of the diameters of the rings the difference in the

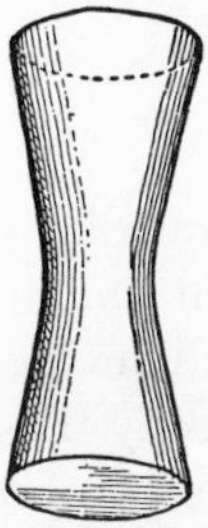

FIG. 99.

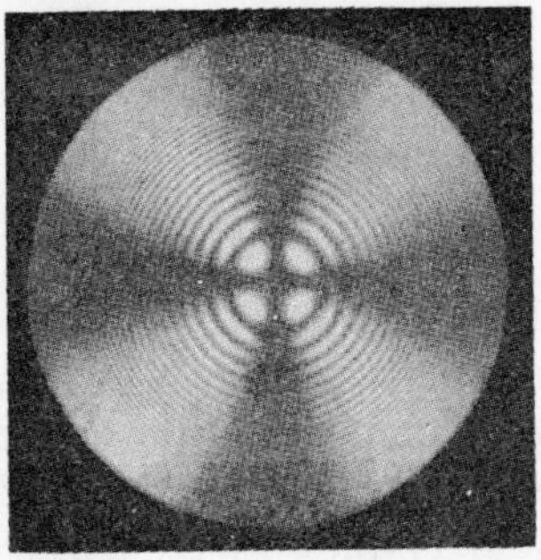

FIG. 100.

two principal indices of refraction of the crystal can be obtained.

For a discussion of methods of distinguishing the character of double refraction by means of a plate of selenite for which $\delta = \frac{\pi}{2}$, as well as for other special cases, cf. Liebisch, Physik. Krystallogr., or Winkelmann's Handbuch der Physik, Optik.

CHAPTER IV

ABSORBING MEDIA

1. Electromagnetic Theory.—Absorbing media will be defined as media in which the intensity of light diminishes as the length of the path of the light within the medium increases. The metals are characterized by specially strong absorbing powers. According to the electromagnetic theory absorption is to be expected in all media which are not perfect dielectrics. For the electric currents arising from conduction produce heat the energy of which must come from the radiant energy of the light.

The electromagnetic theory given above on page 268 sq. will now be extended to include the case of imperfect insulators, i.e. to include media which possess both a dielectric constant ϵ and an electric conductivity σ.

The components of the electric current density will here, as above, be denoted by j_x, j_y, j_z (in electrostatic units), so that for an imperfect insulator

$$j_x = \frac{\epsilon}{4\pi}\frac{\partial X}{\partial t} + \sigma X, \quad j_y = \frac{\epsilon}{4\pi}\frac{\partial Y}{\partial t} + \sigma Y, \quad j_z = \frac{\epsilon}{4\pi}\frac{\partial Z}{\partial t} + \sigma Z. \quad (1)$$

For the total current is composed of the displacement currents which alone were considered in equation (17) on page 269 above, and the conduction currents, which are represented in (1) by the terms σX, σY, σZ. If the current density and the electric force are measured in electrostatic units, then σ represents the absolute conductivity * in the electrostatic system. For mercury it has the value $\sigma = 9.56 \cdot 10^{15}$.

* The dimensions of this quantity are T^{-1}, the second being assumed as the unit of time.

Equations (1) contain the only additions which need be made to the theory of perfect dielectrics previously given. For equations (7) and (11) on pages 265 and 267 will be retained as the fundamental equations of the Maxwell theory for every medium. If the permeability μ be set equal to 1, so that $4\pi s_x = \frac{\partial \alpha}{\partial t}$, etc., then these equations are

$$\frac{4\pi j_x}{c} = \frac{\partial \gamma}{\partial y} - \frac{\partial \beta}{\partial z}, \quad \frac{4\pi j_y}{c} = \frac{\partial \alpha}{\partial z} - \frac{\partial \gamma}{\partial x}, \quad \frac{4\pi j_z}{c} = \frac{\partial \beta}{\partial x} - \frac{\partial \alpha}{\partial y}; \quad (2)$$

$$\frac{1}{c}\frac{\partial \alpha}{\partial t} = \frac{\partial Y}{\partial z} - \frac{\partial Z}{\partial y}, \quad \frac{1}{c}\frac{\partial \beta}{\partial t} = \frac{\partial Z}{\partial x} - \frac{\partial X}{\partial z}, \quad \frac{1}{c}\frac{\partial \gamma}{\partial t} = \frac{\partial X}{\partial y} - \frac{\partial Y}{\partial x}. \quad (3)$$

It may apppear questionable whether it is permissible to set $\mu = 1$ in this case, since the strongly magnetic metals iron, nickel, and cobalt are included under the head of absorbing media. Nevertheless it is shown, both by experiment and by the theory which will be given in Chapter VII, that the permeability of all metals is for light vibrations equal to 1.*

In accordance with the general conclusion reached on page 270, the boundary conditions for the passage of light through the surface separating two different absorbing media are expressed in the same form as above, namely,

$$X_1 = X_2, \quad Y_1 = Y_2, \quad \alpha_1 = \alpha_2, \quad \beta_1 = \beta_2, \quad . \quad (4)$$

provided the xy-plane is parallel to the boundary.

Equations (1) to (4) constitute a complete basis for the electromagnetic theory for isotropic absorbing media.

In order to integrate the differential equations write, as on page 289,

$$X = Ae^{i\frac{2\pi}{T}\left(t - (\mu x + \nu y + \pi z)\right)}, \quad . \quad . \quad . \quad . \quad (5)$$

in which not only A but also μ, ν, and π are complex quantities. The physical meaning of X is obtained from the real

* In the Physik des Aethers, Stuttgart, 1894, Drude has developed the equations which hold for any value of the permeability, and shown that in respect to optical phenomena its value for iron must be unity.

parts of the complex quantities given in (5). It is, however, simpler to ignore the physical meaning of X until the conclusion, i.e. to carry the calculation through with the complex value of X given in (5). Thus, from (5),

$$\frac{\partial X}{\partial t} = i\frac{2\pi}{T}X,$$

so that equations (1) become

$$j_x = \frac{\epsilon - i \cdot 2\sigma T}{4\pi}\frac{\partial X}{\partial t}, \text{ etc.} \quad . \quad . \quad . \quad . \quad . \quad (6)$$

Thus the only difference between isotropic transparent and isotropic absorbing media consists in this, that the constant ϵ, which is real for transparent media, becomes for absorbing media the complex constant

$$\epsilon' = \epsilon - i2\sigma T. \quad . \quad . \quad . \quad . \quad . \quad . \quad (7)$$

All the preceding equations can be applied if ϵ is simply replaced by ϵ'.

Thus, for example, according to equation (3) on page 275,

$$\frac{\epsilon'}{c^2}\frac{\partial^2 X}{\partial t^2} = \Delta X. \quad . \quad . \quad . \quad . \quad . \quad . \quad . \quad (8)$$

This gives, in connection with (5),

$$\frac{\epsilon'}{c^2} = \mu^2 + \nu^2 + \pi^2. \quad . \quad . \quad . \quad . \quad . \quad . \quad (9)$$

Since ϵ' is complex, μ, ν, and π cannot all be real. But this presence of an imaginary always indicates an absorption, i.e. a diminution in the amplitude. If, for example, $\mu = \nu = 0$, $\pi = \frac{1 - i\kappa}{V}$, in which κ and V are to be real, then, from (5),

$$X = Ae^{-2\pi\kappa\frac{z}{\lambda}} \cdot e^{i2\pi\left(\frac{t}{T} - \frac{z}{\lambda}\right)}, \quad . \quad . \quad . \quad (10)$$

in which λ is set equal to $T \cdot V$. But equation (10) asserts that the ratio of the amplitude at any instant to the amplitude after the wave has travelled a distance λ is $1 : e^{-2\pi\kappa}$. Hence κ is called the *coefficient of absorption*.

Equation (10) represents the case in which light falls perpendicularly from air upon the absorbing medium. V is the velocity and λ the wave length of light in the medium. If the ratio $c : V = n$ be called the *index of refraction* of the medium, since it represents the ratio of the velocities of light in air (assumed to be the same as in vacuo) and in the medium, then, by (9),

$$\epsilon' = n^2(1 - \kappa^2 - 2i\kappa),$$

or

$$n^2(1 - \kappa^2) = \epsilon, \quad n^2\kappa = \sigma T. \quad . \quad . \quad . \quad (11)$$

Thus this equation furnishes the means of determining the index of refraction and the coefficient of absorption from the electric constants. It will be shown later that the relation (11) cannot be numerically verified; nevertheless the important point here is to observe that a complex value of ϵ' actually means an absorption of light, and that the real and imaginary parts of ϵ' can be replaced, in accordance with (11), by the more tangible concepts of refraction and absorption coefficients.

2. Metallic Reflection. — Resume the notation on page 279 sq. Let the incident light be plane-polarized at an azimuth of 45° to the plane of incidence. Then $E_p = E_s$. The entire development there given can be applied here if only the real constant ϵ be replaced by a complex quantity ϵ'. ϕ denotes the angle of incidence and χ a complex quantity which may be determined in terms of ϕ by

$$\sin \chi = \frac{\sin \phi}{\sqrt{\epsilon'}}. \quad . \quad . \quad . \quad . \quad . \quad . \quad (12)$$

Then, from (27) on page 285, the ratio of the components of the complex amplitude of the reflected light is

$$\frac{R_p}{R_s} = \rho \cdot e^{i\Delta} = -\frac{\cos(\phi + \chi)}{\cos(\phi - \chi)}. \quad . \quad . \quad . \quad (13)$$

ρ here denotes the ratio of the real amplitudes of the p- and s-components of the reflected light, Δ the relative difference of phase of these components. This is at once evident by setting

$R_p = R_p e^{i\delta_p}$, $R_s = R_s e^{i\delta_s}$, in which R_p, R_s, δ_p, δ_s are real quantities. Then

$$\rho = R_p : R_s, \quad \Delta = \delta_p - \delta_s. \quad . \quad . \quad . \quad (14)$$

Since the right-hand side of (13) is a complex quantity, Δ cannot be zero. *Incident plane-polarized light therefore becomes by reflection at the surface of a metal elliptically polarized.*

From (13) it follows that

$$\frac{1 + \rho \cdot e^{i\Delta}}{1 - \rho \cdot e^{i\Delta}} = \frac{\sin\phi \sin\chi}{\cos\phi \cos\chi}.$$

If in this equation χ be replaced by ϕ and ϵ' in accordance with (12), then

$$\frac{1 + \rho \cdot e^{i\Delta}}{1 - \rho \cdot e^{i\Delta}} = \frac{\sin\phi \tan\phi}{\sqrt{\epsilon' - \sin^2\phi}}. \quad . \quad . \quad . \quad (15)$$

Hence when $\phi = 0$, $\rho \cdot e^{i\Delta} = -1$, or $\Delta = 0$ and $\rho = -1$. When $\phi = \frac{\pi}{2}$, $\rho e^{i\Delta} = +1$, i.e. $\Delta = 0$, $\rho = 1$. Hence the relative difference of phase Δ of the reflected light, i.e. its ellipticity, vanishes at perpendicular and grazing incidence. That angle of incidence $\overline{\phi}$ for which the difference of phase Δ amounts to $\frac{\pi}{2}$ is called the *principal angle of incidence* $\overline{\phi}$. At this angle $e^{i\Delta} = i$; hence, from (15),

$$\frac{1 + i \cdot \overline{\rho}}{1 - i \cdot \overline{\rho}} = \frac{\sin\overline{\phi} \cdot \tan\overline{\phi}}{\sqrt{\epsilon' - \sin^2\overline{\phi}}}. \quad . \quad . \quad . \quad . \quad (16)$$

If this equation be multiplied by the conjugate complex equation

$$\frac{1 - i \cdot \overline{\rho}}{1 + i \cdot \overline{\rho}} = \frac{\sin\overline{\phi} \cdot \tan\overline{\phi}}{\sqrt{\epsilon'' - \sin^2\overline{\phi}}},$$

in which ϵ'' denotes the complex quantity which is conjugate to ϵ', the left-hand side reduces to 1. Hence the principal angle of incidence is determined by

$$\sin^4 \bar{\phi} \cdot \tan^4 \bar{\phi} = n^4(1 + \kappa^2)^2 - 2n^2(1 - \kappa^2) \sin^2 \bar{\phi} + \sin^4 \bar{\phi}. \quad (17)$$

For the numerical calculation it is generally sufficient to take account of the first term only on the right-hand side of this equation, since, for all the metals, $n^2(1 + \kappa^2)$ has a value much greater than 1, somewhere between 8 and 30. With this approximation (17) becomes simply

$$\sin \bar{\phi} \tan \bar{\phi} = n \sqrt{1 + \kappa^2}. \quad . \quad . \quad . \quad . \quad (18)$$

This approximation may be obtained directly from (15) by neglecting in the denominator of the right-hand side $\sin^2 \phi$ in comparison with ϵ'. For, from (11),

$$\sqrt{\epsilon'} = n(1 - i\kappa), \quad . \quad . \quad . \quad . \quad . \quad (19)$$

so that (15) becomes

$$\frac{1 + \rho \cdot e^{i\Delta}}{1 - \rho \cdot e^{i\Delta}} = \frac{\sin \phi \tan \phi}{n(1 - i\kappa)}. \quad . \quad . \quad . \quad . \quad (20)$$

Writing

$$\rho = \tan \psi \quad . \quad . \quad . \quad . \quad . \quad . \quad (21)$$

it appears [cf. (13)] that ψ represents the azimuth of the plane of polarization of the reflected light with respect to the plane of incidence, after it has been made plane-polarized by any means such as the Babinet compensator (cf. page 257). Hence ψ is called the *azimuth of restored polarization.*

Now it is easy to deduce the relation

$$\frac{1 - \rho e^{i\Delta}}{1 + \rho e^{i\Delta}} = \frac{\cos 2\psi - i \sin \Delta \sin 2\psi}{1 + \cos \Delta \sin 2\psi},$$

so that the following may be obtained from (20):

$$\left.\begin{aligned} \kappa &= \sin \Delta \tan 2\psi, \\ n &= \sin \phi \tan \phi \frac{\cos 2\psi}{1 + \cos \Delta \sin 2\psi}, \\ n^2(1 + \kappa^2) &= \sin^2 \phi \tan^2 \phi \cdot \frac{1 - \cos \Delta \sin 2\psi}{1 + \cos \Delta \sin 2\psi}. \end{aligned}\right\} \quad . \quad (22)$$

From these equations the optical constants n and κ of a metal can be determined with sufficient accuracy from observations of ψ and Δ.*

The value of ψ which corresponds to the principal angle of incidence $\phi = \overline{\phi}$ is called the principal azimuth $\overline{\psi}$. From the first of equations (22) it follows that

$$\kappa = \tan 2\overline{\psi}. \quad . \quad . \quad . \quad . \quad . \quad . \quad . \quad (23)$$

Inversely, in order to obtain Δ and ψ from the optical constants, set

$$\tan P = \frac{n\sqrt{1 + \kappa^2}}{\sin \phi \tan \phi}, \quad \tan Q = \kappa. \quad . \quad . \quad . \quad (24)$$

Then from (20), since the right-hand side has the value $\cot P \cdot e^{iQ}$,

$$\begin{aligned} \tan \Delta &= \sin Q \tan 2P, \\ \cos 2\psi &= \cos Q \sin 2P. \quad . \quad . \quad . \quad . \quad (25) \end{aligned}$$

The *reflecting power* of a metal is defined as the ratio of the intensity of the reflected light to that of the incident light when the angle of incidence ϕ is zero. In this case, from equation (26) on page 284, since n is here to be replaced by $n(1 - i\kappa)$ [cf. equation (19)],

$$\frac{\mathrm{R_p}}{E_p} = \frac{R_p \cdot e^{i\delta_p}}{E_p} = \frac{n(1 - i\kappa) - 1}{n(1 - i\kappa) + 1}. \quad . \quad . \quad . \quad (26)$$

If this equation is multiplied by its conjugate complex equation, the value of the reflecting power R is found to be

$$R = \frac{R_p^2}{E_p^2} = \frac{n^2(1 + \kappa^2) + 1 - 2n}{n^2(1 + \kappa^2) + 1 + 2n}. \quad . \quad . \quad . \quad (27)$$

Since for all metals $2n$ is small in comparison with $n^2(1 + \kappa^2)$, R is almost equal to unity, i.e. the reflecting power is very large. A substance which shows this strong reflecting power characteristic of the metals (in the case of silver it

* More rigorous equations, in which $\sin^2 \phi$ has not been neglected in comparison with ϵ', are given in Winkelmann's Handbuch, Optik, p. 822 sq.

amounts to 95 per cent) is said to have metallic lustre.* This is more marked the greater the absorption coefficient of the substance. Since κ is different for different colors, some metals, like gold and copper, have a very pronounced color. Thus a metal appears red if red light is reflected more strongly than the other colors. Hence the light reflected from the surface of a metal is approximately complementary to the color of the light transmitted by it. In order to observe this it is necessary to use sheets of the metal which are only a few thousandths of a millimetre thick. Gold-foil of such thickness actually appears green by transmitted light.

The more often light is reflected between two mirrors of the same substance the more saturated does its color become, for the colors which are most strongly absorbed by the substance are much less weakened by repeated reflection than the others. In this way Rubens and Nichols,† and Aschkinass ‡ have succeeded in isolating heat-waves much longer than any previously observed. An Auer burner without a chimney was used as the source of the radiations. After five reflections upon sylvine an approximately homogeneous beam of wave length $\lambda = 0.061$ mm. was obtained, this being the longest heat-wave yet observed. The reflecting power of sylvine for this radiation is $R = 0.80$, i.e. 80 per cent. Long heat-waves can also be isolated by multiple reflections upon rock salt, fluorspar, and quartz.

It is important to distinguish between the surface colors produced by metallic reflection and those which are shown by weakly absorbing substances with rough surfaces; for example, by colored paper, colored glass, etc. These substances appear colored in diffusely reflected light because the light is reflected in part from the interior particles of the substance, and hence

---

* That this effect is actually due to a high reflecting power is proved by the fact that a bubble of air under water from which the light is totally reflected looks like a drop of mercury.

† Rubens and Nichols, Wied. Ann. 60, p. 418, 1897.

‡ Rubens and Aschkinass, Wied. Ann. 65, p. 241, 1898.

selective absorption is the cause of the color. In such cases the colors in transmitted and reflected light are the same, not complementary as in the case of the metals.

3. The Optical Constants of the Metals.—Equation (22) shows how the optical constants n and κ of a metal can be conveniently determined, namely, by observing the vibration form of the elliptically polarized reflected light when the incident light is plane-polarized, i.e. by measuring Δ and ψ by means of a Babinet compensator and analyzing Nicol in accordance with the method described on page 255 sq. But care must be taken that the surface of the metal be as clean as possible, since surface impurities tend to reduce the value of the principal angle of incidence.* The following table contains some of the values which Drude has obtained by the reflection of yellow light from surfaces which were as clean as possible:

Metals.	$n\kappa$	n	$\overline{\phi}$	$\overline{\psi}$	R
Silver	3.67	0.18	75° 42′	43° 35′	95.3%
Gold	2.82	0.37	72 18	41 39	85.1
Platinum	4.26	2.06	78 30	32 35	70.1
Copper	2.62	0.64	71 35	38 57	73.2
Steel	3.40	2.41	77 3	27 49	58.5
Sodium	2.61	0.005	71 19	44 58	99.7
Mercury	4.96	1.73	79 34	35 43	78.4

The reflecting power R was not measured directly, but calculated from (27).

The optical constants can also be determined by observations upon the transmitted light. By measuring the absorption in a thin film of thickness d a value for $\kappa : \lambda$ may be obtained, as is seen from (10), λ denoting the wave length in the metal. Since now $\lambda = \lambda_0 : n$, and since λ_0, the wave length in air, is known, $n\kappa$ may also be obtained. But reflection at the bounding surfaces of thin sheets of metal is accompanied by a great loss

* Cf. Drude, Wied. Ann. 36, p. 885, 1889; 39, p. 481, 1890.

in intensity. In order to eliminate this difficulty it is necessary to compare the absorptions in films of different thickness. The losses due to reflection are then in both cases nearly the same, so that a conclusion may be drawn as to the value of $n\kappa$ from the difference in the absorptions. The difficulty in making these observations lies in obtaining metal films but a few thousandths of a millimetre in thickness, which are yet uniform and free from holes. For this reason the value of $n\kappa$ as determined by this transmission method usually comes out smaller than by the reflection method.* But in some cases,† for example, silver—which can be easily deposited upon glass from a solution—the values of $n\kappa$ determined by the two methods are in good agreement.

As in the case of transparent media, the index of refraction can be determined from the deviation produced by a prism,‡ but in the case of the metals the angle of the prism must be very small (a fraction of a minute of arc) in order that the intensity of the light transmitted may be appreciable. Since Kundt succeeded in producing metal prisms suitable for this purpose § (generally by electrolytic deposition upon platinized glass), the indices of refraction of the metals have been determined many times by this method.‖ Not only is the production of these prisms troublesome, but also the observations are very difficult, since the result is obtained as the quotient of two very small quantities. In general the results agree well with those obtained from observations of reflection; for example, the remarkable conclusion that for certain metals $n < 1$ has been confirmed.

These small indices of silver, gold, copper, and especially

---

* W. Rathenau, Die Absorption des Lichtes in Metallen. Dissert. Berlin, 1889.

† W. Wernicke, Pogg. Ann. Ergzgbd. 8, p. 75, 1878. Also the observations of Wien (Wied. Ann. 35, p. 48, 1888) furnish an approximate verification.

‡ For the equations cf. W. Voigt, Wien. Ann. 24, p. 144, 1885. P. Drude, Wied. Ann. 42, p. 666, 1891.

§ A. Kundt, Wied. Ann. 34, p. 469, 1888.

‖ Cf., for instance, Du Bois and Rubens, Wied. Ann. 41, p. 507, 1890.

of sodium are particularly surprising; they mean that light travels faster in these metals than in air.

If these optical constants be compared with the demands of the electromagnetic theory [cf. (11)], a contradiction is at once apparent. For since ϵ is to equal $n^2(1 - \kappa^2)$, the dielectric constant of all the metals would be negative, since $\kappa = \tan 2\bar{\psi}$, and since 2ψ is for all metals larger than $45°$, i.e. $\kappa > 1$. But a negative dielectric constant has no meaning. Also, the second of equations (11), namely, $n^2\kappa = \sigma T$, is not confirmed, since, for example, in the case of mercury, for yellow light $\sigma T = 20$, while $n^2\kappa = 8.6$. For silver σT is much greater, while $n^2\kappa$ is much smaller than for mercury.

The same fact is met with here which was encountered above when the indices of refraction of transparent media were compared with the dielectric constants. The electromagnetic theory describes the phenomena well, but the numerical values of the optical constants cannot be determined from electrical relations. The extension of the theory, which removes this difficulty, will be given in the following chapter.

4. Absorbing Crystals.—The extension of the equations for isotropic absorbing media to include the case of absorbing crystals consists simply in assuming different dielectric constants and different conductivities along the three rectangular axes of optical symmetry. If the coordinate axes coincide with these axes of symmetry, equations (12) on page 314 are obtained, with this difference, that ϵ_1, ϵ_2, ϵ_3 are complex quantities, if, in accordance with (5) on page 359, the electrical force is introduced as a complex quantity. To be sure the equations will not be perfectly general, since the axes of symmetry for the dielectric constant do not necessarily coincide with those for the conductivity. These axes must coincide only in crystals which possess at least as much symmetry as the rhombic system. Nevertheless the most general case will not be here discussed, since the essential elements may be obtained from the simplification here presented.*

* This is treated more fully in Winkelmann's Handbuch, Optik, p. 811 sq.

In order to integrate the differential equations given above, namely,

$$\frac{\epsilon_1'}{c^2}\frac{\partial^2 X}{\partial t^2} = \varDelta X - \left(\frac{\partial X}{\partial x} + \frac{\partial Y}{\partial y} + \frac{\partial Z}{\partial z}\right), \text{ etc.}, \quad . \quad (28)$$

let the components u, v, w of the light-vector be represented by the equations

$$\left.\begin{aligned} u &= \epsilon_1' X = M e^{i\frac{2\pi}{T}\left(t - (mx + ny + pz)\frac{1 - i\kappa}{V}\right)}, \\ v &= \epsilon_2' Y = N e^{i\frac{2\pi}{T}(t \ldots)}, \quad w = \epsilon_3' Z = \Pi e^{i\frac{2\pi}{T}(t \ldots)}, \end{aligned}\right\} \quad (29)$$

in which $m^2 + n^2 + p^2 = 1$, and M, N, Π may be complex. These equations correspond to a plane wave whose direction cosines are m, n, p. V is the velocity of the wave, and κ the absorption coefficient (cf. page 360). Let

$$\frac{V}{1 - i\kappa} = \omega. \quad . \quad . \quad . \quad . \quad . \quad . \quad (30)$$

Then Fresnel's law (18) on page 316 may be written

$$\frac{m^2}{a_0^2 - \omega^2} + \frac{n^2}{b_0^2 - \omega^2} + \frac{p^2}{c_0^2 - \omega^2} = 0, \quad . \quad . \quad (31)$$

in which, however, a_0^2, b_0^2, c_0^2 are complex. Hence this equation splits up into two from which V and κ may be calculated separately as functions of the direction m, n, p of the wave normal. According to equations (15), (19), and (20) on pages 315 and 317, the following relations hold for the quantities M, N, Π:

$$Mm + Nn + \Pi p = 0, \quad . \quad . \quad . \quad . \quad (32)$$

$$M : N : \Pi = \frac{m}{a_0^2 - \omega^2} : \frac{n}{b_0^2 - \omega^2} : \frac{p}{c_0^2 - \omega^2}, \quad . \quad (33)$$

$$M_1 M_2 + N_1 N_2 + \Pi_1 \Pi_2 = 0. \quad . \quad . \quad . \quad (34)$$

Since, by (33), M, N, Π are complex, two elliptically polarized rays correspond to every direction m, n, p. For if it be assumed that $M = \mathsf{M} \cdot e^{i\delta_1}$, $N = \mathsf{N} \cdot e^{i\delta_2}$, then $\delta_1 - \delta_2$ denotes the difference of phase between the components u, v of the light-vector. For plane-polarized light $\delta_1 - \delta_2 = 0$. Equation (32) expresses the fact that the plane of the vibration is perpendicular to the wave normal, (34) the fact that the ellipses are similar to each other, while their positions are inverted.*

The relation which can be deduced from (31) between the velocity and the direction m, n, p is very complicated. Hence Fresnel's law, in spite of its apparent identity with (31), is considerably modified. But the relations are much simpler in the case of weakly absorbing crystals such as are always used when observations are made with transmitted light.† For if κ^2 can be neglected in comparison with 1, then $\omega^2 = V^2(1 + 2i\kappa)$. Hence setting

$$a_0^2 = a^2 + ia'^2, \quad b_0^2 = b^2 + ib'^2, \quad c_0^2 = c^2 + ic'^2, \qquad (35)$$

then

$$\frac{m^2}{a_0^2 - \omega^2} = \frac{m^2}{a^2 - V^2 - i(2\kappa V^2 - a'^2)} = \frac{m^2}{a^2 - V^2}\left(1 + i\frac{2\kappa V^2 - a'^2}{a^2 - V^2}\right). \quad (36)$$

Hence (31) splits up into the two equations

$$\frac{m^2}{a^2 - V^2} + \frac{n^2}{b^2 - V^2} + \frac{p^2}{c^2 - V^2} = 0, \quad . \quad . \quad (37)$$

$$2\kappa V^2\left\{\frac{m^2}{(a^2 - V^2)^2} + \frac{n^2}{(b^2 - V^2)^2} + \frac{p^2}{(c^2 - V^2)^2}\right\}$$
$$= a'^2\frac{m^2}{(a^2 - V^2)^2} + b'^2\frac{n^2}{(b^2 - V^2)^2} + c'^2\frac{p^2}{(c^2 - V^2)^2}. \qquad (38)$$

Equation (37) is Fresnel's law. Hence *when the absorption is small this is not modified.* Equation (38) presents κ as a function of m, n, and p. According to (33), when the absorption is small M, N, Π are very nearly real, i.e. the two waves within the crystal have but a slight elliptic polarization. If $\mathfrak{M}$, $\mathfrak{N}$, $\mathfrak{P}$ denote the direction cosines of the principal axis of

* For more complete proof of this, cf. Winkelmann's Handbuch, Optik, p. 813.

† In reflected light the effects of strong absorption are easy to observe, for example, with magnesium- or barium-platinocyanide. Such crystals show metallic lustre and produce polarization.

the vibration ellipse, then, from (33) and (36), since $\mathfrak{M}$ is the real part of M, etc.,

$$\mathfrak{M} : \mathfrak{N} : \mathfrak{P} = \frac{m}{a^2 - V^2} : \frac{n}{b^2 - V^2} : \frac{p}{c^2 - V^2}. \quad . \quad (39)$$

Thus $\mathfrak{M}$, $\mathfrak{N}$, $\mathfrak{P}$ are determined in the same way as the direction of vibration in transparent crystals.

In view of (39) and the relation $\mathfrak{M}^2 + \mathfrak{N}^2 + \mathfrak{P}^2 = 1$, it is possible to write (38) in the form:

$$2\kappa V^2 = a'^2 \mathfrak{M}^2 + b'^2 \mathfrak{N}^2 + c'^2 \mathfrak{P}^2; \quad . \quad . \quad . \quad (40)$$

i.e., in accordance with (18′) on page 317, which also holds here,

$$2\kappa = \frac{a'^2 \mathfrak{M}^2 + b'^2 \mathfrak{N}^2 + c'^2 \mathfrak{P}^2}{a^2 \mathfrak{M}^2 + b^2 \mathfrak{N}^2 + c^2 \mathfrak{P}^2}. \quad . \quad . \quad . \quad (41)$$

Hence the index of absorption κ, like the velocity V, is a single-valued function of the direction of vibration.

This law can be easily verified by observing in transmitted light a cube of colored crystal cut parallel to the planes of symmetry. This shows different colors as the direction of the ray is changed (trichroism for rhombic crystals, dichroism for hexagonal and tetragonal crystals). This phenomenon can be observed in tourmaline, beryl, smoky topaz, iolite, and especially in pennine, which appears bluish green and brownish yellow. If the light transmitted by such a crystal is analyzed with a Nicol, the color depends upon its plane of polarization, the extreme colors being obtained when the Nicol is parallel to an axis of symmetry of the crystal.* The six extreme colors which can be observed in a cube of tricroitic crystal by means of a Nicol reduce in reality to three, since each color appears twice, namely, in the positions for which the direction of vibration in the Fresnel sense is the same (cf. page 253).

Equations (40) and (41) become simpler if the wave normal lies near an optic axis; for example, near A_1. If the angle g_1

* Both colors are seen at the same time if a double-image prism be used instead of a Nicol. Cf. Müller-Pouillet, vol. II, Optics, by Lummer, p. 1005.

which the wave normal N makes with the optic axis A_1 is so small that its square can be neglected in comparison with 1, then $V^2 = b^2$. If, further, the angle between the plane of the optic axes (xz-plane) and the plane (NA_1) defined by A_1 and N be denoted by ψ, then the plane defined by N and the direction of vibration $\mathfrak{M}_1$, $\mathfrak{N}_1$, $\mathfrak{P}_1$ makes an angle $\frac{\psi}{2}$ with the xz-plane. For, from page 322, the plane of vibration bisects the angle included between the planes (NA_1) and (NA_2); but since N is to lie very near to the optic axis, the plane (NA_2) may be identified with the plane (A_1A_2) of the optic axes, i.e. with the xz-plane. Hence the direction of vibration $\mathfrak{M}_1$, $\mathfrak{N}_1$, $\mathfrak{P}_1$ must make an angle of $\frac{\psi}{2}$ with that direction S in the xz-plane which is perpendicular to the wave normal N, i.e. to the optic axis A_1. The direction cosines of S are $\cos q$, 0, $-\sin q$, where q denotes the angle between the optic axis A_1 and the z-axis, i.e. half of the angle included between the optic axes. Hence it follows that

$$\cos\frac{\psi}{2} = \mathfrak{M}_1 \cos q - \mathfrak{P}_1 \sin q. \quad . \quad . \quad . \quad (42)$$

Since now the direction $\mathfrak{M}_1$, $\mathfrak{N}_1$, $\mathfrak{P}_1$ is also perpendicular to the wave normal N, i.e. to the optic axis A_1, whose direction cosines are $\sin q$, 0, $\cos q$, it follows that

$$0 = \mathfrak{M}_1 \sin q + \mathfrak{P}_1 \cos q. \quad . \quad . \quad . \quad . \quad (42')$$

From these last two equations

$$\mathfrak{M}_1 = \cos q \cos\frac{\psi}{2}, \quad \mathfrak{N}_1 = \sin\frac{\psi}{2}, \quad \mathfrak{P}_1 = -\sin q \cos\frac{\psi}{2}. \quad (43)$$

From this the direction $\mathfrak{M}_2$, $\mathfrak{N}_2$, $\mathfrak{P}_2$ may be determined, since it is perpendicular to $\mathfrak{M}_1$, $\mathfrak{N}_1$, $\mathfrak{P}_1$, and to m, n, p. Thus

$$\mathfrak{M}_2 = -\cos q \sin\frac{\psi}{2}, \quad \mathfrak{N}_2 = \cos\frac{\psi}{2}, \quad \mathfrak{P}_2 = \sin q \sin\frac{\psi}{2}. \quad (44)$$

Hence, from (40), in the neighborhood of the optic axis

$$\left.\begin{aligned} 2\kappa_1 b^2 &= (a'^2 \cos^2 q + c'^2 \sin^2 q) \cos^2 \frac{\psi}{2} + b'^2 \sin^2 \frac{\psi}{2}, \\ 2\kappa_2 b^2 &= (a'^2 \cos^2 q + c'^2 \sin^2 q) \sin^2 \frac{\psi}{2} + b'^2 \cos^2 \frac{\psi}{2}. \end{aligned}\right\} \quad (45)$$

These equations show that for any angle $\pm \psi$ the value of κ_1 is the same as that of κ_2 for an angle $\psi' = \pi \pm \psi$. These equations are indeterminate for the optic axis itself, because then ψ has no meaning. In accordance with the preceding discussion, the direction of vibration may be taken arbitrarily (cf. page 319). From (40) it follows that for a wave polarized in the plane of the optic axes, i.e. vibrating perpendicularly to these axes, since in this case $\mathfrak{M} = \mathfrak{P} = 0$, $\mathfrak{N} = 1$,

$$2\kappa_s b^2 = b'^2, \quad \ldots \ldots \quad (46)$$

but for a wave polarized in a plane perpendicular to the plane of the optic axes, and therefore vibrating in that plane, since for this case $\mathfrak{M} = \cos q$, $\mathfrak{N} = 0$, $\mathfrak{P} = -\sin q$,

$$2\kappa_p b^2 = a'^2 \cos^2 q + c'^2 \sin^2 q. \quad \ldots \quad (47)$$

For intermediate positions of the plane of polarization values of κ are obtained which lie between those of κ_s and κ_p. *Hence the absorption of a wave travelling along an optic axis depends upon its plane of polarization.* Upon introduction of the quantities κ_s and κ_p (45) becomes

$$\kappa_1 = \kappa_p \cdot \cos^2 \frac{\psi}{2} + \kappa_s \cdot \sin^2 \frac{\psi}{2}, \quad \kappa_2 = \kappa_p \cdot \sin^2 \frac{\psi}{2} + \kappa_s \cdot \cos^2 \frac{\psi}{2}. \quad (48)$$

For uniaxial crystals ($a = b$, $a' = b'$), if g represent the angle between the wave normal and the optic axis, it is easy to deduce from (40) for the ordinary wave

$$\left.\begin{aligned} &2\kappa_0 V_0^2 = a'^2, \quad V_0^2 = a^2, \\ &\text{for the extraordinary wave} \\ &2\kappa_e V_e^2 = a'^2 \cos^2 g + c'^2 \sin^2 g, \quad V_e^2 = a^2 \cos^2 g + c^2 \sin^2 g. \end{aligned}\right\} . \quad (49)$$

5. Interference Phenomena in Absorbing Biaxial Crystals.—Let a plate of an absorbing crystal be introduced in convergent light between analyzer and polarizer. Resume the notation of §§ 14 and 15 on pages 344 and 349, and consider Fig. 91. A wave W_1, vibrating in a direction H_1, which upon entering a crystal has an amplitude $E \cos \phi$, upon emergence from the crystal has the amplitude $E \cos \phi\, e^{-\frac{2\pi}{T}\frac{\kappa_1}{V_1}l}$, in which l denotes the length of the path traversed in the crystal. If d denote the thickness of the plate of crystal, and r_1 the angle of refraction of the wave W_1, then $l = d : \cos r_1$. Similarly the amplitude of the wave W_2 is, upon emergence from the crystal, $E \sin \phi\, e^{-\frac{2\pi}{T}\frac{\kappa_2}{V_2}l}$ (the length of the path within the crystal is assumed to be for both waves approximately the same). After passing through the analyzer the amplitudes or the two waves are

$$\left.\begin{aligned} &E \cos \phi \cos (\phi - \chi)\cdot e^{-\kappa_1\sigma_1}, \quad \sigma_1 = \frac{2\pi}{TV_1}\frac{d}{\cos r}, \\ &E \sin \phi \sin (\phi - \chi)\cdot e^{-\kappa_2\sigma_2}, \quad \sigma_2 = \frac{2\pi}{TV_2}\frac{d}{\cos r}. \end{aligned}\right\} \qquad (50)$$

The difference in phase δ of the two waves in convergent light is determined by equation (88) on page 350.

The case of crossed Nicols $\left(\chi = \frac{\pi}{2}\right)$ will be more carefully considered. Assume that the plate of crystal is cut perpendicular to the optic axis A_1, and denote by ψ the angle which the plane A_1A_2 of the optic axes makes with the line MA_2 drawn from a point M, which is near the optic axis in the field of view,* to the optic axis A_1; then (cf. Fig. 101) the direction of vibration H_1 makes approximately the angle $\frac{\psi}{2}$ with the direction A_1A_2, provided A_1M is small in comparison with

* The different points of the field of view correspond (cf. p. 351) to the different inclinations of the rays within the plate.

A_1A_2. If, further, the plane of vibration P of the polarizer makes the angle α with the plane A_1A_2 of the optic axes, then

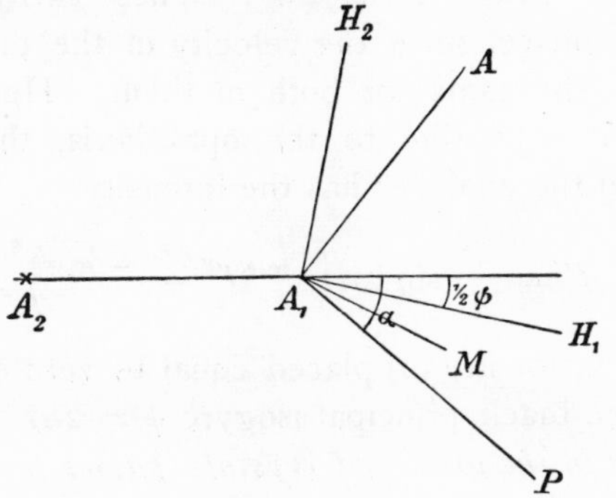

FIG. 101.

in (50) $\phi = \alpha - \frac{\psi}{2}$, $\chi = \frac{\pi}{2}$. The amplitudes of the two interfering waves are therefore

$$\left.\begin{array}{l} + E \cos(\alpha - \psi/2) \sin(\alpha - \psi/2) e^{-\kappa_1\sigma}, \\ - E \sin(\alpha - \psi/2) \cos(\alpha - \psi/2) e^{-\kappa_2\sigma}, \end{array}\right\} \quad . \quad . \quad (51)$$

in which

$$\sigma = \frac{2\pi d}{Tb},$$

since in the neighborhood of the optic axis $V_1 = V_2 = b$, and r is to be small.

Hence the intensity of the light which emerges from the analyzer is

$$J = \frac{E^2}{4} \sin^2(2\alpha - \psi)\{e^{-2\kappa_1\sigma} + e^{-2\kappa_2\sigma} - 2e^{-(\kappa_1+\kappa_2)} \cdot \cos\delta\}. \quad (52)$$

If the wave normal actually coincides with the optic axis, the end sought may be obtained from the following considerations: The amplitude E is resolved into components which are parallel and perpendicular respectively to the plane A_1A_2 of the optic axes. These components are $E \cos\alpha$ and $E \sin\alpha$. After emergence from the crystal the former has the value

$E \cos \alpha\, e^{-\kappa_p \sigma}$, the latter $E \sin \alpha\, e^{-\kappa_s \sigma}$. After passage through the analyzer the former has the amplitude $E \cos \alpha \sin \alpha\, e^{-2\kappa_p \sigma}$, the latter $-E \sin \alpha \cos \alpha\, e^{-\kappa_s \sigma}$. These two waves have no difference in phase, since the velocity in the direction of the optic axis is the same for both of them. Hence when the wave normal is parallel to the optic axis, the light which emerges from the analyzer has the intensity

$$J' = \frac{E^2}{4} \sin 2\alpha \left(e^{-\kappa_p \sigma} - e^{-\kappa_s \sigma}\right)^2. \quad . \quad . \quad (53)$$

The first factor in (52) placed equal to zero determines the position of the black principal isogyre $\psi = 2\alpha$. *But while the black isogyre in the uncolored crystals passes through the optic axis itself, in the pleochroic crystals the point of intersection of the optic axis with the isogyre is bright*, unless $\alpha = 0$ or $\alpha = \frac{\pi}{2}$, i.e. unless the plate lies in the first principal position. For, from (53), J' differs from zero when $\sin 2\alpha \gtrless 0$, and κ_p differs from κ_s.

The second factor in (52) placed equal to zero shows that there are dark rings about the optic axis, since the value of this second factor depends upon $\cos \delta$, and $\cos \delta$ has periodic maxima and minima as the distance from the optic axis increases. Nevertheless even with monochromatic light these rings are perfectly black only where $\kappa_1 = \kappa_2$, i.e., according to (48), when $\psi = \pm \frac{\pi}{2}$, for there the second factor actually vanishes when $\cos \delta = 1$. The whole phenomenon of the rings is less and less distinct the stronger the absorption, i.e. the thicker the plate. For the term in (52) which depends upon the difference in phase δ has a factor which can be written in the form $e^{-(\kappa_p + \kappa_s)\sigma}$. If the crystal is at all colored, then one at least of the two absorption coefficients κ_p and κ_s must differ from zero, i.e. for a sufficiently large value of σ or a sufficiently large thickness d of the plate this term containing cos δ vanishes. This second factor in (52) can be written

$$F = e^{-2\kappa_1\sigma} + e^{-2\kappa_2\sigma}. \quad . \quad . \quad . \quad . \quad (54)$$

Although σ is large, these terms may yet have appreciable values, since κ_1 or κ_2 may be small for certain points M of the field of view provided either κ_p or κ_s is small. It can now be shown that when $\psi = 0$ or π, F is a maximum; when $\psi = \pm\frac{\pi}{2}$, a minimum. For, from (48),

$$\frac{\partial F}{\partial \psi} = \sigma \sin \psi(\kappa_p - \kappa_s)(e^{-2\kappa_1\sigma} - e^{-2\kappa_2\sigma}).$$

Therefore maxima or minima occur when $\psi = 0$ or π, or when $\kappa_1 = \kappa_2$, i.e. $\psi = \pm\frac{\pi}{2}$. But when $\psi = 0$ or π,

$$F = e^{-2\kappa_p\sigma} + e^{-2\kappa_s\sigma} = F_1; \quad . \quad . \quad . \quad (55)$$

and when $\psi = \pm\frac{\pi}{2}$,

$$F = 2 \cdot e^{-(\kappa_p + \kappa_s)\sigma} = F_2. \quad . \quad . \quad . \quad . \quad (56)$$

Writing $e^{-2\kappa_p\sigma} = x$, $e^{-2\kappa_s\sigma} = y$, then $\frac{1}{2}F_1 = \frac{x+y}{2}$, $\frac{1}{2}F_2 = \sqrt{xy}$.

But now, since the arithmetical mean is always greater than the geometrical (the difference between them increasing as the difference between x and y, i.e. between κ_p and κ_s, increases), the values $\psi = 0$ or π correspond to a maximum, the values $\psi = \pm\frac{\pi}{2}$ to a minimum, of F.

In addition to the principal isogyre ($\psi = 2\alpha$), *there is always a black brush traversing the field of view perpendicular to the plane of the optic axes* $\left(\psi = \pm\frac{\pi}{2}\right)$. This brush coincides with the principal isogyre in the second principal position of the plate $\left(\alpha = \frac{\pi}{4}\right)$.

Absorption gives rise to certain peculiar phenomena when either the analyzer or the polarizer is removed. In the first case the two amplitudes which emerge from the crystal have the values $E\cos(\alpha - \frac{1}{2}\psi)e^{-\kappa_1\sigma}$ and $E\sin(\alpha - \frac{1}{2}\psi)e^{-\kappa_2\sigma}$. If these are not brought back to a common plane of vibration, they do not interfere and the resultant intensity is simply the sum of the two components, i.e.

$$J = E^2\{\cos^2(\alpha - \tfrac{1}{2}\psi)e^{-2\kappa_1\sigma} + \sin^2(\alpha - \tfrac{1}{2}\psi)e^{-2\kappa_2\sigma}\}. \quad (57)$$

When the wave normal coincides with the optic axis,

$$J' = E^2\{\cos^2\alpha e^{-2\kappa_p\sigma} + \sin^2\alpha e^{-2\kappa_s\sigma}\}. \quad . \quad . \quad (58)$$

The following principal cases will be investigated:

1. $\alpha = 0$. Then

$$J = E^2\{\cos^2\tfrac{1}{2}\psi e^{-2\kappa_1\sigma} + \sin^2\tfrac{1}{2}\psi e^{-2\kappa_2\sigma}\},$$
$$J' = E^2 e^{-2\kappa_p\sigma}.$$

But since

$$\frac{\partial J}{\partial\psi} \sim \sin\psi\left\{\sigma(\kappa_s - \kappa_p)(\sin^2\tfrac{1}{2}\psi e^{-2\kappa_2\sigma} - \cos^2\tfrac{1}{2}\psi e^{-2\kappa_1\sigma}) + \frac{e^{-2\kappa_2\sigma} - e^{-2\kappa_1\sigma}}{2}\right\},$$

therefore

$$\frac{\partial J}{\partial\psi} = 0 \text{ for } \psi = 0 \text{ or } \pi, \text{ or for } \psi = \pm\pi/2.$$

When $\psi = 0$ or π,

$$J = J_1 = E^2 . e^{-2\kappa_p\sigma};$$

when $\psi = \pm\pi/2$,

$$J = J_2 = E^2 . e^{-(\kappa_p + \kappa_s)\sigma}.$$

If, therefore, $\kappa_p < \kappa_s$ (type II, iolite, epidote), $J_1 > J_2$, i.e. there is a dark brush perpendicular to the plane of the optic axes, which is, however, intercepted by a bright spot on the optic axis. But if $\kappa_p > \kappa_s$ (type I, andalusite, titanite), then $J_2 > J_1$. In this case the dark brush lies in the plane of the optic axes and is continuous.

2. $\alpha = \frac{\pi}{2}$.

$$J = E^2\{\sin^2 \tfrac{1}{2}\psi e^{-2\kappa_1\sigma} + \cos^2 \tfrac{1}{2}\psi e^{-2\kappa_2\sigma}\},$$
$$J' = E^2 . e^{-2\kappa_s\sigma}.$$

When $\psi = 0$ or π,

$$J = J_1 = E^2 . e^{-2\kappa_s\sigma};$$

when $\psi = \pm \pi/2$,

$$J = J_2 = E^2 . e^{-(\kappa_p + \kappa_s)\sigma}.$$

If, therefore, $\kappa_p < \kappa_s$, $J_1 < J_2$, i.e. a continuous dark brush lies in the plane of the optic axes. But if $\kappa_p > \kappa_s$, $J_1 > J_2$, i.e. the dark brush is perpendicular to the plane of the optic axes and is intercepted by a bright spot on the optic axis.

If both analyzer and polarizer are removed, i.e. if a plate of biaxial pleochroic crystal cut perpendicular to one of the optic axes is observed in transmitted natural light, the resultant intensity is

$$J = E^2(e^{-2\kappa_1\sigma} + e^{-2\kappa_2\sigma}); \quad . \quad . \quad . \quad . \quad . \quad (59)$$

while along the optic axis itself it is

$$J' = E^2(e^{-2\kappa_p\sigma} + e^{-2\kappa_s\sigma}). \quad . \quad . \quad . \quad . \quad (60)$$

For natural light may be conceived as composed of two incoherent components of equal amplitudes which vibrate in any two directions which are at right angles to each other. Hence in (60) $2E^2$ denotes the intensity of the incident light. Since now it was shown above [equation (54), page 377] that (59) has a minimum value when $\psi = \pm \frac{\pi}{2}$, *it is evident that a dark brush perpendicular to the plane of the optic axes and intercepted by a bright spot upon the axis will be seen.* These figures produced in natural light were observed by Brewster as long ago as 1819. They may be easily seen in andalusite and epidote.*

---

* For further discussion of these idiocyclophonous figures cf. Winkelmann's Handbuch, Optik, p. 817, note 1.

6. Interference Phenomena in Absorbing Uniaxial Crystals.—Let the plate of crystal be cut perpendicular to the optic axis.

1. Crossed Nicols. Let the plane of vibration of the polarizer make an angle ϕ with the line AM which connects the optic axis A with a point M in the field of view of a polarizing arrangement which furnishes convergent light. Then AM is the direction of vibration H of the extraordinary ray, which, after emergence from the crystal, has the amplitude $E \cos \phi \, e^{-\kappa_e \sigma}$, and, after emergence from the analyzer, the amplitude $E \cos \phi \sin \phi \, e^{-\kappa_e \sigma}$. The ordinary ray has, after emergence from the crystal, the amplitude $E \sin \phi \, e^{-\kappa_o \sigma}$, and, after emergence fıom the analyzer, the amplitude $-E \sin \phi \cos \phi \, e^{-\kappa_o \sigma}$. Hence the intensity of the light emerging from the analyzer is

$$J = \frac{E^2 \sin^2 2\phi}{4} \{ e^{-2\kappa_o \sigma} + e^{-2\kappa_e \sigma} - 2 \cos \delta e^{-(\kappa_o + \kappa_e)\sigma} \}. \quad (61)$$

Along the optic axis $\kappa_o = \kappa_e$, $\delta = 0$; hence

$$J' = 0. \quad . \quad . \quad . \quad . \quad . \quad . \quad . \quad . \quad (62)$$

Interference rings are formed, which, however, disappear when the thickness of the plate is so great that the absorption effects appear. In the field of view there is a dark cross whose arms are parallel to the directions of vibrations of the analyzer and polarizer respectively. Outside of this cross the field of view is bright for those crystals for which a'^2 is small [cf. (49), page 373] and c'^2 large (type I, magnesium-platinocyanide), i.e. for those whose absorption in the direction of the optic axis is small. But for crystals of type II (tourmaline), for which a'^2 is large and c'^2 small, the field of view is everywhere dark.

2. Analyzer or polarizer alone present. These two cases are the same. If only the polarizer is present, and if its plane of vibration makes the angle ϕ with the direction AM, then the intensity of the extraordinary ray is $E^2 \cos^2 \phi \, e^{-2\kappa_e \sigma}$, that of the ordinary ray $E^2 \sin^2 \phi \, e^{-2\kappa_o \sigma}$. Hence

$$J = E^2 (\sin^2 \phi \, e^{-2\kappa_o \sigma} + \cos^2 \phi \, e^{-2\kappa_e \sigma}). \quad . \quad . \quad . \quad (63)$$

Along the optic axis $\kappa_o = \kappa_e$; hence

$$J' = E^2 e^{-2\kappa_o \sigma} \quad . \quad . \quad . \quad . \quad . \quad . \quad . \quad (64)$$

Crystals of the first type ($\kappa_o < \kappa_e$) show, therefore, a dark brush when $\phi = 0$ and $\phi = \pi$, i.e. in a direction parallel to the direction of vibration, or perpendicular to the plane of polarization of the polarizer. The dark brush is intercepted by a bright spot on the axis. In the case of crystals of the second type ($\kappa_o > \kappa_e$) there is a dark brush when $\phi = \pm \frac{\pi}{2}$, i.e. parallel to the plane of polarization of the polarizer. The dark brush passes through the axis itself.

3. Transmitted natural light. The intensity of the ordinary ray is $E^2 e^{-2\kappa_o \sigma}$, that of the extraordinary ray is $E^2 e^{-2\kappa_e \sigma}$, hence

$$J = E^2(e^{-2\kappa_o \sigma} + e^{-2\kappa_e \sigma}) \quad . \quad . \quad . \quad . \quad . \quad (65)$$

Along the optic axis itself $\kappa_o = \kappa_e$, hence

$$J' = 2E^2 e^{-2\kappa_o \sigma} \quad . \quad . \quad . \quad . \quad . \quad . \quad . \quad (66)$$

$2E^2$ denotes the intensity of the incident natural light. In crystals of the first type there is a bright spot on the axis surrounded by a dark field; in crystals of the second type, a dark spot on the axis surrounded by a bright field.

CHAPTER V

DISPERSION

1. Theoretical Considerations.—A theory which accounts well for the observed phenomena of dispersion may be obtained from the assumption that the smallest particles of a body (atoms or molecules) possess natural periods of vibration. These particles are set into more or less violent vibration according as their natural periods agree more or less closely with the periods of the light vibrations which fall upon the body.* That such vibrations can be excited by a source of light, i.e. an oscillating electrical force, is easily comprehended from a generalization of the theory, necessitated by the facts of electrolysis, that every molecule of a substance consists of positively or negatively charged atoms or groups of atoms, the so-called ions.† In a conductor these ions are free to move about, but in an insulator they have certain fixed positions of equilibrium about which they may oscillate. In every element

* As Lord Rayleigh has recently shown (Phil. Mag. (5) 48, p. 151, 1889), Maxwell was the first to found the theory of anomalous dispersion upon such a basis (cf. Cambr. Calendar, 1869, Math. Tripos Exam.). His work did not, however, become known, and, independently of him, Sellmeier, v. Helmholtz, and Ketteler have used this idea for the basis of a theory of dispersion. The assumption that molecules have natural periods can be justified from various points of view, even from that of the mechanical theory of light. From the electric standpoint these natural periods can be looked upon in two different ways: the treatment here given is based upon Reiff's presentation of v. Helmholtz's conception—a presentation which also contains interesting applications to other domains of science (cf. Reiff, Theorie molecularelektrischer Vorgänge, 1896). This conception is more probable than the other which was used by Kolacek (Wied. Ann. 32, p. 224, 1887).

† These are not necessarily identical with the ions in electrolysis.

of volume the sum of the charges of the positive and negative ions must be zero, since free electrification does not appear at any place upon a body which has not been charged from without.

Consider first only the positive ions, and denote by e_1 the charge of a positive ion, by m_1 its mass, by ξ_1 the x-component of its displacement from its position of equilibrium; then the equation of motion of this ion, when an exterior electrical force whose x-component is X is applied, must be of the form *

$$m_1 \frac{\partial^2 \xi_1}{\partial t^2} = e_1 X - \frac{4\pi e_1^2}{\vartheta_1} \xi_1 - r_1 e_1^2 \frac{\partial \xi_1}{\partial t}. \quad . \quad . \quad (1)$$

For the first term of the right-hand side $e_1 X$ is the total impressed force. The second term denotes the (elastic) force which is called into play by the displacement of the ion and which acts to bring it back to its original position. The factor e_1^2 is introduced to indicate that the sign of this force is independent of sign of the charge. The third term represents the force of friction which opposes the motion of the ion. This term also contains the factor e_1^2, since it must also be independent of the sign of the charge. m_1, ϑ_1, r_1 are positive constants. The meaning of ϑ_1 is obtained by determining the position of equilibrium of the ion under the action of the force X. For if ξ_1 is independent of the time t, then, from (1),

$$e_1 \xi_1 = \frac{\vartheta_1}{4\pi} X. \quad . \quad . \quad . \quad . \quad . \quad . \quad (2)$$

ϑ_1 is proportional to the facility with which the ions may be displaced from their positions of rest, i.e. it is inversely proportional to the elastic resistance (or the coefficient of elasticity). For conductors ϑ_1 is to be set equal to ∞.

---

* All quantities are to be measured in electrostatic units. Equation (1) would also hold if the ion had no mass, provided the self-induction due to its motion be taken into consideration.

An entirely similar equation holds for the negatively charged ions, namely,

$$m_2 \frac{\partial^2 \xi_2}{\partial t^2} = e_2 X - \frac{4\pi e_2^2}{\vartheta_2} \xi_2 - r_2 e_2^2 \frac{\partial \xi_2}{\partial t}. \quad . \quad . \quad (3)$$

Here, too, m_2, ϑ_2, r_2, are positive, but e_2 is negative.

Now the electric current along the x-axis consists of three parts:

1. The current which would be produced in the free ether by an electrical force X if no ponderable molecules were present. According to (13) on page 268, the current density has the value

$$(j_x)_0 = \frac{1}{4\pi} \frac{\partial X}{\partial t}. \quad . \quad . \quad . \quad . \quad . \quad . \quad (4)$$

2. The current due to the displacement of the positive charges. If the displacement during the time dt amounts to $d\xi_1$, and if $\mathfrak{N}'$ denotes the number of positive ions in unit length, and $\mathfrak{N}''$ the number in unit cross-section, then there passes in time dt through unit cross-section the quantity

$$e_1 \mathfrak{N}'' \cdot d\xi_1 \mathfrak{N}' = e_1 \mathfrak{N}_1 d\xi_1,$$

in which $\mathfrak{N}_1 = \mathfrak{N}' \cdot \mathfrak{N}''$ denotes the number of ions of the type I which are present in unit volume. Hence in unit time there passes through unit cross-section the quantity

$$(j_x)_1 = e_1 \mathfrak{N}_1 \frac{d\xi_1}{dt} = e_1 \mathfrak{N}_1 \frac{\partial \xi_1}{\partial t}, \quad . \quad . \quad . \quad . \quad (5)$$

in which $\frac{\partial \xi_1}{\partial t}$ is a differential coefficient with respect to the time. $(j_x)_1$ denotes the current density which is produced by the motion of the ions of type I.

3. The current due to the displacement of the negative charges. This may be written in a form similar to the above, thus

$$(j_x)_2 = e_2 \mathfrak{N}_2 \frac{\partial \xi_2}{\partial t}, \quad . \quad . \quad . \quad . \quad . \quad . \quad (6)$$

for a displacement of a negative charge in the negative direction of the x-axis is equivalent to a positive current in the positive direction of the x-axis.

The total current density along the x-axis is then

$$j_x = (j_x)_0 + (j_x)_1 + (j_x)_2 = \frac{1}{4\pi}\frac{\partial X}{\partial t} + \frac{\partial}{\partial t}(e_1\mathfrak{N}_1\xi_1 + e_2\mathfrak{N}_2\xi_2). \quad (7)$$

The components of the current along the y- and z-axes take a similar form

Since no free charge can exist in an element of volume, the following relation holds:

$$e_1\mathfrak{N}_1 + e_2\mathfrak{N}_2 = 0. \quad . \quad . \quad . \quad . \quad . \quad (8)$$

Now the fundamental equations (7) and (11) on pages 265 and 267 are, as always, applicable. The permeability μ will be assumed equal to unity, so that $4\pi s_x = \frac{\partial \alpha}{\partial t}$, etc. Hence these fundamental equations, together with (1), (3), and (7), constitute a complete theoretical basis for all the phenomena of dispersion.

The general integral of differential equations (1) and (2) can be immediately written out if X be assumed to be a periodic function of the time. For ξ_1 and ξ_2 are proportional to the same periodic function of the time plus a certain term which represents the natural vibrations of the ions, which, according to (1) and (3), take place when $X = 0$. But in considering stationary conditions this term can be neglected, since, on account of the resistance factors r_1 and r_2, it disappears in the course of time because of damping. Hence it is possible to set

$$\xi_1 = A_1 \cdot e^{i\frac{t}{\tau}}, \quad \xi_2 = A_2 \cdot e^{i\frac{t}{\tau}}, \quad . \quad . \quad . \quad (9)$$

$$\tau = T : 2\pi, \quad . \quad . \quad . \quad . \quad . \quad . \quad . \quad . \quad . \quad (10)$$

in which A_1 and A_2 are still undetermined functions of the coordinates, which, however, no longer contain the time; while T is the period of the impressed force, i.e. of the light vibrations. In reality ξ_1 and ξ_2 stand for the real parts of the complex quantities written in (9); nevertheless they can be set equal to these complex quantities and the physical meaning can be determined at the end of the calculation from the real parts. This method of procedure makes the calculation much simpler.

Now, from (9),

$$\frac{\partial \xi_1}{\partial t} = \frac{i}{\tau}\xi_1, \quad \frac{\partial^2 \xi_1}{\partial t^2} = -\frac{1}{\tau^2}\xi_1. \quad . \quad . \quad . \quad (11)$$

Hence (1) may be written

$$e_1\xi_1\left(1 + \frac{i}{\tau}\frac{r_1\vartheta_1}{4\pi} - \frac{1}{\tau^2}\frac{m_1\vartheta_1}{4\pi e_1^2}\right) = \frac{\vartheta_1}{4\pi}X;$$

or when

$$a_1 = \frac{r_1\vartheta_1}{4\pi}, \quad b_1 = \frac{m_1\vartheta_1}{4\pi e_1^2}, \quad . \quad . \quad . \quad . \quad (12)$$

it follows that

$$e_1\xi_1 = \frac{1}{4\pi}X\frac{\vartheta_1}{1 + \frac{i}{\tau}a_1 - \frac{b_1}{\tau^2}} \quad . \quad . \quad . \quad . \quad (13)$$

The similar expression for $e_2\xi_2$ is obtained by replacing the subscript 1 by 2. Hence, from (7),

$$j_x = \frac{1}{4\pi}\frac{\partial X}{\partial t}\left\{1 + \frac{\vartheta_1\mathfrak{N}_1}{1 + \frac{i}{\tau}a_1 - \frac{b_1}{\tau^2}} + \frac{\vartheta_2\mathfrak{N}_2}{1 + \frac{i}{\tau}a_2 - \frac{b_2}{\tau^2}}\right\}. \quad (14)$$

A comparison of this equation with (17) on page 269, namely, $j_x = \frac{\epsilon}{4\pi}\cdot\frac{\partial X}{\partial t}$, shows that in place of the dielectric constant ϵ there appears the complex quantity ϵ' which depends upon the period $T(=\tau\cdot 2\pi)$; thus

$$\epsilon' = 1 + \sum_h \frac{\vartheta_h'}{1 + i\frac{a_h}{\tau} - \frac{b_h}{\tau^2}}, \quad . \quad . \quad . \quad (15)$$

in which the following abbreviation has been introduced:

$$\vartheta_h' = \vartheta_h \mathfrak{N}_h. \quad . \quad . \quad . \quad . \quad . \quad . \quad (15')$$

The Σ is to be extended over all the ions which are capable of vibrating. It is possible to assume more than two different kinds of ions. But in the case of the high periods of light vibrations and of dielectrics, these kinds are not to be assumed to be identical with those found in electrolysis.

The meaning of the constants which appear in (15) can be brought out as follows: If the period is very long, i.e. if $\tau = \infty$, a condition which is practically realized in static experiments or in those upon slow electrical oscillations, it follows from (15) that

$$\epsilon = \epsilon'_\infty = 1 + \Sigma \vartheta_h' \quad . \quad . \quad . \quad . \quad . \quad (16)$$

In such experiments ϵ is the dielectric constant of the medium. From (2) and (13) it is evident that ϑ_h' can be called the dielectric constant of the ions of kind h. *The resultant dielectric constant is then the sum of the dielectric constants of the ether and of all the kinds of ions.*

Further, b_h is a constant which is associated with the natural period T_h which the ions of kind h would have if their coefficient of friction a_h could be neglected. For in this case ($X = 0$, $a_h = r_h = 0$) it follows from (1) that

$$b_h = \tau_h^2, \quad \tau_h = T_h : 2\pi. \quad . \quad . \quad . \quad . \quad (17)$$

It has been shown above on page 361 that a complex dielectric constant indicates absorption of light. If n represent the index of refraction and κ the coefficient of absorption, then from the discussion there given [equation (11)], and the equation (15) here deduced,

$$\epsilon' = n^2(1 - i\kappa)^2 = 1 + \sum \frac{\vartheta_h'}{1 + i\dfrac{a_h}{\tau} - \dfrac{\tau_h^2}{\tau^2}}. \quad . \quad (18)$$

By separating the real and the imaginary parts of this equation, two relations may be obtained from which n and κ may be calculated.

2. Normal Dispersion.—In the case of transparent substances there is no appreciable absorption. The assumption must then be made that for these substances the coefficient of friction a_h is so small that the quantity $\frac{a_h}{\tau}$ can be neglected in comparison with $1 - \left(\frac{\tau_h}{\tau}\right)^2$. This is evidently possible only when the period T of the light does not lie close to the natural period T_h of the ions; for if these periods are nearly the same, $\frac{\tau_h}{\tau} = 1$ and absorption would occur even though a_h were small. Transparent substances are to be looked upon as those in which the natural periods of the ions do not coincide with the periods of visible light, and in which the coefficients of friction of the ions are small. If then for this case a_h be neglected, the right-hand side of (18) is real, so that $\kappa = 0$, and the index of refraction is determined by

$$n^2 = 1 + \sum \frac{\vartheta'_h}{1 - \left(\frac{\tau_h}{\tau}\right)^2} . \quad . \quad . \quad . \quad . \quad (19)$$

If the difference between the natural and the impressed periods is great, n^2 can be developed in a rapidly converging series. The natural periods in the ultra-violet τ_v must be separated from the natural periods in the ultra-red τ_r. For the former $\frac{\tau_v}{\tau}$ is a small fraction, hence

$$\frac{1}{1 - \left(\frac{\tau_v}{\tau}\right)^2} = 1 + \left(\frac{\tau_v}{\tau}\right)^2 + \left(\frac{\tau_v}{\tau}\right)^4 + \text{etc.} \quad . \quad . \quad (20)$$

For the latter $\frac{\tau}{\tau_r}$ is a small fraction, hence

$$\frac{1}{1-\left(\frac{\tau_r}{\tau}\right)^2} = -\frac{\tau^2}{\tau_r^{\,2}} \cdot \frac{1}{1-\left(\frac{\tau}{\tau_r}\right)^2} = -\frac{\tau^2}{\tau_r^{\,2}}\left(1+\left(\frac{\tau}{\tau_r}\right)^2+\left(\frac{\tau}{\tau_r}\right)^4 \ldots\right). \quad (21)$$

Using these series and introducing in place of τ the period T itself, in accordance with (10) and (17), (19) becomes

$$n^2 = 1 + \Sigma\vartheta'_v + \frac{\Sigma\vartheta'_v T_v^2}{T^2} + \frac{\Sigma\vartheta'_v T_v^4}{T^4} + \ldots$$
$$- T^2\Sigma\frac{\vartheta'_r}{T_r^2} - T^4\Sigma\frac{\vartheta'_r}{T_r^4} - \ldots \quad (22)$$

Now in fact a dispersion formula with four constants, namely,

$$n^2 = -A'T^2 + A + \frac{B}{T^2} + \frac{C}{T^4}, \quad . \quad . \quad . \quad (23)$$

in which A', A, B, and C are positive, has been found to satisfy observations upon the relation between n and T for transparent substances. (23) is easily recognized as the incompleted series (22), and it is easy to see from (22) why the coefficients A', A, B, and C must be positive. It also appears that the term A of the dispersion equation, which does not contain T, has the following physical significance:

$$A = 1 + \Sigma\vartheta'_v. \quad . \quad . \quad . \quad . \quad . \quad . \quad (24)$$

Since by (16) the dielectric constant ϵ has the meaning

$$\epsilon = 1 + \Sigma\vartheta'_h = 1 + \Sigma\vartheta'_v + \Sigma\vartheta'_r,$$

it appears that

$$\epsilon - A = \Sigma\vartheta'_r, \quad . \quad . \quad . \quad . \quad . \quad . \quad (25)$$

i.e. *the difference between the dielectric constant and the term of the dispersion equation which does not contain T is always positive and is equal to the sum of the dielectric constants of the ions whose natural periods lie in the ultra-red.* In this way the discrepancies mentioned above between Maxwell's original theory and experiment are explained.

Such a difference between ϵ and A must always exist when the dispersion cannot be represented by the three-constant equation

$$n^2 = A + \frac{B}{T^2} + \frac{C}{T^4}, \quad . \quad . \quad . \quad . \quad (26)$$

for the coefficient A' of equation (23) depends upon the ions which have natural periods in the ultra-red. The behavior of water is a striking verification of this conclusion. For the coefficient A' of the four-constant dispersion equation has a larger value for water than for any other transparent substance; and this agrees well with the fact that water absorbs heat-rays more powerfully than any other substance, and also with the fact that for water the difference betwen ϵ and A is greater than for any other substance. If the assumption be made that there be but one region of absorption in the ultra-red, the position of this region can be calculated from A' and $\epsilon - A$. For in this case, from (22), (23), and (25),

$$A' = \frac{\vartheta'_r}{T_r^2}, \quad \epsilon - A = \vartheta'_r, \quad \text{i.e. } T_r^2 = \frac{\epsilon - A}{A'}. \qquad (27)$$

Now, according to Ketteler, for water $A' = 0.0128 \cdot 10^8 \cdot c^2 \sec^{-2}$, in which $c = 3 \cdot 10^{10}$. Further, $\epsilon - A = 77$. From these data the wave length measured in air which corresponds to the region of absorption in the ultra-red is calculated as

$$\lambda_r^2 = c^2 T_r^2 = \frac{77}{0.0128} 10^{-8} = 60 \cdot 10^{-6},$$

i.e.

$$\lambda_r = 7.75 \cdot 10^{-3} \text{ cm.} = 0.08 \text{ mm.} \quad . \quad . \quad (28)$$

This wave length lies in fact far out in the ultra-red. Experiment has shown that water has more than one region of absorption in the ultra-red,* but the order of magnitude of the wave length which is most strongly absorbed is in fact in agreement with (28).†

Experiments upon flint glass, fluor-spar, quartz, rock salt, and sylvine have given further quantitative verifications of the dispersion equation (19) when rays of long wave length have been investigated.‡ If (19) be written in the form

$$n^2 = 1 + \Sigma\vartheta'_h + \Sigma \frac{\vartheta'_h \tau_h^2}{\tau^2 - \tau_h^2},$$

* F. Paschen, Wied. Ann. 53, p. 334, 1894.

† Rubens and Aschkinass, Wied. Ann. 65, p. 252, 1898.

‡ Rubens and Nichols, Wied. Ann. 60, p. 418, 1897; Paschen, Wied. Ann. 54, p. 672, 1895.

i.e. in the form

$$n^2 = b^2 + \Sigma \frac{M_h}{\lambda^2 - \lambda_h^2}, \quad . \quad . \quad . \quad . \quad . \quad (29)$$

it is evident that b^2 must be identified with the dielectric constant ϵ. In the case of the substances just mentioned n^2 can be well represented by equation (29); for example, for quartz, for the ordinary ray, the values of the constants are:

$$M_1 = 0.0106, \quad \lambda_1^2 = 0.0106,$$
$$M_2 = 44.224, \quad \lambda_2^2 = 78.22,$$
$$M_3 = 713.55, \quad \lambda_3^2 = 430.56, \quad b^2 = 4.58.$$

In this $\lambda_h = T_h \cdot V$, and the unit in which λ_h is measured is a thousandth part of a millimetre (μ). According to (29) these seven constants M_1, M_2, M_3, λ_1, λ_2, λ_3, b^2 must satisfy the equation

$$b^2 - 1 = \Sigma\vartheta_h' = \frac{M_1}{\lambda_1^2} + \frac{M_2}{\lambda_2^2} + \frac{M_3}{\lambda_3^2}. \quad . \quad . \quad . \quad (30)$$

The numerical value of the right-hand side is 3.2, that of the left 3.6. The difference is due to molecules whose natural periods of vibration lie so far out in the ultra-violet that $\tau_h = 0$ for them. If the sum of the dielectric constants of these molecules be denoted by ϑ_0', then, from (29),

$$b^2 = 1 + \vartheta_0' + \Sigma\vartheta_h', \quad M_h = \vartheta_h' \cdot \lambda_h^2.$$

Hence the following takes the place of (30):

$$b^2 - 1 - \frac{M_h}{\lambda_h^2} = \vartheta_0'. \quad . \quad . \quad . \quad . \quad . \quad (30')$$

Now the value of the dielectric constant of quartz lies between 4.55 and 4.73, which agrees very well with the value of b^2.

For fluor-spar

$$M_1 = 0.00612, \quad \lambda_1^2 = 0.00888,$$
$$M_2 = 5099, \quad \lambda_2^2 = 1258,$$
$$b^2 = 6.09, \quad \epsilon = 6.7 \text{ to } 6.9.$$

[Here again (30) is not exactly satisfied.]

For rock salt

$$M_1 = 0.018,\quad \lambda_1^2 = 0.0162,$$
$$M_2 = 8977,\quad \lambda_2^2 = 3149,$$
$$b^2 = 5.18,\quad \epsilon = 5.81 \text{ to } 6.29.$$

[(30) is approximately satisfied. $\theta_0' = 0.18$.]

For sylvine

$$M_1 = 0.0150,\quad \lambda_1^2 = 0.0234,$$
$$M_2 = 10747,\quad \lambda_2^2 = 4517,$$
$$b^2 = 4.55,\quad \epsilon = 4.94.$$

[(30) is not satisfied. According to (30') $\theta_0' = 0.53$.]

The conclusion that the difference between ϵ and A of equation (25) indicates natural periods of vibration and absorption in the ultra-red cannot be inverted, i.e. even if the dielectric constant ϵ has the same value as the constant A, which is independent of the period in the dispersion equation, *natural periods and absorption in the ultra-red are not necessarily excluded.* According to (25) it is only necessary that the dielectric constants ϑ_r' of the kinds of ions which lie in the ultra-red be very small. Nevertheless appreciable absorption can occur when $\tau = \tau_r$. For then in (18) the term $\vartheta_r' : i \cdot \dfrac{a_r}{\tau_r}$ appears in the expression for ϵ'. By (12) this term has the value $- i2 T_r \mathfrak{R}_r : r_r$, in which r_r denotes the frictional resistance defined in (1). The value of this term remains finite even when ϑ_r is very small. Thus many substances actually exist, such as the hydro-carbons, for which the difference between ϵ and A is small and which yet absorb heat-rays to a certain extent.

From equations (22) or (23) it follows that n^2 continually decreases as T increases. This can be observed in all transparent substances: it is the normal form of the dispersion curve, and hence this kind of dispersion is said to be *normal.*

3. Anomalous Dispersion. — The dispersion is always normal so long as the investigation is confined to a region of impressed periods which does not include a natural period of the ions. But whenever an impressed period coincides with a natural period, the normal course of the dispersion is disturbed. For it follows from (19) that for periods T which are smaller than a natural period T_h, i.e. for which $1 - \left(\frac{\tau_h}{\tau}\right)^2$ has a negative value, say $-\zeta$, n^2 contains the large negative term $-\vartheta_h' : \zeta$; while for those values of T which are larger than T_h, $1 - \left(\frac{\tau_h}{\tau}\right)^2$ assumes the negative value ζ', so that n^2 contains the positive term $+\vartheta_h' : \zeta'$. *Hence as T increases continuously n^2 in general decreases; but in passing through a region of absorption it increases.* Within the region of absorption (19) cannot be used, but n^2 and κ must be calculated from (18), a_h being now retained in the calculation. In any case n^2 must be a continuous function of T. Hence the general form of the n^2 and κ curves is that shown in Fig 102. The value of κ differs from zero only in the immediate neighborhood of T_h, and there it is larger the smaller the value of a_h. For, from (18), when $T = T_h$,

$$2n^2\kappa = \frac{T}{2\pi}\frac{\vartheta_h'}{a_h} = \frac{2T\mathfrak{N}_h}{r_h}. \quad . \quad . \quad . \quad . \quad (31)$$

Hence if a_h, i.e. r_h, is small, the absorption bands of the substance are sharp and narrow; but if a_h is large, the absorption extends over a large region of wave lengths but has a small intensity.

The form of the *anomalous dispersion curve* shown in Fig. 102 represents well the observations upon substances which exhibit strong selective absorption, for example, fuchsine.* The gases and the vapors of metals are distinguished by very narrow and intense absorption bands, and anomalous dispersion occurs in the neighborhood of these bands.

---

* Cf. Ketteler, Theoret. Optik, Braunschweig, 1885, p. 548 sq. A good verification for the case of cyanine is given by Pflüger, Wied. Ann. 65, p. 173, 1898.

The existence of anomalous dispersion is most simply proved by the fact that a prism of some substances produces from a line source a spectrum in which the order of the colors is not normal. The phenomenon is, however, complicated by the fact that in the spectrum two colors may overlap. Hence it is preferable to use Kundt's method in which a narrow horizontal spectrum formed by a glass prism with a vertical edge is observed through a prism of the substance to be investigated, the refracting edge of the latter being horizontal. If the dispersion produced by the second prism is anomalous, the resultant spectrum is divided into parts which are at different heights and are separated from one another by dark spaces which correspond to the regions of absorption.

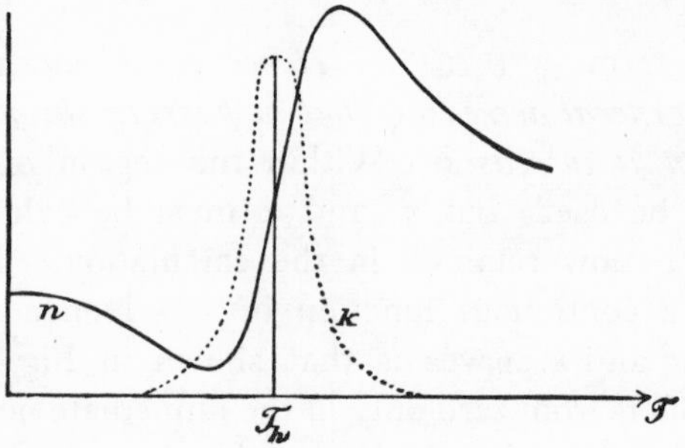

FIG. 102.

An objection to this prism method is this, that when the absorption of the substance under observation is large, only prisms of small refracting angle can be used. Hence the method of Mach and Arbes,* in which total reflection is made use of to determine the anomalous dispersion, is preferable. A solution of fuchsine is placed in the glass trough G and a flint-glass prism P placed upon it. The rays from a line source L, which lies in a vertical plane, are concentrated by means of the lens s_1 upon the bounding surface between the glass and the fuchsine solution. The lens s_2 collects the

* Mach and Arbes, Wied. Ann. 27, p. 436, 1896.

reflected rays and forms a real image of L upon the screen S. This image is spread out into a spectrum by means of a suitably placed glass prism. This spectrum then shows the distribution of light indicated in the figure: the curve *mnpq* represents the limiting curve of total reflection. The break in the curve between n and p shows at a glance the effect of anomalous dispersion. Between n and p there is a dark band, since, for the colors which should appear at this place, the index of refraction of the flint glass is the same as that of the fuchsine solution, so that no reflection whatever takes place. The index of refraction within the region of maximum absorption cannot always be determined by this method, since, on account of the high absorption, the partial reflection in this region is so

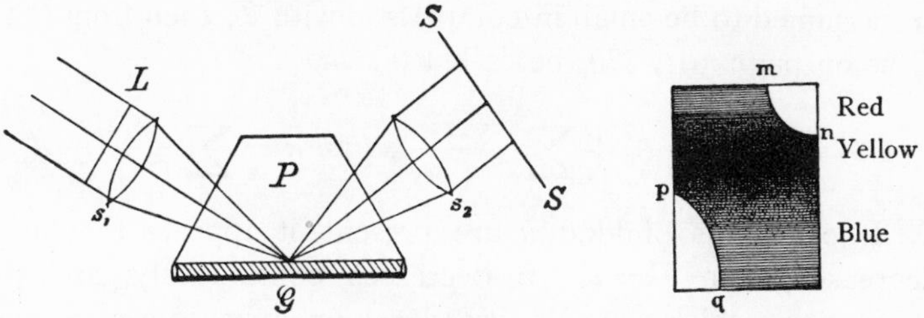

FIG. 103.

large (cf. metallic reflection) that it passes continuously into total reflection, so that no sharp limiting curve appears. n and κ can then be determined from the partial reflection as in the case of the metals.

A striking confirmation * of the theory here presented has recently been brought out by the discovery of the fact that for very long waves ($\lambda = 56\mu$) quartz has a much larger index ($n = 2.18$) than for the shorter visible rays. Equation (29) gives, with the assumption of the values of the constants given for quartz on page 391, $n = 2.20$. Hence if the radiation from an Auer burner be decomposed into a spectrum by means of a prism of quartz, these long waves are found beyond the violet

* Rubens and Aschkinass, Wied. Ann. 67, p. 459, 1899.

end of the spectrum and may therefore be easily isolated by cutting off the other rays with a screen.

The case inverse to that of narrow absorption bands is that in which not a_h but b_h or τ_h are to be neglected in (18) or (15), i.e. the case in which the region of absorption is one in which no natural periods of the ions occur (the impressed periods are larger than the natural periods could possibly be). In this case, from (18),

$$n^2(1 - i\kappa)^2 = 1 + \sum \frac{\vartheta'_h}{1 + \frac{a_h^2}{\tau^2}}\left(1 - i\frac{a_h}{\tau}\right) + \sum \frac{\vartheta'_v}{1 - \left(\frac{\tau_v}{\tau}\right)^2}. \quad (32)$$

The last Σ, that connected with the index v, refers to the natural periods which lie in the ultra-violet. If these periods are assumed to be small in comparison with T, then from (32), if, as on page 391, $\Sigma\vartheta'_v$ be called ϑ'_0,

$$n^2(1 - \kappa^2) = 1 + \vartheta'_0 + \sum \frac{\vartheta'_h \tau^2}{\tau^2 + a_h^2}, \quad 2n^2\kappa = \sum \frac{\vartheta'_h a_h \tau}{\tau^2 + a_h^2}. \quad (33)$$

If only ions of kind h are present, it appears that as T decreases from $T = \infty$, n decreases continuously, and the absorption, which covers a broad region, reaches a maximum for a certain period T. These equations appear to represent well for many substances the dispersion phenomena as they are observed by means of long electrical waves ranging between the limits $\lambda = \infty$ and $\lambda = 1$ cm.*

4. Dispersion of the Metals.—In considering conductors of electricity it is necessary to bear in mind that within these conductors a constant electrical force produces a continuous displacement of quantities of electricity, and that these latter have no definite positions of equilibrium. The idea made use of in electrolysis, that the displaced electrical quantities are connected with definite masses (ions), will be applied to the metals to the extent that the motion of the ions will be assumed to take place in the metals also as though the ions

* Cf. Drude, Wied. Ann. 64, p. 131, 1898.

possessed inert mass m. But this may be only apparent mass, since the inertia may be accounted for by self-induction (cf. note, page 383).

The constant ϑ of these conducting ions must be taken as infinitely great, since, according to (2), ϑ_1 is proportional to the displacement of the ions from their original position because of the influence of a constant electrical force. The equation of motion of these ions is therefore obtained from equation (1) on page 383 by substituting in it $\vartheta_1 = \infty$. It is, therefore,

$$m\frac{\partial^2 \xi}{\partial t^2} = eX - re^2\frac{\partial \xi}{\partial t}, \quad . \quad . \quad . \quad . \quad (34)$$

or if the current due to these ions, which according to (5) is $j_x = e\mathfrak{N}\frac{\partial \xi}{\partial t}$, be introduced,

$$\frac{m}{e^2\mathfrak{N}}\frac{\partial j_x}{\partial t} + \frac{r}{\mathfrak{N}}j_x = X. \quad . \quad . \quad . \quad . \quad . \quad (35)$$

In this equation m is the (apparent or real) mass of an ion, e its charge, $\mathfrak{N}$ the number of ions in unit volume. From (35) it is evident that if two kinds of conducting ions, one charged positively and the other negatively, whose resistance factors are r_1 and r_2, respectively, are present, then for a constant current the following holds:

$$\frac{\mathfrak{N}_1}{r_1} + \frac{\mathfrak{N}_2}{r_2} = \sigma, \quad . \quad . \quad . \quad . \quad . \quad . \quad (36)$$

in which σ is the specific conductivity of the substance measured in electrostatic units (cf. page 358).

For periodic changes, since $X = -i\tau\frac{\partial X}{\partial t}$, by (35),

$$j_x\left\{\frac{i}{\tau}\frac{m}{e^2\mathfrak{N}} + \frac{r}{\mathfrak{N}}\right\} = -i\tau\frac{\partial X}{\partial t},$$

or

$$j_x = \frac{1}{4\pi}\frac{\partial X}{\partial t}\left\{\frac{4\pi\tau\mathfrak{N}}{-\frac{m}{\tau e^2} + ir}\right\}. \quad . \quad . \quad . \quad . \quad (37)$$

Equation (14) on page 386 must then be extended by a term of this kind so that if, for abbreviation,

$$m : e^2 = m', \quad . \quad . \quad . \quad . \quad . \quad . \quad . \quad (38)$$

the resultant complex dielectric constant takes the form

$$\epsilon' = 1 + \sum_h \frac{\vartheta'_h}{1 + i\frac{a_h}{\tau} - \frac{b_h}{\tau^2}} + 4\pi\tau \sum_k \frac{\mathfrak{N}}{ir - \frac{m'}{\tau}}. \quad (39)$$

If it be assumed that the periods are remote from the natural periods of the ions of kind h, so that a_h may be neglected, then since $\epsilon' = n^2(1 - i\kappa)^2$, it follows from (39), by separation of the real and the imaginary parts, that

$$n^2(1 - \kappa^2) = 1 + \sum \frac{\vartheta'_h}{1 - \left(\frac{\tau_h}{\tau}\right)^2} - 4\pi \sum \frac{m'\mathfrak{N}}{r^2 + \left(\frac{m'}{\tau}\right)^2}, \quad (40)$$

$$n^2\kappa = 2\pi\tau \sum \frac{r\mathfrak{N}}{r^2 + \left(\frac{m'}{\tau}\right)^2}. \quad . \quad . \quad . \quad . \quad (41)$$

From this it is evident that in the case of the metals κ may be greater than 1, since the right hand side of (40) may be negative not only on account of the second term, but also on account of the third term, which is proportional to the mass m) of the conducting ions. For a given value of m' and τ the right-hand side of (40) becomes negative sooner the smaller r is, i.e. the larger the specific conductivity. Furthermore, (41) explains the second difficulty which was mentioned on page 368, namely, that for the metals $n^2\kappa$ is smaller than σT. For if $m' = 0$, or $\tau = \infty$, (41) actually gives, in connection with (36), the relation demanded by Maxwell's original theory, namely,

$$n^2\kappa = 2\pi\tau\Sigma\frac{\mathfrak{N}}{r} = \sigma T;$$

but if $\frac{m'}{\tau}$ cannot be neglected in comparison with r, and this is the case when the period is small (τ small) and the conductivity large (r small), then (41) gives $n^2\kappa < \sigma T$.*

Still more general equations than (40) and (41) could be formed by taking account of the conditions represented by (33), which would correspond to the assumption that, in addition to the actually conducting ions, other conducting constituents were present, which constituents, however, under the action of a constant electric force, would be displaced only a finite distance from their original positions. This is the case of so-called internal conductivity which can be roughly imitated by embedding conductors in dielectrics. Whether such an assumption is necessary or not cannot be determined without a more complete investigation of the dispersion of the metals than has as yet been possible.

Equations (40) and (41) also account for the fact that only in the case of substances which are as good conductors as are the metals does the electric conductivity cause absorption of light, while in the very best conducting electrolytes the conductivity is still so small that they can be quite transparent, as observation shows them to be. Thus, for example, the specific conductivity of the best conducting sulphuric acid or nitric acid is only $7 \cdot 10^{-5}$ times that of mercury. Since for the latter (cf. page 358) $\sigma = 10^{16}$, for the best conducting electrolyte $\sigma = 7 \cdot 10^{11}$. Now the period of the light vibrations is about $T = 2 \cdot 10^{-15}$, hence $\sigma T = 14 \cdot 10^{-4}$ or $= 0.0014$. But, from (41), $n^2\kappa$ is always smaller than σT. Thus κ, i.e. the light absorption, or at least that part of it due to conductivity, is very small.

* For a more complete discussion cf. Drude, Phys. Zeitschr. p. 161, January, 1900.

CHAPTER VI

OPTICALLY ACTIVE SUBSTANCES

1. General Considerations.—If a ray of plane-polarized light falls perpendicularly upon a plane-parallel plate of glass, the plane of polarization of the emergent ray is the same as that of the incident ray. This is generally true for all substances, including crystals which are cut perpendicularly to the optic axis.

Nevertheless the so-called *optically active substances* present a striking exception to the rule. Thus, for example, a plate of quartz, cut perpendicularly to the optic axis, rotates the plane of polarization strongly, and even a sugar solution rotates it appreciably. This last fact is the more remarkable because it is customary to look upon a solution as a perfectly isotropic substance; but this phenomenon indicates that it is not isotropic. For, from considerations of symmetry, if a substance were perfectly isotropic, it could produce no change whatever in the plane of polarization of the incident light.

This phenomenon therefore indicates that, optically considered, a sugar solution possesses no plane of symmetry, since otherwise, if the plane of polarization of the incident light coincided with this plane, no rotation could take place. But the nature of a solution is of itself evidence that it has the same properties in all directions. Hence the form of the differential equations which are able to describe the optical processes in a sugar solution must be such that it remains unchanged for any arbitrary rotation of the entire coordinate system; but it must change if only one of the coordinate axes is inverted, i.e. if, for instance, x and y remain unchanged while z is changed to $-z$. Substances for which differential equations of this form hold are called *unsymmetrically isotropic*.

On the other hand a crystal which, like quartz, has no plane of optical symmetry is called an *unsymmetrically crystalline* substance.

2. Isotropic Media.—Lack of symmetry in a solution can have its origin only in the constitution of the molecules, not in their arrangement. In fact le Bel and van't Hoff have been able to bring the rotating power of substances into direct connection with their chemical constitution. In the case of solids the lack of symmetry may be due to the arrangement of the molecules.

An attempt will here be made to extend the preceding theory by altering equation (1) on page 383, Maxwell's fundamental equations being as usual maintained.

The unsymmetrical constitution of a substance can be recognized only by comparing its properties at one point with those at a neighboring point. The extension of the preceding ideas as to the motions of the ions will consist in considering the displacement of an ion to depend not only upon the electric force which exists at the point occupied by the ion, but also upon the components of the electric force in the immediate neighborhood of this point. In order to express this idea mathematically it is necessary that equations (1) or (2) on page 353 contain not only X but also the differential coefficients of X, Y, and Z with respect to the coordinates. Now in view of the condition of isotropy, i.e. that the properties of the substance in one coordinate direction are not to be distinguished from those in another, the only possible extension of (2) is

$$e\xi = \frac{\vartheta}{4\pi}\left(X + f'\left[\frac{\partial Y}{\partial z} - \frac{\partial Z}{\partial y}\right]\right), \quad . \quad . \quad . \quad (1)$$

to which are to be added two similar equations obtained by a cyclical interchange of the letters in (1). So far as isotropy is concerned (1) might also contain the term $\frac{\partial X}{\partial x}$, but this must vanish because otherwise

$$e\left(\frac{\partial \xi}{\partial x}+\frac{\partial \eta}{\partial y}+\frac{\partial \zeta}{\partial z}\right) \sim \frac{\partial^2 X}{\partial x^2}+\frac{\partial^2 Y}{\partial y^2}+\frac{\partial^2 Z}{\partial z^2},$$

i.e. an accumulation of free charge might take place, since in general—for example, in the case of light vibrations—the right-hand side does not vanish.

An unsymmetrical isotropic medium would result if all the molecules were irregular tetrahedra of the same kind,—the tetrahedra of the opposite kind (that which is the image of the first) being altogether wanting. The same would be true if one kind existed in smaller numbers than the other. A graphical representation of equation (1) may be obtained by conceiving that because of the molecular structure the paths of the ions are not short straight lines, but short helixes twisted in the same direction and whose axes are directed at random in space. Consider, for example, a right-handed helical path whose axis is parallel to the x-axis. The component X drives the charged ion always toward the left; but a positive Y drives the ion on the upper side of the helix toward the left, on the lower side toward the right. The result is therefore a force toward the right which is proportional to $-\frac{\partial Y}{\partial z}$, since it depends upon the difference between the value of Y above and its value below. Likewise a positive Z drives the ion on the front side of the helix toward the left, on the back side toward the right. The resultant effect toward the right is therefore proportional to $+\frac{\partial Z}{\partial y}$. These conditions are represented in equation (1), in which f' would be negative if the paths of the ions were right-handed helices and if the coordinate system were chosen as in Fig. 104.

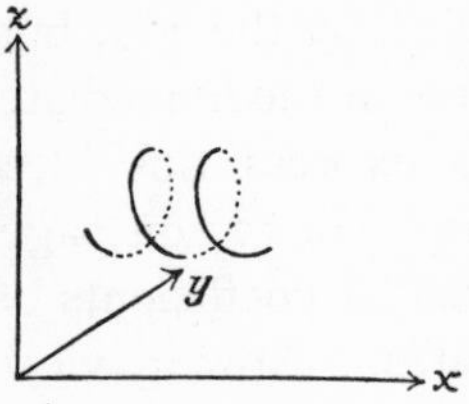

FIG. 104.

In consideration of equation (1), equation (1) on page 383 would become

$$m\frac{\partial^2 \xi}{\partial t^2} = e\left(X + f'\left[\frac{\partial Y}{\partial z} - \frac{\partial Z}{\partial y}\right]\right) - \frac{4\pi e^2}{\vartheta}\xi - re^2\frac{\partial \xi}{\partial t}. \qquad (2)$$

If, as on page 385, ξ be assumed to be a periodic function of the time, then there results, upon introduction of the current $(j_x)_1 = e\mathfrak{N}\frac{\partial \xi}{\partial t}$,

$$(j_x)_1 = \frac{\vartheta \mathfrak{N}}{4\pi\left(1 + i\frac{a}{\tau} - \frac{b}{\tau^2}\right)}\frac{\partial}{\partial t}\left(X + f'\left[\frac{\partial Y}{\partial z} - \frac{\partial Z}{\partial y}\right]\right), \qquad (3)$$

in which

$$a = \frac{r\vartheta}{4\pi}, \quad b = \frac{r\vartheta}{4\pi e^2} = \tau_1^2, \quad . \quad . \quad . \quad . \qquad (4)$$

In what follows $\frac{a}{\tau}$ will be neglected, which is permissible if the periods of the light vibrations are not close to the natural periods of any of the ions. The whole current due to all of the ions and the ether is then

$$j_x = \frac{1}{4\pi}\frac{\partial}{\partial t}\left\{\epsilon X + f\left(\frac{\partial Y}{\partial z} - \frac{\partial Z}{\partial y}\right)\right\}, \quad . \quad . \qquad (5)$$

in which

$$\left.\begin{aligned} \epsilon &= 1 + \Sigma\frac{\vartheta_h \mathfrak{N}_h}{1 - \left(\frac{\tau_h}{\tau}\right)^2}, \\ f &= \Sigma\frac{\vartheta_h f_h' \mathfrak{N}_h}{1 - \left(\frac{\tau_h}{\tau}\right)^2}, \end{aligned}\right\} \quad . \quad . \quad . \quad . \quad . \qquad (6)$$

The fundamental equations (7) and (11) on pages 265 and 267 become therefore, if the permeability $\mu = 1$, so that $4\pi s_x = \frac{\partial \alpha}{\partial}$, etc.,

$$\left.\begin{aligned}\frac{1}{c}\frac{\partial}{\partial t}\left(\epsilon X+f\left[\frac{\partial Y}{\partial z}-\frac{\partial Z}{\partial y}\right]\right)&=\frac{\partial \gamma}{\partial y}-\frac{\partial \beta}{\partial z},\\ \frac{1}{c}\frac{\partial}{\partial t}\left(\epsilon Y+f\left[\frac{\partial Z}{\partial x}-\frac{\partial X}{\partial z}\right]\right)&=\frac{\partial \alpha}{\partial z}-\frac{\partial \gamma}{\partial x},\\ \frac{1}{c}\frac{\partial}{\partial t}\left(\epsilon Z+f\left[\frac{\partial X}{\partial y}-\frac{\partial Y}{\partial x}\right]\right)&=\frac{\partial \beta}{\partial x}-\frac{\partial \alpha}{\partial y},\end{aligned}\right\} \quad . \quad . \quad (7)$$

$$\frac{1}{c}\frac{\partial \alpha}{\partial t}=\frac{\partial Y}{\partial z}-\frac{\partial Z}{\partial y},\quad \frac{1}{c}\frac{\partial \beta}{\partial t}=\frac{\partial Z}{\partial x}-\frac{\partial X}{\partial z},\quad \frac{1}{c}\frac{\partial \gamma}{\partial t}=\frac{\partial X}{\partial y}-\frac{\partial Y}{\partial x}. \quad (8)$$

From the same considerations which were given on page 271, it is evident that the boundary conditions to be fulfilled in the passage of light through the surface separating two different media are continuity of the components parallel to the surface of both the electric and magnetic forces.

In this way a complete theory of light phenomena in optically active substances is obtained.

From equations (7) it follows that

$$\frac{\partial}{\partial t}\left(\frac{\partial X}{\partial x}+\frac{\partial Y}{\partial y}+\frac{\partial Z}{\partial z}\right)=0. \quad . \quad . \quad . \quad . \quad (9)$$

Hence from equations (7) and (8) there results, by the elimination of α, β, γ, as on page 275,

$$\left.\begin{aligned}\frac{1}{c^2}\frac{\partial^2}{\partial t^2}\left(\epsilon X+f\left[\frac{\partial Y}{\partial z}-\frac{\partial Z}{\partial y}\right]\right)&=\Delta X,\\ \frac{1}{c^2}\frac{\partial^2}{\partial t^2}\left(\epsilon Y+f\left[\frac{\partial Z}{\partial x}-\frac{\partial X}{\partial z}\right]\right)&=\Delta Y,\\ \frac{1}{c^2}\frac{\partial^2}{\partial t^2}\left(\epsilon Z+f\left[\frac{\partial X}{\partial y}-\frac{\partial Y}{\partial x}\right]\right)&=\Delta Z.\end{aligned}\right\} \quad . \quad . \quad (10)$$

α, β, γ satisfy equations of the same form.

3. Rotation of the Plane of Polarization.—If a plane wave is travelling along the z-axis, it is possible to set

$$X=Me^{\frac{i}{\tau}(t-pz)},\quad Y=Ne^{\frac{i}{\tau}(t-pz)},\quad Z=0. \quad . \quad (11)$$

p represents the reciprocal of the velocity of the wave. If the values in (11) be substituted in (10), there results

$$\epsilon M - \frac{i}{\tau} fpN = Mp^2c^2,$$

$$\epsilon N + \frac{i}{\tau} fpM = Np^2c^2.$$

These equations are satisfied if

$$\epsilon - p^2c^2 = \frac{pf}{\tau}, \qquad M = iN, \quad . \quad . \quad . \quad . \quad (12)$$

or if

$$\epsilon - p^2c^2 = -\frac{pf}{\tau}, \quad M = -iN. \quad . \quad . \quad . \quad (13)$$

Hence in this case the peculiar result is obtained that two waves exist which have different values of p, i.e. different velocities. Further, the waves have imaginary y-amplitudes if they have real x-amplitudes.

In order to obtain the physical significance of this it is to be remembered that the physical meaning of X and Y is found by taking the real part of the right-hand side of (11). Hence when $iN = M$,

$$X = M \cos \frac{1}{\tau}(t - pz), \quad Y = M \sin \frac{1}{\tau}(t - pz); \quad . \quad (14)$$

when $iN = -M$,

$$X = M \cos \frac{1}{\tau}(t - pz), \quad Y = -M \sin \frac{1}{\tau}(t - px). \quad (15)$$

These equations represent *circularly polarized light;* and since, in accordance with the conventions on page 264, the x-axis is directed toward the right, the y-axis upward to an observer looking in the negative direction of the z-axis, the first is a left-handed circularly polarized wave, since its rotation is counter-clockwise; the second is a right-handed circularly polarized wave (cf. page 249).

Now these two waves have different velocities V, and in fact, from (12), for the first

$$p' = \frac{1}{V'} = -\frac{f}{2\tau c^2} + \frac{1}{c}\sqrt{\frac{f^2}{4\tau^2 c^2} + \epsilon}, \quad . \quad . \quad (16)$$

and, from (13), for the second

$$p'' = \frac{1}{V''} = +\frac{f}{2\tau c^2} + \frac{1}{c}\sqrt{\frac{f^2}{4\tau^2 c^2} + \epsilon}. \quad . \quad . \quad (17)$$

Hence the indices of refraction for right-handed and left-handed circularly polarized light in optically active substances must be somewhat different; and a ray of natural light is decomposed into two circularly polarized rays one of which is right-handed, the other left-handed. When the incidence is oblique these two rays should be separated. These deductions from theory have been actually experimentally verified by v. Fleischl * for the case of sugar solutions and other liquids.

The effect of the superposition of two circularly polarized waves whose velocities are V' and V'' respectively, one of which is right-handed, the other left-handed, is

$$\left.\begin{aligned} X = X' + X'' &= 2M \cos\frac{1}{\tau}\left(t - \frac{p'+p''}{2}z\right)\cos\frac{1}{\tau}\frac{p''-p'}{2}z, \\ Y = Y' + Y'' &= 2M \cos\frac{1}{\tau}\left(t - \frac{p'+p''}{2}z\right)\sin\frac{1}{\tau}\frac{p''-p'}{2}z. \end{aligned}\right\} \quad . \quad (18)$$

Hence in one particular position, i.e. for a certain value of z, the light disturbance is plane-polarized, since, according to (18), X and Y have the same phase. The position of the plane of polarization with respect to the x-axis is determined from

$$Y : X = \tan\frac{1}{\tau}\frac{p'' - p'}{2}z,$$

* E. v. Fleischl, Wied. Ann. 24. p. 127, 1885. It is easier to prove the circular double refraction of quartz along the direction of the optic axis. In quartz the constant f is greater than in liquids.

i.e. this position varies with z. Thus the plane of polarization rotates uniformly about the direction of propagation of the light, the angle of rotation corresponding to a distance z being

$$\delta = \frac{z}{\tau}\frac{p'' - p'}{2} = \frac{f}{2\tau^2c^2}z = 2\pi^2\frac{f}{\lambda_0{}^2}z, \quad . \quad . \quad (19)$$

provided $\lambda_0 = Tc$ denote the wave length in vacuum of the light considered. Since pc represents the index n of the substance with respect to a vacuum,

$$\delta = \frac{z}{\tau c}\frac{n'' - n'}{2} = z\frac{\pi}{\lambda_0}(n'' - n'), \quad . \quad . \quad (19')$$

n'' and n' denoting the respective indices of refraction of the substance for a right-handed and a left-handed circularly polarized wave. Hence, from (19) and (19′),

$$2\pi\frac{f}{\lambda_0} = n'' - n'. \quad . \quad . \quad . \quad . \quad (19'')$$

If, then, plane-polarized light fall perpendicularly upon a plate of an optically active substance of thickness z, the plane of polarization will be rotated an angle δ by the passage of the light through the crystal. The rotation δ may take place in one direction or the other according to the sign of f. $n'' - n'$ may be calculated from δ by (19′).

Special arrangements have been devised for measuring this angle of rotation easily and accurately.* In the half-shadow polarimeter the field of view is divided into two parts in which the planes of polarization are slightly inclined to each other. But even with the use of two simple Nicols, a polarizer and an analyzer, when the light is homogeneous and sufficiently intense the position of the plane of polarization can be determined from the mean of a number of observations to within

* For a description of such instruments cf. Landolt, Das optische Drehungsvermögen der organischer Substanzen, Braunschweig, 2d Edition, 1897; Müller-Pouillet, Optik, p. 1166 sq. Rotation of the plane of polarization has been practically made use of in sugar analysis.

three seconds of arc, provided the setting is made with the aid of the so-called Landolt band. For when Nicol prisms are used the field of view is never polarized uniformly throughout, so that, when the Nicols are crossed, the whole field is not completely dark, but is crossed by a dark curved line which was first observed by Landolt. The position of this band changes very rapidly as the plane of polarization of the light which falls upon the analyzer changes.*

4. **Crystals.**—In order to obtain a law for crystals, it must be borne in mind that the constants ϑ_1, r_1, which appear in equations (1) of the dispersion theory on page 383, depend upon the direction of the coordinates. Also that the terms which have been added in this chapter and which correspond to the optical activity can have a much more general form within a crystal than that given in (1) on page 401. Nevertheless the assumption will be made that, so far as these added terms are concerned, a crystal is to be treated like an unsymmetrically isotropic substance. No objection can be made to this assumption, since the coefficients f of these added terms are so small, in the case of all the actually existing substances, that the change of f with the direction which is due to the crystalline structure can be neglected.

If the coordinate axes be taken in those directions which would be the axes of optical symmetry of the crystal if it were not optically active, the extension of equations (7) and (8) would be †

$$\left.\begin{aligned}\frac{1}{C}\frac{\partial}{\partial t}\left(\epsilon_1 X+f\left[\frac{\partial Y}{\partial z}-\frac{\partial Z}{\partial y}\right]\right)&=\frac{\partial \gamma}{\partial y}-\frac{\partial \beta}{\partial z},\\ \frac{1}{C}\frac{\partial}{\partial t}\left(\epsilon_2 Y+f\left[\frac{\partial Z}{\partial x}-\frac{\partial X}{\partial z}\right]\right)&=\frac{\partial \alpha}{\partial z}-\frac{\partial \gamma}{\partial x},\\ \frac{1}{C}\frac{\partial}{\partial t}\left(\epsilon_3 Z+f\left[\frac{\partial X}{\partial y}-\frac{\partial Y}{\partial x}\right]\right)&=\frac{\partial \beta}{\partial x}-\frac{\partial \alpha}{\partial y},\end{aligned}\right\} \quad . \qquad (20)$$

* Cf. Lippich, Wien. Ber. (2), 85, p. 268, 1892; Müller Pouillet, Optik, p. 1115.

† C is written for c.

$$\frac{1}{C}\frac{\partial \alpha}{\partial t}=\frac{\partial Y}{\partial z}-\frac{\partial Z}{\partial y},\quad \frac{1}{C}\frac{\partial \beta}{\partial t}=\frac{\partial Z}{\partial x}-\frac{\partial X}{\partial z},\quad \frac{1}{C}\frac{\partial \gamma}{\partial t}=\frac{\partial X}{\partial y}-\frac{\partial Y}{\partial x},\qquad (21)$$

in which

$$\left.\begin{aligned} \epsilon_1 = 1 + \Sigma\frac{\vartheta'_h \mathfrak{N}_h}{1-\left(\frac{\tau'_h}{\tau}\right)^2}, \qquad \epsilon_2 = 1 + \Sigma\frac{\vartheta''_h \mathfrak{N}_h}{1-\left(\frac{\tau''_h}{\tau}\right)^2},\\ \epsilon_3 = 1 + \Sigma\frac{\vartheta'''_h \mathfrak{N}_h}{1-\left(\frac{\tau'''_h}{\tau}\right)^2}, \end{aligned}\right\} . \qquad (22)$$

$$f = \Sigma\frac{\vartheta_h f'_h \mathfrak{N}_h}{1-\left(\frac{\tau_h}{\tau}\right)^2}. \quad . \quad . \quad . \quad . \quad . \qquad (23)$$

In this $\vartheta'_h\mathfrak{N}_h$, $\vartheta''_h\mathfrak{N}_h$, $\vartheta'''_h\mathfrak{N}_h$ denote the three different dielectric constants of the ions of kind h along the three coordinate directions, and τ'_h, τ''_h, τ''_h are proportional to the three periods of vibration corresponding to the three axes. In (23) ϑ_h, τ_h are mean values of ϑ'_h, ϑ''_h, ϑ'''_h, and τ'_h, τ''_h, τ'''_h, respectively.

For the sake of integration set, as on page 369,

$$\left.\begin{aligned} u = \epsilon_1 X = Me^{i\psi}, \qquad v = \epsilon_2 Y = Ne^{i\psi}, \qquad w = \epsilon_3 Z = \Pi e^{i\psi},\\ \psi = \frac{2\pi}{T}\left(t - \frac{mx+ny+pz}{V}\right), \end{aligned}\right\} \qquad (24)$$

in which u, v, w may be interpreted as the components of the light-vectors. Then it follows from (20) and (21),* using the abbreviations

$$C^2 : \epsilon_1 = a^2, \quad C^2 : \epsilon_2 = b^2, \quad C^2 : \epsilon_3 = c^2, \quad . \qquad (25)$$

$$\eta = \frac{2\pi f C}{T\epsilon^{\frac{3}{2}}}, \quad . \quad . \quad . \quad . \quad . \quad . \qquad (26)$$

(in which ϵ denotes a mean value of ϵ_1, ϵ_2, ϵ_3) that the expres-

---

* This is more fully developed in Winkelmann's Handbuch, Optik, p. 791. The normal surface and the ray surface are more fully discussed by O. Weder in Die Lichtbewegung in zweiaxigen Crystallen, Diss. Leipzig, 1896, Zeitschr. f. Krystallogr. 1896.

sion for the velocity V in terms of the direction m, n, p of the wave normal takes the form:

$$m^2(V^2-b^2)(V^2-c^2)+n^2(V^2-c^2)(V^2-a^2)$$
$$+p^2(V^2-a^2)(V^2-b^2)=\eta^2. \quad (27)$$

The introduction of the angles g_1 and g_2 which the wave normal makes with the optic axes gives, as on page 320,

$$\left.\begin{aligned}2V_1^2 &= a^2+c^2+(a^2-c^2)\cos g_1\cos g_2\\ &\qquad +\sqrt{(a^2-c^2)^2\sin^2 g_1\sin^2 g_2+4\eta^2},\\ 2V_2^2 &= a^2+c^2+(a^2-c^2)\cos g_1\cos g_2\\ &\qquad -\sqrt{(a^2-c^2)^2\sin^2 g_1\sin^2 g_2+4\eta^2}.\end{aligned}\right\} \quad (28)$$

It appears from this that the two velocities V_1 and V_2 are never identical, not even in the direction of the optic axes.

Thus upon entering an active crystal a wave always divides into two waves which have different velocities. These two waves are elliptically polarized, and the vibration form of both is the same, but the ellipses lie oppositely and the direction of rotation in them is opposite. The ratio h of the axes of the ellipse is given by

$$h+\frac{1}{h}=\frac{\sqrt{(a^2-c^2)^2\sin^2 g_1\sin^2 g_2+4\eta^2}}{\eta}. \quad . \quad (29)$$

Hence in the direction of an optic axis (g_1 or $g_2=0$) $h=1$, i.e. the polarization is circular. But when the wave normal makes but a small angle with the direction of an optic axis, the vibration form is a very flat ellipse, since 2η, even in the case of powerfully active crystals, is always small in comparison with the difference a^2-c^2 of the two velocities.

Biaxial active crystals have not thus far been found in nature; but several uniaxial active crystals exist. Quartz is one of these. It exists in two crystallographic forms, one of which is the image of the other; hence one produces right-handed, the other left-handed, rotation. The rotation of the plane of polarization which is produced by a plate of quartz cut perpendicular to the optic axis is given, as in the case of isotropic media, by the equation

$$\delta = 2\pi^2 \frac{f}{\lambda_0^2} z = \frac{\pi}{\lambda_0} z(n'' - n'). \quad . \quad . \quad . \quad (30)$$

When $z = 1$ mm. and yellow light ($\lambda_0 = 0.000589$ mm.) is used, $\delta = 21.7° = 0.12\pi$ radians. Hence in this case

$$2\pi \frac{f}{\lambda_0} = n'' - n' = 0.12 \cdot \frac{\lambda_0}{z} = 0.000071. \quad . \quad (31)$$

In this n' and n'' denote the two indices of refraction which quartz must have in the direction of its optic axis in consequence of its optical activity. Now a double refraction $n'' - n'$ of the magnitude given in (31) has actually been observed in quartz in the direction of its axis by V. v. Lang. This double refraction can be conveniently demonstrated by the method due to Fresnel, in which the light is successively passed through right- and left-handed quartz prisms whose refracting angles are turned in opposite directions.

If a quartz plate of a few millimetres' thickness, which is cut perpendicular to the axis, be observed between crossed Nicols in white light, it appears colored. For the plane of polarization of the incident light has been rotated a different amount for each of the different colors, and all of those colors must be cut off from the field of view whose planes of polarization are perpendicular to that of the analyzer. Hence the color of the quartz plate changes upon rotation of the analyzer. In convergent white light the interference figure described on page 356 for uniaxial crystals when placed between crossed Nicols are observable only at considerable distance from the centre of the field. Near the centre the circular polarization has the effect of nearly destroying the black cross of the principal isogyre. Hence a quartz plate cut per-

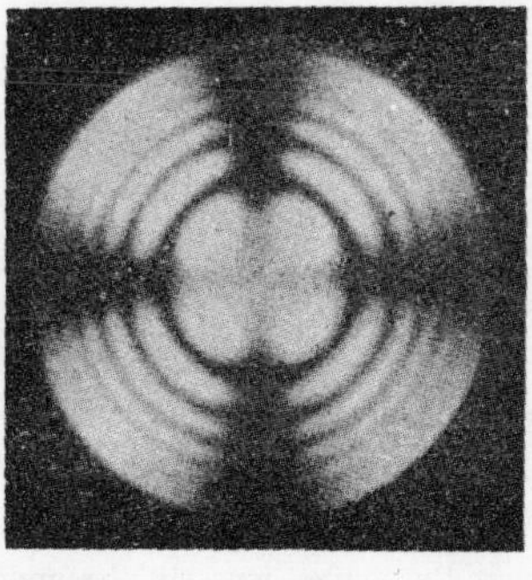

FIG. 105.

pendicular to the axis shows, between crossed Nicols in convergent light, the interference figure represented in Fig. 105.

Spiral interference patterns appear when the incident light is circularly polarized. The calculation of the form of these spirals, which are known as Airy's spirals, is given in Neumann's "Vorlesungen über theoretische Optik," Leipzig, 1885, page 244.

5. Rotary Dispersion.—The rotation δ of the plane of polarization, which is produced by optically active substances, varies with the color. The law of dispersion can be obtained from equations (6) and (19) by setting the thickness of the plate $z = 1$ and introducing for λ_0, the wave length in vacuum, λ, the wave length in air,* thus

$$\delta = \frac{k}{\lambda^2}\Sigma\frac{\vartheta_h f'_h \mathfrak{N}_h}{1 - \left(\frac{\tau_h}{\tau}\right)^2}, \quad . \quad . \quad . \quad . \quad . \quad (32)$$

in which k is a constant.

If the natural periods of the active ions † are so much smaller than the period of the light used that $(\tau_h : \tau)^2$ is negligible in comparison with 1, there results the simplest form of the dispersion equation, namely,

$$\delta = \frac{k'}{\lambda^2}. \quad . \quad . \quad . \quad . \quad . \quad . \quad . \quad (33)$$

This equation, due to Biot, agrees approximately with the facts; yet it is not exact. If all the natural periods of the active ions lie in the ultra-violet, (32) can be developed in ascending powers of $(\tau_h : \tau)^2$ and put into the form

$$\delta = \frac{k_1}{\lambda^2} + \frac{k_2}{\lambda^4} + \frac{k_3}{\lambda^6} + \dots \quad . \quad . \quad . \quad (34)$$

Now in most cases the first two terms of this equation (Boltzmann's equation) are sufficient; nevertheless this is not

* In view of the small dispersion of air this is permissible.

† By active ions will be understood those kinds of ions whose equations of motion are of the form (2) above, while those ions will be called inactive for which he constant f' in equation (2) has the value zero.

so for quartz, in which δ has been measured over a large range of wave lengths, namely, from $\lambda = 2\mu$ to $\lambda = 0.2\mu$. The constants k_1, k_2, k_3 can have different signs, since the f_h' corresponding to the different kinds of active ions need not have the same sign.

If some of the active ions have natural periods τ in the ultra-red, then (32) must be developed in powers of $(\tau : \tau_r)^2$. The equation then takes the form

$$\delta = \frac{k_1}{\lambda^2} + \frac{k_2}{\lambda^4} + \frac{k_3}{\lambda^6} + \ldots + k' + k_1'\lambda^2 + k_2'\lambda^4 + \ldots \quad (35)$$

If, as in the case of quartz, it is desired to represent the dispersion over a large range of colors, some of which have periods which are close to the natural periods, then it is better to avoid development in series and to write, in accordance with (32),

$$\delta = \Sigma \frac{k_h}{\lambda^2 - \lambda_h^2}. \quad \ldots \ldots \quad (36)$$

Now in the case of quartz the wave lengths λ_h of the natural periods which lie closest to those of light are known for the ordinary wave; they are (cf. page 391) $\lambda_1^2 = 0.010627$, $\lambda_2^2 = 78.22$, $\lambda_3^2 = 430.6$. The unit of wave length is here taken as $1\mu = 0.001$ mm. But the conclusion has already been drawn from equation (30′) that quartz has ions for which λ_h is much smaller than the wave length of light. The activity coefficient k' of ions of this kind, for which λ_h^2 may be neglected in (36) in comparison with λ^2, must be taken into consideration, so that the following dispersion equation is obtained for quartz:

$$\delta = \frac{k_1}{\lambda^2 - \lambda_1^2} + \frac{k_2}{\lambda^2 - \lambda_2^2} + \frac{k_3}{\lambda^2 - \lambda_3^2} + \frac{k'}{\lambda^2}. \quad . \quad (37)$$

If this equation be applied to the dispersion of quartz, it is found from observation that $k_2 = k_3 = 0$, i.e. *that the kinds of ions whose natural periods lie in the ultra-red are inactive*, and that k_1 and k' have different signs. Now it argues for the correctness of the foundations of the theory here presented that, with the help of the equation

$$\delta = \frac{k_1}{\lambda^2 - \lambda_1^2} + \frac{k'}{\lambda^2}, \quad . \quad . \quad . \quad . \quad . \qquad (38)$$

which contains but two constants, since λ_1 is a constant which depends upon ordinary dispersion and not upon rotary dispersion, the latter can be well represented, as is shown by the following table,* in which the rotation is given in degrees per mm. of thickness:

$$k_1 = 12.200, \quad k' = -5.046.$$

λ (in μ).	δ obs.	δ calc.
2.140	1.60	1.57
1.770	2.28	2.29
1.450	3.43	3.43
1.080	6.18	6.23
0.67082	16.54	16.56
0.65631	17.31	17.33
0.58932 *	21.72	21.70
0.57905	22.55	22.53
0.57695	22.72	22.70
0.54610	25.53	25.51
0.50861	29.72	29.67
0.49164	31.97	31.92
0.48001	33.67	33.60
0.43586	41.55	41.46
0.40468	48.93	48.85
0.34406	70.59	70.61
0.27467	121.06	121.34
0.21935	220.72	220.57

* The *D*-line.

It is possible that values of the constants k_1 and k' might have been chosen so as to give a somewhat better agreement with the observations. Nevertheless the important fact is that this two-constant equation is in satisfactory agreement with observation, while the three-constant equation, which is obtained from (37) by placing $k' = 0$, does not satisfy the observations. *Hence in quartz ions must be assumed to exist*

* The observed values are taken from Gumlich, Wied. Ann. 64, p. 349, 1898.

whose natural periods are extremely small, much smaller than those corresponding to λ_1.

As the table shows, δ increases as λ decreases. This is the course of normal dispersion. But, as appears from (38), this condition would be disturbed, i.e. anomalous rotary dispersion would take place, if the wave lengths were smaller than λ_1, for then δ would be negative. In general anomalous rotary dispersion is produced whenever λ approaches the wave length λ_h of a natural period. But even when λ is much greater than λ_h, a change in the sign of δ may take place, as is shown by the general equation (36), if two kinds of active ions are present which have activity coefficients k_h of opposite sign. In this case maxima and minima in δ for variations in λ can also appear.

Cases of anomalous rotary dispersion have often been observed. (Cf. Landolt, "Das optische Drehungsvermögen," p. 135.) G. H. v. Wyss has produced anomalous rotary dispersion by mixing right- and left-handed turpentine (Wied. Ann. 33, p. 554, 1888). In general every active substance must show anomalous rotary dispersion in certain regions of vibration, but these regions do not necessarily lie within the limits of the vibrations which can be produced experimentally.

6. Absorbing Active Substances.—If the wave length λ lies close to the wave length λ_h which corresponds to the natural period of an active ion, then, by (36), the rotation δ of the plane of polarization is very large. But in this case the coefficient of friction a_h, which was neglected on page 388, must be taken into consideration. a_h must also be taken into consideration when the substance shows a broad absorption band. In this case ϵ as well as f becomes complex in equation (10); thus

$$\left.\begin{aligned} \epsilon &= 1 + \Sigma \frac{\vartheta_h \mathfrak{N}_h}{1 + i\dfrac{a_h}{\tau} - \dfrac{b_h}{\tau^2}}, \\ f &= \Sigma \frac{\vartheta_h f_h \mathfrak{N}_h}{1 + i\dfrac{a_h}{\tau} - \dfrac{b_h}{\tau^2}}. \end{aligned}\right\} \quad . \quad . \quad . \quad . \quad (39)$$

The quantity p in equation (11) must therefore also be taken as complex. If it be written in the form (cf. page 360)

$$p = \frac{1 - i\kappa}{V}, \quad \dots \dots \quad (40)$$

V represents the velocity and κ the coefficient of absorption of the wave. Since there are two values of p obtained from (16) and (17), there must also be two different coefficients of absorption, κ' and κ'', one of which corresponds to a left-handed and the other to a right-handed circularly polarized wave. This has been experimentally verified by Cotton for solutions of the tartrates of copper and of chromium in caustic potash (C. R. 120, pp. 989, 1044, Ann. de chim. et de phys. (7) 8, p. 347, 1896.) That these solutions also showed anomalous rotary dispersion is easily understood from the foregoing, since the strong absorption which they produce is evidence that λ lies in the region which corresponds to the natural periods.

If the two indices of refraction n' and n'' for left- and right-handed circularly polarized waves be introduced into (16), (17), and (18), there results

$$c(p'' - p') = n'' - n' - i(n''\kappa'' - n'\kappa') = \frac{f}{\tau c} = \frac{2\pi f}{\lambda}. \quad (41)$$

If a sharp absorption band is present, which, according to the above, corresponds to a small value of a_h, then the difference between κ'' and κ' within the absorption band itself becomes very marked. For when $\tau^2 = b_h$, it follows from (39) and (41) that

$$n'' - n' = 0, \quad n''\kappa'' - n'\kappa' = \frac{\vartheta_h f'_h \mathfrak{N}_h}{a_h \cdot c}. \quad . \quad . \quad (42)$$

If τ is farther from the natural period τ_h, and if a_h is sufficiently small, so that it is only necessary to retain terms of the first order in κ or a_h, then, from (39) and (41), the law of dispersion for the difference of the coefficients of absorption takes the form

$$n''\kappa'' - n'\kappa' = \lambda^2 \Sigma \frac{\alpha_h}{(\lambda^2 - \lambda_h^2)^2}. \quad . \quad . \quad . \quad (43)$$

As λ varies, a change in sign, and also maxima and minima of $n''\kappa'' - n'\kappa'$, may occur, provided there are present several kinds of ions which have activity coefficients f'_h of different signs.

Moreover the difference in the absorptions of the right- and the left-handed circularly polarized waves is always small in comparison with the total absorption.

For if f^2 be neglected, and if only one absorption band is present, it is easy to deduce, from (16) and (17),

$$\frac{n''\kappa'' - n'\kappa'}{n''\kappa'' + n'\kappa'} = \frac{2\pi f'_h}{\lambda} n, \quad . \quad . \quad . \quad . \quad . \qquad (44)$$

in which n denotes the mean of n' and n''.

But $f'_h : \lambda$ is always a small number.

Moreover it is to be observed that it is not necessary that every active substance which shows an absorption band should exhibit the phenomena here described. For, in order that this be the case, it is necessary that the ions which cause the absorption should be optically active. It is easily conceivable that absorption and optical activity may be due to different kinds of ions.

CHAPTER VII

MAGNETICALLY ACTIVE SUBSTANCES

A. Hypothesis of Molecular Currents

1. General Considerations.—Peculiar optical phenomena are observed in all substances when they are brought into a strong magnetic field. Furthermore it is well known that the purely magnetic properties of different substances are very different, i.e. the value of the permeability μ varies with the substance (cf. page 269). It is greater than 1 for *paramagnetic* substances, less than 1 for *diamagnetic* ones. Hence a magnetic field is said to produce a greater density of the lines of force in a paramagnetic substance than in the free ether, and a less density in a diamagnetic substance than in the free ether. Ampère and Weber have advanced the theory that so-called molecular currents exist in paramagnetic substances. According to the theory of dispersion which has been here adopted, these currents are due to the ionic charges. When an external magnetic force is applied, these molecular currents are partially or wholly turned into a definite direction so that the magnetic lines due to them are superposed upon the magnetic lines due to the external field.

According to this theory, diamagnetic substances ordinarily have no molecular currents. But as soon as they are brought into a magnetic field, molecular currents are supposed to be produced by induction. These currents remain constant so long as the external field does not change. The ionic charges must be assumed to rotate without friction so that the maintenance of these currents requires the expenditure of no energy. The lines of force due to these induced molecular currents must oppose the lines of the external field, since, according to Lenz's law, induced currents always flow in such a direction that they tend to oppose a change in the external magnetic field.

If it is desired to determine the optical properties of a substance when placed in a strong magnetic field, it is always necessary to bear in mind that both in para- and diamagnetic substances certain ions are supposed to be in rotation and to produce molecular currents. If e be the charge of a rotating ion of kind 1, and T its period of rotation, the strength of the molecular current produced by it is

$$i = e : \mathrm{T}. \quad . \quad . \quad . \quad . \quad . \quad . \quad (1)$$

If now such an ion, rotating about a point $\mathfrak{P}$, be struck by the electric force of a light-wave, its path must be changed. If the period of rotation T is very small in comparison with the period of the light, the path of the ion remains unchanged in form and period, but the point about which it rotates is changed from $\mathfrak{P}$ to a point $\mathfrak{P}'$ distant ξ from $\mathfrak{P}$ in the direction of the electrical force. The ion then oscillates back and forth between $\mathfrak{P}$ and $\mathfrak{P}'$ in the period of the light-wave. The same mean effect must be produced if the period of rotation is large, provided it is not a multiple of the period T of the light vibration. Any rotation of the plane of the path, which is produced by the magnetic force of the light-wave, may be neglected, since this is always much smaller than the external magnetic force. This displacement of the molecular current also produces a displacement of the magnetic lines of force which arise from it, so that a peculiar induction effect takes place, an effect which must be considered when a wave of light falls upon a molecular current.

This inductive effect can be at once calculated if the number of lines of force associated with a molecular current is known.

Now this number can easily be found. Let the paths of

the molecular currents all be parallel to a plane which is perpendicular to the direction R of the external magnetic field. Consider first a line of length l parallel to the direction R. Let $\mathfrak{N}'$ denote the number of molecular currents due to ions of kind 1 upon unit length; then $l \cdot \mathfrak{N}'$ denotes the number upon the length l. These currents may be looked upon as a solenoid of cross-section q, q being the area of the ionic orbit. The number of lines of force in this solenoid is *

$$M = 4\pi\mathfrak{N}'iq : c.$$

If now there are $\mathfrak{N}''$ such solenoids per unit area, then the number of magnetic lines per unit area due to these molecular currents is

$$M_1 = 4\pi\frac{\mathfrak{N}'\mathfrak{N}''iq}{c} = 4\pi iq\frac{\mathfrak{N}}{c},$$

in which $\mathfrak{N}$ is the number of rotating ions of kind 1 in unit of volume.

The components of M_1 in the direction of the coordinates are

$$\left.\begin{array}{c} \alpha_1 = \dfrac{4\pi}{c}iq\mathfrak{N}\cos(Kx), \quad \beta_1 = \dfrac{4\pi}{c}iq\mathfrak{N}\cos(Ky), \\ \gamma_1 = \dfrac{4\pi}{c}iq\mathfrak{N}\cos(Kz). \end{array}\right\} \quad . \quad (2)$$

2. Deduction of the Differential Equations.—The discussion will be based upon equations (7) and (11) (cf. pages 265 and 267) of the Maxwell theory, namely,

$$\frac{4\pi}{c}j_x = \frac{\partial\gamma}{\partial y} - \frac{\partial\beta}{\partial z} \text{ etc.,} \quad \frac{4\pi}{c}s_x = \frac{\partial Y}{\partial z} - \frac{\partial Z}{\partial y} \text{ etc.} \quad (3)$$

But while in the extensions of the Maxwell theory which have thus far been made only the expression j_x for the electric current density was modified by the hypothesis of the existence of ions, the magnetic current density s_x retaining always the

* The number of lines of force in a solenoid is $4\pi niq$, where n is the number of turns in unit length and i the strength of the current in electromagnetic units. Since here i is defined electrostatically, c occurs in the denominator.

constant value $\frac{1}{4}\pi\cdot\frac{\partial\alpha}{\partial t}$, here, because of the introduction of the concept of rotating ions, s_x must also assume another form. $4\pi j_x$ and $4\pi s_x$ are defined by (12) on page 268 as the change in the density of the electric and the magnetic lines of force in unit time.

Now in order to calculate $4\pi s_x$ it is necessary to take account of the fact that it consists of several parts. The change which is produced directly by a light-wave in the flow of lines of force through the rectangle $dy\,dz$ in the ether is represented by $dy\,dz\cdot\frac{\partial\alpha}{\partial t}$. But another quantity must be added to this—a quantity which is due to the motion, produced by the light-wave, of the point $\mathfrak{P}$ about which the ions rotate, since the lines of force M_1 move with the point P.

In order to calculate the amount of this portion of s_x, consider a rectangular element $dy\,dz$ perpendicular to the x-axis, and inquire what number of lines of force cut the four sides $abcd$ of the rectangle because of the motion of $\mathfrak{P}$, the components of the motion being ξ, η, ζ.

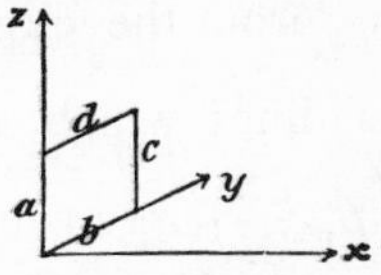

FIG. 106.

Consider first only the lines of force α_1 which are parallel to the x-axis. In unit time the number of lines of force which pass into the rectangle through the side a is $\left(\alpha_1\cdot\frac{\partial\eta}{\partial t}\right)_a dz$; and the number which pass out through the side c is $\left(\alpha_1\cdot\frac{\partial\eta}{\partial t}\right)_c dz$. The subscripts a and c are to indicate that the value of the expression $\alpha_1\cdot\frac{\partial\eta}{\partial t}$ is to be calculated along these sides respectively. Hence

$$\left(\alpha_1\cdot\frac{\partial\eta}{\partial t}\right)_c = \left(\alpha_1\cdot\frac{\partial\eta}{\partial t}\right)_a + dy\frac{\partial}{\partial y}\left(\alpha_1\cdot\frac{\partial\eta}{\partial t}\right).$$

In the last term α_1 is left under the sign of differentiation in order to include the case of non-homogeneous media for which

α_1, β_1, γ_1 are functions of the coordinates. In homogeneous substances α_1, β_1, γ_1 are constant. The number of lines α_1, which in their motion cut the sides a and c, increase the number of lines which pass through the rectangle by the amount $-dy\,dz\frac{\partial}{\partial y}\left(\alpha_1\frac{\partial \eta}{\partial t}\right)$. Similarly the number of lines α_1 which in their motion cut the sides b and d of the rectangle add to the total flow through the rectangle the amount $-dy\,dz\frac{\partial}{\partial z}\left(\alpha_1\frac{\partial \zeta}{\partial t}\right)$.

Because of the component ξ of the motion of $\mathfrak{P}$, the lines of force β_1, which are parallel to the y-axis, can cut only the sides a and c of the rectangle. Now the number of lines which pass through the rectangle changes only because of a rotation of the lines β_1 about the z-axis, this change being positive if the lines β_1 rotate from the + direction of y to the + direction of x. The effect of this rotation can be calculated by subtracting from the expression $\left(\beta_1\cdot\frac{\partial \xi}{\partial t}\right)_c dz$, which gives the number of lines which cut the side c in a second, the expression $\left(\beta_1\cdot\frac{\partial \xi}{\partial t}\right)_a dz$, which represents the number which cut a in a second. Since now

$$\left(\beta_1\cdot\frac{\partial \xi}{\partial t}\right)_c = \left(\beta_1\cdot\frac{\partial \xi}{\partial t}\right)_a + dy\frac{\partial}{\partial y}\left(\beta_1\cdot\frac{\partial \xi}{\partial t}\right),$$

the rotation of β_1 adds to the flow of lines through the rectangle the amount $+dy\,dz\frac{\partial}{\partial y}\left(\beta_1\frac{\partial \xi}{\partial t}\right)$.

Similarly the rotation of the lines γ_1 about the y-axis adds the amount $+dy\,dz\frac{\partial}{\partial z}\left(\gamma_1\frac{\partial \xi}{\partial t}\right)$ to the flow of lines through the rectangle.

The total flow through the rectangle, obtained by adding these amounts, is

$$dy\,dz\left\{\frac{\partial \alpha}{\partial t} - \frac{\partial}{\partial y}\left(\alpha_1\frac{\partial \eta}{\partial t}\right) - \frac{\partial}{\partial z}\left(\alpha_1\frac{\partial \zeta}{\partial t}\right) + \frac{\partial}{\partial y}\left(\beta_1\frac{\partial \xi}{\partial t}\right) + \frac{\partial}{\partial z}\left(\gamma_1\frac{\partial \xi}{\partial t}\right)\right\}.$$

The change in unit time in the number of lines which pass through an element of unit area perpendicular to the x-axis is therefore, since for a constant external field α_1, β_1, γ_1 are independent of the time t,

$$4\pi s_x = \frac{\partial}{\partial t}\left\{\alpha + \frac{\partial}{\partial z}(\gamma_1\xi - \alpha_1\zeta) - \frac{\partial}{\partial y}(\alpha_1\eta - \beta_1\xi)\right\}. \quad (4)$$

Strictly speaking, the current density is modified in a complicated way by the rotation of the ions. But if the ratio of the period of rotation of the ion to the period of the light is not rational, it is only necessary, in order to find the mean effect, to take account of the motion ξ, η, ζ of the centre of rotation $\mathfrak{P}$.

The current density j_x may therefore be written as above [cf. equation (7), page 385] in the form

$$j_x = \frac{1}{4\pi}\frac{\partial X}{\partial t} + e\mathfrak{N}\frac{\partial \xi}{\partial t}. \quad . \quad . \quad . \quad . \quad . \quad (5)$$

For the motion of a point $\mathfrak{P}$, which is the mean position of a rotating ion of kind 1, two equations will be assumed. The first is the same as that given above on page 383, namely,

$$m\frac{\partial^2 \xi}{\partial t^2} = eX - \frac{4\pi e^2}{\vartheta}\xi - re^2\frac{\partial \xi}{\partial t}, \quad . \quad . \quad . \quad . \quad (6)$$

and corresponds to the case in which $\mathfrak{P}$ can oscillate about a position of equilibrium (ions of a dielectric). The second is equation (34) on page 397, namely,

$$m\frac{\partial^2 \xi}{\partial t^2} = eX - re^2\frac{\partial \xi}{\partial t}, \quad . \quad . \quad . \quad . \quad . \quad (7)$$

and corresponds to the case in which $\mathfrak{P}$ moves continually in the direction of the constant force X, i.e. the case in which e is the ion of a conductor, for example a metal. m denotes the ponderable mass of the ion.

If the changes are periodic, so that every X and every ξ is proportional to $e^{i\frac{t}{\tau}}$, there results from (6)

$$e\frac{\partial \xi}{\partial t}\left\{1 + i\frac{r\vartheta}{4\pi\tau} - \frac{m\vartheta}{4\pi e^2}\cdot\frac{1}{\tau^2}\right\} = \frac{\vartheta}{4\pi}\frac{\partial X}{\partial t}, \quad . \quad . \quad (8)$$

while from (7)

$$e\frac{\partial \xi}{\partial t}\left(r + \frac{i}{\tau}\frac{m}{e^2}\right) = X = -i\tau\frac{\partial X}{\partial t}. \quad . \quad . \quad . \quad (9)$$

Hence, setting as above

$$\frac{r\vartheta}{4\pi} = a, \quad \frac{m\vartheta}{4\pi e^2} = b = \tau_1^{\,2}, \quad \frac{m}{e^2} = m', \quad . \quad . \quad . \quad (10)$$

(5) gives, in case e is an ion of a non-conductor,

$$j_x = \frac{1}{4\pi}\frac{\partial X}{\partial t}\left\{1 + \frac{\mathfrak{N}\vartheta}{1 + ia/\tau - b/\tau^2}\right\}, \quad . \quad . \quad . \quad (11)$$

But if e is the ion of a conductor,

$$j_x = \frac{1}{4\pi}\frac{\partial X}{\partial t}\left\{1 + \frac{4\pi\tau\mathfrak{N}}{ir - m'/\tau}\right\}. \quad . \quad . \quad . \quad (12)$$

In any case it is possible to set

$$j_x = \frac{\epsilon'}{4\pi}\frac{\partial X}{\partial t}, \quad j_y = \frac{\epsilon'}{4\pi}\frac{\partial Y}{\partial t}, \quad j_z = \frac{\epsilon'}{4\pi}\frac{\partial Z}{\partial t}, \quad . \quad (13)$$

in which ϵ' is in general a complex quantity depending upon τ.

Moreover from (1), (2), and (8) there results, for an ion of a non-conductor,

$$\gamma_1\xi = \frac{\mathfrak{N}\vartheta}{1 + ia/\tau - b/\tau^2}\cdot\frac{q}{cT}\cos(Kz)\,X, \quad . \quad . \quad (14)$$

and from (9), for an ion of a conductor,

$$\gamma_1\xi = \frac{4\pi\tau\mathfrak{N}}{ir - m'/\tau}\cdot\frac{q}{cT}\cos(Kz)\,X. \quad . \quad . \quad . \quad (15)$$

In both cases it is possible to set

$$\gamma_1\xi = \nu\cos(Kz)\,X, \quad . \quad . \quad . \quad . \quad (16)$$

in which ν is in general a complex quantity depending upon τ. A similar expression may be obtained for $\alpha_1\zeta$, etc. Setting further

$$\nu\cos(Kx) = \nu_x, \quad \nu\cos(Ky) = \nu_y, \quad \nu\cos(Kz) = \nu_z, \quad (17)$$

then from (13), (4), and (16) the fundamental equations (3) become

$$\left.\begin{aligned}
\frac{1}{c}\frac{\partial}{\partial t}\left\{\alpha+\frac{\partial}{\partial z}(\nu_z X-\nu_x Z)-\frac{\partial}{\partial y}(\nu_x Y-\nu_y X)\right\}&=\frac{\partial Y}{\partial z}-\frac{\partial Z}{\partial y},\\
\frac{1}{c}\frac{\partial}{\partial t}\left\{\beta+\frac{\partial}{\partial x}(\nu_x Y-\nu_y X)-\frac{\partial}{\partial z}(\nu_y Z-\nu_z Y)\right\}&=\frac{\partial Z}{\partial x}-\frac{\partial X}{\partial z},\\
\frac{1}{c}\frac{\partial}{\partial t}\left\{\gamma+\frac{\partial}{\partial y}(\nu_y Z-\nu_z Y)-\frac{\partial}{\partial x}(\nu_z X-\nu_x Z)\right\}&=\frac{\partial X}{\partial y}-\frac{\partial Y}{\partial x},
\end{aligned}\right\} \quad (18)$$

$$\frac{\epsilon'}{c}\frac{\partial X}{\partial t}=\frac{\partial \gamma}{\partial y}-\frac{\partial \beta}{\partial z},\quad \frac{\epsilon'}{c}\frac{\partial Y}{\partial t}=\frac{\partial \alpha}{\partial z}-\frac{\partial \gamma}{\partial x},\quad \frac{\epsilon'}{c}\frac{\partial Z}{\partial t}=\frac{\partial \beta}{\partial x}-\frac{\partial \alpha}{\partial y}. \quad (19)$$

When several kinds of molecules are present the same equations (18) and (19) still hold, but the constants ϵ' and ν are sums; thus

$$\epsilon' = 1 + \Sigma\frac{\mathfrak{N}_h\vartheta_h}{1+i\frac{a_h}{\tau}-\frac{b_h}{\tau^2}} + 4\pi\tau\Sigma\frac{\mathfrak{N}_h}{ir_k-\frac{m_k'}{\tau}}, \quad . \quad . \quad (20)$$

$$\nu = \frac{1}{c}\Sigma\frac{\mathfrak{N}_h\vartheta_h}{1+i\frac{a_h}{\tau}-\frac{b_h}{\tau^2}}\cdot\frac{q_h}{T_h} + \frac{4\pi\tau}{c}\Sigma\frac{\mathfrak{N}_k}{ir_k-\frac{m_k'}{\tau}}\frac{q_k}{T_k}. \quad (21)$$

The index h refers to the ions of a dielectric, the index k to those of a conductor. T_h is positive or negative according as the positively charged rotating ion strengthens or weakens the external magnetic field. In the case of a negatively charged ion T_h is to be taken as negative when the lines of force of the molecular current lie in the same direction as those of the external magnetic field. In the case of paramagnetic substances T_h is positive for the positively charged ions and negative for those charged negatively. For diamagnetic ions the case is the inverse. Further, q_h is to be considered as dependent upon the strength of the outer magnetic field, for when the magnetization is not carried to saturation all of the molecular currents have not been made parallel to one another

—a fact that is most simply expressed by saying that the value of q_h is then smaller. q_h is therefore to be assumed proportional to the magnetization of the substance. From their method of derivation (cf. page 422) it is evident that equations (18) and (19) are perfectly general, i.e. hold also in *non-homogeneous bodies* for which ϵ' and ν are functions of the coordinates.

3. The Magnetic Rotation of the Plane of Polarization.—Assume that the direction of the beam of light is parallel to the direction of magnetization, and let this direction coincide with the z-axis. Then X, Y, α, β depend only upon z and t, provided plane waves are propagated along the z-axis. Furthermore, $Z = \gamma = 0$, and

$$\nu_x = \nu_y = 0, \quad \nu_z = \nu.$$

Hence the fundamental equations (18) and (19) become

$$\left.\begin{aligned} \frac{1}{c}\frac{\partial}{\partial t}\left\{\alpha + \nu\frac{\partial X}{\partial z}\right\} &= \frac{\partial Y}{\partial z}, \\ \frac{1}{c}\frac{\partial}{\partial t}\left\{\beta + \nu\frac{\partial Y}{\partial z}\right\} &= -\frac{\partial X}{\partial z}, \end{aligned}\right\} \quad . \quad . \quad . \quad (22)$$

$$\frac{\epsilon'}{c}\frac{\partial X}{\partial t} = -\frac{\partial \beta}{\partial z}, \quad \frac{\epsilon'}{c}\frac{\partial Y}{\partial t} = \frac{\partial \alpha}{\partial z}. \quad . \quad . \quad . \quad (23)$$

A differentiation of these equations with respect to t and a substitution in them of the values of $\frac{\partial \alpha}{\partial t}, \frac{\partial \beta}{\partial t}$ taken from (22) gives

$$\left.\begin{aligned} \frac{\epsilon'}{c^2}\frac{\partial^2 X}{\partial t^2} &= \frac{\partial^2 X}{\partial z^2} + \frac{\nu}{c}\frac{\partial^3 Y}{\partial t \partial z^2}, \\ \frac{\epsilon'}{c^2}\frac{\partial^2 Y}{\partial t^2} &= \frac{\partial^2 Y}{\partial z^2} - \frac{\nu}{c}\frac{\partial^3 X}{\partial t \partial z^2}. \end{aligned}\right\} \quad . \quad . \quad . \quad . \quad (24)$$

For the sake of integration write, as above on page 404,

$$X = Me^{\frac{i}{\tau}(t - pz)}, \quad Y = Ne^{\frac{i}{\tau}(t - pz)} \quad . \quad . \quad . \quad (25)$$

Then there results from (24)

$$\epsilon' M = p^2 c^2 (M + i \frac{\nu}{c\tau} N),$$

$$\epsilon' N = p^2 c^2 (N - i \frac{\nu}{c\tau} M).$$

These equations can be satisfied in two different ways, namely, if

$$p^2 c^2 \left(1 + \frac{\nu}{c\tau}\right) = \epsilon', \quad M = iN, \quad . \quad . \quad . \quad . \quad (26)$$

or if

$$p^2 c^2 \left(1 - \frac{\nu}{c\tau}\right) = \epsilon', \quad M = -iN. \quad . \quad . \quad . \quad (27)$$

From the interpretation given on page 405 of the analogous equations (12) and (13) it appears that equations (26) and (27) represent right-handed and left-handed circularly polarized waves and that these waves travel with different velocities. The first (26) is a left-handed circularly polarized wave, and the value of p corresponding to it is

$$p' c = \sqrt{\frac{\epsilon'}{1 + \frac{\nu}{c\tau}}}. \quad . \quad . \quad . \quad . \quad . \quad (28)$$

The value of p corresponding to the right-handed circularly polarized wave is

$$p'' c = \sqrt{\frac{\epsilon'}{1 - \frac{\nu}{c\tau}}}. \quad . \quad . \quad . \quad . \quad . \quad (29)$$

In case ϵ' and ν, i.e. p' and p'', are assumed to be real, a superposition of the two circularly polarized waves gives plane-polarized light whose plane of polarization rotates, while the wave travels a distance z, through the angle

$$\delta = \frac{z}{\tau} \frac{p'' - p'}{2}. \quad . \quad . \quad . \quad . \quad . \quad . \quad (30)$$

If, as is generally the case, $\nu : c\tau$ is small in comparison with 1, then, from (30),

$$\delta = \frac{\nu\sqrt{\epsilon'}}{2c^2\tau^2}z. \quad . \quad . \quad . \quad . \quad . \quad . \quad . \quad (30')$$

When ν is positive the direction of the rotation is from right to left, i.e. counter-clockwise, to an observer looking opposite to the direction of propagation. The positive paramagnetic ions rotate in the same direction when the magnetization has the direction of the positive z-axis. *Hence when ν is positive the rotation of the plane of polarization is in the direction of the molecular currents in paramagnetic substances.*

Since the direction of rotation depends only upon the direction of magnetization, for a given magnetization the rotation of the plane of polarization is doubled if the light after passing through the magnetized substance is reflected and made to traverse it again in the opposite direction. By such a double passage of light through a naturally active substance no rotation of the plane of polarization is produced. For in an optically active substance the direction of rotation of the plane of polarization is always the same to an observer looking in a direction opposite to that of propagation, i.e. the rotation changes its absolute direction when the direction of propagation changes.

Whether the rotation δ is in the direction of the paramagnetic molecular currents or opposite to it cannot be determined from the magnetic character of the substance (whether para- or diamagnetic), for the sign of ν cannot be calculated from the permeability μ of a substance when more than one kind of rotating ions is present.* In accordance with (19) on page 270, the permeability μ is defined by setting the entire density of the lines of force M_2 in the direction of the z-axis equal to $\mu\gamma$. Now by (2), when the magnetization is in the

* Reiff called attention to this point in his book, "Theorie molecularelektrischer Vorgänge," 1896. His standpoint differs from that here taken in that he assumes, not rotating ions, but molecular magnets which have no electric charge but are capable of turning about an axis.

direction of the z-axis, the total number of lines in unit section (the so-called induction) is

$$M_z = \mu\gamma = \gamma + \frac{4\pi}{c}\Sigma iq\mathfrak{N} = \gamma + \frac{4\pi}{c}\Sigma e\mathfrak{N}\frac{q}{T}. \quad (31)$$

Hence the substance is para- or diamagnetic according as

$$\frac{4\pi}{c}\Sigma e\mathfrak{N}\frac{q}{T} \gtrless 0. \quad . \quad . \quad . \quad . \quad . \quad (32)$$

But no conclusion as to the sign of ν can be drawn from the sign of this sum. Take, for example, the simplest case, namely, that in which two different kinds, 1 and 2, of paramagnetic ions are present. Let $e_1 = -e_2 = e$, $\mathfrak{N}_1 = \mathfrak{N}_2 = \mathfrak{N}$, $T_1 = -T_2 = T$, $q_1 = q_2 = q$. Then, from (31),

$$(\mu - 1)\gamma = \frac{4\pi}{c} \cdot 2e\mathfrak{N}\frac{q}{T} > 0.$$

But, from (21), when a_h and b_h are negligible,

$$\nu = \frac{\mathfrak{N}}{c}\frac{q}{T}(\vartheta_1 - \vartheta_2).$$

Thus the sign of ν depends upon the difference of the two dielectric constants $\mathfrak{N}\vartheta_1$ and $\mathfrak{N}\vartheta_2$.

Observation also shows that the magnetic character of a substance furnishes no criterion for determining the direction of the magnetic rotation of the plane of polarization.

4. Dispersion in Magnetic Rotation of the Plane of Polarization. — If the wave length in vacuo $\lambda_0 = Tc$ of the light used be introduced into (30′), it becomes

$$\delta = \frac{2\pi^2\nu\sqrt{\epsilon'}}{\lambda_0^2}z = \frac{2\pi^2\nu n}{\lambda_0^2}z, \quad . \quad . \quad . \quad . \quad (33)$$

in which $\sqrt{\epsilon'} = n$ represents the index of refraction of the substance (unmagnetized).

If n be assumed to be constant, as is roughly the case, ν

must also be considered constant. Hence in this case δ is inversely proportional to λ_0^2, as it is in the case of the natural rotation of the plane of polarization. · This is in fact approximately true.

But if the expression for $\epsilon' = n^2$ be written in the form * (λ, the wave length in air, is introduced instead of λ_0)

$$n^2 = 1 + \frac{A_1}{1 - \left(\frac{\lambda_1}{\lambda}\right)^2} + \frac{A_2}{1 - \left(\frac{\lambda_2}{\lambda}\right)^2} + \frac{A_3}{1 - \left(\frac{\lambda_3}{\lambda}\right)^2} + \ldots, \qquad (34)$$

then, from (21),

$$\nu = \frac{A_1'}{1 - \left(\frac{\lambda_1}{\lambda}\right)^2} + \frac{A_2'}{1 - \left(\frac{\lambda_2}{\lambda}\right)^2} + \frac{A_3'}{1 - \left(\frac{\lambda_3}{\lambda}\right)^2} + \ldots, \qquad (35)$$

in which A_1', A_2', A_3', . . . are constants which are independent of A_1, A_2, A_3, . . .

Thus the number of constants which appear in the dispersion equation for the magnetic rotation of the plane of polarization depends upon the number of constants which is necessary to represent ordinary dispersion, i.e. upon the number of natural periods which must be taken into consideration.

In order to represent the dispersion within the visible spectrum it is in general sufficient to assume one natural period in the ultra-violet, whose wave length λ_1 is not negligible with respect to λ, and in addition a number of other natural periods whose wave lengths λ_2, λ_3, etc., are negligible in comparison with λ. The dispersion equation (34) then becomes

$$n^2 = 1 + A_2 + A_3 + \ldots + \frac{A_1\lambda^2}{\lambda^2 - \lambda_1^2}$$

$$= 1 + A_1 + A_2 + A_3 + \ldots + \frac{A_1\lambda_1^2}{\lambda^2 - \lambda_1^2},$$

* Cf. equation (19) on page 388. This form holds only in the region of normal dispersion and in cases in which no conduction ions are present.

or

$$n^2 = a + \frac{b}{\lambda^2 - \lambda_1^2}. \quad . \quad . \quad . \quad . \quad . \quad (36)$$

In this case, from (35), the dispersion equation must be written

$$\nu = \frac{A_1'\lambda^2}{\lambda^2 - \lambda_1^2} + A_2' + A_3' + \ldots = a' + \frac{b'\lambda^2}{\lambda^2 - \lambda_1^2}, \quad (37)$$

i.e. the dispersion equation for the magnetic rotation δ is, from (33), when $2\pi^2 z$ is set equal to 1,

$$\delta = n\left(\frac{a'}{\lambda^2} + \frac{b'}{\lambda^2 - \lambda_1^2}\right). \quad . \quad . \quad . \quad . \quad (38)$$

This is a two-constant dispersion equation, since λ_1 is obtained from the equation for ordinary dispersion. The experimental results are in good agreement with (38), as is shown by the following table: *

BISULPHIDE OF CARBON.

$\lambda_1 = 0.212\mu$, $\lambda_1^2 = 0.0450$,
$a = 2.516$, $b = 0.0433$,
$a' = -0.0136$, $b' = +0.1530$.

Spectr. Line.	n calc.	n obs.	δ calc.	δ obs.
A	1.6115	1.6118	....	....
B	1.6179	1.6181	....	....
C	1.6210	1.6214	0.592	0.592
D	1.6307	1.6308	0.762	0.760
E	1.6439	1.6438	0.999	1.000
F	1.6560	1.6555	1.232	1.234
G	1.6805	1.6800	1.704	1.704
H	1.7033	1.7032	....	....

* Poincaré has published a collection of other single-constant dispersion equations which have been proposed in L'éclairage électrique, XI. p. 488, 1897. None of these equations agree well with the observations.

CREOSOTE.

$$\lambda_1 = 0.1845\mu, \quad \bar{\lambda}_1^2 = 0.0340,$$
$$a = 2.2948, \quad b = 0.0227,$$
$$a' = -0.1799, \quad b' = +0.3140.$$

Spectr. Line.	n calc.	n obs.	δ calc.	δ obs.
B	1.5319	1.5319	0.515	....
C	1.5336	1.5335	0.573	0.573
D	1.5386	1.5383	0.745	0.758
E	1.5454	1.5452	0.990	1.000
F	1.5515	1.5515	1.226	1.241
G	1.5636	1.5639	1.723	1.723
H	1.5744	1.5744	2 206	....

If the simplest possible supposition be made, namely, that two kinds of rotating ions are present, one charged positively, the other negatively, then the difference in the signs of a' and b' shows that these ions rotate in opposite directions.

The equations of dispersion (33), (34), and (35) show that the rotation δ is very large if λ is nearly equal to the λ_1 which corresponds to a natural period. This result has recently been confirmed by Macaluso and Corbino * in experiments upon sodium vapor. Nevertheless their observations are not represented by the equations here developed. For, as appears from equation (38) and as can be shown by a more rigorous discussion in which the frictional resistance $\frac{a}{\tau}$ is not neglected, the rotation δ should have a different sign on the two sides of the absorption band, i.e. for $\lambda \gtrless \lambda_1$. But according to the observations the sign of δ is the same on both sides of the absorption band.

Thus for this case, and probably for all gases and vapors, the theory here presented does not represent the facts. Another

* Rend. d. R. Accad. d. Lincei (5) 7, p. 293, 1898.

fact which will be discussed in the next paragraph leads to the same conclusion.

5. Direction of Magnetization Perpendicular to the Rays.—Let the z-axis be the direction of the magnetization, the x-axis that of the ray. Then x and t are the only independent variables and $\nu_x = \nu_y = 0$, $\nu_z = \nu$. In the last of equations (18) the coefficient ν appears only in the term $-\nu\frac{\partial X}{\partial x}$, but this term vanishes, because from the first of equations (19) $X = 0$. *Hence from the preceding discussion the magnetization has no effect upon the optical relations when the ray is perpendicular to the direction of magnetization.* But as a matter of fact such an effect has recently been observed in the case of the vapors of metals. *This is a second reason for seeking another hypothesis upon which to base the explanation of the optical behavior of substances in the magnetic field.*

The above theory might be extended by assuming that the structure of the magnetized substance becomes non-isotropic because of the mutual attractions of the molecular currents in the direction of the lines of force. Nevertheless another hypothesis leads more directly and completely to the end sought. This hypothesis also is suggested by certain observed properties of substances in a magnetic field.

B. Hypothesis of the Hall Effect.

1. General Considerations.—The assumption of rotating ions will now be dropped and the previous conception of movable ions again taken into consideration. Now a strong magnetic field must exert special forces upon the ions, because an ion in motion represents an electrical current, and every element of current experiences in a magnetic field a force which is perpendicular to the element and to the direction of magnetization. Consequently the current lines in a magnetic field tend to move sideways in a direction at right angles to their direction. This phenomenon, known as the Hall effect, is actually observed in all metals, particularly in bismuth and antimony.

If an element of current of length dl and intensity i_m (in electromagnetic units) lies perpendicular to a magnetic field of intensity $\mathfrak{H}$,* then the force $\mathfrak{K}$ which acts upon the element is

$$\mathfrak{K} = i_m dl \mathfrak{H} = \frac{i}{c} dl \mathfrak{H}, \quad . \quad . \quad . \quad . \quad . \quad (39)$$

in which i represents the strength of the current in electrostatic units. When the coordinate system is chosen as on page 264, $\mathfrak{K}$ lies in the direction of the x-axis if i and $\mathfrak{H}$ lie in the directions of the y- and z-axes respectively.

If an ion carrying a charge e be displaced a distance $d\eta$ along the y-axis in the time dt, then, according to page 384, the strength of current along $d\eta$ is $i = e\mathfrak{N}'\frac{\partial \eta}{\partial t}$, in which $\mathfrak{N}'$ is the number of ions in unit length. Hence from (39), since $dl = d\eta$,

$$\mathfrak{K} = \frac{e}{c} \mathfrak{N}' d\eta \frac{\partial \eta}{\partial t} \mathfrak{H}.$$

This is the force acting upon the whole number of ions along the length $d\eta$. The number of these ions is $\mathfrak{N}'d\eta$. The force impelling a single ion along the x-axis is therefore

$$\mathfrak{K}_x = \frac{e}{c} \frac{\partial \eta}{\partial t} \mathfrak{H}_z. \quad . \quad . \quad . \quad . \quad . \quad . \quad (40)$$

If in addition there is a magnetization in the direction of the y-axis, a displacement ζ would add a force

$$\mathfrak{K}_x = -\frac{e}{c} \frac{\partial \zeta}{\partial t} \mathfrak{H}_y. \quad . \quad . \quad . \quad . \quad . \quad (41)$$

These two terms, (40) and (41), must be added to the right-hand side of the equations of motion of the ions, (6) and

* If μ is not equal to 1 then $\mathfrak{H}$ must be replaced by the density of the lines of force, i.e. by the induction.

(7) on page 423. If it be assumed that the ions are dielectric ions, not conduction ions, an assumption which is permissible for the case of all substances which have small conductivity, then

$$m\frac{\partial^2\xi}{\partial t^2} = eX - \frac{4\pi e^2}{\vartheta}\xi - re^2\frac{\partial\xi}{\partial t} + \frac{e}{c}\left(\frac{\partial\eta}{\partial t}\mathfrak{H}_z - \frac{\partial\zeta}{\partial t}\mathfrak{H}_y\right),$$

and by a cyclical interchange of letters

$$m\frac{\partial^2\eta}{\partial t^2} = eY - \frac{4\pi e^2}{\vartheta}\eta - re^2\frac{\partial\eta}{\partial t} + \frac{e}{c}\left(\frac{\partial\zeta}{\partial t}\mathfrak{H}_x - \frac{\partial\xi}{\partial t}\mathfrak{H}_z\right),$$

$$m\frac{\partial^2\zeta}{\partial t^2} = eZ - \frac{4\pi e^2}{\vartheta}\zeta - re^2\frac{\partial\zeta}{\partial t} + \frac{e}{c}\left(\frac{\partial\xi}{\partial t}\mathfrak{H}_y - \frac{\partial\eta}{\partial t}\mathfrak{H}_x\right). \qquad (42)$$

2. Deduction of the Differential Equations.—The fundamental equations (3) on page 420 remain as always unchanged. Since it has been assumed that there are no rotating ions, the ions do not carry with them in their motion magnetic lines of force, hence the permeability $\mu = 1$, and the previous relation (cf. page 269) holds, namely,

$$4\pi s_x = \frac{\partial\alpha}{\partial t}, \quad 4\pi s_y = \frac{\partial\beta}{\partial t}, \quad 4\pi s_z = \frac{\partial\gamma}{\partial t}. \quad . \quad . \quad (43)$$

Furthermore, as above (page 384),

$$4\pi j_x = \frac{\partial}{\partial t}(X + 4\pi\Sigma e\mathfrak{N}\xi),$$

$$4\pi j_y = \frac{\partial}{\partial t}(Y + 4\pi\Sigma e\mathfrak{N}\eta), \quad . \quad . \quad . \quad . \quad (44)$$

$$4\pi j_z = \frac{\partial}{\partial t}(Z + 4\pi\Sigma e\mathfrak{N}\zeta).$$

Equations (3), (42), (43), and (44) contain the complete theory.*

* The most general equations can be obtained from the theory of rotating ions presented above in Section A in connection with equation (42). The system of equations thus obtained would cover all possible cases in which movable ions are present in a strong magnetic field. For the sake of simplicity the two theories are separately presented in Sections A and B.

When the conditions change periodically and the former abbreviations are used, namely,

$$\frac{r\vartheta}{4\pi} = a, \quad \frac{m\vartheta}{4\pi e^2} = b, \quad . \quad . \quad . \quad . \quad . \quad (45)$$

(42) becomes

$$e\xi\left(1 + i\frac{a}{\tau} - \frac{b}{\tau^2}\right) - \frac{i\vartheta}{4\pi c\tau}(\eta\mathfrak{H}_z - \zeta\mathfrak{H}_y) = \frac{\vartheta}{4\pi}X. \quad . \quad (46)$$

If the z-axis be taken in the direction of the magnetic field so that $\mathfrak{H}_x = \mathfrak{H}_y = 0$, $\mathfrak{H}_z = \mathfrak{H}$, then, by use of the abbreviations

$$1 + i\frac{a}{\tau} - \frac{b}{\tau^2} = \Theta, \quad \frac{\vartheta}{4\pi c\tau e}\mathfrak{H} = \Phi, \quad . \quad . \quad (47)$$

there results from (46)

$$\left.\begin{aligned} e\xi \cdot \Theta - i \cdot e\eta \cdot \Phi &= \frac{\vartheta}{4\pi}X, \\ e\eta \cdot \Theta + i \cdot e\xi \cdot \Phi &= \frac{\vartheta}{4\pi}Y, \\ e\zeta \cdot \Theta \qquad\qquad &= \frac{\vartheta}{4\pi}Z. \end{aligned}\right\} \quad . \quad . \quad . \quad . \quad (48)$$

If these equations be solved with respect to ξ, η, and ζ, there results

$$\left.\begin{aligned} 4\pi e\xi(\Theta^2 - \Phi^2) &= \vartheta(\Theta X + i\Phi Y), \\ 4\pi e\eta(\Theta^2 - \Phi^2) &= \vartheta(\Theta Y - i\Phi X), \\ 4\pi e\zeta \cdot \Theta &= \vartheta Z. \end{aligned}\right\} \quad . \quad . \quad . \quad (49)$$

Hence, from (44),

$$\left.\begin{aligned} 4\pi j_x &= \frac{\partial X}{\partial t}\left(1 + \sum\frac{\vartheta\mathfrak{N}\Theta}{\Theta^2 - \Phi^2}\right) + i\frac{\partial Y}{\partial t}\sum\frac{\vartheta\mathfrak{N}\Phi}{\Theta^2 - \Phi^2}, \\ 4\pi j_y &= \frac{\partial Y}{\partial t}\left(1 + \sum\frac{\vartheta\mathfrak{N}\Theta}{\Theta^2 - \Phi^2}\right) - i\frac{\partial X}{\partial t}\sum\frac{\vartheta\mathfrak{N}\Phi}{\Theta^2 - \Phi^2}, \\ 4\pi j_z &= \frac{\partial Z}{\partial t}\left(1 + \sum\frac{\vartheta\mathfrak{N}}{\Theta}\right). \end{aligned}\right\} \quad . \quad (50)$$

These equations will be written in the abbreviated form

$$\left.\begin{aligned}4\pi j_x &= \epsilon'' \frac{\partial X}{\partial t} + i\nu \frac{\partial Y}{\partial t},\\ 4\pi j_y &= \epsilon'' \frac{\partial Y}{\partial t} - i\nu \frac{\partial X}{\partial t},\\ 4\pi j_z &= \epsilon' \ \frac{\partial Z}{\partial t}.\end{aligned}\right\} \quad . \quad . \quad . \quad . \quad (51)$$

3. Rays Parallel to the Direction of Magnetization.—In this case z and t are the only independent variables, and equations (3), (43), and (51) give

$$\left.\begin{aligned}&\frac{1}{c}\left(\epsilon''\frac{\partial X}{\partial t} + i\nu\frac{\partial Y}{\partial t}\right) = -\frac{\partial \beta}{\partial z}, \quad \frac{1}{c}\left(\epsilon''\frac{\partial Y}{\partial t} - i\nu\frac{\partial X}{\partial t}\right) = \frac{\partial \alpha}{\partial z},\\ &\quad \frac{1}{c}\frac{\partial \alpha}{\partial t} = \frac{\partial Y}{\partial z}, \quad \frac{1}{c}\frac{\partial \beta}{\partial t} = -\frac{\partial X}{\partial z}, \quad \gamma = Z = 0.\end{aligned}\right\} \quad (52)$$

If α and β be eliminated, there results

$$\left.\begin{aligned}\frac{\epsilon''}{c^2}\frac{\partial^2 X}{\partial t^2} &= \frac{\partial^2 X}{\partial z^2} - \frac{i\nu}{c^2}\frac{\partial^2 Y}{\partial t^2},\\ \frac{\epsilon''}{c^2}\frac{\partial^2 Y}{\partial t^2} &= \frac{\partial^2 Y}{\partial z^2} + \frac{i\nu}{c^2}\frac{\partial^2 X}{\partial t^2}.\end{aligned}\right\} \quad . \quad . \quad . \quad (53)$$

For the sake of integration set, as above on pages 404 and 426,

$$X = Me^{\frac{i}{\tau}(t - pz)}, \quad Y = Ne^{\frac{i}{\tau}(t - pz)} \quad . \quad . \quad . \quad . \quad (54)$$

Then there results, from (53),

$$\epsilon''M = p^2c^2M - i\nu N, \quad \epsilon''N = p^2c^2N + i\nu M,$$

i.e. the two sets of equations

$$\left.\begin{aligned}p^2c^2 &= n'^2(1 - i\kappa')^2 = \epsilon'' + \nu, \quad M = iN,\\ p^2c^2 &= n''^2(1 - i\kappa'')^2 = \epsilon'' - \nu, \quad M = -iN.\end{aligned}\right\} \quad . \quad (55)$$

n', κ' correspond to left-handed, n'', κ'' to right-handed circularly polarized waves. From the meanings given to ϵ'' and ν in (50) and (51) it follows that

$$\left.\begin{aligned}n'^2(1 - i\kappa')^2 &= 1 + \sum \frac{\vartheta \mathfrak{N}}{\Theta - \Phi},\\ n''^2(1 - i\kappa'')^2 &= 1 + \sum \frac{\vartheta \mathfrak{N}}{\Theta + \Phi}.\end{aligned}\right\} \quad . \quad . \quad . \quad (56)$$

If τ does not lie close to a natural period, then the imaginary term in Θ, namely, $i\frac{a}{\tau}$, can be neglected, so that $\kappa' = \kappa'' = 0$, and since Θ is always small in comparison with 1, and therefore in comparison with Θ,

$$\left.\begin{aligned} n'^2 &= 1 + \sum \frac{\vartheta \mathfrak{N}}{\Theta}\left(1 + \frac{\Phi}{\Theta}\right), \\ n''^2 &= 1 + \sum \frac{\vartheta \mathfrak{N}}{\Theta}\left(1 - \frac{\Phi}{\Theta}\right). \end{aligned}\right\} \quad . \quad . \quad . \quad . \quad (57)$$

From (19) on page 407 the rotation δ of the plane of polarization is

$$\delta = z\frac{\pi}{\lambda_0}(n'' - n') = z\frac{\pi}{\lambda_0}\frac{n''^2 - n'^2}{n'' + n'}. \quad . \quad . \quad . \quad (58)$$

If the mean of n'' and n' be denoted by n, then

$$\delta = z\frac{\pi}{\lambda_0}\frac{n''^2 - n'^2}{2n}. \quad . \quad . \quad . \quad . \quad . \quad (59)$$

Hence, from (57),

$$\delta = -\frac{\pi}{n}\cdot\frac{z}{\lambda_0}\sum\frac{\vartheta\mathfrak{N}\Phi}{\Theta^2}. \quad . \quad . \quad . \quad . \quad (60)$$

Thus the index of refraction n is given, to terms of the first order in Φ, by

$$n^2 = 1 + \sum\frac{\vartheta\mathfrak{N}}{\Theta}. \quad . \quad . \quad . \quad . \quad . \quad (61)$$

4. Dispersion in the Magnetic Rotation of the Plane of Polarization.—Upon introduction of the values of Θ and Φ from (47) in the last equations they become

$$\delta = -\frac{\pi}{2n}\frac{z}{\lambda_0^2}\mathfrak{H}\sum\frac{\vartheta\mathfrak{N}}{\left(1 - \frac{b}{\tau^2}\right)^2}\cdot\frac{\vartheta}{e}, \quad . \quad . \quad . \quad (62)$$

$$n^2 = 1 + \sum\frac{\vartheta\mathfrak{N}}{1 - \frac{b}{\tau^2}}. \quad . \quad . \quad . \quad . \quad (63)$$

Hence, as in hypothesis A, to a first approximation δ is inversely proportional to λ_0^2.

If n^2 can be represented with sufficient accuracy by the two-constant dispersion equation (cf. page 431)

$$n^2 = a + \frac{b}{\lambda^2 - \lambda_1^{\ 2}} \quad . \quad . \quad . \quad . \quad . \quad (64)$$

(λ, the wave length in air, is written for λ_0), then, from (62), it must be possible to represent δ by the two-constant dispersion equation

$$\delta = \frac{1}{n}\left(\frac{a'}{\lambda^2} + \frac{b'\lambda^2}{(\lambda^2 - \lambda_1^{\ 2})^2}\right). \quad . \quad . \quad . \quad . \quad (65)$$

a' and b' must have different signs if but two different kinds of ions, one charged positively, the other negatively, are present. This is the simplest assumption that can be made.

The agreement between (65) and observations upon carbon bisulphide and creosote is shown in the following tables:

BISULPHIDE OF CARBON.

$$\lambda_1^{\ 2} = 0.0450, \quad a' = +0.1167, \quad b' = +0.2379.$$

Spectr. Line.	δ calc.	δ obs.
C	0.592	0.592
D	0.760	0.760
E	0.996	1.000
F	1.225	1.234
G	1.704	1.704

CREOSOTE.

$$\lambda_1^{2} = 0.0340, \quad a' = -0.070, \quad b' = +0.380.$$

Spectr. Line.	δ calc.	δ obs.
C	0.573	0.573
D	0.744	0.758
E	0.987	1.000
F	1.222	1.241
G	1.723	1.723

The agreement between theory and observation is almost as good as that obtained by the hypothesis of molecular currents (cf. page 431).

5. The Impressed Period Close to a Natural Period.—When the period of the light lies close to a natural period, the friction term $\frac{a}{\tau}$ cannot be neglected. Assume that T is close to the natural period T_1 of the ions of kind 1, and write, therefore, $\tau = \sqrt{b_1}(1 + g) = \tau_1(1 + g)$, in which g is small in comparison with 1. Then in equation (56), since Φ is small, it is possible to write in all the terms which are under the sign Σ and do not correspond to the ions of kind 1

$$\frac{1}{\Theta - \Phi} = \frac{1}{1 - \frac{b}{\tau_1^2}}\left(1 + \frac{\Phi}{1 - \frac{b}{\tau_1^2}}\right), \quad . \quad . \quad . \quad (66)$$

so that, using the abbreviations

$$\left.\begin{aligned} 1 + \sum \frac{\vartheta\mathfrak{N}}{1 - \frac{b}{\tau_1^2}} = A, \quad & \sum \frac{\Phi\vartheta\mathfrak{N}}{\left(1 - \frac{b}{\tau_1^2}\right)^2} = A', \\ \frac{a_1}{\tau_1} = h, \quad \frac{\vartheta_1}{4\pi c\tau_1 e_1}\mathfrak{H} = \phi, \quad & \vartheta_1\mathfrak{N}_1 = B, \end{aligned}\right\} \quad . \quad (67)$$

it follows from (56), if terms containing g in powers higher than the first be neglected, and if $g \cdot \phi$ be also neglected in comparison with g or ϕ, that

$$n'^2(1 - i\kappa')^2 = A + A' + \frac{B}{2g + ih - \phi}, \quad . \quad . \quad (68)$$

$$n''^2(1 - i\kappa'')^2 = A - A' + \frac{B}{2g + ih + \phi}. \quad . \quad . \quad (69)$$

The imaginary part of the right-hand side of (68) reaches its largest value, i.e. a left-handed circularly polarized wave experiences maximum absorption, when

$$2g = +\phi, \text{ i.e. } \tau^2 = \tau_l^2 = \tau_1^2(1 + \phi). \quad . \quad . \quad (70)$$

But the maximum absorption for a right-handed circularly polarized wave occurs when

$$2g = -\phi, \text{ i.e. } \tau^2 = \tau_r^2 = \tau_1^2(1 - \phi). \quad . \quad . \quad (71)$$

Thus a small absorption band in incident natural light is doubled by the presence of the magnetic field when the direction of the field is parallel to that of the light. In one of the bands the left-handed circularly polarized wave is strongly absorbed so that the transmitted light is weakened and shows right-handed circular polarization; in the other band the right-handed circularly polarized light is wanting.

The same result would be reached from the hypothesis A of the molecular currents.

If g is not small and if $2g$ is numerically larger than ϕ, so that h is negligible in comparison with $2g \pm \phi$, then in (68) and (69) κ' and κ'' can be placed equal to zero, provided the right-hand sides are positive. Hence at some distance from the absorption band

$$n'^2 = A + A' + \frac{B}{2g - \phi}, \quad n''^2 = A - A' + \frac{B}{2g + \phi}.$$

(In order that the right-hand sides may be positive, the numerical value of A must be greater than that of $\frac{B}{2g \pm \phi}$).
From equation (59) on page 438, the amount of the rotation of the plane of polarization is

$$\left.\begin{aligned} \delta &= -\frac{\pi}{n} \cdot \frac{z}{\lambda_0}\left(A' + B\frac{\phi}{4g^2 - \phi^2}\right), \\ &\text{in which} \\ n &= \frac{1}{2}\left(\sqrt{A + \frac{B}{2g - \phi}} + \sqrt{A + \frac{B}{2g + \phi}}\right). \end{aligned}\right\} \quad (72)$$

From this it appears that the rotation δ has the same sign upon both sides of the absorption band, and is nearly symmetrical with respect to this band, for, at least approximately, δ depends only upon g^2. The same result follows from equation (62). If δ is positive, it appears from page 428, that the rotation takes place in the direction of paramagnetic Ampèrian currents. Since the sign of δ is not determined by the sign of the small term A', but by the much larger term $B\phi : 4g^2 - \phi^2$, and since the numerical value of $2g$ is to be larger than ϕ, and since further B is always positive, the sign of δ depends only upon ϕ, i.e. upon the charge e_1. When e_1 is positive, i.e. when $\phi > 0$, the direction of δ is opposite to that of the molecular currents, and further, $\tau_l > \tau_r$, i.e. that wave (l) whose direction of rotation is in the sense of the molecular currents reaches its maximum absorption for a slower period T than the wave (r) whose direction of rotation is opposite to that of the molecular currents. When e_1 is negative the plane of polarization is rotated in the direction of the molecular currents. Then $\tau_l < \tau_r$, i.e. in general that wave whose direction of rotation is the same as that of the rotation δ of the plane of polarization reaches its maximum absorption for a shorter period than the wave which rotates in the opposite direction.

All these results have been verified by experiments upon sodium vapor. These experiments will be discussed later. For both absorption lines of this vapor (the two D lines) e is found to be negative. *The two D lines of sodium vapor are then produced by negatively charged ions.*

The absorption at a place where $g = 0$ may be small provided ϕ is large in comparison with h. Then, by (68) and (69),

$$n'^2 = A + A' - \frac{B}{\phi}, \quad n''^2 = A - A' + \frac{B}{\phi}.$$

The right-hand sides of these equations must be positive if they are to have any meaning, i.e. the numerical value of A must be greater than that of $\frac{B}{\phi}$. The rotation δ of the plane of polarization is then proportional to

$$\delta \sim \frac{n''^2 - n'^2}{2} = B/\phi - A'. \quad . \quad . \quad . \quad (73)$$

δ is therefore large since ϕ is small. If e_1 is positive, the rotation δ is in the same direction as the molecular currents, i.e. within the absorption band the rotation is opposite to that just outside of the absorption band. Nevertheless the rotation δ need not pass through zero values, for at places where $n'\kappa'$ and $n''\kappa''$ have large but different values it is meaningless to speak of a rotation of the plane of polarization.

6. Rays Perpendicular to the Direction of Magnetization.—Let the z-axis be taken in the direction of the magnetization, the x-axis in that of the wave normal. Then x and t are the independent variables and equations (3), (43), and (51) give

$$\left.\begin{array}{c} \epsilon'' \dfrac{\partial X}{\partial t} + i\nu \dfrac{\partial Y}{\partial t} = 0, \\ \dfrac{1}{c}\left(\epsilon'' \dfrac{\partial Y}{\partial t} - i\nu \dfrac{\partial X}{\partial t}\right) = -\dfrac{\partial \gamma}{\partial x}, \\ \dfrac{\epsilon'}{c}\dfrac{\partial Z}{\partial t} = \dfrac{\partial \beta}{\partial x}, \\ \alpha = 0, \quad \dfrac{1}{c}\dfrac{\partial \beta}{\partial t} = \dfrac{\partial Z}{\partial x}, \quad \dfrac{1}{c}\dfrac{\partial \gamma}{\partial t} = -\dfrac{\partial Y}{\partial x}. \end{array}\right\} \quad . \quad . \quad (74)$$

Elimination of β and γ gives

$$\left.\begin{array}{c} \epsilon'' X + i\nu Y = 0, \\ \dfrac{\epsilon''}{c^2}\dfrac{\partial^2 Y}{\partial t^2} = \dfrac{\partial^2 Y}{\partial x^2} + i\dfrac{\nu}{c^2}\dfrac{\partial^2 X}{\partial t^2} \\ \dfrac{\epsilon'}{c^2}\dfrac{\partial^2 Z}{\partial t^2} = \dfrac{\partial^2 Z}{\partial x^2}. \end{array}\right\} \quad . \quad . \quad . \quad . \quad (75)$$

If X be eliminated from the first two equations, there results

$$\left(\epsilon'' - \frac{\nu^2}{\epsilon''}\right)\frac{\partial^2 Y}{\partial t^2} = c^2\frac{\partial^2 Y}{\partial x^2}. \quad . \quad . \quad . \quad . \quad (76)$$

Setting, for the sake of integration,

$$X = M \cdot e^{\frac{i}{\tau}(t - p'x)}, \quad Y = Ne^{\frac{i}{\tau}(t - p'x)}, \quad Z = \Pi e^{\frac{i}{\tau}(t - px)},$$

it follows from (75) and (76) that

$$\epsilon'' - \frac{\nu^2}{\epsilon''} = p'^2c^2, \quad \epsilon' = p^2c^2, \quad M = -\frac{i\nu}{\epsilon''}N. \quad . \quad (77)$$

The velocities of Z and Y are then different, i.e. *the substance acts like a doubly refracting medium.* For Z, i.e. for a wave polarized at right angles to the direction of magnetization, the index of refraction and the coefficient of absorption are obtained from

$$p^2c^2 = n^2(1 - i\kappa)^2 = \epsilon' = 1 + \sum\frac{\vartheta\mathfrak{N}}{\Theta}; \quad . \quad . \quad (78)$$

for a wave polarized parallel to the direction of magnetization the following holds:

$$n'^2(1 - i\kappa')^2 = 1 + \sum\frac{\vartheta\mathfrak{N}\Theta}{\Theta^2 - \Phi^2} - \frac{\left(\sum\frac{\vartheta\mathfrak{N}\Phi}{\Theta^2 - \Phi^2}\right)^2}{1 + \sum\frac{\vartheta\mathfrak{N}\Theta}{\Theta^2 - \Phi^2}}. \quad . \quad . \quad (79)$$

The difference between n' and n is in general very small, since it is of the second order in Φ provided Θ is not small. Hence this magnetic double refraction can only be observed in the neighborhood of a natural period, since then Θ is very small.

7. The Impressed Period in the Neighborhood of a Natural Period.—Set as above $\tau = \tau_1(1 + g) = \sqrt{b_1}(1 + g)$, and assume that g is small in comparison with 1.

Then in every term under the sign Σ, save that which corresponds to ions of kind 1, Θ is to be considered a real quantity which is not very small. Φ^2 is then negligible in comparison with Θ^2.

Hence, using the abbreviations (67) on page 440,

$$n'^2(1 - i\kappa')^2 = A + \frac{B}{(2g + ih)^2 - \phi^2}$$

$$\cdot\left\{2g + ih - \frac{B\phi^2}{[(2g + ih)^2 - \phi^2]A + (2g + ih)B}\right\},$$

or

$$n'^2(1 - i\kappa')^2 = A + \frac{B[(2g + ih)A + B]}{A[(2g + ih)^2 - \phi^2] + B(2g + ih)}. \quad (80)$$

Now for a metallic vapor the index of refraction is always nearly equal to 1, even when g is quite small. Hence it follows (cf. equation for n^2 on page 441) that A is almost equal to 1 and B must be very small, so that in the second term of the right-hand side of (80), which contains the small factor B, B can be neglected in comparison with A. Therefore

$$n'^2(1 - i\kappa)^2 = A + \frac{B(2g + ih)}{(2g + ih)^2 - \phi^2}. \quad . \quad . \quad (81)$$

The imaginary part, i.e. the absorption, will therefore be a maximum, provided h is small, when

$$4g^2 - \phi^2 = 0, \quad \text{i.e.} \quad 2g = \pm \phi. \quad . \quad . \quad . \quad (82)$$

Hence when the plane of polarization of the wave is parallel to the direction of magnetization, there are two absorption bands, one on each side of the single band which appears when the magnetic field is not present.

For a wave whose plane of polarization is perpendicular to the direction of magnetization (78) gives

$$n^2(1 - i\kappa)^2 = A + \frac{B}{2g + ih}. \quad . \quad . \quad . \quad (83)$$

The absorption is a maximum at a place where $g = 0$. *Thus for a wave whose plane of polarization is perpendicular to the direction of magnetization the absorption is not altered by the presence of the field.*

If $2g$ is large in comparison with h and ϕ, κ and κ' are very small, and approximately

$$n'^2 = A + \frac{B}{2g}\,\frac{A \cdot 4g^2 + B \cdot 2g}{A(4g^2 - \phi^2) + B \cdot 2g}, \quad n^2 = A + \frac{B}{2g};$$

hence

$$n'^2 - n^2 = \frac{B}{2g} \cdot \frac{A\phi^2}{4g^2n^2 - A\phi^2},$$

or, since $4g^2$ is large in comparison with ϕ^2, approximately

$$n' - n = \frac{AB\phi^2}{16n^3g^3}, \quad . \quad . \quad . \quad . \quad . \quad . \quad . \quad . \quad (84)$$

i.e. the sign of $n' - n$ depends upon the sign of g, but is independent both of the direction of magnetization and of the sign of ϕ. Voigt and Wiechert have succeeded in verifying this law of magnetic double refraction in the case of sodium vapor.*

8. The Zeeman Effect.—Zeeman discovered that when the vapor of a metal, like sodium or cadmium, is brought to incandescence in a magnetic field, a narrow line in its emission spectrum is resolved into two or three lines (a doublet or a triplet) of slightly different periods.† The doublet is produced when the direction of the magnetic lines is the same as the direction of emission, the triplet when these directions are at right angles to each other. These observations are explained by the theoretical considerations given above ‡ in connection with the law, which will be presented later, that the emission lines of a gas correspond to the same periods of vibration as the absorption lines.§ According to the preceding discussion the two separate lines of the doublet ought to show right- and left-handed circular polarization, while in the triplet the middle line ought to be polarized in a plane which is perpendicular to the direction of the magnetization, and the two outer lines in a plane which is parallel to it. These conclusions are actually verified by the experiment. From measurements upon the two triplets into which the two sodium lines (D_1 and D_2) are

* W. Voigt, Wied. Ann. 67, p. 360, 1899.

† P. Zeeman, Phil. Mag. (5) 43, p. 226; 44, p. 255, 1897.

‡ This method of explaining the Zeeman effect is due to Voigt (Wied. Ann. 67, p. 345, 1899). The differential equations upon which Voigt bases his theory are the same as those deduced in § 2, but he refrains from giving any physical meaning to the coefficients in the differential equations.

§ This law results both from experiment and from Kirchhoff's law as to the proportionality between the emission and absorption of heat-rays. The radiation from a metallic vapor brought to incandescence in a Bunsen flame does not appear to be a case of pure temperature radiation (cf. Part III), nevertheless theory shows that even for luminescent rays the emission and absorption lines must coincide.

resolved, Zeeman obtained for the distance $2g$ between the two outer lines of the triplet, when the strength of the magnetic field was $\mathfrak{H} = 22{,}400$, the value $2g = 2 : 17{,}800$. Now, from (82) and (67),

$$2g = \phi = \frac{\vartheta_1 \mathfrak{H}}{2\pi c \tau_1 e_1},$$

or since $\tau_1 = \sqrt{b_1}$, and consequently, from (45) on page 436, $\vartheta_1 = 4\pi\tau_1^2 e_1^2 : m_1$, it follows that

$$2g = \phi = \mathfrak{H}\tau_1 \frac{e_1}{cm_1} = \frac{\mathfrak{H} T_1}{2\pi} \cdot \frac{e_1}{cm_1} \cdot \quad . \quad . \quad . \quad (85)$$

If the values of $2g$, $\mathfrak{H}$, and T_1 for sodium light be introduced, there results

$$\frac{e_1}{cm_1} = 1.6 \cdot 10^7.$$

This number represents the ratio of the charge of the ion, measured in electromagnetic units, to its apparent mass (cf. note on page 383). From observations upon a cadmium line ($\lambda = 0.48\mu$) this ratio is determined as $2.4 \cdot 10^7$.*

Michelson has shown from more accurate observations, made both with the interferometer and with the echelon spectroscope, that in general the emission lines are not resolved simply into doublets and triplets but into more complicated forms.† This is to be expected when, as is the case with

---

* It is to be noted that Kaufmann obtained from the magnetic deflection of the kathode rays (Wied. Ann. 65, p. 439, 1898) almost the same number ($1.86 \cdot 10^7$) for the ratio of the charge to the mass of the particles projected from the kathode. For the ions of electrolysis this ratio is much smaller ($9.5 \cdot 10^3$ for hydrogen, $4.1 \cdot 10^2$ for sodium). This can be accounted for either by assuming that an electrolytic ion contains a large number of positively and negatively charged particles (electrons) which are held firmly together in electrolysis but are free to move by themselves in a high vacuum, or to vibrate so as to give out light; or that the electrolytic ion consists of a combination of an electric charge e_1 of apparent mass m_1 with a large uncharged mass M. In a slowly changing electric field or in a constant current the electron clings fast to the mass M. But in a rapidly changing electric field, such as corresponds to light vibrations, only the electron moves, and in a high vacuum the electron becomes separated from its mass M.

† Cf. Phil. Mag. (5) 45, p. 348. Astrophys. Journ. 7, p. 131; 8, p. 37, 1898. Wied. Beibl. 1898, p. 797.

Michelson's experiments, the method of investigation is carried to such a degree of refinement that the emission lines are found, even in the absence of the magnetic field, to have a structure more complicated than is assumed in the above theoretical discussion, i.e. when an emission line is shown to be a close double. Furthermore, a theoretical extension of equation (46) is possible if the influence of the motion of neighboring ions is taken into account. In this case in that equation the second differential coefficient of the electric force with respect to the coordinates would appear, and the magnetic resolution of the absorption and emission lines would be more complicated.*

A very powerful grating or prism is necessary for observing the Zeeman effect directly. Hence it is more convenient to use a method of investigation described by Konig † in which a sodium flame in a magnetic field is observed through another such flame outside the field. If the line of sight is perpendicular to the field, the first flame appears bright and polarized. From Kirchhoff's law as to the equality of emission and absorption, only those vibrations of the magnetized sodium flame whose period in the magnetic field is the same as without the field can be absorbed by the unmagnetized sodium flame. Perhaps the phenomenon observed by Egoroff and Georgiewsky, ‡ that a sodium flame in a magnetic field emits partially polarized light in a direction perpendicular to the field, can also be explained in this way, i.e. by absorption in the outer layers of the flame, the field being non-homogeneous. But even if the field were perfectly homogeneous, this phenomenon could be theoretically explained, since the total absorption $n'\kappa'$ for the waves polarized in the direction of magnetization, when calculated from equation (80) for all

* Voigt (Wied. Ann. 68, p. 352) accounts for the anomalous Zeeman effects by longitudinal magnetic effects. What is the physical significance of such an effect has not yet been shown.

† Wied. Ann. 63, p. 268, 1897.

‡ C. R. 127, pp. 748, 949, 1897.

possible values of g, is found to be somewhat different from the total absorption $n\kappa$ of the waves polarized in a plane which is perpendicular to the magnetization when this is calculated from (83) for all possible values of g.*

9. **The Magneto-optical Properties of Iron, Nickel, and Cobalt.**—Although it has been shown above that in the case of metallic vapors the conception of molecular currents does not lead to a satisfactory explanation of the phenomena, yet this concept must be retained in order to account for the magneto-optical properties of the strongly magnetic metals. This is most easily proved by the fact that, in the case of these metals, the magneto-optical effects are proportional to the magnetization, and therefore reach a limiting value when the magnetization is carried to saturation, even though the outer magnetic field is continuously increased.† The explanation based upon the Hall effect would not lead to such a limiting value,‡ since the magneto-optical effects would then be proportional to the magnetic induction of the substance, i.e. proportional to the total density of the lines of force. It is true that, strictly speaking, the Hall effect is never entirely absent, even upon the hypothesis of molecular currents; nevertheless the experimental results show that, in the case of iron, nickel, and cobalt, the influence of the molecular currents is very much greater than that of the Hall effect, so that, for simplicity, the terms which represent the Hall effect will now be neglected.

---

* Voigt (Wied. Ann. 69, p. 290, 1899) accounts for the phenomenon observed by Egoroff and Georgiewsky, as well as for the variations in intensity in the Zeeman effect, by the assumption that the friction coefficient r in equations (42) on page 435 depends upon the strength of the magnetic field in different ways for vibrations of different directions. This assumption cannot be simply and plausibly obtained from physical conceptions.

† This is proved by observations of Kundt (Wied. Ann. 27, p. 191, 1886) and DuBois (Wied. Ann. 39, p. 25, 1890).

‡ This, together with the difference in form of the deduced laws of dispersion, is the difference between the two theories. They would be identical if the equations deduced from the hypothesis of the Hall effect were developed only to the first order in the added magneto-optical terms. This is allowable because in the case of the metals no narrow absorption bands occur.

a. Transmitted Light.—When a plane wave passes normally through a thin film of iron which is magnetized perpendicularly to its surface, the equations in § 3 on page 426 are applicable. Denote by n and κ the index of refraction and the coefficient of absorption of the unmagnetized metal, by n' and κ' the corresponding quantities for the left-handed circularly polarized wave, by n'' and κ'' the same quantities for the right-handed circularly polarized wave. Then from (28) and (29) on page 427, retaining only terms of the first order in ν,

$$\left.\begin{aligned} p'c &= n'(1 - i\kappa') = \sqrt{\epsilon'}\left(1 - \frac{\nu}{2c\tau}\right), \\ p''c &= n''(1 - i\kappa'') = \sqrt{\epsilon'}\left(1 + \frac{\nu}{2c\tau}\right), \\ n(1 &- i\kappa) = \sqrt{\epsilon}. \end{aligned}\right\} \quad . \quad . \quad (86)$$

If ν be supposed to have the form

$$\nu = a + bi, \quad . \quad . \quad . \quad . \quad . \quad . \quad . \quad (87)$$

in which a and b are real, then

$$n'' - n' = \frac{n}{c\tau}(a + b\kappa), \quad n''\kappa'' - n'\kappa' = \frac{n}{c\tau}(a\kappa - b). \quad (88)$$

The second of these equations asserts that the right- and left-handed circularly polarized waves are absorbed in different amounts; while the first one, in connection with (19′) on page 407 (provided the difference between $n''\kappa''$ and $n'\kappa'$ is small so that the emergent light is approximately plane-polarized), shows that the rotation δ* of the plane of polarization is determined by

$$\delta = \frac{z}{2c\tau}(n'' - n') = 2\frac{\pi^2}{\lambda_0^2}zn(a + b\kappa), \quad . \quad . \quad (89)$$

in which it is assumed that $\lambda_0 = cT = 2\pi c\tau$.

The film of metal must be very thin (a fraction of λ_0) in order that it may be transparent. Nevertheless appreciable

---

* Unless $n''\kappa''$ and $n'\kappa'$ are nearly equal, so that the emergent light is approximately plane-polarized, δ has no meaning.

rotation is observable; for example, when $z = 0.332\lambda_0$ the rotation of red light ($\lambda_0 = 0.00064$ mm.) in the case of iron magnetized to saturation is $\delta = 4.25°$. *This would give for the rotation produced by a plate of iron 1 cm. thick the enormous value* $\delta = 200\,000°$. From these observations and (89) there results, for red light and for iron magnetized to saturation, the centimetre being the unit of length,

$$n(a + b\kappa) = 0.758 \cdot 10^{-6}. \quad . \quad . \quad . \quad . \quad (90)$$

The sign of $a + b\kappa$ is positive since the rotation δ takes place in the direction of the molecular currents in paramagnetic substances.

The relation between the rotation δ and the period τ or the wave length λ_0 is obtained from equations (20) and (21) on page 425, taken in connection with (87) and (89). It is a noteworthy fact that δ decreases as λ_0 decreases.* This result is seen from equation (89) to be probable, since n and $n\kappa$ actually decrease rapidly as λ_0 decreases, and since, from (21), it appears that a and b likewise decrease as λ_0 decreases, provided only one kind of conduction ions is particularly effective in producing the magneto-optical phenomena.

b. Reflected Light (*Kerr Effect*).—In order that the properties of the light reflected from a magnetized mirror may be calculated, the boundary conditions which hold at the surface of the mirror must be set up. These conditions can be obtained from the differential equations (18) and (19) on page 425, and the consideration that the surface of the mirror is in reality a very thin non-homogeneous transition layer in which these differential equations also hold (cf. page 426).

If the surface of the mirror is taken as the xy-plane, the boundary conditions are found, by a method similar to that used on page 271, to be

Continuity of

$$\alpha,\ \beta,\ X - \frac{1}{c}\frac{\partial}{\partial t}(\nu_y Z - \nu_z Y),\quad Y - \frac{1}{c}\frac{\partial}{\partial t}(\nu_z X - \nu_x Z). \qquad (91)$$

* Cf. experiments of Lobach, Wied. Ann. 39, p. 347, 1890.

From these conditions a theoretical explanation of the effect discovered by Kerr can be deduced.* This effect † consists in a slight rotation of the plane of polarization of light reflected from a magnetized mirror, when the incident light is plane-polarized either in or perpendicular to the plane of incidence. This can only be due to some peculiar effect of magnetization, since without magnetization there is complete symmetry and no such effect would be possible.

10. The Effects of the Magnetic Field of the Ray of Light.—It has been shown above that a powerful external magnetic field produces a change in the optical properties of a substance. Now the question arises whether, with delicate methods of observation, an effect due to the magnetic field of the light itself might not be detected in the absence of an external field.

If, first, only the terms representing the Hall effect be taken into account, i.e. if it be assumed that there are no molecular currents (revolving ions), then the equations to be used are (cf. page 435)

$$\frac{4\pi j_x}{c} = \frac{\partial \gamma}{\partial y} - \frac{\partial \beta}{\partial z}, \text{ etc.}, \quad \frac{1}{c}\frac{\partial \alpha}{\partial t} = \frac{\partial Y}{\partial z} - \frac{\partial Z}{\partial y}, \quad . \quad (92)$$

$$4\pi j_x = \frac{\partial X}{\partial t} + 4\pi \Sigma e \mathfrak{N} \frac{\partial \xi}{\partial t}, \quad . \quad . \quad . \quad . \quad (93)$$

$$4\pi e \xi = \frac{\vartheta}{\Theta}\left(X + \frac{1}{c}\left[\gamma \frac{\partial \eta}{\partial t} - \beta \frac{\partial \zeta}{\partial t}\right]\right), \quad . \quad . \quad (94)$$

if

$$\Theta = 1 + i\frac{a}{\tau} - \frac{b}{\tau^2}. \quad . \quad . \quad . \quad . \quad . \quad (95)$$

---

* This deduction was made by Drude, Wied. Ann. 46, p. 353, 1892. The constant b which appeared there and was assumed to be real must here be taken as complex, since from (21) on page 425 ν is complex. This change makes the result of the theory identical with that given by Goldhammer, Wied. Ann. 46, p. 71, 1892. The theory is in agreement with practically all of the facts. For the effect of the surface layer on the phenomenon cf. Micheli, Diss. Lpz. 1900. Ann. d. Phys. 1, 1900.

† Kerr, Phil. Mag. (5) 3, p. 321, 1877; 5, p. 161, 1878.

(94) is the characteristic equation of this problem. This shows, since η and ζ are approximately proportional to Y and Z, that the differential equations of the electromagnetic field are no longer linear in $X, Y, Z, \alpha, \beta, \gamma$. This means that *the optical properties must depend upon the intensity of the light.* Such a dependence has never yet been observed, and it can easily be shown that the correction terms in (94), which represent the departures from the equation heretofore used, namely,

$$4\pi e\xi = \frac{\vartheta}{\Theta}X,$$

are so small that their effect could not be observed. Since the magnetic force α, β, γ is equal to, or at least of the same order of magnitude as, the electric force X, Y, Z, it is necessary to find the value of $\frac{1}{c}\frac{\partial\eta}{\partial t}, \frac{1}{c}\frac{\partial\xi}{\partial t}$, i.e. *to find the ratio of the velocity of the ion to the velocity of light.* Now approximately, from (94),

$$\xi = \frac{\vartheta}{4\pi e\Theta}X;$$

i.e., when

$$X = A\cdot\sin 2\pi\left(\frac{t}{T} - \frac{z}{\lambda}\right),$$

$$\frac{1}{c}\frac{\partial\xi}{\partial t} = \frac{2\pi}{cT}\cdot\frac{\vartheta}{4\pi e\Theta}A\cdot\cos 2\pi\left(\frac{t}{T} - \frac{z}{\lambda}\right). \quad . \quad . \quad (96)$$

Now, according to page 436, the natural period T_0 of the ion is determined in the following way:

$$\tau_0^2 = \left(\frac{T_0}{2\pi}\right)^2 = b = \frac{m\vartheta}{4\pi e^2},$$

or

$$\frac{\vartheta}{4\pi e} = \frac{T_0^2}{4\pi^2}\cdot\frac{e}{m}. \quad . \quad . \quad . \quad . \quad (97)$$

A substitution of this value in (96) shows that the largest value which $\frac{1}{c}\frac{\partial\xi}{\partial t}$ can have as the time changes is

$$\frac{1}{c}\frac{\partial\xi}{\partial t} = \frac{T_0^2}{2\pi T\Theta}\cdot\frac{e}{mc}A.$$

If in this Θ be set equal to $1 - \frac{T_0^2}{T^2}$, a substitution which is permissible provided T is not close to T_0, it follows that

$$\frac{1}{c}\frac{\partial\xi}{\partial t} = \frac{T}{2\pi}\cdot\frac{e}{mc}\cdot\frac{T_0^2}{T^2 - T_0^2}\cdot A. \quad . \quad . \quad . \quad (98)$$

$e : mc$ has for sodium vapor the value $1.6 \cdot 10^7$ (cf. page 447). This value will be used in what follows. Further, in the visible spectrum $T = 2 \cdot 10^{-15}$ approximately. Hence (98) may be written

$$\frac{1}{c}\frac{\partial\xi}{\partial t} = A\cdot\frac{T_0^2}{T^2 - T_0^2}\cdot 5 \cdot 10^{-9}. \quad . \quad . \quad . \quad (99)$$

It is first necessary to find a value for A, i.e. for the strength of field in an intense ray of light. A square metre on the surface of the earth receives from the sun about 124 kilogrammetres of energy in a second, i.e. $1.22 \cdot 10^6$ absolute units (ergs) to the square centimeter. But from equation (25) on page 273, for a plane wave of natural light of amplitude A, the energy flow dE in unit time through unit surface (cm.^{2}) in air or in vacuum is *

$$dE\,(\text{in 1 sec per cm.}^2) = \frac{c}{4\pi}A^2. \quad . \quad . \quad . \quad (100)$$

* Without using Poynting's equation, the result contained in (100) may be deduced as follows: The electromagnetic energy which in unit time passes through 1 cm.^{2} must be that contained in a volume of V cm.^{3}, V being the velocity of light. In air or vacuum $V = c$. Further, from page 272 the electromagnetic energy in unit volume of air for the case of natural light is equal to $A^2 : 4\pi$. Hence $dE = cA^2 : 4\pi$.

From which, if half of the energy of the sun's radiation is ascribed to visible rays, the maximum strength of the electric field in sunlight is *

$$A = \sqrt{\frac{4\pi}{c} \cdot 0.61 \cdot 10^3} = 1.6 \cdot 10^{-2} = 0.016.\dagger \quad . \quad (101)$$

Hence for intense sunlight

$$\frac{1}{c}\frac{\partial \xi}{\partial t} = 8 \cdot 10^{-11} \frac{T_0^2}{T^2 - T_0^2} \quad . \quad . \quad . \quad . \quad (102)$$

This expression is always small provided T is not close to T_0. But even if, for example, $T : T_0 = 60 : 59$ (sodium flame illuminated by light of wave length $\lambda = 0.0006$ mm.), $T_0^2 : T^2 - T_0^2 = 30$, and the value of (101) is still very small.

If the velocity of a plane wave be calculated from (94), it is easy to see that its dependence upon the magnetic correction terms is of the second order, i.e. the change in the velocity of light produced by an increase in intensity from zero to that of sunlight would be of the order $10^{-20} V$. Hence the conclusion may be drawn that *an observable magneto-optical effect due to the magnetic field of the light itself does not exist.* There might be some question as to this conclusion in the case in which the period of the incident light very nearly coincides with the natural period (sodium vapor illuminated by sodium light). But the absorption which would then take place would render impossible a decisive test as to whether or not in this case the index of refraction varies with the intensity.

If now molecular currents (revolving ions) be assumed, equations (3), (4), (5) on page 420 sq. become applicable. If it were necessary to consider only one kind of revolving ion, then, from (31) on page 429, the density γ_1 of the lines of force might be set equal to $(\mu - 1)\gamma$, μ being the permeability

---

* As a matter of fact this ratio is only about $\frac{1}{3}$.

† The maximum strength of the magnetic field has the same value. This would therefore be about $\frac{1}{12}$ of the horizontal intensity of the earth's magnetic field in Germany.

of the substance. In this it is assumed that the magnetization of the substance can follow instantaneously the rapid changes in γ. If this should not be the case, it would be necessary to give μ a value smaller than that which is obtained with a constant field. Hence equations (3) and (4) take the form

$$\frac{1}{c}\frac{\partial}{\partial t}\left(\alpha + (\mu - 1)\gamma\frac{\partial \xi}{\partial z} + \ldots\right) = \frac{\partial Y}{\partial z} - \frac{\partial Z}{\partial y}. \qquad (103)$$

Now $\frac{\partial \xi}{\partial z}$ is of the same order of magnitude as $\frac{1}{c}\frac{\partial \xi}{\partial t}$ (in vacuo the two quantities are the same). Hence the magneto-optical correction terms of (103) are very small even when $\bar{\mu} - 1$ has as large a value as 1000, as is the case for iron; for then these terms are of the order of magnitude $1000 \cdot 10^{-10} = 10^{-7}$; so that *the magneto-optical effect due to the magnetic field of the light itself could never be detected in iron even if the magnetization of the iron were able to follow completely the rapid changes of field which take place in a light-wave.* This also explains why in a constant magnetic field the molecular currents give rise to a permeability which is greater than unity, *while for light-vibrations the same substance acts as though its permeability were equal to unity. But this is not due to any sort of lag in the magnetization,* for the conclusions here drawn are independent of such lag.

CHAPTER VIII

BODIES IN MOTION

1. General Considerations.—In what has preceded the optical properties of substances have been explained on the assumption of movable ionic charges. In this explanation the substance as a whole was considered to be at rest. But a motion of a substance as a whole produces a modification in its optical properties. In order to be able to develop a theory for this case, an hypothesis must be made as to whether the charged ions alone are carried along by the motion of the substance, or whether the ether which lies between these ions is also carried along in whole or in part. The assumption which will be adopted here is *that the ether always remains completely at rest*. Upon this basis H. A. Lorentz * has developed a complete and elegant theory. It is essentially this theory which is here presented. The conception of an ether absolutely at rest is the most simple and the most natural,—at least if the ether is conceived to be not a substance but merely space endowed with certain physical properties. Moreover the explanation of aberration presents insuperable difficulties if the ether is not assumed to be at rest. Lorentz has shown that the theory of a stationary ether is essentially in agreement with all the observations which bear upon this point. This matter will be more fully discussed below.

2. The Differential Equations of the Electromagnetic Field Referred to a Fixed System of Coordinates.—The starting-point will be, as always, the fundamental equations

* H. A. Lorentz, Versuch einer Theorie der elektrischen und optischen Erscheinungen in bewegten Körpern. Leiden, 1895.

(7) and (11) of the Maxwell electromagnetic theory (cf. pages 265 and 267), namely,

$$\frac{4\pi}{c} j_x = \frac{\partial \gamma}{\partial y} - \frac{\partial \beta}{\partial z}, \text{ etc.,} \quad \frac{4\pi}{c} s_x = \frac{\partial Y}{\partial z} - \frac{\partial Z}{\partial y}, \text{ etc.} \quad . \quad (1)$$

It has already been shown [equation (7), page 385] that when there is present only one kind of ion, whose charge is e and whose number in unit volume is $\mathfrak{N}$, the components of the electric current density are given by

$$4\pi j_x = \frac{\partial X}{\partial t} + 4\pi e \mathfrak{N} \frac{\partial \xi}{\partial t}.$$

In this ξ denotes the x-component of the displacement of the ion from its position of equilibrium within the substance. If the ions be given a constant velocity whose components are v_x, v_y, v_z, then the above equations take the more general form:

$$\left.\begin{aligned} 4\pi j_x &= \frac{\partial X}{\partial t} + 4\pi e \mathfrak{N} \frac{d\xi}{dt} + 4\pi e \mathfrak{N} v_x, \\ 4\pi j_y &= \frac{\partial Y}{\partial t} + 4\pi e \mathfrak{N} \frac{d\eta}{dt} + 4\pi e \mathfrak{N} v_y, \\ 4\pi j_z &= \frac{\partial Z}{\partial t} + 4\pi e \mathfrak{N} \frac{d\zeta}{dt} + 4\pi e \mathfrak{N} v_z. \end{aligned}\right\} \quad . \quad . \quad . \quad (2)$$

In these equations the differential coefficients with respect to the time are purposely written in the two forms $\frac{\partial}{\partial t}$ and $\frac{d}{dt}$. The first means that the change with respect to the time of some quantity at a definite *point in space* is considered, the second that the change in some quantity with respect to the time at a definite *point in the substance* is under consideration. Hence, if the components of the velocity of the substance are v_x, v_y, v_z, then in the formation of the differential coefficient the observed point is displaced in the element of time dt the distances $v_x dt$, $v_y dt$, $v_z dt$ along the coordinate axes. This change in position alters the quantities to be differentiated by $v_x dt\frac{\partial}{\partial x}$, $v_y dt\frac{\partial}{\partial y}$, $v_z dt\frac{\partial}{\partial z}$, when x, y, z are referred to a fixed system of coordinates, so that finally the relation holds

$$\frac{d}{dt} = \frac{\partial}{\partial t} + v_x\frac{\partial}{\partial x} + v_y\frac{\partial}{\partial y} + v_z\frac{\partial}{\partial z}. \quad . \quad . \quad . \quad (3)$$

Now the terms $\frac{d\xi}{dt}$, etc., must appear in equations (2) because the entire velocity of the ions is composed of the velocity of translation v_x of the substance, and the velocity of the ion with respect to the substance. This last is represented by $\frac{d\xi}{dt}$, not by $\frac{\partial\xi}{\partial t}$.

For the components of the magnetic current density the equations (13) on page 268 hold, namely,

$$4\pi s_x = \frac{\partial\alpha}{\partial t}, \quad 4\pi s_y = \frac{\partial\beta}{\partial t}, \quad 4\pi s_z = \frac{\partial\gamma}{\partial t}, \quad . \quad . \quad (4)$$

since it is proposed to neglect the effect of any external magnetic field, and since, in accordance with page 456, the permeability μ of all substances is equal to unity for optical periods.

If the substance has no velocity of translation, i.e. if $v_x = v_y = v_z = 0$, then the equation of motion of an ion is (cf. page 383)

$$m\frac{\partial^2\xi}{\partial t^2} + re^2\frac{\partial\xi}{\partial t} + \frac{4\pi e^2}{\vartheta}\xi = eX.$$

Now it will be assumed that the influence of the substance upon the ion is not affected by the motion of the substance. Nevertheless the differential equation must be modified because of the fact that the ions share in the motion of the sustance, and a moving ion is equivalent to an electric current whose components are proportional to ev_x, ev_y, ev_z. The magnetic force α, β, γ acts upon this current. Hence the equation of motion of an ion is (cf. similar discussion on page 434)*

$$m\frac{d^2\xi}{dt^2}+re^2\frac{d\xi}{dt}+4\pi\frac{e^2}{\vartheta}\xi=eX+\frac{e}{c}(v_y\gamma-v_z\beta). \quad . \quad (5)$$

Here, too, it is to be observed that $\frac{d}{dt}$ appears, but not $\frac{\partial}{\partial t}$, since (5) expresses the relative motion of the ions with respect to the substance.

When the changes in X or ξ are periodic, it is possible to write

$$\frac{d\xi}{dt}=\frac{i}{\tau'}\xi, \quad \frac{d^2\xi}{dt^2}=-\frac{1}{\tau'^2}\xi. \quad . \quad . \quad . \quad . \quad (6)$$

τ' is then equal to the period T' divided by 2π. Nevertheless it is to be observed that this period T' is the *relative period* with respect to the moving substance, and not the *absolute period* T referred to a fixed system of coordinates. It is important to distinguish between T and T'; thus, for example, $T'>T$ when the substance moves in the direction of the propagation of the light. In the case of plane waves in which all the quantities are proportional to

$$e^{\frac{i}{\tau}\left(t-\frac{p_1x+p_2y+p_3z}{\omega}\right)},$$

in which x, y, and z refer to a fixed coordinate system, $\tau=T:2\pi$ is proportional to the absolute period T.

---

* For the reasons discussed on page 455 the terms $\frac{\gamma}{c}\frac{d\eta}{dt}$, etc., are omitted from the right-hand side of (4), for they are too small to be considered. For the motion of the earth $v:c=10^{-4}$, i.e. it is of an entirely different order of magnitude from $\frac{d\eta}{dt}:c$. Also in Fizeau's experiment with running water, which will be described later, in which $v:c$ has a still smaller value, it is only the terms which depend upon v which have an appreciable effect upon the optical phenomena. The ionic velocities $\frac{d\xi}{dt}$, etc., do not have such an effect.

Now, from (3) and (6),

$$\frac{1}{\tau'} = \frac{1}{\tau}\left(1 - \frac{p_1 v_x + p_2 v_y + p_3 v_z}{\omega}\right);$$

i.e., if the velocity v is small in comparison with ω,

$$\frac{\tau'}{\tau} = \frac{T'}{T} = 1 + \frac{p_1 v_x + p_2 v_y + p_3 v_z}{\omega} = 1 + \frac{v_n}{\omega}, \quad . \quad (7)$$

in which v_n denotes the velocity of the substance in the direction of the wave normal.

If the abbreviations used on page 386, namely,

$$a = \frac{r\vartheta}{4\pi}, \quad b = \frac{m\vartheta}{4\pi e^2}, \quad . \quad . \quad . \quad . \quad . \quad (8)$$

be introduced into (5), there results

$$4\pi e\xi\left(1 + i\frac{a}{\tau'} - \frac{b}{\tau'^2}\right) = \vartheta\left(X + \frac{v_y\gamma - v_z\beta}{c}\right). \quad . \quad (9)$$

In equations (2) $e\mathfrak{N}$ means the charge present in unit volume.

If the value of $e\mathfrak{N}$ [cf. page 270, equation (20)] obtained from (the dielectric constant ϵ of the ether is set equal to 1)

$$4\pi e\mathfrak{N} = \frac{\partial X}{\partial x} + \frac{\partial Y}{\partial y} + \frac{\partial Z}{\partial z} \quad . \quad . \quad . \quad . \quad (10)$$

be substituted in (2), there results

$$4\pi j_x = \frac{\partial X}{\partial t} + v_x\left(\frac{\partial X}{\partial x} + \frac{\partial Y}{\partial y} + \frac{\partial Z}{\partial z}\right)$$

$$+ \frac{\mathfrak{N}\vartheta}{1 + i^a/\tau' - {}^b/\tau'^2} \frac{d\left(X + \frac{v_y\gamma - v_z\beta}{c}\right)}{dt}. \quad (11)$$

If several kinds of molecules are present, the first factor of the last term of this equation becomes, provided $i\frac{a}{\tau'}$ be neglected, i.e. provided the substance has no appreciable absorption,

$$\sum \frac{\mathfrak{N}\vartheta}{1 + i^a/\tau' - {}^b/\tau'^2} = n^2 - 1. \quad . \quad . \quad . \quad (12)$$

In this equation n is the index of refaction *corresponding to the period* $T' = 2\pi\tau'$ when the substance is at rest. Equation (12) is derived from the theory of dispersion [cf. equation (18) on page 387]. If now in equation (11) the differential coefficient $\frac{d}{dt}$ be replaced by its value in terms of $\frac{\partial}{\partial t}$ taken from (3), and if the resulting value for $4\pi \dot{j}_x$ be substituted in (1), a differential equation is obtained for the substance in motion referred to a fixed system of coordinates. This equation is much simplified if only terms in the first order in v be retained. It is always permissible to neglect the other terms, since, even when v represents the velocity of the earth in space, it is still very small in comparison to the velocity of light. It is then possible to replace $\frac{d}{dt}$ by $\frac{\partial}{\partial t}$ in those terms in (11) which are multiplied by v, and also to neglect, in the case of homogeneous substances, the second term of (11) which is multiplied by v_x, since approximately, i.e. for $v = 0$, for a periodic change of condition in such substances the following relation holds (cf. page 275):

$$\frac{\partial X}{\partial x} + \frac{\partial Y}{\partial y} + \frac{\partial Z}{\partial z} = 0. \quad . \quad . \quad . \quad . \quad . \quad (13)$$

Thus (11) becomes

$$4\pi \dot{j}_x = n^2 \frac{\partial X}{\partial t} + (n^2 - 1)\left\{ v_x \frac{\partial X}{\partial x} + v_y \frac{\partial X}{\partial y} + v_z \frac{\partial X}{\partial z} \right.$$
$$\left. + \frac{1}{c}\left(v_y \frac{\partial \gamma}{\partial t} - v_z \frac{\partial \beta}{\partial t} \right) \right\}. \quad (14)$$

But, from (1) and (4),

$$\frac{1}{c}\frac{\partial \gamma}{\partial t} = \frac{\partial X}{\partial y} - \frac{\partial Y}{\partial x}, \quad \frac{1}{c}\frac{\partial \beta}{\partial t} = \frac{\partial Z}{\partial x} - \frac{\partial X}{\partial z};$$

hence $4\pi j_x$ may be written in the form

$$4\pi j_x = n^2\frac{\partial X}{\partial t} + (n^2 - 1)\left\{2\left(v_x\frac{\partial X}{\partial x} + v_y\frac{\partial X}{\partial y} + v_z\frac{\partial X}{\partial z}\right) - \frac{\partial}{\partial x}(v_xX + v_yY + v_zZ)\right\}.$$

Hence, in view of (1) and (4), there result for a *moving, homogeneous, isotropic medium whose points are referred to a fixed system of coordinates* the following differential equations:

$$\left.\begin{aligned}
&\frac{n^2}{c}\frac{\partial X}{\partial t} + \frac{n^2-1}{c}\left\{2\left(v_x\frac{\partial X}{\partial x} + v_y\frac{\partial X}{\partial y} + v_z\frac{\partial X}{\partial z}\right) - \frac{\partial}{\partial x}(v_xX + v_yY + v_zZ)\right\} = \frac{\partial\gamma}{\partial y} - \frac{\partial\beta}{\partial z},\\
&\frac{n^2}{c}\frac{\partial Y}{\partial t} + \frac{n^2-1}{c}\left\{2\left(v_x\frac{\partial Y}{\partial x} + v_y\frac{\partial Y}{\partial y} + v_z\frac{\partial Y}{\partial z}\right) - \frac{\partial}{\partial y}(v_xX + v_yY + v_zZ)\right\} = \frac{\partial\alpha}{\partial z} - \frac{\partial\gamma}{\partial x},\\
&\frac{n^2}{c}\frac{\partial Z}{\partial t} + \frac{n^2-1}{c}\left\{2\left(v_x\frac{\partial Z}{\partial x} + v_y\frac{\partial Z}{\partial y} + v_z\frac{\partial Z}{\partial z}\right) - \frac{\partial}{\partial z}(v_xX + v_yY + v_zZ)\right\} = \frac{\partial\beta}{\partial x} - \frac{\partial\alpha}{\partial y},
\end{aligned}\right\} \quad (15)$$

$$\frac{1}{c}\frac{\partial\alpha}{\partial t} = \frac{\partial Y}{\partial z} - \frac{\partial Z}{\partial y},\quad \frac{1}{c}\frac{\partial\beta}{\partial t} = \frac{\partial Z}{\partial x} - \frac{\partial X}{\partial z},\quad \frac{1}{c}\frac{\partial\gamma}{\partial t} = \frac{\partial X}{\partial y} - \frac{\partial Y}{\partial x}. \quad (15')$$

Differentiation of equations (15) with respect to x, y, and z respectively and addition gives, with the use of the abbreviation

$$\frac{\partial X}{\partial x} + \frac{\partial Y}{\partial y} + \frac{\partial Z}{\partial z} = F,$$

$$\frac{n^2}{c}\frac{\partial F}{\partial t} + \frac{n^2-1}{c}\left\{2\left(v_x\frac{\partial F}{\partial x} + v_y\frac{\partial F}{\partial y} + v_z\frac{\partial F}{\partial z}\right) - (v_x\Delta X + v_y\Delta Y + v_z\Delta Z)\right\} = 0. \quad (16)$$

In the terms which are multiplied by v_x, etc., the following approximations may be used:

$$F = 0,$$

$$\Delta X = \frac{n^2}{c^2}\frac{\partial^2 X}{\partial t^2}, \quad \Delta Y = \frac{n^2}{c^2}\frac{\partial^2 Y}{\partial t^2}, \quad \Delta Z = \frac{n^2}{c^2}\frac{\partial^2 Z}{\partial t^2}. \quad (17)$$

Hence, from (16),

$$F = \frac{\partial X}{\partial x} + \frac{\partial Y}{\partial y} + \frac{\partial Z}{\partial z} = \frac{n^2 - 1}{c^2}\frac{\partial}{\partial t}(v_x X + v_y Y + v_z Z). \quad (18)$$

This equation asserts that *in the moving substance the electrical force cannot be propagated as a plane transverse wave*, since F is not equal to zero. *But the magnetic force, on the other hand, can be so propagated*, since, from (15′),

$$\frac{\partial}{\partial t}\left(\frac{\partial \alpha}{\partial x} + \frac{\partial \beta}{\partial y} + \frac{\partial \gamma}{\partial z}\right) = 0. \quad . \quad . \quad . \quad . \quad (19)$$

The differential equations (15) and (15′) may easily be transformed into equations each of which contains but one of the quantities X, Y, Z, α, β, γ. For example, if the first of equations (15) be differentiated with respect to t, and if $\frac{\partial \gamma}{\partial t}$ and $\frac{\partial \beta}{\partial t}$ be replaced by their values taken from (15′), there results

$$\frac{n^2}{c^2}\frac{\partial^2 X}{\partial t^2} + \frac{n^2 - 1}{c^2}\left\{2\frac{\partial}{\partial t}\left(v_x\frac{\partial X}{\partial x} + v_y\frac{\partial X}{\partial y} + v_z\frac{\partial X}{\partial z}\right)\right.$$
$$\left. - \frac{\partial^2}{\partial t \partial x}(v_x X + v_y Y + v_z Z)\right\} = \Delta X - \frac{\partial}{\partial x}\left(\frac{\partial X}{\partial x} + \frac{\partial Y}{\partial y} + \frac{\partial Z}{\partial z}\right).$$

In consideration of (18) this becomes

$$\frac{n^2}{c^2}\frac{\partial^2 X}{\partial t^2} + 2\frac{n^2 - 1}{c^2}\frac{\partial}{\partial t}\left(v_x\frac{\partial X}{\partial x} + v_y\frac{\partial X}{\partial y} + v_z\frac{\partial X}{\partial z}\right) = \Delta X. \quad (20)$$

The differential equations in Y, Z, α, β, γ have the same form.

3. The Velocity of Light in Moving Media.—From the last equation the velocity of light in a moving medium can be simply calculated. Setting

$$X = A \cdot e^{\frac{i}{\tau}\left(t - \frac{p_1 x + p_2 y + p_3 z}{\omega}\right)}, \quad . \quad . \quad . \quad (21)$$

there results, from (20),

$$\frac{n^2}{c^2} - \frac{2(n^2 - 1)}{c^2} \frac{p_1 v_x + p_2 v_y + p_3 v_z}{\omega} = \frac{1}{\omega^2},$$

or

$$\frac{n^2}{c^2}\left(1 - \frac{2(n^2 - 1)}{n^2} \frac{v_n}{\omega}\right) = \frac{1}{\omega^2}, \quad . \quad . \quad . \quad (22)$$

in which v_n denotes the velocity of translation of the medium in the positive direction of the wave normal. Hence, to terms of the first order in v_n,

$$\omega^2 = \frac{c^2}{n^2}\left(1 + \frac{2(n^2 - 1)}{n^2} \cdot \frac{v_n}{\omega}\right),$$

i.e.

$$\omega = \frac{c}{n}\left(1 + \frac{n^2 - 1}{n^2} \cdot \frac{v_n}{\omega}\right).$$

If, in the term on the right-hand side which contains v_n, ω be replaced by its approximate value $c : n$,

$$\omega = \frac{c}{n} + \frac{n^2 - 1}{n^2} v_n. \quad . \quad . \quad . \quad . \quad (23)$$

This equation asserts *that the motion of a medium has the same effect upon the velocity of light as though it communicated to the ether a certain fraction* (namely, $\frac{n^2 - 1}{n^2}$) *of its velocity of translation.*

This conclusion was drawn by Fresnel from the experiments of Fizeau in which the velocity of light in running water was measured. However, this interpretation of equation (23) is not quite rigorous, for the effect of the motion of the medium is not entirely contained in the second term of the right-hand side of (23). It appears also in the first. For, from page 462,

n does not denote the index of refraction for the absolute period T, but for the relative period T'. Now, according to (7),

$$T' = T\left(1 + \frac{v_n}{\omega}\right). \quad . \quad . \quad . \quad . \quad . \quad (24)$$

Hence if ν represent the index of the medium at rest for the absolute period T,

$$n = \nu + \frac{\partial \nu}{\partial T} \cdot T\frac{v_n}{\omega} = \nu + \frac{\partial \nu}{\partial \lambda}\lambda\frac{v_n}{\omega},$$

in which $\lambda = cT$ represents the wave length of the light in vacuo. Hence, from (23),

$$\omega = \frac{c}{\nu}\left(1 - \frac{\partial \nu}{\partial \lambda} \cdot \frac{\lambda}{\nu}\frac{v_n}{\omega}\right) + \frac{n^2 - 1}{n^2}v_n,$$

or, since in the terms which contain v_n the approximate values $n = \nu$, $\omega = c : \nu$ may be introduced,

$$\omega = \frac{c}{\nu} + v_n\left(\frac{\nu^2 - 1}{\nu^2} - \frac{\lambda}{\nu}\frac{\partial \nu}{\partial \lambda}\right). \quad . \quad . \quad . \quad (25)$$

$\frac{c}{\nu}$ is the velocity V of light for waves of absolute period T in the medium at rest; hence the term in (25) which contains v_n as a factor represents the change in the velocity which is due to the motion of the medium. This term is larger than Fresnel assumed it to be, since $\frac{\partial \nu}{\partial \lambda}$ is negative for normal dispersion. However, the difference is smaller than the errors of observation.

The experiment was first performed by Fizeau* and repeated later by Michelson and Morley.† In this experiment water was forced in opposite directions through two parallel tubes, and the velocities of the light in the tubes were compared by an interference method. The coefficient of ether drift, i.e.

* C. R. 33, p. 349, 1851; Pogg. Ann. Ergbd. 3, p. 457; Ann. chim. et phys. (3) 57, p. 385.

† Michelson and Morley, Am. Jo. Sci. (3) 31, p. 377, 1886.

the coefficient of v_n in the expression for ω, was found by experiment to have the value 0.434 ± 0.02, while for water and the Fraunhofer line D equation (25) gives its value as 0.451. The value of this coefficient given by the assumption of Fresnel is, for this case, $\nu^2 - 1 : \nu^2 = 0.438$.

4. The Differential Equations and the Boundary Conditions Referred to a Moving System of Coordinates which is Fixed with Reference to the Moving Medium.—If x', y', z' represent the coordinates of a point referred to an origin within the moving medium, then

$$x = x' + v_x \cdot t, \quad y = y' + v_y \cdot t, \quad z = z' + v_z \cdot t. \quad (26)$$

Since v_x, v_y, v_z do not depend on x, y, z, the partial differentiation with respect to x, y, z can be replaced by a partial differentiation with respect to x', y', z', i.e. in the equations of the preceding paragraph the differential coefficients with respect to x, y, z may be considered as taken with respect to x', y', z'. In what follows this will be done and x, y, z will be understood to represent simply the coordinates referred to a point of the moving medium. But in place of the differential coefficients $\frac{\partial X}{\partial t}$, etc., $\frac{dX}{dt}$, etc., must be introduced, since here the dependence of X upon the time is to be investigated, and hence X must be referred to a point whose position relative to other points in the moving medium is fixed. This change is made with the aid of equation (3) on page 459, so that, for example,

$$\frac{\partial X}{\partial t} = \frac{dX}{dt} - v_x \frac{\partial X}{\partial x} - v_y \frac{\partial X}{\partial y} - v_z \frac{\partial X}{\partial z}. \quad . \quad (27)$$

If this equation be substituted in (2), then for any number of kinds of ions, in consideration of (9), (10), and (12),

$$4\pi j_x = \frac{dX}{dt} - v_x \frac{\partial X}{\partial x} - v_y \frac{\partial X}{\partial y} - v_z \frac{\partial X}{\partial z}$$

$$+ (n^2 - 1) \frac{d}{dt}\left(X + \frac{v_y \gamma - v_z \beta}{c}\right) + v_x\left(\frac{\partial X}{\partial x} + \frac{\partial Y}{\partial y} + \frac{\partial Z}{\partial z}\right). \quad (28)$$

Hence equations (1), (3), (4), and (28) give, in connection with (19),

$$\left.\begin{aligned}
&\frac{n^2}{c}\frac{dX}{dt}+\frac{n^2-1}{c^2}\frac{d}{dt}(v_y\gamma-v_z\beta)=\frac{\partial}{\partial y}\left(\gamma+\frac{v_yX-v_xY}{c}\right)\\
&\qquad\qquad-\frac{\partial}{\partial z}\left(\beta+\frac{v_xZ-v_zX}{c}\right),\\
&\frac{n^2}{c}\frac{dY}{dt}+\frac{n^2-1}{c^2}\frac{d}{dt}(v_z\alpha-v_x\gamma)=\frac{\partial}{\partial z}\left(\alpha+\frac{v_zY-v_yZ}{c}\right)\\
&\qquad\qquad-\frac{\partial}{\partial x}\left(\gamma+\frac{v_yX-v_xY}{c}\right),\\
&\frac{n^2}{c}\frac{dZ}{dt}+\frac{n^2-1}{c^2}\frac{d}{dt}(v_x\beta-v_y\alpha)=\frac{\partial}{\partial x}\left(\beta+\frac{v_xZ-v_zX}{c}\right)\\
&\qquad\qquad-\frac{\partial}{\partial y}\left(\alpha+\frac{v_zY-v_yZ}{c}\right).\\
&\frac{1}{c}\frac{d\alpha}{dt}=\frac{\partial}{\partial z}\left(Y+\frac{v_z\alpha-v_x\gamma}{c}\right)-\frac{\partial}{\partial y}\left(Z+\frac{v_x\beta-v_y\alpha}{c}\right),\\
&\frac{1}{c}\frac{d\beta}{dt}=\frac{\partial}{\partial x}\left(Z+\frac{v_x\beta-v_y\alpha}{c}\right)-\frac{\partial}{\partial z}\left(X+\frac{v_y\gamma-v_z\beta}{c}\right),\\
&\frac{1}{c}\frac{d\gamma}{dt}=\frac{\partial}{\partial y}\left(X+\frac{v_y\gamma-v_z\beta}{c}\right)-\frac{\partial}{\partial x}\left(Y+\frac{v_z\alpha-v_x\gamma}{c}\right).
\end{aligned}\right\}\quad(29)$$

These equations hold also for non-homogeneous (isotropic) media, since the approximate equation (13), which does not hold for such media, has not been made use of in deducing them; while all the equations which have been so used are applicable to both homogeneous and non-homogeneous media. Hence, in accordance with the considerations presented on page 271, it follows at once from (29) that the boundary conditions which must be fulfilled in passing from one medium to another are, provided the boundary is perpendicular to the z-axis, that

$$\left.\begin{aligned}
&X+\frac{v_y\gamma-v_z\beta}{c},\quad Y+\frac{v_z\alpha-v_x\gamma}{c},\\
&\alpha+\frac{v_zY-v_yZ}{c},\quad \beta+\frac{v_xZ-v_zX}{c},
\end{aligned}\right\}\text{ be continuous at the boundary.}\quad(30)$$

From this and (29) the following additional conditions are obtained, namely, that

$$n^2 Z + \frac{n^2 - 1}{c}(v_x \beta - v_y \alpha), \ \gamma \text{ be continuous at the boundary.} \quad (30')$$

Since in (30), in the terms multiplied by v_x, v_y, v_z, the approximate values which are obtained when $v_x = v_y = v_z = 0$ may be substituted, the boundary conditions may be put in the form

$$X, Y, \alpha - \frac{v_y Z}{c}, \quad \beta + \frac{v_x Z}{c} \left\} \begin{matrix} \text{must be continuous at} \\ \text{the boundary.} \end{matrix} \right\} \cdot \quad (30'')$$

For *a homogeneous medium* differential equations can easily be obtained each of which contains but one of the quantities $X, Y, Z, \alpha, \beta, \gamma$. For it follows from (27), when terms of the first order only in v_x, v_y, v_z are retained, that

$$\frac{\partial^2 X}{\partial t^2} = \frac{d^2 X}{dt^2} - 2\frac{d}{dt}\left(v_x \frac{\partial X}{\partial x} + v_y \frac{\partial X}{\partial y} + v_z \frac{\partial X}{\partial z}\right);$$

hence (20) becomes

$$\frac{n^2}{c^2}\frac{d^2 X}{dt^2} - \frac{2}{c^2}\frac{d}{dt}\left(v_x \frac{\partial X}{\partial x} + v_y \frac{\partial X}{\partial y} + v_z \frac{\partial X}{\partial z}\right) = \Delta X. \quad (31)$$

Equations of the same form may be obtained for $Y, Z, \alpha, \beta, \gamma$. The preceding equations (18) and (19) also hold here, i.e. the electric force is not propagated as a transverse wave; but the magnetic force is so propagated.

Writing

$$X = A \cdot e^{\frac{i}{\tau}\left(t - \frac{p_1' x + p_2' y + p_3' z}{\omega'}\right)},$$

in which, since it is assumed that $p_1'^2 + p_2'^2 + p_3'^2 = 1$, p_1', p_2', p_3' denote the direction cosines of the wave normal, ω' the velocity of light referred to the moving system of coordinates. Then, from (31),

$$\frac{n^2}{c^2} + \frac{2}{c^2 \omega'}(p_1' v_x + p_2' v_y + p_3' v_z) = \frac{1}{\omega'^2},$$

or

$$\frac{n^2}{c^2}\left(1+\frac{2(p_1'v_x+p_2'v_y+p_3'v_z)}{n^2\omega'}\right)=\frac{1}{\omega'^2},$$

$$\omega'=\frac{c}{n}\left(1-\frac{p_1'v_x+p_2'v_y+p_3'v_z}{n^2\omega'}\right).$$

Writing on the right-hand side for ω' the approximate value $\omega' = c : n$, there results

$$\omega'=\frac{c}{n}-\frac{p_1'v_x+p_2'v_y+p_3'v_z}{n^2}. \quad . \quad . \quad . \quad (32)$$

5. The Determination of the Direction of the Ray by Huygens' Principle.—The velocity ω' of the wave along its normal depends upon the direction p_1' p_2', p_3' of the normal. In order to find the direction $\mathfrak{p}_1$, $\mathfrak{p}_2$, $\mathfrak{p}_3$ of the ray corresponding to the direction of the normal p_1', p_2', p_3', it is convenient to pursue the method used on page 330 in the case of crystals, namely, to find by means of Huygens' principle the point of intersection of three adjacent wave fronts. Thus differentiate the equation

$$p_1'x+p_2'y+p_3'z+f(p_1'^2+p_2'^2+p_3'^2)=\omega'+f \quad (33)$$

with respect to p_1', p_2', p_3' [cf. equation (59), page 330]. The result is

$$x+2fp_1'=\frac{\partial\omega'}{\partial p_1'},\quad y+2fp_2'=\frac{\partial\omega'}{\partial p_2'},\quad z+2fp_3'=\frac{\partial\omega'}{\partial p_3'};$$

i.e., in consideration of (32),

$$x+2fp_1'=-\frac{v_x}{n^2},\quad y+2fp_2'=-\frac{v_y}{n^2},\quad z+2fp_3'=-\frac{v_z}{n^2}. \quad (34)$$

If these three equations be multipled by p_1', p_2', p_3', respectively, and added, there results, since $p_1'^2+p_2'^2+p_3'^2=1$,

$$p_1'x+p_2'y+p_3'z+2f=-\frac{p_1'v_x+p_2'v_y+p_3'v_z}{n^2}$$

But, from (33), $p_1'x + p_2'y + p_3'z = \omega'$; i.e., in consideration of (32), $2f = -c:n$. Hence, from (34), the direction of the ray is determined from the proportion

$$\mathfrak{p}_1 : \mathfrak{p}_2 : \mathfrak{p}_3 = x : y : z = \frac{cp_1'}{n} - \frac{v_x}{n^2} : \ldots,$$

or

$$\mathfrak{p}_1 : \mathfrak{p}_2 : \mathfrak{p}_3 = p_1' - \frac{v_x}{nc} : p_2' - \frac{v_y}{nc} : p_3' - \frac{v_z}{nc}. \quad . \quad (35)$$

Thus the ray does not coincide with the wave normal.

Neglecting terms of the second order in v, (35) may be written

$$p_1' : p_2' : p_3' = \mathfrak{p}_1 + \frac{v_x}{nc} : \mathfrak{p}_2 + \frac{v_y}{nc} : \mathfrak{p}_3 + \frac{v_z}{nc}. \quad . \quad (35')$$

6. The Absolute Time replaced by a Time which is a Function of the Coordinates.—In place of the variables x, y, z, t, in which t denotes the absolute time and x, y, z the coordinates referred to a point in the moving medium, the quantities x, y, z, and

$$t' = t - \frac{v_x x + v_y y + v_z z}{c^2} \quad . \quad . \quad . \quad . \quad (36)$$

will be introduced as independent variables.

t' may conveniently be called a sort of "position" time, since it depends upon the position of the point under consideration, i.e. upon x, y, z. The partial differential coefficients with respect to x, y, z will then be denoted by $\left(\frac{\partial}{\partial x}\right)'$, $\left(\frac{\partial}{\partial y}\right)'$, $\left(\frac{\partial}{\partial z}\right)'$, while $\frac{\partial}{\partial x}$, etc., will be used as above to denote the partial differential coefficients when x, y, z, t are the independent variables. From (36),

$$\left.\begin{aligned} &\frac{d}{dt} = \frac{d}{dt'}, \quad \frac{\partial}{\partial x} = \left(\frac{\partial}{\partial x}\right)' - \frac{v_x}{c^2}\frac{d}{dt'}, \quad \frac{\partial}{\partial y} = \left(\frac{\partial}{\partial y}\right)' - \frac{v_y}{c^2}\frac{d}{dt'}, \\ &\qquad\qquad \frac{\partial}{\partial z} = \left(\frac{\partial}{\partial z}\right)' - \frac{v_z}{c^2}\frac{d}{dt'}. \end{aligned}\right\} (37)$$

If the following abbreviations be used,

$$\left.\begin{aligned} X+\frac{v_y\gamma - v_z\beta}{c} = X', \quad Y+\frac{v_z\alpha - v_x\gamma}{c} = Y', \\ Z+\frac{v_x\beta - v_y\alpha}{c} = Z', \\ \alpha+\frac{v_zY - v_yZ}{c} = \alpha', \quad \beta+\frac{v_xZ - v_zX}{c} = \beta', \\ \gamma+\frac{v_yX - v_xY}{c} = \gamma', \end{aligned}\right\} \quad (38)$$

then the introduction of the values (37) in (29) gives, when terms in the first order only in v are retained, and when the differentiation $\left(\frac{\partial}{\partial x}\right)$ is again denoted simply by $\frac{\partial}{\partial x}$,

$$\left.\begin{aligned} \frac{n^2}{c}\frac{dX'}{dt'} = \frac{\partial\gamma'}{\partial y} - \frac{\partial\beta'}{\partial z}, \quad \frac{n^2}{c}\frac{dY'}{dt'} = \frac{\partial\alpha'}{\partial z} - \frac{\partial\gamma'}{\partial x}, \\ \frac{n^2}{c}\frac{dZ'}{dt'} = \frac{\partial\beta'}{\partial x} - \frac{\partial\alpha'}{\partial y}. \\ \frac{1}{c}\frac{d\alpha'}{dt'} = \frac{\partial Y'}{\partial z} - \frac{\partial Z'}{\partial y}, \quad \frac{1}{c}\frac{d\beta'}{dt'} = \frac{\partial Z'}{\partial x} - \frac{\partial X'}{\partial z}, \\ \frac{1}{c}\frac{d\gamma'}{dt'} = \frac{\partial X'}{\partial y} - \frac{\partial Y'}{\partial x}. \end{aligned}\right\} \quad (39)$$

According to (30) and (38) the boundary conditions, when the boundary is perpendicular to the z-axis, are that

$$X', \ Y', \ \alpha', \ \beta' \text{ be continuous at the boundary.} \quad (40)$$

Now equations (39) and (40) have the same form as the differential equations and boundary conditions of the electromagnetic field for the case of a medium at rest. Hence the important conclusion:

If, for a system at rest, X, Y, Z, α, β, γ are certain known functions of x, y, z, t, and the period T, then, for the system in motion, X', Y', Z', α', β', γ' are the same functions *of* $x, y, z, t - \frac{v_x x + v_y y + v_z z}{c^2}$, *and* T; in which now x, y, z are the relative coordinates referred to a point of the medium, and T is the relative period with respect to a point of the moving medium. From (7) on page 461, the absolute period is in the latter case to be assumed as $T\left(1 - \frac{v_n}{\omega}\right)$.

7. The Configuration of the Rays Independent of the Motion.—The last proposition is capable of immediate application to the relative configuration of the rays. For, in a system at rest, let the space which is filled with light be bounded by a certain surface S so that outside of S both X, Y, Z, and α, β, γ vanish. Then when the system is in motion X', Y', Z', and α', β', γ' vanish for points outside of S, i.e. *in the moving system also the surface S is the boundary of the space which is filled with light.* Now suppose that S is the surface of a cylinder (a beam of light), an assumption which can be made if the cross-section of the cylinder is large in comparison with the wave length. The generating lines of this cylinder are called the *light-rays.* According to the above proposition, the boundary of the beam of light, even though it be frequently reflected and refracted, is unchanged by the common motion of the whole, i.e. *in the moving system light-waves of the relative period T are reflected and refracted according to the same laws as rays of the absolute period T in the system at rest.*

The laws of lenses and mirrors need therefore no modification because of the motion. Likewise the motion has no influence upon interference phenomena. For these phenomena differ from the others only in that the form of the surface S which bounds the light-space is more complicated, and, as above remarked, this form is not altered by the motion.

For crystals * also the configuration of the rays is independent of the motion, for the differential equations and

* Whether this is true for naturally and magnetically active substances will not here be discussed. To determine this a special investigation is necessary.

boundary conditions applicable to these can be put into forms similar to (39) and (40), so that it is only necessary to refer to the laws of refraction of the crystal at rest.

8. The Earth as a Moving System.—The last considerations are especially fruitful in discussing the motion of the earth through space. For, according to what has been said, *the motion of the earth* can never have an influence of the first order in v upon the phenomena which are produced with terrestrial sources of light;* for the periods emitted by such sources are merely the relative periods of the above discussion, i.e. they are wholly independent of the motion of the earth, so that the configuration of the rays cannot be altered by this motion. Now in fact numerous experiments by Respighi,† Hoeck,‡ Ketteler,§ and Mascart ‖ upon refraction and interference (some of them upon crystals) have proved that the phenomena are independent of the orientation of the apparatus with respect to the direction of the earth's motion. On the other hand, when celestial sources of light are used the effect of the earth's motion can be detected, for in this case the relative period depends upon that motion. As a matter of fact the spectral lines of some of the fixed stars appear somewhat displaced. This is to be explained by the relative motion of the earth, or of the whole solar system, with respect to the fixed stars. For the laws of refraction and interference are concerned with relative periods, and from equation (7) these are given by $T\left(1 - \frac{v_n}{\omega}\right)$, in which T is the absolute period. Thus T varies with the magnitude and sign of v_n, and hence also the position of the spectral lines formed upon the moving earth by

---

* Substances which show natural or magnetic optical activity are here neglected.

† Mem. di Bologna (2) II, p. 279.

‡ Astr. Nachr. 73, p. 193.

§ Astron. Undulat. Theorie, pp. 66, 158, 166, 1873.

‖ Ann. de l'école norm. (2) 1, p. 191, 1872; 3, p. 376, 1874.

refraction or diffraction. This is known as *Doppler's Principle.**

Since the path of the earth about the sun is nearly a circle, v_n is in this case equal to zero. Hence, as has been also experimentally shown by Mascart,† the motion of the earth causes no shifting in the Fraunhofer lines of the solar spectrum.‡

9. Aberration of Light.—Although, as was shown in § 7, the configuration of the rays is not influenced by the motion of the earth, yet the direction of the wave normal which corresponds to a given direction of the ray does depend upon that motion. This has already been shown on page 470; but it is worth while to here deduce directly the definition of the ray without using Huygens' principle as was done above. Consider, for example, the case of a plane wave in a system at rest: all the quantities involved are functions of $t - \frac{p_1x + p_2y + p_3z}{\omega}$. In a system at rest p_1, p_2, p_3 are the direction cosines of both the wave normal and the ray. The physical criterion for the direction of the ray will be that the light pass through

---

* In the above it is assumed that the source A is at rest and the point of observation B in motion. The considerations also hold in case both A and B move. v_n is then the relative velocity of B with respect to A measured in the direction of the propagation of the light. In this case the rigorous calculation shows that the actual period T and the relative period T' observed at B stand to each other in the ratio $T : T' = \omega - v' : \omega - v$, in which v' is the absolute velocity of B, v that of A in the direction of the ray, and ω that of the light in the medium between A and B. It is only when v' and v are both small in comparison with ω that this rigorous equation reduces to that given in the text, i.e. to the customary form of Doppler's principle. Now we know nothing whatever about the absolute velocities of the heavenly bodies; hence in the ultimate analysis the application of the usual equation representing Doppler's principle to the determination of the relative motion in the line of sight of the heavenly bodies with respect to the earth might lead to errors. Attention was first called to this point by Moessard (C. R. 114, p. 1471, 1892).

† Ann. de l'école norm. (2) 1, pp. 166, 190, 1872.

‡ No account is here taken of the displacement, due to the rotation of the sun, of the lines which are obtained from light which comes from the rim of the sun. In experiments the light from the entire disk of the sun is generally used.

two small openings whose line of connection has the direction cosines p_1, p_2, p_3. If now the whole system moves with a velocity v_x, v_y, v_z, there must always be one ray (called a relative ray when referred to a moving system) whose direction cosines are p_1, p_2, p_3. But according to page 473 this ray is produced by waves which are periodic functions of

$$t - \frac{v_x x + v_y y + v_z z}{c^2} - \frac{p_1 x + p_2 y + p_3 z}{\omega}. \quad . \quad (41)$$

This expression corresponds to plane waves for which the direction cosines of the wave normal p_1', p_2', p_3' are proportional to

$$p_1' : p_2' : p_3' = \frac{p_1}{\omega} + \frac{v_x}{c^2} : \frac{p_2}{\omega} + \frac{v_y}{c^2} : \frac{p_3}{\omega} + \frac{v_z}{c^2}. \quad (42)$$

This relation (42) makes possible the calculation of the direction of the wave normal in the moving system from the direction of the ray, and *vice versa*. This relation is also identical with that deduced on page 471 [cf (35')], from Huygens' principle, for the quantities $\mathfrak{p}_1, \mathfrak{p}_2, \mathfrak{p}_3$ there correspond to p_1, p_2, p_3 here, and approximately $c : \omega = n$.

Hence if upon the moving earth a star appears to lie in the direction p_1, p_2, p_3, referred to a coordinate system connected with the earth, its real direction is somewhat different, for this latter coincides with the direction of the normal to the wave from the star to the earth, i.e. the position of the star is obtained from $p_1' \, p_2' \, p_3'$.

The case in which the line of sight to the star and the motion of the earth are at right angles to each other will be considered more in detail. Thus set $p_1 = p_2 = 0$, $p_3 = 1$, $v_y = v_z = 0$, $v_x = v$; then from (42), if the velocity in air ω be identified with c,—as is here permissible,—the position of the star is given by

$$p_1' : p_2' : p_3' = v : 0 : c, \quad . \quad . \quad . \quad . \quad (43)$$

i.e. the real direction of the star differs from its apparent direction by the angle of aberration ζ which is determined by

$\tan \zeta = v : c$. This angle of aberration is not changed when the star is observed through a telescope whose tube is filled with water, since it has been shown that the relative configuration in any sort of a refracting system is not changed by the motion.* This conclusion may be reached directly as follows: If ω differs appreciably from c, as is the case when the observation is made through water, then the wave normal in the water is no longer given by (43), but, in accordance with (42), by

$$p_1' : p_2' : p_3' = v : 0 : \frac{c^2}{\omega} = v : 0 : cn, \quad . \quad . \quad (44)$$

from which the angle of aberration ζ' is determined by $\tan \zeta' = v : cn$. The corresponding wave normal in air or in vacuo makes, however, another angle ζ with the z-axis such that, since the boundary between air and water is to be assumed perpendicular to the direction of the ray, according to Snell's law $\sin \zeta : \sin \zeta' = n$. Since now, on account of the smallness of ζ and ζ', the sin is equal to the tan, it follows that $\tan \zeta = v : c$, i.e. the angle of aberration is the same as though the position of the star had been observed directly in air.

10. Fizeau's Experiment with Polarized Light.—Although in accordance with the theory the motion of the earth should have no influence upon optical phenomena save those of aberration and the change in the period of vibration in accordance with Doppler's principle, and although experiments designed to detect the existence of such an effect have in general given negative results, nevertheless Fizeau † thought that he discovered in one case such an effect. When a beam of plane-polarized light passes obliquely through a plate of glass, the azimuth of polarization is altered (cf. p. 286). The apparatus used consisted of a polarizing prism, a bundle of glass plates, and an analyzer. At the time of the solstice, generally about noon,

---

* Cf. p. 116 above.

† Ann. de chim. et de phys. (3) 58, p. 129, 1860; Pogg. Ann. 114, p. 554, 1861.

a beam of sunlight was sent, by means of suitably placed mirrors, through the apparatus from east to west, and then from west to east. It was thought that a slight difference in the positions of the analyzer in the two cases was detected.

According to the theory here given no such difference can exist. For if in any position of the apparatus the analyzer is set for extinction, then the light disturbance is limited to a space which does not extend behind the analyzer. According to the discussion on page 473, the boundary of this space does not change because of the motion of the earth, provided the configuration of the rays with respect to the apparatus remains fixed; and this is true even when crystalline media are used for producing the bounding surface S of the light-space. Hence the position of extinction of the analyzer must be independent of the orientation of the apparatus with respect to the earth's motion. In any case it is to be hoped that this experiment of Fizeau's will be repeated. Until this is done it is at least doubtful whether there is in reality a contradiction in this matter between experiment and the theory here presented.

11. **Michelson's Interference Experiment.** — The time which light requires to pass between two stationary points A and B whose distance apart is l is $t_1 = \frac{l}{c}$, where c represents the velocity of light. It will be assumed that the medium in which the light is travelling is the ether, or, what amounts to the same thing, air. If the two points A and B have a common velocity v in the direction of the ray, then the time of passage t_1' of the light from A to B is somewhat different. For the light must travel in the time t_1' not only the distance l, but also the distance over which the point B has moved in the time t_1', i.e. the total distance travelled by the light is $l + vt_1'$, so that

$$t_1'c = l + vt_1 \quad . \quad . \quad . \quad . \quad . \quad . \quad (45)$$

If the light is reflected at B, in order to return to A it requires a time t_2' such that

$$t_2'c = l - vt_2' \quad . \quad . \quad . \quad . \quad . \quad . \quad (46)$$

For this case differs from the preceding only in this, that now A moves in a direction opposite to that of the reflected light. Hence the time t' required for the light to pass from A to B and back again to A is, from (45) and (46),

$$t' = t_1' + t_2' = \frac{l}{c}\left(\frac{1}{1 - v/c} + \frac{1}{1 + v/c}\right),$$

or

$$t' = \frac{2l}{c}\left(1 + \left[\frac{v}{c}\right]^2\right), \quad . \quad . \quad . \quad . \quad (47)$$

provided the development be carried only to terms of the second order in $\frac{v}{c}$. Now although the influence of the common motion of the points A and B upon the time t' is of the second order, it should be possible to detect it by a sensitive interference method.

The experiment was performed by Michelsen in tho year 1881.* The instrument used was a sort of an interferential refractor furnished with two horizontal arms P and Q set at right angles to each other and of equal length (cf. Fig. 57, page 149). Two beams of light were brought to interference, one of which had travelled back and forth along P, the other along Q. The entire apparatus could be rotated about a vertical axis so that it could be brought into two positions such that first P, then Q coincided with the direction of the earth's motion. Upon rotating the apparatus from one position to the other a displacement of the interference bands is to be expected.

The amount of this displacement will now be more accurately calculated. Let the arm P coincide with the direction v of the earth's motion, the arm Q be perpendicular to it. Let A be the point in which P and Q intersect. The time t' required for the light to pass the length of P and back is given by (47). But the time t'' required for the light to travel the

* Am. Jo. Sci. (3) 22, p. 120, 1881.

length of Q and back is not simply $t'' = 2l : c$; for it is necessary to remember that the point of intersection A of the two arms P and Q, from which the light starts and to which it returns after an interval of time t', has in this time changed its position in space. Thus the distance through which this point A has moved is vt' (Fig. 107). The first position of the point A will be denoted by A_1, the last by A_2. In order that the light from A_1 may return to A_2 after reflection at the end of the arm Q, it is necessary that the reflecting mirror at Q be somewhat inclined to the wave normal. The distance travelled by the light is $2s$ and the relation holds,

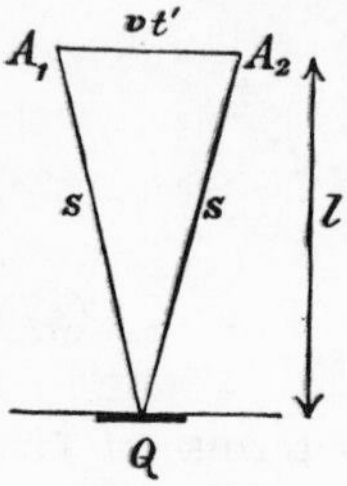

FIG. 107.

$$s^2 = l^2 + \left(\frac{vt'}{2}\right)^2.$$

Also, $t'' = 2s : c$ denotes the time which the light requires to travel the length of Q and back. Now, from (47), if terms of higher order than the second in v be neglected,

$$t'' = \frac{2l}{c}\left(1 + \frac{v^2}{8l^2}t'^2\right) = \frac{2l}{c}\left(1 + \frac{v^2}{2c^2}\right), \quad . \quad . \quad . \quad (48)$$

hence

$$t' - t'' = \frac{l}{c} \cdot \frac{v^2}{c^2}. \quad . \quad . \quad . \quad . \quad . \quad . \quad (49)$$

If this difference in time were one whole period T, the interference fringes would be displaced just one fringe from the position which they would occupy if the earth were at rest, i.e. if $v = 0$. Hence if the displacement δ be expressed as a fractional part of a fringe, there results from (49)

$$\delta = \frac{t' - t''}{T} = \frac{l}{cT} \cdot \frac{v^2}{c^2} = \frac{l}{\lambda}\zeta^2, \quad . \quad . \quad . \quad (50)$$

in which ζ is the angle of aberration. According to page 116, $\zeta = 20.5'' = 20.5 \cdot \pi : 180 \cdot 60^2 = 0.995 \cdot 10^{-4}$ radians.

The displacement produced by turning the instrument from the position in which P coincides with the direction of the earth's motion to that in which Q coincides with this direction should be 2δ.

But no displacement of the interference fringes was observed. The sensitiveness of the method was afterwards increased by Michelson and Morley* by reflecting each beam of light several times back and forth by means of mirrors. The effect of this is to multiply several times the length of the arms P and Q. Each beam of light was in this way compelled to travel a distance of 22 metres, i.e. l was 11 metres. The apparatus was mounted upon a heavy plate of stone which floated upon mercury and could therefore be easily rotated about a vertical axis. According to (50) this rotation ought to have produced a displacement of $2\delta = 0.4$ of a fringe, but the observed displacement was certainly not more than 0.02 of a fringe,—a difference which might easily arise from errors of observation.

This difficulty † may be explained by giving up the theory that the ether is in absolute rest and assuming that it shares in the earth's motion. The explanation of aberration becomes then involved in insuperable difficulties. Another way of explaining the negative results of Michelson's experiment has been proposed by Lorentz and Fitzgerald. These men assume that *the length of a solid body depends upon its absolute motion in space.*

As a matter of fact, if the arm which lies in the direction of the earth's motion were shorter than the other by an amount $l\frac{v^2}{2c^2}$, the difference in time $t' - t''$, as calculated in (49), would

---

* Am. Jo. Sci. (3) 34, p. 333, 1887; Phil. Mag. (5) 24, p. 449, 1887.

† Sutherland (Phil. Mag. (5) 45, p. 23, 1898) explains Michelson's negative result by a lack of accuracy in the adjustment of the apparatus. But, according to a communication which I have recently received from H. A. Lorentz, this objection is not tenable if, as is always the case, the observation is made with a telescope which is focussed upon the position of maximum sharpness of the fringes.

be just compensated, i.e. no displacement of the fringes would be produced.

However unlikely the hypothesis that the dimensions of a substance depend upon its absolute motion may at first sight seem to be, it is not so improbable if the assumption be made that the so-called molecular forces, which act between the molecules of a substance, are transmitted by the ether like the electric and magnetic forces, and that therefore a motion of translation in the ether must have an effect upon them, just as the attraction or repulsion between electrically charged bodies is modified by a motion of translation of the particles in the ether. Since $\frac{v^2}{c^2}$ has the value 10^{-8}, the diameter of the earth which lies in the direction of its motion would be shortened only 6.5 cm.

PART III

RADIATION

CHAPTER I

ENERGY OF RADIATION

1. Emissive Power.—The fundamental laws of photometry were deduced above (page 77) from certain definitions whose justification lay in the fact that intensities and brightnesses calculated with the aid of these definitions agreed with observations made by the eye. But it is easy to replace this physiological, subjective method by a physical, objective means of measuring the effect of a source of light. Thus it is possible to measure the amount of heat developed in any substance which absorbs the light-rays. To be sure this introduces into the photometric definition a new idea which was unnecessary so long as the physiological unit was used, namely, the idea of time, since the heat which is developed in an absorbing substance is proportional to the time. According to the principle of energy, the heat developed must be due to a certain quantity of energy which the source of light has transmitted to the absorbing substance. Therefore the *emission* E of a source Q is defined as the amount of energy which is radiated from Q into the surrounding medium in unit time.

Now radiant energy consists of vibrations of widely differing wave lengths. It must be possible to express the amount of energy transmitted in unit time by waves whose lengths lie between λ and $\lambda + d\lambda$ in the form $E_\lambda d\lambda$. *The factor E_λ will be called the emission for the wave length λ.*

The emission between the wave lengths λ_1 and λ_2 is therefore

$$E_{12} = \int_{\lambda_1}^{\lambda_2} E_\lambda \cdot d\lambda, \quad . \quad . \quad . \quad . \quad . \quad . \quad (1)$$

and the total emission is

$$E = \int_0^\infty E_\lambda \cdot d\lambda. \quad . \quad . \quad . \quad . \quad . \quad . \quad (2)$$

The emission of a body depends not only upon its nature, but also upon the size and form of its surface. In order to be independent of these secondary considerations, the term *emissive power* will be introduced and defined as the emission (outward) of unit surface.

2. The Intensity of Radiation of a Surface.—The fundamental law stated on page 77 that the quantity of light is the same at every section of a tube of light, i.e. of a tube whose surface is formed by rays of light, appears necessary from the energy standpoint, since the quantity of light is interpreted as the energy flow in unit time. For, as was shown on page 273, the rays of light are the paths of the energy flow, i.e. energy passes neither in nor out of a tube of light. Hence the flow of energy must be the same through every section of a tube, since the same amount of energy must flow out of every element of volume as flows into it, provided this element neither contains a source of light nor absorbs radiant energy.

Hence the energy flow which a surface element ds sends by radiation into an elementary cone of angular aperture $d\Omega$ may be written in the form [cf. equation (69), page 83]

$$dL = i ds \cos \phi \, d\Omega, \quad . \quad . \quad . \quad . \quad . \quad . \quad (3)$$

in which ϕ denotes the angle included between the element of surface ds and the axis of the elementary cone, i.e. the direction of the rays under consideration. i will be called the *intensity of radiation* of the surface ds.

If all parts of a curved radiating surface appear to the eye equally bright, then, as was shown on page 82, i must be constant, i.e. independent of the inclination ϕ. The discussion as to whether or not i is constant when considered from the energy standpoint will be reserved till later. If, for the present, i be assumed to be constant, then from (3) the energy flow which passes from ds into a finite circular cone whose generating lines make an angle U with the normal to ds is found to be [cf. (73) on page 83]

$$L = \pi i ds \sin^2 U. \quad . \quad . \quad . \quad . \quad . \quad (4)$$

Setting $U = \frac{\pi}{2}$ and dividing by ds, the emissive power e of ds is obtained in the form

$$e = \pi i. \quad . \quad . \quad . \quad . \quad . \quad . \quad . \quad (5)$$

Here again i, the total intensity of radiation, must be distinguished from i_λ, the intensity of radiation for wave length λ. If e_λ denote the emissive power for the wave length λ, then

$$e_\lambda = \pi i_\lambda. \quad . \quad . \quad . \quad . \quad . \quad . \quad . \quad (6)$$

3. The Mechanical Equivalent of the Unit of Light.—On page 81 the flame of a Hefner lamp was assumed as the unit of light. Tumlirz * has found the emission within a horizontal cone of unit solid angle from such a flame to be 0.1483 gram-calories a second; Angström's † value for the same is 0.22 gram-calories a second. If such a lamp be assumed to radiate uniformly in all directions, then its total emission, i.e. the energy which it emits in all directions (into the solid angle 4π), is calculated from the value of Tumlirz as

$$E = 4\pi \cdot 0.1483 \frac{\text{gr cal}}{\text{sec}} = 1.86 \frac{\text{gr cal}}{\text{sec}},$$

* Wied. Ann. 38, p. 650, 1889.

† Wied. Ann. 67, p. 648, 1899.

or, since one gram-calorie is equal to $419 \cdot 10^5$ ergs, the value of E in the C.G.S. system is

$$E = 78 \cdot 10^6 \frac{\text{erg}}{\text{sec}}. \quad . \quad . \quad . \quad . \quad . \quad . \quad (7)$$

Only 2.4 per cent of this energy corresponds to visible rays.* Hence the light emission amounts to

$$E' = 1.9 \cdot 10^6 \frac{\text{erg}}{\text{sec}}. \quad . \quad . \quad . \quad . \quad . \quad . \quad (8)$$

Hence if the unit of light is understood to mean the energy of the light-rays emitted by a Hefner lamp in a second in a horizontal direction within a cone of unit solid angle, i.e. upon 1 cm.² at a distance of 1 cm., then

$$1 \text{ unit of light} = 1.51 \cdot 10^5 \frac{\text{erg}}{\text{sec}}. \quad . \quad . \quad . \quad . \quad (9)$$

This is then the mechanical equivalent of the unit of light.

The candle-metre is taken as the unit of intensity of illumination (cf. page 81). It is defined as the quantity of light which a Hefner lamp radiates upon 1 cm.² at a distance of 1 m. The solid angle amounts in this case to $1 : 100 \cdot 100$. Hence, from (9),

$$1 \text{ candle-metre} = 15 \cdot \frac{\text{erg}}{\text{sec}} \quad . \quad . \quad . \quad . \quad (10)$$

Hence when the intensity of illumination is 1 candle-metre, i.e. when an eye is at a distance of 1 m. from a standard candle, it receives, assuming that the diameter of the pupil is 3 mm., about 1 erg of energy in a second. This rate of energy flow would require 1 year and 89 days to heat 1 gm. of water 1° C. This calculation gives some idea of the enormous sensitiveness of the eye. When the eye perceives a star of the 6th magnitude it responds to an intensity of illumination of about $1 \cdot 10^{-8}$ candle-metres, since a star of the 6th

* In the experimental determination of this number the heat-rays were absorbed by a layer of water.

magnitude has about the same brightness as a Hefner lamp at a distance of 11 km. In this case the eye receives about $1 \cdot 10^{-8}$ ergs per second.

The so-called normal candle (a paraffine candle of 2 cm. diameter and 50 mm. flame) has an emission about 1.24 times that of the Hefner lamp.

4. The Radiation from the Sun.—According to Langley about one third of the energy of the sun's radiation is absorbed by the earth's atmosphere when the sun is in the zenith. According to his measurements, if there were no atmospheric absorption, the sun would radiate upon 1 cm.^{2} of the earth's surface at perpendicular incidence about 3 gr. cal. (more accurately 2.84) per minute (*solar constant*). Angström obtained a value of 4 gr. cal. a minute. Hence, making allowance for the absorption of the earth's atmosphere, the flow of energy to the earth's surface is, according to Langley, about 2 gr. cal. a minute = $1.3 \cdot 10^6$ erg/sec. Pouillet's value, which was given on page 454, is somewhat smaller. The energy of the visible light between the Fraunhofer lines A and H_2 amounts to about 35% of the total radiation, i.e. the so-called intensity of illumination B of the sun, without allowing for the absorption in the air, is, from Langley's measurements,

$$B = 6.9 \cdot 10^5 \frac{\text{erg}}{\text{sec}} = 46\,300 \text{ candle-metres.} \quad (11)$$

If the mean distance of the sun from the earth be taken as $149 \cdot 10^9$ m., the candle-power of the sun is found to be $1.02 \cdot 10^{27}$.

5. The Efficiency of a Source of Light.—The efficiency g of a source of light is defined as the ratio of the energy of the light radiated per second to the energy required to maintain the source for the same time.

Thus a Carcel lamp of 9.4 candle-power consumes 42 gm. of oil in an hour or $1.16 \cdot 10^{-2}$ gm. in a second. The heat of combustion of the oil is 9500 calories per gram, i.e.

$39.7 \cdot 10^{10}$ ergs. Now equation (8) gives the emission of the standard unit, hence the efficiency of the lamp is

$$g = \frac{9.4 \cdot 1.9 \cdot 10^{6}}{1.16 \cdot 10^{-2} \cdot 39.7 \cdot 10^{10}} = 0.4 \cdot 10^{-2} = 0.4\%.$$

Thus the efficiency is very small; only 0.4% of the energy contained in the oil is used for illumination.

The electric light is much more efficient. With the arc light 1 candle-power can be obtained with an expenditure of $\frac{1}{2}$ watt, i.e. $5 . 10^{6}$ erg/sec. Hence for the arc light

$$g = \frac{1.9 \cdot 10^{6}}{5 \cdot 10^{6}} = 0.38 = 38\%.$$

For the incandescent lamp g has about the value 5.5%.

These figures show that it is more economical to use the heat of combustion of oil to drive a motor which runs a dynamo which in turn feeds an arc light, than to use the oil directly for lighting purposes. A Diesel motor transforms about 70% of the energy of the oil into mechanical energy, and 90% of this can be transformed into electrical energy by the dynamo which feeds the arc light; hence the efficiency of the electric light, upon the basis of the energy of the oil used, may be increased to

$$g = 0.38 \cdot 0.7 \cdot 0.9 = 24\%.$$

In this calculation no account has been taken of the fact that the carbons in the lamp are also consumed. For an incandescent lamp of the ordinary construction, which requires about $3\frac{1}{2}$ watts per candle-power, g would be equal to 3.4% calculated upon the basis of the fuel consumption of the motor. For a Nernst incandescent lamp which requires 1 watt per candle-power,* g would be as high as 12%.

6. The Pressure of Radiation.—Consider the case of a plane wave from a constant source of light falling perpendicu-

* The consumption of energy varies from .5 to 1.8 watts according to conditions.

larly upon a *perfectly black body*. Such a body is defined as one which does not reflect at all, but completely absorbs all the rays which fall upon it, transmitting none.* According to the theory of reflection given above, an ideally black body must have the same index of refraction as the surrounding medium, otherwise reflection would take place.† Moreover it must have a coefficient of absorption, which must, however, be infinitely small, since otherwise reflection would take place (cf. chapter on Metallic Reflection), even though the index of refraction were equal to that of the surrounding medium. Hence, in order that no light may be transmitted by the body, it must be infinitely thick. An approximately black body can be realized by applying a coat of lamp-black or, since lamp-black is transparent to heat-rays, of platinum-black; likewise pitch or obsidian immersed in water, not in air, are nearly black bodies. The most perfect black body is a small hole in a hollow body. The rays which enter the hole are repeatedly reflected from the walls of the hollow body even though these walls are not perfectly black. Only a very small part of the rays are again reflected out of the hole. This part is smaller the smaller the hole in comparison with the surface of the body.

Let plane waves, travelling along the positive z-axis, fall upon a black body $\mathfrak{K}$. Conceive a cylindrical tube of light parallel to the z-axis and of cross-section q. Let energy flow in at $z = 0$. This energy will be completely absorbed, i.e. transformed into heat within the black body, which is supposed to extend from $z = a$ to $z = \infty$. The amount of energy thus absorbed in any time t is $E \cdot q \cdot V \cdot t$, if E denote the radiant energy which is present in unit of volume of the medium in front of $\mathfrak{K}$, and V the velocity of the waves in this medium.

* A perfectly black body can emit light if its temperature is sufficiently high. Hence it would be preferable to use the term "perfectly absorbing" instead of "perfectly black."

† This shows that the definition of a black body depends upon the nature of the medium surrounding it.

If now the black body be displaced a distance dz in the direction of light, then the energy which falls upon the body in the time t is less than before by the amount of the energy contained in the volume $q \cdot dz$ of the medium, i.e. by the amount $q \cdot dz \cdot E$. Hence the amount of heat developed in the body is smaller than before by the same amount (measured in mechanical units). But the same amount of radiant energy always enters the tube in the time t no matter whether the body $\mathfrak{K}$ is displaced or not. Further, the electromagnetic energy contained in the volume $q \cdot dz$, which has been vacated by the motion of the body, is always the same, i.e. it is independent of whether this volume is occupied by $\mathfrak{K}$ or not, since the index of refraction, and therefore also the dielectric constant, of $\mathfrak{K}$ is to be identical with that of the surrounding medium, so that reflection does not occur, i.e. the electric and magnetic forces at the surface of the body are the same in the medium and in $\mathfrak{K}$. If, therefore, because of the displacement of $\mathfrak{K}$ a distance dz, the same energy which has entered the light-tube in the time t develops less heat than when $\mathfrak{K}$ is not displaced, then, according to the principle of the conservation of energy, this loss in heat must be represented by work gained in the displacement of $\mathfrak{K}$. If this work be expressed in the form $p \cdot q \cdot dz$, *p represents the pressure which is exerted upon $\mathfrak{K}$ by the radiation.* Hence

$$p \cdot q \cdot dz = q \cdot dz \cdot \mathrm{E},$$

i.e.

$$p = \mathrm{E}. \quad . \quad . \quad . \quad . \quad . \quad . \quad . \quad . \quad (12)$$

Thus the pressure of radiation which is exerted by plane waves falling perpendicularly upon a perfectly black body is equal to the amount of energy of the incident waves contained in unit of volume of the medium outside.

Since, according to § 4, the energy flow from the sun to the earth amounts to $1.3 \cdot 10^6$ erg/sec. per cm.², this is the amount of energy contained in $3 \cdot 10^{10}$ cm.^{3} of air. Hence the energy in 1 cm.^{3} is

$$E = \frac{1.3 \cdot 10^6}{3 \cdot 10^{10}} = 4 \cdot 10^{-5}.$$

Therefore the sun's rays exert this pressure upon 1 cm.^{2} of a black body. This pressure is about equal to a weight of $4 \cdot 10^{-5}$ mgr., i.e. it is so small that it cannot be detected experimentally. Nevertheless this pressure is of great theoretical importance, as will be seen in the next chapter.

7. Prevost's Theory of Exchanges.—Every body, even when it is not self-luminous, radiates an amount of energy which is greater and contains more waves of short period the higher the temperature of the body. If, therefore, two bodies *A* and *B* of different temperatures are placed opposite to each other, then each of them both radiates and receives energy. The temperatures of the two bodies become equal because the hotter one radiates more energy than it receives and absorbs from the colder, while the colder receives more than it radiates. This conception of the nature of the process of radiation was first brought forward by Prevost.

If, therefore, the emission of a body *A* be determined by measuring the rise in temperature produced in a black body which absorbs the rays from *A*, the result obtained depends upon the difference in temperature between the bodies *A* and *B*. The rise in the temperature of *B* would be so much more correct a measure of the entire emission of *A* the smaller the amount of energy which *B* itself radiates. Hence if it is desired to measure the energy of the light-rays from a source *A*, whose ultra-red rays are all absorbed in a vessel of water, it can be done by measuring the absorption in a black body *B* which has the same temperature as the water. For at the temperature of a room the body *B* emits only long heat-rays, and it receives from the water as many of these rays as it emits. On the other hand the total emission of a source of light is somewhat greater than that which is represented by the absorption of the body B at the temperature of the room; nevertheless, in consideration of the greater temperature of the source (the sun or a flame), the result of the measurements is practically independent of the variations in temperature of the body B. But the temperature of B must be taken into account in measuring the emission of a body A which is not much hotter than B. This subject will be resumed in the next chapter.

CHAPTER II

APPLICATION OF THE SECOND LAW OF THERMODYNAMICS TO PURE TEMPERATURE RADIATION

1. **The Two Laws of Thermodynamics.**—The first law of thermodynamics is the principle of energy, according to which mechanical work is obtained only by the expenditure of a certain quantity of energy, i.e. by a change in the condition of the substance which feeds the machine. Although this law asserts that it is impossible to produce perpetual motion, i.e. to make a machine which accomplishes work without producing a permanent change in the substance which feeds it, yet a machine which works without expense is conceivable. For there is energy in abundance all about us; for example, consider the enormous quantity of it which is contained as heat in the water of the ocean. Now, so far as the first law is concerned, a machine is conceivable which continually does work at the expense of heat withdrawn from the water of the ocean. Now mankind has gained the conviction that such a machine, which would practically be a sort of perpetual motion, is impossible. In all motors which, like the steam-engine, transform heat into work, at least two reservoirs of heat of different temperatures must be at our disposal. These two reservoirs are the boiler and the condenser. This latter may be the air. In general heat can be transformed into work only when a certain quantity of heat Q is taken from the reservoir of higher temperature and a smaller quantity Q' is given up to a reservoir of lower temperature.

Hence the following law is asserted as the result of universal experience: *Mechanical work can never be continually obtained at the expense of heat if only one reservoir of heat of uniform temperature is at disposal.* This idea is the essence of the second law of thermodynamics.

Only one consequence of this law will be here made use of. *If a system of bodies, so protected that no exchanges of heat or work can take place between it and the external medium, has at any time the same temperature in all its parts, then,* **if no changes take place in the nature of any of the bodies,** *no difference of temperature can ever arise in the system.* For such a difference of temperature might be utilized for driving a machine. If, then, this difference of temperature should be equalized by the action of the machine, it would again arise of itself in such a system, and could again be used for the production of work, and so on indefinitely, although originally but one source of heat at uniform temperature was at disposal. This would be in contradiction to the second law. It is important to observe that heat originally of one temperature could be used in this way for the continual production of work *only if the nature of the bodies of the system remained unchanged.* For if this nature changes, if, for example, chemical changes take place, then the capacity of the system for work ultimately comes to an end. A condition of equality can indeed be disturbed by chemical changes; this is not, however, in contradiction with the second law. This phenomenon can be observed in any case of combustion.

2. Temperature Radiation and Luminescence. — Every body radiates energy, at least in the form of long heat-rays. Now two cases are to be distinguished: either (1) the nature of the body is not changed by this radiation, in which case it would radiate continuously in the same way if its temperature were kept constant by the addition of heat. This process will be called *pure temperature radiation.* Or (2) the body changes because of the radiation, in which case, in general, the same radiation would not continue indefinitely even though the temperature were kept constant. This process is called *luminescence.* The cause of the radiation does not in this case lie in the temperature of the system, but in some other source of energy. Thus the radiation due to chemical changes is called chemical luminescence. This occurs in the slow oxidation of phosphorus or of decaying wood. The phenomenon of phosphorescence which is shown by other substances, i.e. the radiation of light after exposure to a source of light, is called photo-luminescence. Here the source of energy of the radiation is the light to which the substance has been exposed, which has perhaps produced some change in the nature, for instance in the molecular structure, of the substance, which change then takes place in the opposite sense in producing phosphorescence. The radiation produced in Geissler tubes by high-tension currents is called electro-luminescence.

From what was said in § 1 it is clear that *the second law of thermodynamics leads to conclusions with respect to pure temperature radiations only.* From the conception of heat exchanges mentioned on page 491 it follows, for example, *that if an equilibrium of temperature has once been established in a closed system of bodies, it can never be disturbed by pure temperature radiation.* But a disturbance of the equilibrium might be produced by luminescence.

In what follows only pure temperature radiations will be considered.

3. The Emissive Power of a Perfect Reflector or of a Perfectly Transparent Body is Zero.—Consider a very large plate of any substance *K* enclosed between two plates of perfectly reflecting substance *SS*. A perfectly reflecting body is understood to be one which reflects all of the radiant energy which falls upon it. Let *K* and *SS* have originally the same temperature. *K* and *SS* may be thought of as parts of a large system of uniform temperature which is closed to outside influences. If now *K* emits energy, it also receives the same amount back again by reflection from *SS*. Assume that the absorption coefficient of *K* is not equal to zero. The *absorbing power a* of a body * or of a surface may be defined as the

* The absorbing power *a* must be carefully distinguished from the coefficient

ratio of the energy absorbed to the energy radiated upon it from without. If the incident energy is 1, then the quantity absorbed is a, the quantity reflected $1 - a$, provided the body transmits no energy. Hence this quantity $1 - a$ is the *reflecting power* $r = 1 - a$, provided the body is so thick that no energy is transmitted; otherwise $r < 1 - a$.

The energy reflected to K from the mirrors SS is now partially absorbed in K and partially reflected to SS. This reflected part is again entirely reflected back to K from SS, and so on. It is easy to see, since SS absorb no energy, that, when a stationary condition has been reached, the body K reabsorbs all the energy which it emits. If, therefore, the mirrors SS also emitted energy, the temperature of the body K would rise, since then K would absorb not only all the energy which it itself sends out, but also a part of the energy emitted by SS. On the other hand the temperature of the mirrors would fall, since they radiate but do not absorb. Now since, according to the second law, the original equilibrium of temperature cannot be disturbed by pure temperature radiation, the conclusion is reached that *the emissive power of a perfect mirror is zero.* If, therefore, a system of bodies is surrounded on all sides by a perfect mirror, it is completely protected from loss by radiation. In a similar way the conclusion may be reached that *the emissive power of a perfectly transparent body is zero.* For conceive an absorbing body K surrounded by a transparent body, the whole being enclosed within a perfectly reflecting shell, then the temperature of the transparent body must fall if it emits anything, since it does not absorb.

4. Kirchhoff's Law of Emission and Absorption.—Consider a small surface element ds of an absorbing body at the centre of a hollow spherical reflector of radius 1, which has at opposite ends of a diameter two small equal openings $d\Omega$ (cf. Fig. 108).

---

of absorption mentioned on page 360. A metal, e.g. silver, has a very large coefficient of absorption κ, but an extremely small absorbing power a, since silver reflects almost all of the incident light.

Let ds be small in comparison with $d\Omega$. The energy radiated by ds through each of the openings $d\Omega$ is, according to (3) on page 484,

$$dL = i ds \cos \phi \, d\Omega, \quad . \quad . \quad . \quad . \quad . \quad (1)$$

in which ϕ is the angle between the normal to ds and the line connecting the middle points of ds and $d\Omega$. i is called the intensity of radiation from ds in the direction ϕ. Whether or

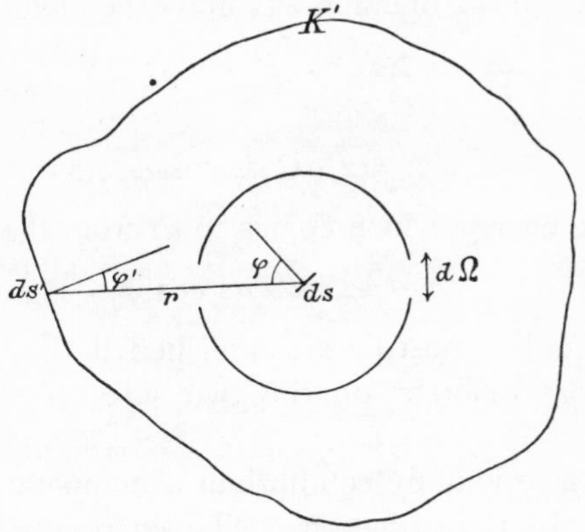

FIG. 108.

not i depends upon ϕ will not here be discussed. All the energy which ds emits in other directions it again receives and completely absorbs because of the repeated reflections which take place at the surface of the hollow sphere. Suppose now that the hollow sphere is surrounded by a black body K', whose outer surface is a perfect reflector. K' then radiates towards the interior only. Part (dE') of the energy emitted from K' passes through the two openings $d\Omega$ to the element ds and is there partially absorbed. The element ds subtends at a surface element ds' of the black body a solid angle

$$d\Omega' = \frac{ds}{r^2} \cos \phi \quad . \quad . \quad . \quad . \quad . \quad . \quad (2)$$

if r denotes the distance between ds and ds'. The energy radiated from ds' to ds is then

$$dL' = i' ds' \cos \phi' d\Omega', \quad . \quad . \quad . \quad . \quad . \quad (3)$$

in which i' represents the intensity of radiation of the black surface at an angle ϕ' from its normal. The sum of all the surface elements ds' which radiate upon ds is

$$\Sigma ds' = r^2 d\Omega : \cos\phi', \quad . \quad . \quad . \quad . \quad . \quad . \quad (4)$$

in which r and ϕ' are to be considered constant for the different elements of surface ds'. Hence the entire energy radiated from K' through the opening $d\Omega$ upon the element ds is

$$dE' = \Sigma dL' = i' \cdot r^2 \cdot d\Omega\, d\Omega', \quad . \quad . \quad . \quad . \quad . \quad (5)$$

or, from (2),

$$dE' = i' d\Omega\, ds \cos\phi. \quad . \quad . \quad . \quad . \quad . \quad . \quad (6)$$

Similarly the energy which comes to ds from the other side is

$$dE'' = i'' d\Omega\, ds \cos\phi, \quad . \quad . \quad . \quad . \quad . \quad . \quad (7)$$

in which i'' and i' must be distinguished if they depend upon ϕ' and if ϕ' is different on the two sides of the enveloping black body.

If there is originally equilibrium of temperature, it cannot be disturbed by the radiation. The energy $2dL$ sent out by ds through the two openings $d\Omega$ must be compensated by the energy $a(dE' + dE'')$ absorbed, a being the absorbing power of *ds corresponding to the direction* ϕ. According to the second law and (1), (6), and (7),

$$2i = a(i' + i''). \quad . \quad . \quad . \quad . \quad . \quad . \quad . \quad (8)$$

This equation must remain unchanged when the enveloping black body K' changes its form, thus varying ϕ'. Hence $i'(= i'')$ must be independent of ϕ', i.e. *the intensity of radiation i' of a black body is independent of the direction of radiation.* Hence, from (8),

$$i = a \cdot i'. \quad . \quad . \quad . \quad . \quad . \quad . \quad . \quad . \quad (9)$$

If different black bodies be taken for the surface ds', while the substance ds remains unchanged, then, according to (9), i' must always remain constant, i.e. *the intensity of radiation of a black body does not depend upon its particular nature, but is* *always the same function p of the temperature.** Hence (9) may be stated as follows:

The ratio between the emission and the absorption of any body at a given angle of inclination depends upon the temperature only: this ratio is equal to the emission of a black body at the same temperature. These laws are due to Kirchhoff.† They hold not only for the total intensity of emission, *but also for the emission of any particular wave length,* thus

$$i_\lambda = a_\lambda \cdot i_\lambda' \quad . \quad . \quad . \quad . \quad . \quad . \qquad (9')$$

For if a perfectly transparent dispersing prism be placed behind the opening $d\Omega$ outside of the hollow sphere (page 497), then one particular wave length from ds can be made to fall upon the black body, the others being returned by perfect mirrors through the prism and the opening $d\Omega$ to ds. Then within a small region of wave lengths which lie between λ and $\lambda + d\lambda$ the considerations which lead to equation (9) are applicable.

Equations (9) and (9′) must *hold for each particular azimuth of polarization of the rays.* For if a prism of a transparent doubly refracting crystal be introduced behind $d\Omega$, the waves of different directions of polarization will be separated into two groups. One of these groups may now be allowed to fall upon a black body while the other is returned by a suitably placed perfect mirror. The above considerations then lead to equation (9′), which therefore also holds for any particular direction of polarization.

5. Consequences of Kirchhoff's Law.—If a black body is slowly heated, there is a particular temperature, namely, about 525° C., at which it begins to send out light. This is at first light of long wave length (red); but as the temperature is raised smaller wave lengths appear in appreciable amount (at

* This function can depend upon the index of refraction of the space through which the rays pass. This will be considered later. Here this index will be assumed to be 1, i.e. the space will be considered a vacuum.

† Cf. Ostwald's Klassiker, No. 100.

about 1000° the body becomes yellow, at 1200° white).* Now equation (9′) asserts that no body can begin to emit light at a lower temperature than a black body, but that all bodies begin to emit red rays at the same temperature (about 525° C.) (*Draper's law*).† The intensity of the emitted light depends, to be sure, upon the absorbing power a_λ of the body at the temperature considered. Polished metals, for example, which keep their high reflecting power even at high temperatures emit much less light than lamp-black. Hence a streak of lamp-black upon a metallic surface appears, when heated to incandescence, as a bright streak upon a dark background. Likewise a transparent piece of glass emits very little light at high temperature because its absorbing power is small. If a hollow shell with a small hole in it be made of any metal, the hole acts like a nearly ideally black body (cf. page 489). It must therefore appear, at the temperature of incandescence, as a bright spot upon the surface of the hollow shell, since the metal has but a small absorbing power.

In the case of all smooth bodies which are not black, the reflecting power increases as the angle of incidence increases; hence the absorbing power must decrease. *Hence, according to (9′), the intensity of emission i of all bodies which are not black is greater when it takes place perpendicular to the surface than when it is oblique. Hence the cosine law of emission holds rigorously only for black surfaces.*

At oblique incidence, as was shown on page 282, the

* The first light which can be perceived is not red but a ghostly gray. This can be explained by the fact that the retina of the human eye consists of two organs sensitive to light, the rods and the cones. The former are more sensitive to light, but cannot distinguish color. The yellow spot, i.e. the most sensitive point of the retina, has many cones but few rods. Hence the first impression of light is received from the peripheral portions of the retina. But as soon as the eye is focussed upon the object, i.e. as soon as its image is formed upon the yellow spot, the impression of light vanishes, hence the ghostliness of the phenomenon.

† Every exception to Draper's law, as for example phosphorescence at low temperatures, signifies that the case is not one of pure temperature radiation, but that, even when the temperature remains constant, some energy transformation is the cause of the radiation.

reflecting power, and therefore the absorbing power, depends upon the condition of polarization of the incident rays. *Hence the radiation emitted obliquely by a body is partially polarized.* That component of the radiation which is polarized in a plane perpendicular to the plane defined by the normal and the ray must be the stronger, because it is the component which is less powerfully reflected, and is therefore more strongly absorbed. In the case of crystals like tourmaline, the absorbing power, even at perpendicular incidence, depends upon the condition of polarization of the incident light. If, therefore, tourmaline retains this property at the temperature of incandescence, a glowing tourmaline plate must emit partially polarized light even in a direction normal to its surface. Kirchhoff has experimentally confirmed this result. To be sure the dependence of the absorption upon the condition of polarization is much less at the temperature of incandescence than at ordinary temperatures.

Kirchhoff made an important application of his law to the explanation of such inversion of spectral lines as is shown in the Fraunhofer lines in the solar spectrum. For if the light from a white-hot body (an electric arc) be passed through a sodium flame of lower temperature than the arc, the spectrum shows a dark *D*-line upon a bright ground. For at high temperatures sodium vapor emits strongly only the *D*-line, consequently it must absorb strongly only light of this wave length. Hence the sodium flame absorbs from the arc light the light which has the same wave length as the *D*-line. To be sure it also emits the same wave length, but if the sodium flame is cooler than the arc, it emits that light in smaller intensity than the latter. Hence in the spectrum the intensity in the position of the *D*-line is less than the intensities in the positions corresponding to other wave lengths which are transmitted without absorption by the flame.* According to this view the Fraunhofer lines in the solar spectrum are explained by the

* For further discussion cf. Müller-Pouillet, Optik, p. 333 sq., 1897.

absorption of the light which comes from the hot centre of the sun by the cooler metallic vapors and gases upon its surface. Nevertheless this application of Kirchhoff's law assumes that the incandescence of gases and vapors is a case of pure temperature radiation. According to experiments by Pringsheim this does not seem to be in general the case. This point will be further discussed in § 1 of Chapter III.

6. The Dependence of the Intensity of Radiation upon the Index of Refraction of the Surrounding Medium.—Consider two infinitely large plates PP' of two black substances placed parallel to one another. Let the outer sides of PP' be coated with a layer of perfectly reflecting substance SS' so that radiation can pass neither out of nor into the space PP'. It has thus far been assumed that the space into which the radiation is to take place is absolutely empty, or filled with a homogeneous perfectly transparent medium like air. Instead of this the assumption will now be made that an empty space

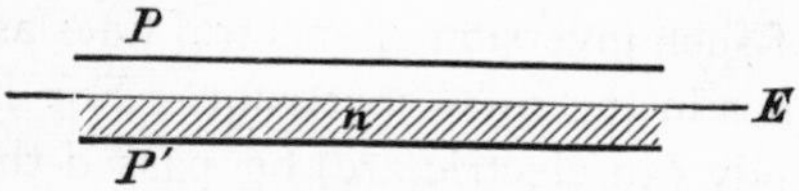

FIG. 109.

adjoins P, while a perfectly transparent substance, whose index is n for any given wave length λ, adjoins P'.* Let the boundary of this medium be the infinitely large plane E (cf. Fig. 109), which is assumed to be parallel to the plates PP' in order that P may be everywhere adjacent to a vacuum.

Now, according to page 83, an element of surface ds upon P radiates into a circular conical shell, whose generating lines make the angles ϕ and $\phi + d\phi$ with the normal to ds, the energy

$$dL = 2\pi i ds \sin \phi \cos \phi \, d\phi, \quad . \quad . \quad . \quad (10)$$

* In order that P and P' may both be ideally black bodies they must in this case consist of different substances, since a black body must have the same index as the surrounding medium

in which i denotes the intensity of radiation from P. Part of the emitted energy aL is reflected at the plane E and again absorbed by P. Let the amount thus reflected be

$$dL_r = 2\pi i ds \sin\phi \cos\phi \, d\phi \cdot r_\phi, \quad . \quad . \quad . \qquad (11)$$

in which r_ϕ denotes the factor of reflection at the boundary E for the angle of incidence ϕ. The rest of the energy, $dL - dL_r$, reaches P' and is there absorbed.

Similarly the energy emitted from an element of surface ds upon P' into a circular conical shell whose generating lines make the angles χ and $\chi + d\chi$ with the normal to P' is

$$dL' = 2\pi i' ds \sin\chi \cos\chi \, d\chi,$$

in which i' denotes the intensity of radiation from P'. There is returned to P' by reflection at E the energy

$$dL'_r = 2\pi i' ds \sin\chi \cos\chi \, d\chi \cdot r_\chi,$$

hence the energy

$$dL'' = dL' - dL'_r = 2\pi i' ds \sin\chi \cos\chi \, d\chi \, (1 - r_\chi) \qquad (12)$$

reaches P and is there absorbed.

Since the temperature of P is to remain constant, it follows that

$$\int dL = \int dL_r + \int dL'',$$

i.e. from (10), (11), and (12), since, according to page 498, the intensities of radiation i and i' are independent of the angles ϕ and χ,

$$i\int_0^{\pi/2} \sin\phi \cos\phi \, d\phi \, (1 - r_\phi) = i'\int_0^{\pi/2} \sin\chi \cos\chi \, d\chi \, (1 - r_\chi). \quad (13)$$

Now it is to be noted that for angles χ, for which $\sin\chi > \frac{1}{n}$, $r_\chi = 1$, since in this case total reflection takes place at E. Hence it is only necessary to extend the integral (13) from $\chi = 0$ to $\chi = \bar{\chi}$, where $\sin\bar{\chi} = \frac{1}{n}$. It will for the present be assumed that n is constant for all wave lengths. Hence in (13) ϕ and χ can be thought of as a corresponding pair of angles of incidence and refraction for which the following holds:

$$\sin \phi : \sin \chi = n, \quad . \quad . \quad . \quad . \quad . \quad . \quad (14)$$

and the integration can then be carried out with respect to ϕ between the limits $\phi = 0$ and $\phi = \frac{\pi}{2}$. Now, from (14),

$$\sin \chi \cos \chi \, d\chi = \frac{1}{n^2} \sin \phi \cos \phi \, d\phi. \quad . \quad . \quad (15)$$

Moreover, according to equations (24) on page 282, for every direction of polarization, and hence also for natural light, $r_\phi = r_\chi$. For, according to those equations (disregarding the sign, which need not here be considered), the reflected amplitude is always the same fraction of the incident amplitude; whence it is immaterial whether ϕ is the angle of incidence and χ that of refraction or the inverse, i.e. the reflection factors are the same whether the light is incident from above upon the plane E at the angle ϕ or from below at the angle χ, so long as $\sin \phi : \sin \chi = n$. Hence from (13) and (15), when $r_\chi = r_\phi$,

$$i \int_0^{\pi/2} \sin \phi \cos \phi (1 - r_\phi) d\phi = \frac{i'}{n^2} \int_0^{\pi/2} \sin \phi \cos \phi (1 - r_\phi) d\phi. \quad (16)$$

Since the integral which appears upon both sides of this equation is not equal to zero, there results at once

$$i' : i = n^2, \quad . \quad . \quad . \quad . \quad . \quad . \quad . \quad (17)$$

i.e. *the intensities of radiation of two black surfaces are proportional to the squares of the indices of refraction of the surrounding media.**

* This law is also due to Kirchhoff (Ostwald's Klassiker, No. 100, p. 33). It is often falsely ascribed to Clausius, who did not publish it till several years after Kirchhoff had done so. The law has been experimentally tested by Smolochowski de Smolan (C. R. 123, p. 230, 1896; Wied. Beibl. 20, p. 974, 1896) by comparing the radiations in air and bisulphide of carbon. His results agree fairly with the theory.

This proof relates only to the total radiation, and the index n was assumed constant for all wave lengths. *But equation (17) holds also for the partial radiations of any one particular period T.* Let the intensity of emission of P for rays whose periods lie between T and $T + dT$ be denoted by $i_T dT$. Similarly denote the intensity of radiation from P' for the same rays by $i'_T dT$. Then, from (16),

$$\sum dT\left(i_T - \frac{i'_T}{n^2}\right)\int_0^{\pi/2} \sin\phi \cos\phi(1 - r_\phi)d\phi = 0. \quad . \quad (18)$$

The Σ is to be extended over all periods between $T = 0$ and $T = \infty$.

Between the two bodies P and P' conceive a layer introduced which is transparent to a certain wave length λ, but reflects other wave lengths. Equation (18) must always hold, but the functional relation between r_ϕ and T varies according to the thickness and nature of the layer. Now in order that (18) may hold as r_ϕ is indefinitely varied, every term of the Σ in (18) must vanish, i.e. for every value of T*

$$i'_T : i_T = n^2. \quad . \quad . \quad . \quad . \quad . \quad . \quad (19)$$

According to Kirchhoff's law (9'), for a body which is not black the ratio of the emission i_λ to the absorption a_λ is proportional to the square of the index n of the surrounding medium. Since the change of a_λ with n may be calculated from the reflection equations, the relation between i_λ and n is at once obtained. *In any case, then, for bodies that are not black the intensity of radiation is not strictly proportional to* n^2.

7. The Sine Law in the Formation of Optical Images of Surface Elements.—If ds' is the optical image of a surface element ds formed by a bundle of rays which are symmetrical

* Equation (17) can also be obtained by the method employed on page 497 if the space outside of the hollow sphere be conceived as filled with a medium different from that inside the sphere, but the calculation is somewhat more complicated. Since in such an arrangement the waves of different periods T may be separated from one another by refraction and diffraction, (19) results at once from (17) in consideration of the conclusions upon page 497.

to the normal to ds and have an angle of aperture u in the object space, u' in the image space, then the whole energy emitted by ds within the bundle under consideration must fall upon ds'; and inversely, ds' must radiate upon ds, since the rays denote the path of the energy flow. Hence if ds and ds' be considered black surfaces of the same temperature, and coated on their remote sides by perfectly reflecting layers, then, since no difference in temperature between ds and ds' can arise because of the radiation, the energy dL sent out from ds must be equal to the energy dL' received by it from ds'. If now ds lies in a medium of refractive index n, ds' in one of index n', and if the intensity of emission of a black body in vacuo be denoted by i_0, then, by (17), the intensity of emission of ds is $i = n^2 i_0$, that of ds', $i' = n'^2 i_0$. Moreover, from (4) on page 485,

$$dL = \pi \cdot ds \cdot i \cdot \sin^2 u, \quad dL' = \pi \cdot ds' \cdot i' \cdot \sin^2 u'.$$

Hence, since $dL = dL'$,

$$\pi ds n^2 i_0 \sin^2 u = \pi ds' n'^2 i_0 \sin^2 u',$$

i.e.

$$ds n^2 \sin^2 u = ds' n'^2 \sin^2 u'. \quad . \quad . \quad . \quad . \quad . \quad (20)$$

This is the sine law deduced on page 61 [cf. equation (46)]. The deduction there given, which was purely geometrical, is more complicated than the above, which is based upon considerations of energy.

8. Absolute Temperature.—As was noted on page 493, work can be obtained, with the aid of a suitable machine, by withdrawing a certain quantity of heat W_1 from a reservoir 1, and giving up a smaller quantity of heat W_2 to another reservoir 2, which is colder than 1. In this process the machine may return to its original condition, i.e. it may perform a so-called *cycle*. The principle of the conservation of energy then demands that the work A performed be equal to the difference between the quantities of heat W_1 and W_2 when these are measured in mechanical units, i.e.

$$A = W_1 - W_2. \quad . \quad . \quad . \quad . \quad . \quad . \quad . \quad . \quad (21)$$

Now compare two machines M and M', both of which withdraw in one cycle the same quantity of heat W_1 from reservoir 1. They may, however, give up different quantities W_2 and W_2' to reservoir 2. In that case the two quantities of work A and A' done by them are different, for from (21)

$$A = W_1 - W_2, \quad A' = W_1 - W_2'.$$

Now consider M to be so constructed that it can be made to work backwards (i.e. let it describe *a reversible cycle*). In so doing it withdraws the quantity of heat W_2 from reservoir 2, gives up the quantity W_1 to reservoir 1, and performs the work $-A$. If now a cycle of machine M' be combined with such an inverted cycle of machine M, the resultant work accomplished is

$$A' - A = W_2 - W_2'. \quad . \quad . \quad . \quad . \quad (22)$$

This process can be conceived to be repeated indefinitely. Hence according as $W_2 - W_2'$ is positive or negative heat is continually withdrawn from or added to reservoir 2, while on the whole heat is neither withdrawn from nor added to reservoir 1. Hence in this case reservoir 1 may be assumed to be finite and may be considered to be part of the machine which describes the cycle; while reservoir 2 may be conceived to be the surrounding medium, for example the water of the ocean, whose heat capacity may be considered infinite. If now $A' - A$ were greater than 0, then a machine would have been constructed which, with the aid of *one* infinitely large heat-reservoir, would do an indefinite amount of work. But by the second law of thermodynamics this is impossible (cf. page 493), hence*

$$A' - A < 0, \quad \text{i.e.} \quad A > A', \quad . \quad . \quad . \quad (23)$$

i.e. of all machines which take up a quantity of heat W_1 at a definite temperature and give up heat to a colder reservoir, and

* That in general the equality $A = A'$ does not hold is evident from a consideration of many irreversible processes, e.g. friction. As soon as useless heat is developed $A' < A$.

which work in a cycle, *that machine does the largest amount of work which describes a reversible cycle.* In the case of such a machine, the work A which is obtained from a given quantity of heat W_1 taken from the higher reservoir is therefore perfectly definite, since it is a finite maximum, i.e. this work A is determined by the amount of heat W_1 taken up and by the temperatures of the two reservoirs, and is wholly independent of the nature of the machine. Evidently A must be proportional to W_1 so that the relation holds,

$$A = W_1 f(\tau_1, \tau_2), \quad . \quad . \quad . \quad . \quad . \quad (24)$$

in which f denotes a universal function of the reservoir temperatures measured according to any scale whatever. A combination of (21) and (24) gives

$$W_2 = W_1(1 - f[\tau_1, \tau_2]),$$

or

$$W_1 : W_2 = \phi(\tau_1, \tau_2), \quad . \quad . \quad . \quad . \quad (25)$$

in which ϕ is a universal function, i.e. one which is independent of the nature of the machine.

Now it can be easily shown that this function ϕ must be the product of two functions, one of which depends only upon τ_1, the other only upon τ_2. For if another machine be considered which works reversibly between the temperatures τ_2 and τ_3, taking up the amount of heat W_2 and giving up the amount W_3, then, by (25),

$$W_2 : W_3 = \phi(\tau_2, \tau_3). \quad . \quad . \quad . \quad . \quad (26)$$

If now a cycle of the first machine, working between τ_1 and τ_2, be combined with a cycle of the last machine, then the quantity of heat W_1 is taken up at the temperature τ_1, the quantity W_3 given up at the temperature τ_3; but the reservoir at temperature τ_2 can be left out of account, since just as much heat W_2 is given up to it by the first machine as is taken from it by the last machine. Hence

$$W_1 : W_3 = \phi(\tau_1, \tau_3). \quad . \quad . \quad . \quad . \quad . \quad (27)$$

A multiplication of (25) by (26) gives

$$W_1 : W_3 = \phi(\tau_1, \tau_2) \cdot \phi(\tau_2, \tau_3). \quad . \quad . \quad . \quad (28)$$

Hence from a comparison of (27) and (28)

$$\phi(\tau_1, \tau_3) = \phi(\tau_1, \tau_2) \cdot \phi(\tau_2, \tau_3). \quad . \quad . \quad . \quad (29)$$

In this equation τ_2 can be looked upon as an arbitrary parameter whose value need not be considered. Thus the right-hand side of (29) represents the product of two factors one of which depends only upon τ_1, the other only upon τ_2. These factors will be denoted by ϑ_1 and $\frac{1}{\vartheta_3}$,* so that, from (29),

$$\phi(\tau_1, \tau_3) = \vartheta_1 : \vartheta_3. \quad . \quad . \quad . \quad . \quad . \quad (30)$$

Hence in (25) $\phi(\tau_1, \tau_2) = \vartheta_1 : \vartheta_2$ and there results

$$\frac{W_1}{W_2} = \frac{\vartheta_1}{\vartheta_2} \quad . \quad . \quad . \quad . \quad . \quad . \quad . \quad (31)$$

ϑ_1 and ϑ_2 are functions of the two reservoir temperatures τ_1 and τ_2 measured upon any scale. ϑ_1 and ϑ_2 *are called the absolute temperatures of the reservoirs.* The ratio of the absolute temperatures of any two bodies means then the ratio of the quantities of heat which a machine working in a reversible cycle withdraws from one and gives up to the other of these bodies, provided the bodies may be considered infinitely large so that their temperatures are not appreciably changed by the gain or loss of the quantities of heat W_1 or W_2.

Since this merely defines the *ratio* of the absolute temperatures of the two bodies, it is necessary to establish a second relation in order to establish a scale of temperature. This relation is fixed by the following convention: The difference between the absolute temperatures of melting ice and boiling water, both at atmospheric pressure, shall be called 100. It

* It is desirable to write the second factor $\frac{1}{\vartheta_3}$ instead of ϑ_3, because then the parameter τ_2 disappears from (29), as can be seen at once by writing

$$\phi(\tau_1, \tau_2) = \vartheta_1 : \vartheta_2 \quad \text{and} \quad \phi(\tau_2, \tau_2) = \vartheta_2 : \vartheta_3.$$

is shown in the theory of heat that the absolute temperature is approximately obtained by adding the number 273 to the temperature measured in centigrade degrees upon an air-thermometer.

9. **Entropy.**—Consider again a machine M which, in performing a reversible cycle, takes up the quantity of heat W_1 at the absolute temperature ϑ_1 and gives up the quantity W_2 at the absolute temperature ϑ_2. If heat be always considered positive when it is given up by the machine, then, from (31),

$$\frac{W_1}{\vartheta_1} + \frac{W_2}{\vartheta_2} = 0. \quad . \quad . \quad . \quad . \quad . \quad . \quad (32)$$

If now there be combined with this a similar machine which works between the temperatures ϑ_3 and ϑ_4., then, from (32),

$$\frac{W_1}{\vartheta_1} + \frac{W_2}{\vartheta_2} + \frac{W_3}{\vartheta_3} + \frac{W_4}{\vartheta_4} = 0. \quad . \quad . \quad . \quad (33)$$

In general, then, it may be said that when a reversible cycle is described, in which the elements of heat δW are given up at the temperatures ϑ,

$$\sum \frac{\delta W}{\vartheta} = \int \frac{\delta W}{\vartheta} = 0, \quad . \quad . \quad . \quad . \quad (34)$$

in which the sum or the integral is to be extended over all the quantities of heat given up, and θ denotes the *corresponding* absolute temperatures of the machine or of the reservoirs.*

Hence if a reversible cycle between two different conditions 1 and 2 of a body be considered, it is possible to write, in accordance with (34),

$$\frac{\delta W}{\vartheta} = -dS, \quad . \quad . \quad . \quad . \quad . \quad (35)$$

$$\int_1^2 \frac{\delta W}{\vartheta} = S_1 - S_2, \quad . \quad . \quad . \quad . \quad (35')$$

* In a reversible process the temperature of the machine must be the same as that of the source, otherwise an exchange of heat could not take place equally well in either direction and the process would not be reversible.

in which S represents a single-valued function of the state of the body, and dS the differential of this function. For then, according to (34), the right-hand side of (35′) always reduces to zero as soon as a cycle is described in which the final condition 2 of the substance is identical with the initial condition 1. This function S of the state of a body or of a system of bodies is called *the entropy of the body*.

The energy E is also a function of the state of the body. It is defined by means of the assertion of the first law of thermodynamics, that in any change of the body the work δA done by the body plus the heat δW given up (measured in mechanical units) is equal to the decrease $-d\mathrm{E}$ in the energy of the body, i.e. it is defined by the equation

$$\delta A + \delta W = -d\mathrm{E}. \qquad (36)$$

10. General Equations of Thermodynamics.—It is convenient to choose as the independent variables which determine the state of a body or of a system, the absolute temperature ϑ and some other variables x, whose meaning will for the present be left undetermined. x will be so chosen that when the temperature changes in such a way that x remains constant, no work is done by the body. Then, since A does not change when x remains constant, the following relations hold:

$$\delta A = M\delta x, \quad \delta W = X\delta x + Y\delta\vartheta. \qquad (37)$$

δx and $\delta\vartheta$ represent any changes in x and ϑ; δA and δW, the corresponding work done and heat given up by the body. The process will be assumed to be reversible, i.e. the equations (37) will be assumed to hold for either sign of δx and $\delta\vartheta$. Now from (35), (36), (37),

$$-dS = \frac{X}{\vartheta}\delta x + \frac{Y}{\vartheta}\delta\vartheta, \quad -d\mathrm{E} = (M + X)\delta x + Y\delta\vartheta. \qquad (38)$$

Since in general

$$dS = \frac{\partial S}{\partial x}\delta x + \frac{\partial S}{\partial \vartheta}\delta\vartheta,$$

it follows that

$$\frac{X}{\vartheta} = -\frac{\partial S}{\partial x}, \quad \frac{Y}{\vartheta} = -\frac{\partial S}{\partial \vartheta}, \quad . \quad . \quad . \quad (39)$$

$$M + X = -\frac{\partial E}{\partial x}, \quad Y = -\frac{\partial E}{\partial \vartheta}. \quad . \quad . \quad (40)$$

Differentiation of these equations gives

$$\frac{\partial(X/\vartheta)}{\partial \vartheta} = \frac{\partial(Y/\vartheta)}{\partial x}, \quad \frac{\partial(M+X)}{\partial \vartheta} = \frac{\partial Y}{\partial x}, \quad . \quad . \quad (41)$$

or, after a few transformations,

$$\frac{X}{\vartheta} = -\frac{\partial M}{\partial \vartheta}, \quad \frac{\partial Y}{\partial x} = -\vartheta \frac{\partial^2 M}{\partial \vartheta^2}. \quad . \quad . \quad . \quad (42)$$

11. The Dependence of the Total Radiation of a Black Body upon its Absolute Temperature.—Consider a cylinder which has unit cross-section and length x and whose walls consist of a perfectly black body. Let these walls be covered with perfect mirrors so as to prevent radiation into the space outside. Within the cylinder temperature equilibrium will occur at a certain temperature ϑ. Let the energy in unit volume at this temperature be denoted by $\psi(\vartheta)$. This radiant energy exerts a definite pressure upon the walls of the cylinder. It was shown above on page 490 that the pressure exerted upon a black surface by plane waves at normal incidence is equal to the energy contained in unit volume. If the radiation is irregular, taking place in all directions, the normal pressure due to any set of waves may be resolved into three rectangular components in such a way that one is perpendicular to a surface s of the walls of the cylinder. Only this component exerts a pressure upon s. Consequently the whole pressure upon s is not $\psi(\vartheta)$, but $\frac{1}{3}\psi(\vartheta)$.*

If unit area of the cylinder wall moves a distance δx outward, the work done is

$$\delta A = \tfrac{1}{3}\psi(\vartheta)\delta x. \quad . \quad . \quad . \quad . \quad . \quad (43)$$

* For a deduction of this factor $\frac{1}{3}$ cf. Boltzmann, Wied. Ann. 22, p. 291, 1884; or Galitzine, Wied. Ann. 47, p. 488, 1892.

Again, if the temperature of the entire cylinder is increased an amount $\delta\vartheta$, while x remains constant, the energy increases by

$$dE = \frac{\partial\psi}{\partial\vartheta}\delta\vartheta\cdot x, \quad . \quad . \quad . \quad . \quad . \quad (44)$$

since the volume of the cylinder is x. No work is done so long as x remains constant.

A comparison of (43) with (37) and of (44) with (38) shows, since by (38), when $\delta x = 0$, $dE = -Y\delta\vartheta$, that

$$M = \tfrac{1}{3}\psi, \quad Y = -x\frac{\partial\psi}{\partial\vartheta}. \quad . \quad . \quad . \quad . \quad (45)$$

It follows, therefore, from (42), since ψ depends only upon ϑ and not upon x, that

$$\frac{\partial\psi}{\partial\vartheta} = \tfrac{1}{3}\vartheta\frac{\partial^2\psi}{\partial\vartheta^2} = \frac{1}{3}\frac{\partial}{\partial\vartheta}\left(\vartheta\frac{\partial\psi}{\partial\vartheta} - \psi\right).$$

Integration of this equation with respect to ϑ gives

$$3\psi = \vartheta\frac{\partial\psi}{\partial\vartheta} - \psi. \quad . \quad . \quad . \quad . \quad . \quad (46)$$

An integration constant need not be added, because when $\vartheta = 0$ the body contains no heat, and hence no radiation can take place. It follows from (46) that

$$4\psi = \vartheta\frac{\partial\psi}{\partial\vartheta}, \quad \text{i.e. } 4\frac{d\vartheta}{\vartheta} = \frac{d\psi}{\psi};$$

hence

$$4 lg\vartheta = lg\psi + \text{const.},$$

or

$$\psi(\vartheta) = C\cdot\vartheta^4. \quad . \quad . \quad . \quad . \quad . \quad . \quad (47)$$

If now a small hole be made in the wall of this cylinder, radiation will take place from the hole as though it were a black body (cf. page 489).* The intensity of radiation i must

* This also occurs if the walls of the cylinder are not perfectly black. Hence in this case also $\psi(\vartheta)$ is the energy in unit volume for the condition of temperature equilibrium, and $\tfrac{1}{3}\psi$ is the pressure on the wall of the cylinder. Only if the walls

evidently be proportional to the energy in unit volume $\psi(\vartheta)$ within the cylinder. Hence the intensity of radiation of a black body is

$$i = a \cdot \vartheta^4, \quad . \quad . \quad . \quad . \quad . \quad . \quad (48)$$

i.e. *the total intensity of emission of a black body is proportional to the fourth power of its absolute temperature.*

This law, which Stefan * first discovered experimentally and Boltzmann deduced theoretically in a way similar to the above, has been since frequently verified. The most accurate work is that of Lummer and Pringsheim,† who found by bolometric measurements that within the temperature interval 100° to 1300° C. the radiation from a hole in a hollow shell followed the Stefan-Boltzmann law. It is of course necessary in such experiments to take account of the temperature of the bolometer (cf. page 491). The radiation of the small surface ds upon the surface ds' at a distance r amounts, when ds and ds' are perpendicular to r [cf. the definition of intensity of radiation, equation (3), page 484], to

$$dL = i\frac{ds\, ds'}{r^2}.$$

The radiation from ds' upon ds amounts, if i' denote the intensity of radiation of ds', to

$$dL' = i'\frac{ds\, ds'}{r^2}.$$

---

of the cylinder had been perfect mirrors and no heat had been originally admitted into the cylinder would the energy in unit volume $\psi = 0$. The energy in unit volume would reach the normal value ψ if the walls of the cylinder contained a spot, no matter how small, which was not a perfect mirror. If this spot were perfectly black, the pressure upon it would be $\frac{1}{3}\psi$. But in that case every part of the cylinder wall, even that formed of perfect mirrors, would experience the same pressure, since otherwise the cylinder would be set into continuous motion of translation or rotation.

* Wien. Ber. 79, (2), p. 391, 1879. Stefan thought that this law held for all bodies. It is only strictly true for black bodies.

† Wied. Ann. 63, p. 395, 1897.

Hence if i and i' follow the law (48), the total quantity of heat transmitted in unit time to the element ds' is

$$dW = dL - dL' = a\frac{ds\,ds'}{r^2}(\vartheta^4 - \vartheta'^4), \quad . \quad . \quad (49)$$

in which ϑ' denotes the absolute temperature of ds'.

The constant a has recently been determined in absolute units by F. Kurlbaum * by means of bolometric measurements. In these experiments the temperature to which the bolometer was raised by the radiation was noted; the radiation was then cut off, and the bolometer raised to the same temperature by a measured electric current. The radiation is thus measured in absolute units by means of the heat developed by the current. Kurlbaum found that the difference between the emissive power of unit surface of a black body between 100° and 0°, i.e. the difference between the energy radiated in all directions, was

$$e_{100} - e_0 = 0.01763\,\frac{\text{gr-cal}}{\text{sec}}. \quad . \quad . \quad . \quad . \quad (50)$$

Now [cf. equation (5), page 485] $e = \pi i$, in which i is the intensity of radiation. Further, 1 gm-cal $= 419\cdot 10^5$ ergs, hence

$$i_{100} - i_0 = a(373^4 - 273^4) = \frac{0.01763\cdot 419\cdot 10^5}{\pi},$$

i.e. *the radiation constant a for a black body in absolute C. G. S. units is*

$$a = 1.71\cdot 10^{-5}\ {}^{\text{erg}}/_{\text{sec}}, \quad . \quad . \quad . \quad . \quad . \quad . \quad (51)$$

or, in gm-cal,

$$a = 0.408\cdot 10^{-12}\ {}^{\text{gr cal}}/_{\text{sec}}. \quad . \quad . \quad . \quad . \quad . \quad (51')$$

12. The Temperature of the Sun Calculated from its Total Emission.—If the sun were a perfectly absorbing (i.e. a black) body which emitted only pure heat radiations, its tem-

* Wied. Ann. 65, p. 746, 1898.

perature could be calculated from the solar constant (page 487) and the absolute value of the constant a.* If ϑ denote the absolute temperature of the sun, ϑ' that of the earth, then from (49) and (51′) the solar constant, i.e. the energy radiated in a minute upon unit area of the earth, would be

$$dW = 0.408 \cdot 10^{-12} \cdot 60 \frac{ds}{r^2} (\vartheta^4 - \vartheta'^4). \quad . \quad . \quad (52)$$

But

$$ds : r^2 = \pi \cdot (\tfrac{1}{2}\phi)^2,$$

in which ϕ is the apparent diameter of the sun $= 32'$.

If, therefore, Langley's value of the solar constant be taken, namely, $dW = 3$ gm-cal per minute,† the effective temperature of the sun would be $\vartheta = 6500°$, i.e. about 6200° C. If Angström's value be taken, namely, 4 gm-cal per minute, the effective temperature would be about 6700° C.

13. The Effect of Change in Temperature upon the Spectrum of a Black Body.—The spectrum of a black body is understood to mean the distribution of the energy among the different wave lengths. The investigation will be based upon the principle of the equilibrium of temperature within a closed hollow shell. The intensity of radiation of a black surface (conceived as a small hole in the wall of the hollow shell) is proportional to the energy in unit volume within the shell. Following the method used on page 513 (cf. note 1) it appears that the temperature at which temperature equilibrium is attained is not dependent upon the nature of the walls of the hollow shell, provided they do not consist entirely of perfect mirrors.

The effect of a change in temperature upon the spectrum

---

* The temperature obtained by this calculation is called the effective temperature of the sun. Its actual temperature would be higher if its absorbing power is less than 1, but lower if luminescence is involved in the sun's radiation.

† ϑ' can be neglected, since, according to (52), ϑ'^4 is small in comparison with ϑ^4..

of a black body can now be determined by means of the following device, due to W. Wien.*

Conceive a cylinder of unit cross-section within which two pistons S and S', provided with light-tight valves, move. Let K and K' be two black bodies of absolute temperatures ϑ

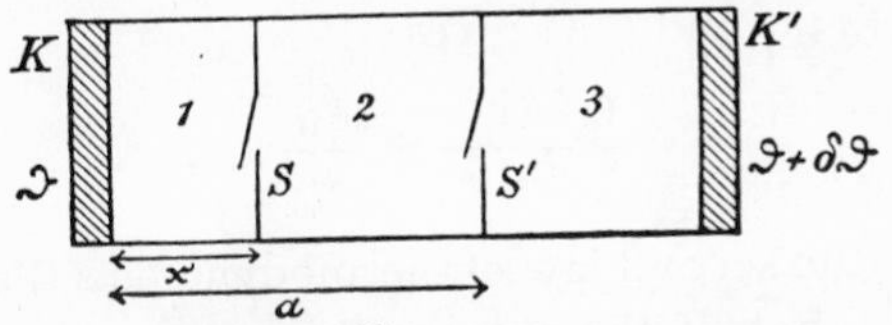

FIG. 110.

and $\vartheta + \delta\vartheta$. Let the side walls of the cylinder, as well as the pistons S and S', be perfect mirrors. Let also the outer sides of K and K' be coated with perfect mirrors. Let there be a vacuum within the cylinder.

At first let S' be closed and S be open. Then K radiates into the spaces 1 and 2, K' into 3. The energy in unit volume is greater in 3 than in 2 because the temperature of K' is greater by $\delta\vartheta$ than that of K. Let now S be closed and moved a distance δx toward S', until the energy in unit volume in 2 is equal to that in 3. The value which δx must have in order that this condition may be fulfilled will now be calculated. If $\mathfrak{E}$ denote the original amount of radiant energy contained in space 2, then the original energy in unit volume in this space is

$$\psi(\vartheta) = \frac{\mathfrak{E}}{a - x}.$$

Hence the change in energy in unit volume corresponding to a change in x is

$$d\psi = \frac{d\mathfrak{E}}{a - x} + \mathfrak{E}\frac{\delta x}{(a - x)^2}.$$

Now $d\mathfrak{E}$ is the work which is done in pushing forward the piston S. Hence, from page 512, $d\mathfrak{E} = \frac{1}{3}\psi\delta x$. Hence

$$d\psi = \frac{\delta x}{a - x}\left(\frac{1}{3}\psi + \frac{\mathfrak{E}}{a - x}\right) = \frac{\delta x}{a - x} \cdot \frac{4}{3}\psi. \quad . \quad (53)$$

* Berl. Ber. 1893. Sitzung vom 9 Febr.

But, by (47), ψ is proportional to the fourth power of ϑ, hence

$$d\psi = 4\psi \frac{\delta\vartheta}{\vartheta}. \quad . \quad . \quad . \quad . \quad . \quad . \quad (54)$$

If, therefore, the energy in unit volume in space 2 is to be made equal to that in 3 by a displacement δx of the piston S, a comparison of (53) and (54) gives

$$\frac{1}{3}\frac{\delta x}{a - x} = \frac{\delta\vartheta}{\vartheta}. \quad . \quad . \quad . \quad . \quad . \quad (55)$$

Now from the second law of thermodynamics the conclusion may be drawn that, if the total radiant energy in unit volume is the same in spaces 1 and 2, the distribution of energy throughout the spectrum must be the same within the two spaces.

For if this were not the case there would be waves of some wave lengths which would have a larger energy in unit volume in 3 than in 2. For it would be possible to place in front of the valve in S' a thin layer which would transmit waves of the length considered, but reflect all others. If then the valve were opened, a greater quantity of energy would pass from 3 to 2 than in the inverse direction, and the energy in unit volume would become greater in 2 than in 3. Suppose now that S' were closed, the layer removed, and the piston S' pushed back by the excess of pressure in 2 until the energy in unit volume in the two spaces became again equal. Let the work which would be thus gained be denoted by A. Then let S' be again opened and brought into its original position. This operation would require no work. Let then S' be closed and S pushed back to its original position. In this operation the same work would be gained which was expended in the displacement of S through the distance δx. If, finally, the valve in S were again opened, the original condition would be restored; no heat would have been taken from or added to the body K, but a certain amount would have been withdrawn from K' (by radiation through the layer before the valve in S'). Further, a certain amount of work A would have been gained.

But, according to the second law, work A can never be gained by means of a cycle in which heat is withdrawn from only one source K', the heat being thus entirely transformed into work. Hence the conclusion that *when the two spaces 2 and 3 contain the same quantity of energy in unit volume, the distribution of energy in their spectra is always the same.*

But, according to Doppler's principle, the distribution of energy in the spectrum is changed by the motion of the piston S. Let the total energy in unit volume in space 2 be given by

$$\psi(\vartheta) = \int_0^\infty \phi(\lambda, \vartheta) d\lambda, \quad . \quad . \quad . \quad . \quad (56)$$

then the expression $\phi(\lambda, \vartheta)d\lambda$ represents the energy in unit volume of the waves whose lengths lie between λ and $\lambda + d\lambda$. Consider the plane waves which are reflected back and forth at normal incidence between the pistons S and S' in the space 2. The wave length of these waves is changed by the motion of S. Consider first a ray which starts from a point P and has been reflected but once upon S. If the vibration at the point P due to the incident wave has the period T, then the vibration at P due to the wave reflected from S will have some other period T'. For if a disturbance starts out from P at the time $t = 0$, it returns to P after reflection upon S at a time $t' = 2b_1 : c$, in which c is the velocity of light in space 2 (in vacuo), and b_1 the distance of P from the mirror at the time t_1 when the disturbance from P reached S.

If at the time $t = 0$ the distance between P and S is b, then evidently $b = b_1 + s_1$, in which s_1 denotes the distance travelled by the mirror S in the time t_1. If S moves with a velocity v with respect to P, then $s_1 = vt_1$, and $b_1 = ct_1$; hence it follows from $b = (c + v)t_1$ that $t_1 = b : c + v$, or

$$b_1 = b\frac{c}{c + v}, \quad t' = 2\frac{b_1}{c} = \frac{2b}{c + v}.$$

After the interval T the distance between P and S has diminished to $b' = b - vT$. Hence a disturbance which starts from P at a time $t = T$ returns to P after reflection at a time $T + t''$, in which

$$t'' = \frac{2b'}{c + v} = \frac{2(b - vT)}{c + v}.$$

The reflected wave therefore produces at P a vibration which has a period T' such that

$$T' = T + t'' - t' = T - \frac{2vT}{c + v} = T\frac{c - v}{c + v}.$$

A wave reflected twice at S has at P a period T'' such that

$$T'' = T'\frac{c - v}{c + v} = T\left(\frac{c - v}{c + v}\right)^2.$$

A wave reflected n times has a period

$$T^{(n)} = T\left(\frac{c - v}{c - v}\right)^n. \quad . \quad . \quad . \quad . \quad . \qquad (57)$$

Now n will be considered to be the number of times that the rays which are travelling back and forth in the space 2 between S and S' are reflected from S while it is moving a distance δx. If the distance between S and S' had the constant value $a - x$, the time δt required for n reflections at S would be

$$\delta t = n\frac{2(a - x)}{c}. \quad . \quad . \quad . \quad . \quad . \qquad (58)$$

It will be assumed that the motion δx is so small with respect to $a - x$ that $a - x$ may be taken as a constant. In this time δt, S traverses a distance $\delta x = v \cdot \delta t$. Hence, from (58),

$$\delta x = vn\frac{2(a - x)}{c},$$

i.e.

$$n = \frac{\delta x}{2(a - x)} \cdot \frac{c}{v}. \quad . \quad . \quad . \quad . \quad . \qquad (59)$$

It will now be assumed that v is small in comparison with c. Then from (57), retaining only terms of the first order in $v : c$,

$$T^{(n)} = T\left(1 - 2n\frac{v}{c}\right);$$

i.e., in consideration of (59),

$$T^{(n)} = T\left(1 - \frac{\delta x}{a - x}\right).$$

The change in the period due to the motion of the piston S amounts then to

$$\delta T = T^{(n)} - T = -T\frac{\delta x}{a - x},$$

and also the change $\delta_1\lambda$ in the wave length λ due to the motion of S is

$$\delta_1\lambda = -\lambda\frac{\delta x}{a - x}. \quad . \quad . \quad . \quad . \quad . \quad (60)$$

When δx is positive $\delta_1\lambda$ is negative, i.e. the wave length is shortened.

Moreover, it must be remembered that only one third of that part of the energy which is represented by (56) and which corresponds to the wave length λ can be looked upon as due to waves which travel at right angles to S (cf. page 512). The waves which travel parallel to S undergo no change in wave length because of the motion of S. If, therefore, that part of the energy which is originally present in space 2 and which corresponds to waves whose lengths lie between λ and $\lambda + d\lambda$ is

$$dL = \phi(\lambda, \vartheta)d\lambda, \quad . \quad . \quad . \quad . \quad . \quad (61)$$

then, neglecting the increase of energy in unit volume due to the motion (cf. page 517), the energy dL' which, after the motion of the piston, corresponds to wave lengths between λ and $\lambda + d\lambda$, would consist of two thirds of dL and one third of $\phi(\lambda - \delta_1\lambda, \vartheta)d\lambda$, in which $\delta_1\lambda$ denotes the increase in wave length due to the motion of the piston as worked out in (60). Thus

$$dL' = [\tfrac{2}{3}\phi(\lambda, \vartheta) + \tfrac{1}{3}\phi(\lambda - \delta_1\lambda, \vartheta)]d\lambda.$$

Now, from Taylor's theorem,

$$\phi(\lambda - \delta_1\lambda, \vartheta) = \phi(\lambda, \vartheta) - \delta_1\lambda\frac{\partial\phi}{\partial\lambda}.$$

Hence

$$dL' = \phi(\lambda, \vartheta) - \frac{\delta_1\lambda}{3}\cdot\frac{\partial\phi}{\partial\lambda},$$

or again, from Taylor's theorem, by setting $\frac{1}{3}\delta_1\lambda = \delta\lambda$,

$$dL' = \phi(\lambda - \delta\lambda, \vartheta)d\lambda. \quad . \quad . \quad . \quad . \quad (62)$$

The energy which corresponds to the wave length λ at the temperature $\vartheta + \delta\vartheta$, i.e. after the motion of the piston, is the same as the energy corresponding to the wave length $\lambda - \delta\lambda$ at the temperature ϑ. But now, from (60) and (55),

$$\delta\lambda = \tfrac{1}{3}\delta_1\lambda = -\frac{\lambda}{3}\frac{\delta x}{a - x}, \quad \delta\vartheta = \frac{\vartheta}{3}\frac{\delta x}{a - x},$$

i.e. the relation holds

$$\frac{\delta\vartheta}{\vartheta} + \frac{\delta\lambda}{\lambda} = 0, \quad . \quad . \quad . \quad . \quad . \quad (63)$$

which can be written as $\delta(\vartheta\lambda) = 0$, i.e.

$$\vartheta\lambda = \text{const.} \quad . \quad . \quad . \quad . \quad . \quad . \quad (64)$$

Hence neglecting the increase in the energy in unit volume due to the motion of the piston, i.e. neglecting the increase in energy due to rise in temperature, *the same energy in unit* *'olume exists at a temperature* ϑ *in waves of length* λ *as exists* *the lower temperature* ϑ' *in waves of length* λ', *provided* - $\lambda'\vartheta'$.

t if the increase in the total energy in unit volume, proportional to ϑ^4, be taken into consideration, the ven may still be shown to hold if the distribution of vestigated in the expression $\psi : \vartheta^4$ instead of in ψ.

The above law then asserts *that for a black body one and the same curve expresses the functional relationship between* $\psi : \vartheta^4$ *and* $\lambda\vartheta$ *at any temperature.* Now, from (56),

$$\frac{\psi(\vartheta)}{\vartheta^4} = \int_0^\infty \frac{\phi(\lambda, \vartheta)}{\vartheta^5} d(\lambda\vartheta). \quad . \quad . \quad . \quad . \quad (65)$$

Hence $\phi(\lambda, \vartheta) : \vartheta^5$ must be a function of $\lambda\vartheta$, thus

$$\frac{\phi(\lambda, \vartheta)}{\vartheta^5} = f(\lambda\vartheta). \quad . \quad . \quad . \quad . \quad . \quad (66)$$

If, therefore, for any temperature ϑ the curve of the distribution of energy be plotted using $\lambda\vartheta$ as abscissæ and $\phi(\lambda, \vartheta) : \vartheta^5$ as ordinates, then this curve holds for all temperatures, and it is easy to construct from this curve the actual distribution of energy for other temperatures, when the λ's are taken as abscissæ and the ϕ's as ordinates. Hence the following theorem:

If at a temperature ϑ *the maximum radiation of a black body corresponds to the wave length* λ_m, *then at the temperature* ϑ' *it must correspond to a wave length* λ'_m *such that*

$$\lambda_m \cdot \vartheta = \lambda'_m \cdot \vartheta'. \quad . \quad . \quad . \quad . \quad . \quad . \quad . \quad (67)$$

Further, it follows from (66) and (67), if the function ϕ which corresponds to the wave length λ_m be denoted by ϕ_m, that

$$\phi_m : \phi'_m = \vartheta^5 : \vartheta'^5; \quad . \quad . \quad . \quad . \quad . \quad (68)$$

i.e. *if two black bodies have different temperatures, the intensity of radiation of those wave lengths which correspond to the maxima of the intensity curves for the two bodies are proportional to the fifth power of the absolute temperatures of the bodies.*

14. The Temperature of the Sun Determined from the Distribution of Energy in the Solar Spectrum.—Equation (67) has been frequently verified by experiment.* The mean

---

* Cf. Paschen and Wanner, Berl. Ber. 1899, Jan., Apr.; Lummer and Pringsheim, Verh. d. deutsch phys. Ges. 1899, p. 23. For low temperatures, cf. Langley, Ann. de chim. et de phys. (6) 9, p. 443, 1886. With the use of a bolom-

value of $\lambda_m\vartheta$ as determined from a number of experiments in good agreement is $\lambda_m\vartheta = 2887$, the unit of wave length being 0.001 mm. Since now, according to Langley, the maximum energy of the sun's radiation corresponds to the wave length $\lambda'_m = 0.0005$, it would follow that the temperature of the sun is

$$\vartheta' = 5774° = 5501° \text{ C.}$$

This result is of the same order of magnitude as that calculated on page 516. It is, however, questionable whether the sun is a perfectly absorbing (black) body which emits only pure temperature radiation. If chemical luminescence exists in the sun, its temperature may be wholly different.

15. The Distribution of the Energy in the Spectrum of a Black Body.—The preceding discussion relates to the change in the distribution of the energy in the spectrum of a black body with the temperature; but nothing has been said about the distribution of the energy for a given temperature. In order to determine the law of this distribution W. Wien proceeds as follows: *

If the radiating black body be assumed to be a gas, then, upon the assumption of the kinetic theory of gases, Maxwell's law of the distribution of velocity of the molecules would hold. According to this law the number of molecules whose velocities lie between v and $v + dv$ is proportional to the quantity

$$v^2 \cdot e^{-v^2/\beta^2} dv, \quad . \quad . \quad . \quad . \quad . \quad . \quad . \quad (69)$$

in which β is a constant which can be expressed in terms of the mean velocity $\bar{v}$ as follows:

$$\bar{v}^2 = \tfrac{3}{2}\beta^2. \quad . \quad . \quad . \quad . \quad . \quad . \quad . \quad (70)$$

...oled to $-20°$ C. he found that the maximum radiation of a blackened ...late at a temperature $-2°$ C. corresponded to $\lambda_m = 0.0122$ mm. From ...87 it would follow that at $-2°$ C. $\lambda'_m = 0.0107$. To be sure the copper ...ot an ideal black body and it was only its maximum relative to a ... $-20°$ that was measured. This relative maximum corresponds to ... the absolute maximum, as can be seen by drawing the intensity

... p. 662, 1896.

According to the kinetic theory the absolute temperature is proportional to the mean kinetic energy of the molecules, i.e.

$$\vartheta \sim \overline{v}^2 \sim \beta^2. \quad . \quad . \quad . \quad . \quad . \quad . \quad . \quad (71)$$

Now Wien makes the hypotheses:

1. That the length λ of the waves which every molecule emits depends only upon the velocity v of the molecule. Hence v must also be a function of λ.

2. The intensity of the radiations whose wave lengths lie between λ and $\lambda + d\lambda$ is proportional to the number of molecules which emit vibrations of this period, i.e. proportional to the expression (69). If this intensity of radiation be written in the form

$$\phi(\lambda, \vartheta)a\lambda,$$

then from (69), (70), and (71), since v is a function of λ,

$$\phi(\lambda, \vartheta) = F(\lambda)\cdot e^{-\frac{f(\lambda)}{\vartheta}}.^* \quad . \quad . \quad . \quad . \quad . \quad (72)$$

Since now, from (66), $\phi : \vartheta^5$ must be a function of the argument $\lambda\vartheta$, it follows that $F(\lambda) = c_1 : \lambda^5$ and $f(\lambda) = c_2 : \lambda$, so that the following law of radiation results:

$$\phi(\lambda, \vartheta) = \frac{c_1 \cdot e^{-c_2 : \lambda\vartheta}}{\lambda^5}, \quad . \quad . \quad . \quad . \quad . \quad . \quad (73)$$

and the total radiation is

$$i = c_1 \int_0^\infty \frac{e^{-c_2 : \lambda\vartheta}}{\lambda^5} d\lambda. \quad . \quad . \quad . \quad . \quad . \quad (74)$$

This law of radiation must hold for all black bodies whether they be gases or not, since, as was shown on page 498, the law of radiation of a black body does not depend upon the nature of the body.

This law has been frequently verified by experiment.†

---

* Planck deduces the same radiation law from electromagnetic theory (Berl. Ber. 1899; Ann. de Phys. 1, 1900).

† Cf. note on page 523. Recently certain deviations from Wien's law have been found (cf. Lummer and Pringsheim, Verh. deutsch. phys. Ges. 1, p. 23, 215, 1899; Beckmann, Diss. Tübingen, 1898; Rubens, Wied. Ann. 69, p. 582).

That wave length, λ_m, at which the intensity of radiation is a maximum is determined from the equation $\frac{\partial\phi}{\partial\lambda} = 0$. Now, from (73),

$$lg\phi = lgc_1 - \frac{c_2}{\lambda\vartheta} - 5lg\lambda,$$

hence

$$\frac{1}{\phi}\frac{\partial\phi}{\partial\lambda} = \frac{c^2}{\lambda^2\vartheta} - \frac{5}{\lambda}.$$

Hence the relation obtains,

$$\lambda_m \cdot \vartheta = c_2 : 5. \quad . \quad . \quad . \quad . \quad . \quad . \quad (75)$$

Since $\lambda_m\vartheta$ has the value 2887 (cf. page 524),

$$c_2 = 14\,435 \quad . \quad . \quad . \quad . \quad . \quad . \quad (76)$$

when the unit of wave length is 0.001 mm.* In cm.,

$$c_2 = 1.4435. \quad . \quad . \quad . \quad . \quad . \quad (76')$$

Writing $\frac{1}{\lambda} = y$, $\frac{c_2}{\vartheta} = c'$, (74) becomes

$$i = -c_1\int_\infty^0 y^3 \cdot e^{-c'y}dy.$$

But

$$\int y^3 \cdot e^{-c'y}dy = -\left(\frac{1}{c'}y^3 + \frac{3}{c'^2}y^2 + \frac{6}{c'^3}y + \frac{6}{c'^4}\right)e^{-c'y}.$$

Hence

$$\int_\infty^0 y^3 \cdot e^{-c'y}dy = -\frac{6}{c'^4},$$

and

$$i = \frac{6c_1}{c'^4} = \frac{6c_1}{c_2^4}\vartheta^4. \quad . \quad . \quad . \quad . \quad . \quad (77)$$

---

* According to Beckmann (Diss. Tübingen, 1898) and Rubens (Wied. Ann. 69, p. 576, 1899) the constant c_2, when calculated from the emission of waves of great length, is considerably larger. According to this Wien's law is not rigorously correct.

If this equation be compared with (48) on page 514, it appears that

$$a = 6c_1 : c_2^4, \quad . \quad . \quad . \quad . \quad . \quad . \quad . \quad (78)$$

in which a is the constant of the Boltzmann-Stefan law of radiation. Now from equation (51), page 515,

$$a = 1.71 \cdot 10^{-5} \, {}^{\text{erg}}/_{\text{sec.}}$$

Hence in consideration of (76′) the constant c_1 has the value in C.G.S. units

$$c_1 = \tfrac{1}{6} a c_2^4, \quad \text{i e.} \quad c_1 = 1.24 \cdot 10^{-5}. \quad . \quad . \quad (79)$$

The law of radiation (73), which is universal, furnishes a means of establishing * a truly absolute system of units of length, mass, time, and temperature—a system which is based upon universal properties of the ether and does not depend upon any particular properties of any body. Thus universal gravitation and the velocity of light represent two universal laws. The absolute system is then obtained from the assumption that the constant of gravitation, the velocity of light, and the two constants c_1 and c_2 in the law of radiation all have the value 1.

---

* Planck, Berl. Ber. 1899, p. 479.

CHAPTER III

INCANDESCENT VAPORS AND GASES

1. Distinction between Temperature Radiation and Luminescence.—The essential distinction between temperature radiation and luminescence has already been mentioned on page 494. What is now the criterion by which it is possible to decide whether a luminous body shines by virtue of luminescence or by pure temperature radiation?

In the case of luminescence Kirchhoff's law as to the proportionality between emission and absorption is not applicable; nevertheless even in this case the emission of sharp spectral lines is accompanied by selective absorption of these same lines, since both are closely connected with the existence of but slightly damped natural periods of the ions.

A criterion for the detection of luminescence can be obtained from measurements of the absolute value of the emissive power or of the intensity of radiation. For if the intensity of radiation of a body within any region of wave lengths is greater than that of a black body at the same temperature, and within the same region of wave lengths, then luminescence must be present. By means of this criterion E. Wiedemann,* F. Paschen,† and E. Pringsheim ‡ have shown that the yellow light which is radiated when common salt is burned in the flame of a Bunsen burner is due at least partially to chemical luminescence (according to Pringsheim the

* Wied. Ann. 37, p. 215, 1889.

† Wied. Ann. 51, p. 42, 1894.

‡ Wied. Ann. 45, p. 428, 1892; 49, p. 347, 1893.

reduction of the sodium from the salt). The latter concludes, after many experiments, that in general, in all methods which are used for the production of the spectra of gases, the incandescence is a result of electrical * or chemical † processes. Nevertheless at sufficiently high temperatures all gases and vapors must emit temperature radiations which correspond to Kirchhoff's law,‡ since otherwise the second law of thermodynamics would be violated. It is, to be sure, possible that the absorption, and hence also the temperature radiation, when chemical processes are excluded, is small, and gives possibly no sharp spectral lines because the absorbing power reaches an appreciable value only because of chemical processes. For example, it would be conceivable that the natural vibration of the ions, which occasion strong selective absorption, become possible only upon a change in the molecular structure of the molecule.

2. The Ion-hypothesis.—According to the electromagnetic theory, the vibrations of the ions produce electromagnetic waves of their own period, i.e. light-waves of a given color. The attempt will be made to find out whether this hypothesis can be carried to its conclusions without contradicting other results deduced from the kinetic theory of gases.

Consider a stationary condition, in which the vibrations of the ionic charges have a constant amplitude. Since this amplitude would necessarily diminish because of radiation and

---

* E. Wiedemann has shown that a low temperature exists in Geissler tubes (Wied. Ann. 6, p. 298, 1879).

† Pringsheim (Wied. Ann. 45, p. 440) obtained photographic effects from CS_2 flame at a temperature of 150° C. Pure temperature radiation could in this case have produced no photographic effect. According to E. St. John (Wied. Ann. 56, p. 433, 1895) the effectiveness of the Auer burner does not depend upon luminescence, but is due to the use in the flame of a substance of little mass, small conducting power, large surface, and large emissive power. But according to Rubens (Wied. Ann. 69, p. 588, 1899) the Auer burner is probably chemically active for long waves.

‡ According to Paschen (Wied. Ann. 50, p. 409, 1893) CO_2 and water vapor show pure temperature radiation. Their absorbing power for certain regions of wave lengths is also very great.

friction, it is necessary to suppose that it is kept constant by a continuous supply of energy. In the case of temperature radiation this supply of energy comes from the impacts of the molecules; in the case of luminescence, from chemical or electrical energy.

If the distance between two equal electric charges (measured in electrostatic units) of opposite sign (they may be at rest or in motion) undergoes a periodic change of amplitude l and period T, then, according to Hertz,* the electromagnetic energy emitted in a half-period is

$$L' = \frac{8\pi^4}{3\lambda^3} e^2 l^2, \quad . \quad . \quad . \quad . \quad . \quad . \quad (1)$$

in which λ denotes the wave length in vacuo.

Hence the amount of energy radiated in unit time from two oppositely charged ions is

$$L = \frac{16}{3} \pi^4 \frac{e^2 l^2}{\lambda^3 T} = \frac{16}{3} \pi^4 c \frac{e^2 l^2}{\lambda^4}. \quad . \quad . \quad . \quad (2)$$

Now, according to measurements of E. Wiedemann,† the energy emitted in a second, in the two D-lines, by 1 gm. of sodium is

$$L_1 = 3210 \text{ gr-cal} = 13.45 \cdot 10^{10} \text{ ergs}. \quad . \quad . \quad (3)$$

The atomic weight of sodium is 23. It is next necessary to calculate the absolute weight of an atom of sodium. According to Avogadro's law, in every gas or vapor, at a given temperature and pressure, there exists the same number of molecules in unit volume. This number, at a pressure of 1 atmosphere and at 0° C., is calculated from the kinetic theory ‡ as $N = 10^{20}$ in a cm.^{3}. According to Regnault 1 cm.^{3} of air at 0° C. and atmospheric pressure weighs 0.001293 gm.

---

* Wied. Ann. 36, p. 12, 1889. A different numerical factor is here given because T is defined differently.

† Wied. Ann. 37, p. 395, 1889.

‡ Cf. Richarz, Wied. Ann. 52, p. 395, 1894.

Hydrogen is 14.4 times lighter than air; hence the weight g of one molecule of hydrogen is given by

$$g \cdot 10^{20} = \frac{0.001293}{14.4};$$

$$g = 9 \cdot 10^{-25} \text{ gr.}$$

Since a molecule of hydrogen (H_2) consists of two atoms, the weight of an atom of hydrogen is $4.5 \cdot 10^{-25}$ gm. An atom of sodium is 23 times heavier; hence it weighs $1.03 \cdot 10^{-23}$ gm.

Sodium is a univalent atom. Each atom is connected with one ion whose charge will be denoted by e. If, therefore, two atoms with charges $\pm e$ are required to produce one vibrating system, then in one gram of sodium there are present $\frac{1}{2} : 1.03 \cdot 10^{-23} = 4.85 \cdot 10^{22}$ such systems. Hence, from (2) and (3),

$$\frac{16}{3} \pi^4 c \frac{e^2 l^2}{\lambda^4} \cdot 4.85 \cdot 10^{22} = 13.45 \cdot 10^{10}. \quad . \quad . \quad . \quad (4)$$

Now e is a universal constant, since it represents the electrical charge which is connected with a univalent atom (it is the charge corresponding to a valence 1); for since, according to Faraday's law of electrolysis, a given electrical current always decomposes the same number of valences in unit time, the charge corresponding to a valence 1 must be a universal constant which does not depend upon the special nature of the atom. Now an electric current of 1 ampere decomposes in one second 0.1160 cm.^{3} of hydrogen at 0° C. and atmospheric pressure. Now the quantity of electricity carried in a second through any cross-section of a conductor conveying 1 ampere of current is $\frac{1}{10}$ electromagnetic units or $3 \cdot 10^9$ electrostatic units. Half of this flows as positive electricity in one direction, half as negative in the other. Hence in 0.116 cm.^{3} of hydrogen at 0° C. and atmospheric pressure, the total positive charge is $1.5 \cdot 10^9$ electrostatic units, the negative charge being the same. In 1 cm.^{3} there would therefore be $1.29 \cdot 10^{10}$ units. Since, according to page 530, the number of molecules in a cm.^{3} is $N = 10^{20}$, and since each molecule contains a positive and a negative charge, the charge of a univalent ion (the element of electric quantity) is

$$e = 1.29 \cdot 10^{-10}.* \quad \ldots \ldots \quad (5)$$

The introduction of this value into (4) gives, since $c = 3 \cdot 10^{10}$ and $\lambda = 0.000589$, for the value of l,

$$l = 1.13 \cdot 10^{-11} \text{ cm.} \quad \ldots \ldots \quad (6)$$

The diameter of a molecule as calculated from the kinetic theory is about $d = 2 \cdot 10^{-8}$ cm.† Since from (6) l is seen to be considerably smaller than d, the relatively strong emission of sodium vapor appears to be due to an oscillation of the ions (the valence charge) within the molecule (sphere of action of the molecule).

On page 447 the ratio of the charge e to the mass m of a negative ion of sodium vapor was calculated as

$$e : m = c \cdot 1.6 \cdot 10^7.$$

Hence

$$m = 2.7 \cdot 10^{-28} \text{ gr.}, \quad \ldots \ldots \quad (7)$$

i.e. the mass of the ion is the 38000th part of the mass of an atom of sodium.

On page 383 the equation of motion of an ion vibrating under the influence of an electrical force X was written in the form ‡

$$m \frac{\partial^2 \xi}{\partial t^2} + re^2 \frac{\partial \xi}{\partial t} + \frac{4\pi e^2}{\vartheta} \xi = eX, \quad \ldots \quad (8)$$

ξ denoting the displacement of the ion from its position of rest. When r is small the natural period T' of the ion is given by

$$T'^2 = \frac{\pi m \vartheta}{e^2}. \quad \ldots \ldots \quad (9)$$

* J. J. Thomson (Phil. Mag. (5) 46, p. 29, 1898) has calculated from certain observations e as 6–$7 \cdot 10^{-10}$, which is in good agreement with the value above given.

† Cf. Richarz, Wied. Ann. 52, p. 395, 1894.

‡ Here ϑ no longer denotes absolute temperature.

Since for sodium vapor $T' = 2 \cdot 10^{-15}$, it follows from (5) and (7) that

$$\vartheta = 7.6 \cdot 10^{-23}. \quad . \quad . \quad . \quad . \quad . \quad . \quad (10)$$

Finally, in order to determine the constant r, it is possible to make use of the conclusion reached on page 387, namely, that the index of refraction n and the coefficient of absorption κ are determined from the equation

$$n^2(1 - i\kappa)^2 = 1 + \frac{\mathfrak{N}\vartheta}{1 + i\frac{a}{\tau} - \frac{b}{\tau^2}}, \quad . \quad . \quad . \quad (11)$$

in which $\mathfrak{N}$ denotes the number of ions in a cm.³, and in which also

$$\tau = T : 2\pi, \quad a = \frac{r\vartheta}{4\pi}, \quad b = \frac{m\vartheta}{4\pi e^2}. \quad . \quad . \quad . \quad (12)$$

Hence the value of r could be obtained from observations upon κ. Such measurements of κ for sodium vapor have not been made and would be very difficult to make, since the absorption in the neighborhood of a natural period would vary rapidly with the period T. But an estimation of the value of r may be obtained in another way: From the sharpness of the absorption lines of sodium vapor it is evident that $\frac{a}{\tau}$ must be very small. But when $\tau = T' : 2\pi$,

$$\frac{a}{\tau} = r \cdot e\sqrt{\frac{\vartheta}{4\pi m}} = r \cdot 1.9 \cdot 10^{-8}. \quad . \quad . \quad . \quad (13)$$

r must then in any case have an order of magnitude less than 10^4. There is also another way for obtaining an upper limit for r.

If the ions, after being set into vibration, are cut off from external influences, they execute damped vibrations of the form

$$\xi = l \cdot e^{-\gamma\frac{t}{T'}} \cdot e^{i2\pi\frac{t}{T'}}. \quad . \quad . \quad . \quad . \quad (14)$$

Hence, from (8), when r is small,

$$\gamma = \frac{re^2}{2m} T' = r \cdot 0.6 \cdot 10^{-7}, \quad . \quad . \quad . \quad . \quad (15)$$

in which T' is determined by (9). Now the damping factor must be very small, since interference has been observed with sodium light with a difference of path of 200 000λ. Also if $t = 200\,000 T'$, ξ cannot be very small. Hence 200 000γ must be less than 1, i.e.

$$r \leqq 10^2. \quad . \quad . \quad . \quad . \quad . \quad . \quad (16)$$

In what follows a lower limit for the value of r will be derived.

3. The Damping of Ionic Vibrations because of Radiation.—If at the time $t = 0$ a negatively charged ion $-e$ is at a distance l from a positively charged ion $+e$, and if in the course of the time T' this distance has changed by dl, then the change $d\mathfrak{E}$ in the electrostatic energy is

$$d\mathfrak{E} = \frac{e^2}{l^2} \cdot dl. \quad . \quad . \quad . \quad . \quad . \quad . \quad (17)$$

Now, from (14), in the course of the period of time T' the amplitude of the motion of the ion has changed by $dl = -\gamma l$, provided γ is small. Further, by (1) on page 530, the decrease in energy in the time T' is

$$d\mathfrak{E}' = -\frac{16}{3} \frac{\pi^4}{\lambda^3} e^2 l^2. \quad . \quad . \quad . \quad . \quad . \quad (18)$$

Now the decrease in energy $d\mathfrak{E}$ must at least be equal to the decrease $d\mathfrak{E}'$ which is due to radiation. Hence, from (17) and (18), there results, if dl is set equal to $-\gamma l$,

$$\frac{e^2}{l} \gamma \geqq \frac{16}{3} \cdot \frac{\pi^4}{\lambda^3} e^2 l^2, \quad \text{i.e. } \gamma \geqq \frac{16\pi^4}{3} \left(\frac{l}{\lambda}\right)^3. \quad . \quad . \quad (19)$$

Introducing the value of l from (6),

$$\gamma \geqq 10^{-16},$$

i.e., from (15),

$$r \geqq 1.6 \cdot 10^{-9},$$

It will be shown below that r must be considerably above the lower limit thus determined, and that, for the value of l used, the damping of the ionic vibrations, because of their own radiation, would be altogether negligible.

Even if l were assumed to be of the order of magnitude of the diameter of a molecule, i.e. if $l = 2 \cdot 10^{-8}$, then $\gamma = 2 \cdot 10^{-8}$, while it is probable that γ is considerably larger.

4. The Radiation of the Ions under the Influence of External Radiations.—Under the influence of an external force of period $T = 2\pi\tau$ and of amplitude A the ions take up a motion of the same period whose amplitude may be written [cf. (8) and the abbreviations (12)]

$$l = A \,.\, \frac{\vartheta}{4\pi e\sqrt{\left[1 - \left(\frac{b}{\tau}\right)^2\right]^2 + \frac{a^2}{\tau^2}}}. \quad . \quad . \quad (20)$$

The energy emitted in unit time by a layer of thickness dz and of area 1 is, according to (2) on page 530,

$$dL = \frac{1}{3}\pi^2 cN dz \frac{A^2\vartheta^2}{\lambda^4\left\{\left[1 - \left(\frac{b}{\tau}\right)^2\right]^2 + \frac{a^2}{\tau^2}\right\}}. \quad . \quad . \quad (21)$$

On the other hand the energy $\frac{c}{4\pi}A^2$ enters the layer in unit time (cf. page 454; the electric energy is equal to the magnetic), while the energy $\frac{c}{4\pi}A'^2$ passes out, provided A' represents the amplitude of the impressed electric force after it has passed through the layer dz. Hence

$$A' = A \cdot e^{-2\pi n\kappa\frac{dz}{\lambda}}.$$

The energy absorbed in unit time within the layer amounts then to

$$d\mathfrak{E} = \frac{c}{4\pi}(A^2 - A'^2) = \frac{c}{4\pi}A^2 . 4\pi n\kappa\frac{dz}{\lambda}. \quad . \quad . \quad . \quad (22)$$

But now, from (11) on page 533, in the neighborhood of a natural period

$$2n^2\kappa = \frac{\mathfrak{N}\vartheta^a/\tau}{\left(1 - \frac{b}{\tau^2}\right)^2 + \frac{a^2}{\tau^2}}. \quad . \quad . \quad . \quad . \quad (23)$$

In consideration of this equation the ratio of the emitted to the absorbed energy is

$$\frac{dL}{d\mathfrak{E}} = \frac{2\pi^2}{3}\frac{\vartheta\tau}{\lambda^3 a}n = \frac{4\pi^2}{3}.\frac{n}{c\lambda^2 r}. \quad . \quad . \quad . \quad . \quad (24)$$

This ratio is larger the smaller the value of r. For $n = 1$ and $\lambda = 5.9 \cdot 10^{-5}$ (24) gives

$$\frac{dL}{d\mathfrak{E}} = \frac{0.126}{r}.$$

Since in any case this ratio must be considerably less than 1, as otherwise a reversal of the sodium line (cf. page 501) would be impossible, then, in consideration of the inequality (16), the value of r must be about

$$r = 10 \text{ to } 100. \quad . \quad . \quad . \quad . \quad . \quad (25)$$

5. **Fluorescence.**—If r had the value 1 for sodium vapor, an appreciable radiation of light would of necessity take place under the influence of radiation from without. This effect has not as yet been observed, although no delicate experiments have been made to attempt to discover it. In the case of the fluorescent bodies an appreciable radiation is actually produced by exposure to light. The attempt might be made to explain this phenomenon by assuming a small value of r. The character of the absorption of a body can in this way be made very variable, since this absorption depends upon the quantity a, i.e. upon $r\vartheta$. Nevertheless any attempt to found a theory of fluorescence upon the equation of motion (8) of the ions can

be seen at once to be useless. For, according to that equation, when a stationary condition has been reached, the vibrations of the ions must have the same period as that of the incident force X. But this will not explain one of the chief characteristics of fluorescence, namely this, that fluorescent light is of a different color from that of the light most strongly absorbed.

Fluorescence is to be looked upon as a case of luminescence which is due to certain special (chemical) changes whose cause is to be found in the illumination to which the body is exposed. The mathematical equations thus far given would therefore need to be considerably extended.*

6. The Broadening of the Spectral Lines due to Motion in the Line of Sight.†—If the natural vibrations of the ions were altogether undamped, they would nevertheless give sharp spectral lines only when their centres of vibration remained at rest. But since this centre is within the molecule, and since, according to the kinetic theory, the molecule is moving hither and thither with great velocity, the vibration produced by the ions must, according to Doppler's principle, be of somewhat variable period, i.e. the spectral lines cannot be perfectly sharp.

If an ion which has the period T moves toward the observer with the velocity v, then, according to Doppler's principle, the light which comes to the observer has the period

$$T' = T\left(1 \pm \frac{v}{c}\right), \quad . \quad . \quad . \quad . \quad . \quad (26)$$

in which c is the velocity of light in the space between the ion and the observer. Since the index of refraction of gases differs

* No satisfactory theory has yet been brought forward. That of Lommel (Wied. Ann. 3, p. 113, 1878) has been compared with experiment by G. C. Schmidt (Wied. Ann. 58, p. 117, 1896) and has been found faulty.

† This question was first treated by Ebert (Wied. Ann. 36, p. 466, 1889). According to his calculations the difference of path over which interference can be obtained is smaller than it would be if the finite width of the lines depended upon Doppler's principle. But Rayleigh has removed this difficulty in a more complete discussion (Phil. Mag. (5) 27, p. 298, 1889).

but slightly from 1, $c = 3\cdot 10^{10}$ cm./sec.. If then the assumption were made that all the molecules had the same velocity v, the emitted wave lengths would all lie within the limits $\lambda\left(1 \pm \frac{c}{v}\right)$. The width $d\lambda$ of the spectral line would therefore be

$$d\lambda = \lambda\frac{2v}{c}. \quad . \quad . \quad . \quad . \quad . \quad . \quad (27)$$

Now, according to the kinetic theory,* the mean value of the square of the velocities is given by

$$\text{Mean} \quad (v^2) = \frac{248\cdot 10^6 . \vartheta}{M}, \quad . \quad . \quad . \quad . \quad (28)$$

in which M is the molecular weight of the gas, ϑ its absolute temperature. Hence, setting

$$v = \sqrt{\text{mean } (v^2)} = 15.8\cdot 10^2\sqrt{\frac{\vartheta}{M}}, \quad . \quad . \quad (29)$$

the velocity of a hydrogen molecule, for example ($M = 2$), at 50° C. ($\vartheta = 323$) would be $v = 2010\cdot 10^2$ cm./sec. = 2010 m./sec. Hence, from (27), the width of a spectral line would be $d\lambda = \lambda\cdot 1.34\cdot 10^{-5}$. According to (27) the lines in the red end of the spectrum should be broader than those in the blue. This corresponds to the facts.†

The width of a spectral line is connected with the greatest difference of path over which the light can be made to produce interference (cf. page 152). If a spectral line be decomposed into two parts and if these parts be brought together after having traversed paths which differ by d cm., then, according to equation (28) on page 153, these parts can produce interference fringes whose visibility V, for the case in which the intensity of the light is constant throughout the whole width of the line, is given by

$$V = \frac{\sin 4\pi da}{4\pi da}. \quad . \quad . \quad . \quad . \quad . \quad (30)$$

* L. Boltzmann, Gastheorie, I, p. 14.

† Winkelmann, Handb. der Physik, Optik, p. 424.

In this, according to equations (22) and (20) on page 151, the quantity a is connected with the width $d\lambda = \lambda_1 - \lambda_2$ of the spectral line in the following way:

$$2a = \frac{1}{\lambda_2} - \frac{1}{\lambda_1} = \frac{d\lambda}{\lambda^2}. \quad . \quad . \quad . \quad . \quad (31)$$

The visibility V of the fringes is defined by equation (26) on page 152. According to Rayleigh the interference fringes are still visible when the ratio $J_{\text{min.}} : J_{\text{max.}}$ of the intensities at the positions of greatest darkness and of greatest brightness is 0.95. In this case V would have the value 0.025. If this value be substituted in (30), then from (27) and (31) it appears that the maximum difference in path d at which interference could still be observed would be

$$0.025 = \frac{\sin (4\pi\, {}^d/_\lambda \cdot {}^v/_c)}{4\pi\, {}^d/_\lambda \cdot {}^v/_c} = \frac{\sin \pi x}{\pi x}, \quad . \quad . \quad (32)$$

in which, for brevity, $4\frac{d}{\lambda}\frac{v}{c}$ is replaced by x. Since the right-hand side of (32) is small, the smallest root of x is to be looked for in the neighborhood of 1. Setting $x = 1 - \epsilon$, (32) gives

$$0.025 = \frac{\pi\epsilon}{\pi(1 - \epsilon)} = \epsilon.$$

Hence

$$\frac{d}{\lambda} = x \cdot \frac{c}{4v} = 0.975 \cdot \frac{c}{4v}. \quad . \quad . \quad . \quad . \quad (33)$$

If account be taken of the fact that all the molecules have not the same velocity v, the value of d would be still greater, namely, approximately*

$$\frac{d}{\lambda} = 0.345 \frac{c}{v}. \quad . \quad . \quad . \quad . \quad . \quad (34)$$

If, for example, the temperature of incandescent hydrogen

---

*Cf. Rayleigh, Phil. Mag. (5) 27, p. 298, 1889.

in a Geissler tube is 50° C., the ability of its spectral lines to produce interference would vanish for a difference of path

$$\frac{d}{\lambda} = 51\,600.$$

For sodium vapor in a Bunsen flame $M = 2 \cdot 23 = 46$. Assuming the temperature to be 1500° C., i.e. assuming $\vartheta = 1773$, then from (29) it would follow that $v = 98.2 \cdot 10^3$, and from (34) that $\frac{d}{\lambda} = 105\,000$.

The ability to produce interference would be higher if the temperature were lower. As a matter of fact interference can be obtained over a longer difference of path if the sodium light is produced by an electric discharge in a vacuum tube. In this electro-luminescence the temperature is much lower. Michelson estimates it in one case at 250° C. $\frac{d}{\lambda}$ would then have the value 205 000. At 50° C. $\frac{d}{\lambda} = 245\,000$. The ability of the mercury lines to produce interference over a large difference of path is accounted for by the large atomic weight of mercury (which, since the vapor is monatomic, is equal to the molecular weight). For, according to (29), a large value of M means a small velocity v of the molecule. For mercury $M = 200$; hence for $\vartheta = 273 + 50° = 323$, $v = 2 \cdot 10^4$, $\frac{d}{\lambda} = 517\,000$.

The numbers calculated in this way agree approximately with the results of Michelson's observations.* Michelson could also directly observe the effect of temperature upon the ability to produce interference when the source of light was a hydrogen tube placed in a copper box and heated to 300° C.† Heating decreased the clearness of the fringes. This phenomenon furnishes additional evidence that the temperature in a vacuum tube is low, i.e. that the light emitted is due to lumi-

---

* Phil. Mag. (5) 34, p. 280, 1892.

† Astrophys. Jour. 2, p. 251, 1896.

nescence rather than to a high temperature. For the heating of the gas to 300° C. could only appreciably change the molecular velocity if the temperature ϑ were low, for example 50° C.

Although the results of the above calculation are in good agreement with the facts, nevertheless the considerations here presented do not completely cover the case. For on the one hand, according to Ebert,* the distance between two lines in the solar spectrum which can still be resolved is smaller than is consistent with Doppler's principle, and on the other hand, according to Lord Rayleigh,† the consideration of the rotation of the molecules would reduce the ability of the transmitted light to produce interference much more than the consideration of their motion of translation. To be sure the revolution of the molecules would have to be considered only in the case of molecules composed of more than one atom; hence the explanation given above of the great capacity for interference shown by the mercury lines would still stand.

7. Other Causes of the Broadening of the Spectral Lines. —The motion of the molecules is not the only cause of the broadening of the spectral lines. The change in the period of the ionic vibrations due to damping must set a limit to the ability to produce interference, and hence must broaden the spectral line,‡ since the ability to produce interference and the homogeneity of the spectral lines are closely connected. When a stationary condition of emission has been reached the ions are continually set into vibration by the collisions of the molecules. The more frequently these collisions occur, the smaller becomes the ability of the emitted light to produce interference. Since now the number of collisions increases

* Sitz.-Ber. d. phys. med. Soc. Erlangen, 1889. Wied. Beibl. 1889, p. 944.

† Phil. Mag. (5) 34, p. 410, 1892.

‡ This is the view of Lommel (Wied. Ann. 3, p. 251, 1877) and Jaumann (Wied. Ann. 53, p. 832, 1894; 54, p. 178, 1895), who have also worked it out mathematically. Cf. also Garbasso, (Atti d. R. Acad. d. Scienc. di Torino, XXX, 1894).

with the density of a gas, an increase in density must also produce a broadening of the spectral lines. Experiment shows this to be the case.* On the other hand a simple increase in the thickness of the incandescent layer (within certain limits) produces no broadening but only brightening of the lines.† However, if the thickness of the incandescent layer is so great that it possesses appreciable absorption for all wave lengths, then, if the case is one of pure temperature radiation, it must, according to Kirchhoff's law, show broad emission lines, or, in the limit, emit a continuous spectrum.‡

* Cf. Winkelmann's Handbuch, Optik, p. 419 sq. The broadening of the spectral lines because of the mutual electrodynamic effect of the ionic vibrations has been theoretically investigated by Galitzine (Wied. Ann. 56, p. 78, 1895). Cf. also Mebius, Wied. Beibl. 1899, p. 419.

† Cf. Paschen, Wied. Ann. 51, p. 33, 1894.

‡ Cf. Wanner, Wied. Ann. 68, p. 143, 1899; who observed a remarkable reversal of the sodium line upon increasing the thickness of a sodium flame by repeated reflections.

INDEX

"Singularly successful in making the work intelligible to readers who lack a somewhat extended mathematical equipment . . . admirably reviewed and discussed, not only from the mathematical viewpoint, but also with reference to the physical implications," **NATURE** (London)

THE MATHEMATICAL ANALYSIS OF ELECTRICAL AND OPTICAL WAVE-MOTION

by Harry Bateman

Written by one of the greatest mathematical physicists of our time, this volume is an outstandingly clear, concise, and well-organized development of the mathematics of electricity and light. Developing theory by use of Maxwell's equations, the author analyzes fundamental equations and electromagnetic fields, and then proceeds to methods of solving the wave equations. Polar coordinates and cylindrical coordinates, transformation of coordinates of surfaces of rotation, and diffraction follow, together with homogeneous solutions of the wave equations. Extensive and adequate discussions of electromagnetic fields with moving singularities are given for you.

You will find authoritative examinations of such important topics as Bessel's equation, Fourier series, convergence, boundary conditions. The theories of Green and Kirchhoff are developed, as are homogeneous solutions to the wave equations by the methods of Green and Stieltjes. This classic text contains much material that is essential to the mathematical physicist. It has been estimated that about one third of its material is not readily available elsewhere in English. Treatment is thorough for most topics, although a number of relations have been presented without proof to enable the reader to gain a quick understanding of the subject and its potentialities.

Unabridged, corrected text. 60 examples at chapter endings. Over 150 bibliographic footnotes. 17 illustrations. vi + 159pp. 5⅜ x 8.

S14 Paperbound **$1.60**

APPLIED OPTICS AND OPTICAL DESIGN

by A. E. Conrady

This monumental work is an exhaustive coverage of both physical and mathematical aspects of applied optics and optical design. A systematic presentation, it limits itself mostly to "real optics," applying both algebraic and trigonometrical methods. Considerable attention is paid to the practical problem of maximum aberration permissable (for all ordinary aberrations) without affecting proper performance.

The author covers all ordinary ray tracing methods, together with the complete theory of primary aberrations, and as much of higher aberration as is needed for the design of telescopes, low-powered microscopes, and photographic equipment. Treatment is detailed and easily followed. For most of the book, no knowledge of mathematics above trigonometry is required, but in occasional sections acquaintance with calculu and analytical geometry is desirable.

Such special topics are exhaustively treated as: fundamental equations, chromatic aberration, extra-axial image points, optical sine theorem, general theory of perfect optical systems; accuracy in numerical calculation, longitudinal achromaticism, transverse chromatic aberration, angular magnification, aplanatic optical systems, bending of lenses, differential correction of approximate solutions, the powers of the human eye, eyepieces (Ramsden, achromaticized Ramsden, Huyghens, Kellner), fundamental laws of oblique pencils, physical aspects of optical images, optical tolerances, secondary spectrum, Seidel aberrations, spherical aberration (angular, longitudinal, transverse, zonal), thin lenses, and dozens of similar topics.

Summary of important points at the end of each chapter. Index. Tables of functions of N. Over 150 clear optical diagrams. x + 518pp. 6⅛ x 9¼.

S366 Paperbound **$2.95**

THE PRINCIPLES OF PHYSICAL OPTICS

by Ernst Mach

In this volume Ernst Mach has set down a detailed account of the experimental and theoretical evolution of our understanding of light phenomena and apparatus. He begins with a discussion of the philosophic and physiological speculation occasioned by early experiments on light and color perception and proceeds to a thorough examination of the history of diopterics and the roles of such men as Huyghens, Galileo, Descartes, the Bernoullis, Kepler, and others.

Newton's theory of color and dispersion, his concept of the periodicity of light, the development of the theory of interference, and the perfection and elaboration of these ideas to the mid-nineteenth century are treated in detail and hundreds of experiments described in full. Polarization is covered from Bartholinus's paper on double refracting Iceland spar through work by Malus, Brewster, Biot, Arago, to the definitive work of Young and Fresnel. The final third of the book considers the mathematical representation of the properties of light, refinements in the theory of linear, circular, and elliptic polarization, and advanced diffraction experiments including the theory of the diffraction grating.

Physicists, engineers, designers of optical systems, students and teachers of science, historians of science, in fact everyone interested in the gradual development and perfection of scientific research will discover an enormous array of stimulating material in this classic exposition.

2 Appendices of original papers by Malus. 279 figures and 10 portraits. Separate name and subject indices. x + 324pp.

S178 Paperbound **$1.75**

"Thorough and yet not overdetailed. Unreservedly recommended," NATURE (London).

FOUNDATIONS OF PHYSICS

by Robert Bruce Lindsay and Henry Margenau

A bridge between semipopular works for the general reader and technical treatises written for specialists, this excellent work discusses the foundation ideas and background of modern physics. It is not a text on theoretical physics, but a discussion of the methods of physical description and construction of theory. It is especially valuable for the physicist with a background in elementary calculus who is interested in the ideas which give meaning to the data and tools of modern physics.

Contents include a thorough discussion of theory, data, symbolism, mathematical equations; space and time in physics, foundations of mechanics; probability and its application; the statistical point of view; the physics and continua; the electron theory and special relativity; the general theory of relativity; quantum mechanics; the problem of causality.

Unabridged, newly corrected edition. New listing of recommended readings. 35 illustrations. xi + 537pp. 5 3/8 x 8.

Paperbound $2.45

Catalogue of Dover SCIENCE BOOKS

BOOKS THAT EXPLAIN SCIENCE

THE NATURE OF LIGHT AND COLOUR IN THE OPEN AIR, M. Minnaert. Why is falling snow sometimes black? What causes mirages, the fata morgana, multiple suns and moons in the sky; how are shadows formed? Prof. Minnaert of U. of Utrecht answers these and similar questions in optics, light, colour, for non-specialists. Particularly valuable to nature, science students, painters, photographers. "Can best be described in one word—fascinating!" Physics Today. Translated by H. M. Kremer-Priest, K. Jay. 202 illustrations, including 42 photos. xvi + 362pp. 5⅜ x 8. T196 Paperbound **$1.95**

THE RESTLESS UNIVERSE, Max Born. New enlarged version of this remarkably readable account by a Nobel laureate. Moving from sub-atomic particles to universe, the author explains in very simple terms the latest theories of wave mechanics. Partial contents: air and its relatives, electrons and ions, waves and particles, electronic structure of the atom, nuclear physics. Nearly 1000 illustrations, including 7 animated sequences. 325pp. 6 x 9. T412 Paperbound **$2.00**

MATTER AND LIGHT, THE NEW PHYSICS, L. de Broglie. Non-technical papers by a Nobel laureate explain electromagnetic theory, relativity, matter, light, radiation, wave mechanics, quantum physics, philosophy of science. Einstein, Planck, Bohr, others explained so easily that no mathematical training is needed for all but 2 of the 21 chapters. "Easy simplicity and lucidity . . . should make this source-book of modern physcis available to a wide public," Saturday Review. Unabridged. 300pp. 5⅜ x 8. T35 Paperbound **$1.60**

THE COMMON SENSE OF THE EXACT SCIENCES, W. K. Clifford. Introduction by James Newman, edited by Karl Pearson. For 70 years this has been a guide to classical scientific, mathematical thought. Explains with unusual clarity basic concepts such as extension of meaning of symbols, characteristics of surface boundaries, properties of plane figures, vectors, Cartesian method of determining position, etc. Long preface by Bertrand Russell. Bibliography of Clifford. Corrected. 130 diagrams redrawn. 249pp. 5⅜ x 8. T61 Paperbound **$1.60**

THE EVOLUTION OF SCIENTIFIC THOUGHT FROM NEWTON TO EINSTEIN, A. d'Abro. Einstein's special, general theories of relativity, with historical implications, analyzed in non-technical terms. Excellent accounts of contributions of Newton, Riemann, Weyl, Planck, Eddington, Maxwell, Lorentz, etc., are treated in terms of space, time, equations of electromagnetics, finiteness of universe, methodology of science. "Has become a standard work," Nature. 21 diagrams. 482pp. 5⅜ x 8. T2 Paperbound **$2.00**

BRIDGES AND THEIR BUILDERS, D. Steinman, S. R. Watson. Engineers, historians, everyone ever fascinated by great spans will find this an endless source of information and interest. Dr. Steinman, recent recipient of Louis Levy Medal, is one of the great bridge architects, engineers of all time. His analysis of great bridges of history is both authoritative and easily followed. Greek, Roman, medieval, oriental bridges; modern works such as Brooklyn Bridge, Golden Gate Bridge, etc. described in terms of history, constructional principles, artistry, function. Most comprehensive, accurate semi-popular history of bridges in print in English. New, greatly revised, enlarged edition. 23 photographs, 26 line drawings. xvii + 401pp. 5⅜ x 8. T431 Paperbound **$1.95**

CONCERNING THE NATURE OF THINGS, Sir William Bragg. Christmas lectures at Royal Society by Nobel laureate, dealing with atoms, gases, liquids, and various types of crystals. No scientific background is needed to understand this remarkably clear introduction to basic processes and aspects of modern science. "More interesting than any bestseller," London Morning Post. 32pp. of photos. 57 figures. xii + 232pp. 5⅜ x 8. T31 Paperbound **$1.35**

THE RISE OF THE NEW PHYSICS, A. d'Abro. Half million word exposition, formerly titled "The Decline of Mechanism," for readers not versed in higher mathematics. Only thorough explanation in everyday language of core of modern mathematical physical theory, treating both classical, modern views. Scientifically impeccable coverage of thought from Newtonian system through theories of Dirac, Heisenberg, Fermi's statistics. Combines history, exposition; broad but unified, detailed view, with constant comparison of classical, modern views. "A must for anyone doing serious study in the physical sciences," J. of the Franklin Inst. "Extraordinary faculty . . . to explain ideas and theories . . . in language of everyday life," Isis. Part I of set: philosophy of science, from practice of Newton, Maxwell, Poincaré, Einstein, etc. Modes of thought, experiment, causality, etc. Part II: 100 pp. on grammar, vocabulary of mathematics, discussions of functions, groups, series, Fourier series, etc. Remainder treats concrete, detailed coverage of both classical, quantum physics: analytic mechanics, Hamilton's principle, electromagnetic waves, thermodynamics, Brownian movement, special relativity, Bohr's atom, de Broglie's wave mechanics, Heisenberg's uncertainty, scores of other important topics. Covers discoveries, theories of d'Alembert, Born, Cantor, Debye, Euler, Foucault, Galois, Gauss, Hadamard, Kelvin, Kepler Laplace, Maxwell, Pauli, Rayleigh Volterra, Weyl, more than 180 others. 97 illustrations. ix + 982pp. 5⅜ x 8.
T3 Vol. 1 Paperbound **$2.00**
T4 Vol. II Paperbound **$2.00**

SPINNING TOPS AND GYROSCOPIC MOTION, John Perry. Well-known classic of science still unsurpassed for lucid, accurate, delightful exposition. How quasi-rigidity is induced in flexible, fluid bodies by rapid motions; why gyrostat falls, top rises; nature, effect of internal fluidity on rotating bodies; etc. Appendixes describe practical use of gyroscopes in ships, compasses, monorail transportation. 62 figures. 128pp. 5⅜ x 8.
T416 Paperbound **$1.00**

FOUNDATIONS OF PHYSICS, R. B. Lindsay, H. Margenau. Excellent bridge between semi-popular and technical writings. Discussion of methods of physical description, construction of theory; valuable to physicist with elementary calculus. Gives meaning to data, tools of modern physics. Contents: symbolism, mathematical equations; space and time; foundations of mechanics; probability; physics, continua; electron theory; relativity; quantum mechanics; causality; etc. "Thorough and yet not overdetailed. Unreservedly recommended," Nature. Unabridged corrected edition. 35 illustrations. xi + 537pp. 5⅜ x 8. S377 Paperbound **$2.45**

FADS AND FALLACIES IN THE NAME OF SCIENCE, Martin Gardner. Formerly entitled "In the Name of Science," the standard account of various cults, quack systems, delusions which have masqueraded as science: hollow earth fanatics, orgone sex energy, dianetics, Atlantis, Forteanism, flying saucers, medical fallacies like zone therapy, etc. New chapter on Bridey Murphy, psionics, other recent manifestations. A fair reasoned appraisal of eccentric theory which provides excellent innoculation. "Should be read by everyone, scientist or non-scientist alike," R. T. Birge, Prof. Emeritus of Physics, Univ. of Calif; Former Pres., Amer. Physical Soc. x + 365pp. 5⅜ x 8. T394 Paperbound **$1.50**

ON MATHEMATICS AND MATHEMATICIANS, R. E. Moritz. A 10 year labor of love by discerning, discriminating Prof. Moritz, this collection conveys the full sense of mathematics and personalities of great mathematicians. Anecdotes, aphorisms, reminiscences, philosophies, definitions, speculations, biographical insights, etc. by great mathematicians, writers: Descartes, Mill, Locke, Kant, Coleridge, Whitehead, etc. Glimpses into lives of great mathematicians, from Archimedes to Euler, Gauss, Weierstrass. To mathematicians, a superb browsing-book. To laymen, exciting revelation of fullness of mathematics. Extensive cross index. 410pp. 5⅜ x 8. T489 Paperbound **$1.95**

GUIDE TO THE LITERATURE OF MATHEMATICS AND PHYSICS, N. G. Parke III. Over 5000 entries under approximately 120 major subject headings, of selected most important books, monographs, periodicals, articles in English, plus important works in German, French, Italian, Spanish, Russian. (many recently available works). Covers every branch of physics, math, related engineering. Includes author, title, edition, publisher, place, date, number of volumes, number of pages. 40 page introduction on basic problems of research, study provides useful information on organization, use of libraries, psychology of learning, etc. Will save you hours of time. 2nd revised edition. Indices of authors, subjects. 464pp. 5⅜ x 8. S447 Paperbound **$2.49**

THE STRANGE STORY OF THE QUANTUM, An Account for the General Reader of the Growth of Ideas Underlying Our Present Atomic Knowledge, B. Hoffmann. Presents lucidly, expertly, with barest amount of mathematics, problems and theories which led to modern quantum physics. Begins with late 1800's when discrepancies were noticed; with illuminating analogies, examples, goes through concepts of Planck, Einstein, Pauli, Schroedinger, Dirac, Sommerfield, Feynman, etc. New postscript through 1958. "Of the books attempting an account of the history and contents of modern atomic physics which have come to my attention, this is the best," H. Margenau, Yale U., in Amer. J. of Physics. 2nd edition. 32 tables, illustrations. 275pp. 5⅜ x 8. T518 Paperbound **$1.45**

DOVER SCIENCE BOOKS

HISTORY OF SCIENCE AND PHILOSOPHY OF SCIENCE

THE VALUE OF SCIENCE, Henri Poincaré. Many of most mature ideas of "last scientific universalist" for both beginning, advanced workers. Nature of scientific truth, whether order is innate in universe or imposed by man, logical thought vs. intuition (relating to Weierstrass, Lie, Riemann, etc), time and space (relativity, psychological time, simultaneity), Hertz's concept of force, values within disciplines of Maxwell, Carnot, Mayer, Newton, Lorentz, etc. iii + 147pp. 5⅜ x 8. S469 Paperbound **$1.35**

PHILOSOPHY AND THE PHYSICISTS, L. S. Stebbing. Philosophical aspects of modern science examined in terms of lively critical attack on ideas of Jeans, Eddington. Tasks of science, causality, determinism, probability, relation of world physics to that of everyday experience, philosophical significance of Planck-Bohr concept of discontinuous energy levels, inferences to be drawn from Uncertainty Principle, implications of "becoming" involved in 2nd law of thermodynamics, other problems posed by discarding of Laplacean determinism. 285pp. 5⅜ x 8. T480 Paperbound **$1.65**

THE PRINCIPLES OF SCIENCE, A TREATISE ON LOGIC AND THE SCIENTIFIC METHOD, W. S. Jevons. Milestone in development of symbolic logic remains stimulating contribution to investigation of inferential validity in sciences. Treats inductive, deductive logic, theory of number, probability, limits of scientific method; significantly advances Boole's logic, contains detailed introduction to nature and methods of probability in physics, astronomy, everyday affairs, etc. In introduction, Ernest Nagel of Columbia U. says, "[Jevons] continues to be of interest as an attempt to articulate the logic of scientific inquiry." liii + 786pp. 5⅜ x 8. S446 Paperbound **$2.98**

A HISTORY OF ASTRONOMY FROM THALES TO KEPLER, J. L. E. Dreyer. Only work in English to give complete history of cosmological views from prehistoric times to Kepler. Partial contents: Near Eastern astronomical systems, Early Greeks, Homocentric spheres of Euxodus, Epicycles, Ptolemaic system, Medieval cosmology, Copernicus, Kepler, much more. "Especially useful to teachers and students of the history of science . . . unsurpassed in its field," Isis. Formerly "A History of Planetary Systems from Thales to Kepler." Revised foreword by W. H. Stahl. xvii + 430pp. 5⅜ x 8. S79 Paperbound **$1.98**

A CONCISE HISTORY OF MATHEMATICS, D. Struik. Lucid study of development of ideas, techniques, from Ancient Near East, Greece, Islamic science, Middle Ages, Renaissance, modern times. Important mathematicians described in detail. Treatment not anecdotal, but analytical development of ideas. Non-technical—no math training needed. "Rich in content, thoughtful in interpretations," U.S. Quarterly Booklist. 60 illustrations including Greek, Egyptian manuscripts, portraits of 31 mathematicians. 2nd edition. xix + 299pp. 5⅜ x 8. S255 Paperbound **$1.75**

THE PHILOSOPHICAL WRITINGS OF PEIRCE, edited by Justus Buchler. A carefully balanced expositon of Peirce's complete system, written by Peirce himself. It covers such matters as scientific method, pure chance vs. law, symbolic logic, theory of signs, pragmatism, experiment, and other topics. "Excellent selection . . . gives more than adequate evidence of the range and greatness," Personalist. Formerly entitled "The Philosophy of Peirce." xvi + 368pp. T217 Paperbound **$1.95**

SCIENCE AND METHOD, Henri Poincaré. Procedure of scientific discovery, methodology, experiment, idea-germination—processes by which discoveries come into being. Most significant and interesting aspects of development, application of ideas. Chapters cover selection of facts, chance, mathematical reasoning, mathematics and logic; Whitehead, Russell, Cantor, the new mechanics, etc. 288pp. 5⅜ x 8. S222 Paperbound **$1.35**

SCIENCE AND HYPOTHESIS, Henri Poincaré. Creative psychology in science. How such concepts as number, magnitude, space, force, classical mechanics developed, how modern scientist uses them in his thought. Hypothesis in physics, theories of modern physics. Introduction by Sir James Larmor. "Few mathematicians have had the breadth of vision of Poincaré, and none is his superior in the gift of clear exposition," E. T. Bell. 272pp. 5⅜ x 8. S221 Paperbound **$1.35**

ESSAYS IN EXPERIMENTAL LOGIC, John Dewey. Stimulating series of essays by one of most influential minds in American philosophy presents some of his most mature thoughts on wide range of subjects. Partial contents: Relationship between inquiry and experience; dependence of knowledge upon thought; character logic; judgments of practice, data, and meanings; stimuli of thought, etc. viii + 444pp. 5⅜ x 8. T73 Paperbound **$1.95**

WHAT IS SCIENCE, Norman Campbell. Excellent introduction explains scientific method, role of mathematics, types of scientific laws. Contents: 2 aspects of science, science and nature, laws of chance, discovery of laws, explanation of laws, measurement and numerical laws, applications of science. 192pp. 5⅜ x 8. S43 Paperbound **$1.25**

FROM EUCLID TO EDDINGTON: A STUDY OF THE CONCEPTIONS OF THE EXTERNAL WORLD, Sir Edmund Whittaker. Foremost British scientist traces development of theories of natural philosophy from western rediscovery of Euclid to Eddington, Einstein, Dirac, etc. 5 major divisions: Space, Time and Movement; Concepts of Classical Physics; Concepts of Quantum Mechanics; Eddington Universe. Contrasts inadequacy of classical physics to understand physical world with present day attempts of relativity, non-Euclidean geometry, space curvature, etc. 212pp. 5⅜ x 8. T491 Paperbound **$1.35**

THE ANALYSIS OF MATTER, Bertrand Russell. How do our senses accord with the new physics? This volume covers such topics as logical analysis of physics, prerelativity physics, causality, scientific inference, physics and perception, special and general relativity, Weyl's theory, tensors, invariants and their physical interpretation, periodicity and qualitative series. "The most thorough treatment of the subject that has yet been published," The Nation. Introduction by L. E. Denonn. 422pp. 5⅜ x 8. T231 Paperbound **$1.95**

LANGUAGE, TRUTH, AND LOGIC, A. Ayer. A clear introduction to the Vienna and Cambridge schools of Logical Positivism. Specific tests to evaluate validity of ideas, etc. Contents: function of philosophy, elimination of metaphysics, nature of analysis, a priori, truth and probability, etc. 10th printing. "I should like to have written it myself," Bertrand Russell. 160pp. 5⅜ x 8. T10 Paperbound **$1.25**

THE PSYCHOLOGY OF INVENTION IN THE MATHEMATICAL FIELD, J. Hadamard. Where do ideas come from? What role does the unconscious play? Are ideas best developed by mathematical reasoning, word reasoning, visualization? What are the methods used by Einstein, Poincaré, Galton, Riemann? How can these techniques be applied by others? One of the world's leading mathematicians discusses these and other questions. xiii + 145pp. 5⅜ x 8. T107 Paperbound **$1.25**

GUIDE TO PHILOSOPHY, C. E. M. Joad. By one of the ablest expositors of all time, this is not simply a history or a typological survey, but an examination of central problems in terms of answers afforded by the greatest thinkers: Plato, Aristotle, Scholastics, Leibniz, Kant, Whitehead, Russell, and many others. Especially valuable to persons in the physical sciences; over 100 pages devoted to Jeans, Eddington, and others, the philosophy of modern physics, scientific materialism, pragmatism, etc. Classified bibliography. 592pp. 5⅜ x 8. T50 Paperbound **$2.00**

SUBSTANCE AND FUNCTION, and **EINSTEIN'S THEORY OF RELATIVITY, Ernst Cassirer.** Two books bound as one. Cassirer establishes a philosophy of the exact sciences that takes into consideration new developments in mathematics, shows historical connections. Partial contents: Aristotelian logic, Mill's analysis, Helmholtz and Kronecker, Russell and cardinal numbers, Euclidean vs. non-Euclidean geometry, Einstein's relativity. Bibliography. Index. xxi + 464pp. 5⅜ x 8. T50 Paperbound **$2.00**

FOUNDATIONS OF GEOMETRY, Bertrand Russell. Nobel laureate analyzes basic problems in the overlap area between mathematics and philosophy: the nature of geometrical knowledge, the nature of geometry, and the applications of geometry to space. Covers history of non-Euclidean geometry, philosophic interpretations of geometry, especially Kant, projective and metrical geometry. Most interesting as the solution offered in 1897 by a great mind to a problem still current. New introduction by Prof. Morris Kline, N.Y. University. "Admirably clear, precise, and elegantly reasoned analysis," International Math. News. xii + 201pp. 5⅜ x 8. S233 Paperbound **$1.60**

THE NATURE OF PHYSICAL THEORY, P. W. Bridgman. How modern physics looks to a highly unorthodox physicist—a Nobel laureate. Pointing out many absurdities of science, demonstrating inadequacies of various physical theories, weighs and analyzes contributions of Einstein, Bohr, Heisenberg, many others. A non-technical consideration of correlation of science and reality. xi + 138pp. 5⅜ x 8. S33 Paperbound **$1.25**

EXPERIMENT AND THEORY IN PHYSICS, Max Born. A Nobel laureate examines the nature and value of the counterclaims of experiment and theory in physics. Synthetic versus analytical scientific advances are analyzed in works of Einstein, Bohr, Heisenberg, Planck, Eddington, Milne, others, by a fellow scientist. 44pp. 5⅜ x 8. S308 Paperbound **60¢**

A SHORT HISTORY OF ANATOMY AND PHYSIOLOGY FROM THE GREEKS TO HARVEY, Charles Singer. Corrected edition of "The Evolution of Anatomy." Classic traces anatomy, physiology from prescientific times through Greek, Roman periods, dark ages, Renaissance, to beginning of modern concepts. Centers on individuals, movements, that definitely advanced anatomical knowledge. Plato, Diocles, Erasistratus, Galen, da Vinci, etc. Special section on Vesalius. 20 plates. 270 extremely interesting illustrations of ancient, Medieval, Renaissance, Oriental origin. xii + 209pp. 5⅜ x 8. T389 Paperbound **$1.75**

SPACE-TIME-MATTER, Hermann Weyl. "The standard treatise on the general theory of relativity," (Nature), by world renowned scientist. Deep, clear discussion of logical coherence of general theory, introducing all needed tools: Maxwell, analytical geometry, non-Euclidean geometry, tensor calculus, etc. Basis is classical space-time, before absorption of relativity. Contents: Euclidean space, mathematical form, metrical continuum, general theory, etc. 15 diagrams. xviii + 330pp. 5⅜ x 8. S267 Paperbound **$1.75**

MATTER AND MOTION, James Clerk Maxwell. Excellent exposition begins with simple particles, proceeds gradually to physical systems beyond complete analysis; motion, force, properties of centre of mass of material system; work, energy, gravitation, etc. Written with all Maxwell's original insights and clarity. Notes by E. Larmor. 17 diagrams. 178pp. 5⅜ x 8. S188 Paperbound **$1.25**

PRINCIPLES OF MECHANICS, Heinrich Hertz. Last work by the great 19th century physicist is not only a classic, but of great interest in the logic of science. Creating a new system of mechanics based upon space, time, and mass, it returns to axiomatic analysis, understanding of the formal or structural aspects of science, taking into account logic, observation, a priori elements. Of great historical importance to Poincaré, Carnap, Einstein, Milne. A 20 page introduction by R. S. Cohen, Wesleyan University, analyzes the implications of Hertz's thought and the logic of science. 13 page introduction by Helmholtz. xlii + 274pp. 5⅜ x 8. S316 Clothbound **$3.50**
S317 Paperbound **$1.75**

FROM MAGIC TO SCIENCE, Charles Singer. A great historian examines aspects of science from Roman Empire through Renaissance. Includes perhaps best discussion of early herbals, penetrating physiological interpretation of "The Visions of Hildegarde of Bingen." Also examines Arabian, Galenic influences; Pythagoras' sphere, Paracelsus; reawakening of science under Leonardo da Vinci, Vesalius; Lorica of Gildas the Briton; etc. Frequent quotations with translations from contemporary manuscripts. Unabridged, corrected edition. 158 unusual illustrations from Classical, Medieval sources. xxvii + 365pp. 5⅜ x 8. T390 Paperbound **$2.00**

A HISTORY OF THE CALCULUS, AND ITS CONCEPTUAL DEVELOPMENT, Carl B. Boyer. Provides laymen, mathematicians a detailed history of the development of the calculus, from beginnings in antiquity to final elaboration as mathematical abstraction. Gives a sense of mathematics not as technique, but as habit of mind, in progression of ideas of Zeno, Plato, Pythagoras, Eudoxus, Arabic and Scholastic mathematicians, Newton, Leibniz, Taylor, Descartes, Euler, Lagrange, Cantor, Weierstrass, and others. This first comprehensive, critical history of the calculus was originally entitled "The Concepts of the Calculus." Foreword by R. Courant. 22 figures. 25 page bibliography. v + 364pp. 5⅜ x 8. S509 Paperbound **$2.00**

A DIDEROT PICTORIAL ENCYCLOPEDIA OF TRADES AND INDUSTRY, Manufacturing and the Technical Arts in Plates Selected from "L'Encyclopédie ou Dictionnaire Raisonné des Sciences, des Arts, et des Métiers" of Denis Diderot. Edited with text by C. Gillispie. First modern selection of plates from high-point of 18th century French engraving. Storehouse of technological information to historian of arts and science. Over 2,000 illustrations on 485 full page plates, most of them original size, show trades, industries of fascinating era in such great detail that modern reconstructions might be made of them. Plates teem with men, women, children performing thousands of operations; show sequence, general operations, closeups, details of machinery. Illustrates such important, interesting trades, industries as sowing, harvesting, beekeeping, tobacco processing, fishing, arts of war, mining, smelting, casting iron, extracting mercury, making gunpowder, cannons, bells, shoeing horses, tanning, papermaking, printing, dying, over 45 more categories. Professor Gillispie of Princeton supplies full commentary on all plates, identifies operations, tools, processes, etc. Material is presented in lively, lucid fashion. Of great interest to all studying history of science, technology. Heavy library cloth. 920pp. 9 x 12. T421 2 volume set **$18.50**

DE MAGNETE, William Gilbert. Classic work on magnetism, founded new science. Gilbert was first to use word "electricity," to recognize mass as distinct from weight, to discover effect of heat on magnetic bodies; invented an electroscope, differentiated between static electricity and magnetism, conceived of earth as magnet. This lively work, by first great experimental scientist, is not only a valuable historical landmark, but a delightfully easy to follow record of a searching, ingenious mind. Translated by P. F. Mottelay. 25 page biographical memoir. 90 figures. lix + 368pp. 5⅜ x 8. S470 Paperbound **$2.00**

HISTORY OF MATHEMATICS, D. E. Smith. Most comprehensive, non-technical history of math in English. Discusses lives and works of over a thousand major, minor figures, with footnotes giving technical information outside book's scheme, and indicating disputed matters. Vol. I: A chronological examination, from primitive concepts through Egypt, Babylonia, Greece, the Orient, Rome, the Middle Ages, The Renaissance, and to 1900. Vol. II: The development of ideas in specific fields and problems, up through elementary calculus. "Marks an epoch . . . will modify the entire teaching of the history of science," George Sarton. 2 volumes, total of 510 illustrations, 1355pp. 5⅜ x 8. Set boxed in attractive container. T429, 430 Paperbound, the set **$5.00**

THE PHILOSOPHY OF SPACE AND TIME, H. Reichenbach. An important landmark in development of empiricist conception of geometry, covering foundations of geometry, time theory, consequences of Einstein's relativity, including: relations between theory and observations; coordinate definitions; relations between topological and metrical properties of space; psychological problem of visual intuition of non-Euclidean structures; many more topics important to modern science and philosophy. Majority of ideas require only knowledge of intermediate math. "Still the best book in the field," Rudolf Carnap. Introduction by R. Carnap. 49 figures. xviii + 296pp. 5⅜ x 8. S443 Paperbound **$2.00**

FOUNDATIONS OF SCIENCE: THE PHILOSOPHY OF THEORY AND EXPERIMENT, N. Campbell. A critique of the most fundamental concepts of science, particularly physics. Examines why certain propositions are accepted without question, demarcates science from philosophy, etc. Part I analyzes presuppositions of scientific thought: existence of material world, nature of laws, probability, etc; part 2 covers nature of experiment and applications of mathematics: conditions for measurement, relations between numerical laws and theories, error, etc. An appendix covers problems arising from relativity, force, motion, space, time. A classic in its field. "A real grasp of what science is," Higher Educational Journal. xiii + 565pp. 5⅝ x 8⅜. S372 Paperbound **$2.95**

THE STUDY OF THE HISTORY OF MATHEMATICS and **THE STUDY OF THE HISTORY OF SCIENCE, G. Sarton.** Excellent introductions, orientation, for beginning or mature worker. Describes duty of mathematical historian, incessant efforts and genius of previous generations. Explains how today's discipline differs from previous methods. 200 item bibliography with critical evaluations, best available biographies of modern mathematicians, best treatises on historical methods is especially valuable. 10 illustrations. 2 volumes bound as one. 113pp. + 75pp. 5⅜ x 8. T240 Paperbound **$1.25**

MATHEMATICAL PUZZLES

MATHEMATICAL PUZZLES OF SAM LOYD, selected and edited by **Martin Gardner.** 117 choice puzzles by greatest American puzzle creator and innovator, from his famous "Cyclopedia of Puzzles." All unique style, historical flavor of originals. Based on arithmetic, algebra, probability, game theory, route tracing, topology, sliding block, operations research, geometrical dissection. Includes famous "14-15" puzzle which was national craze, "Horse of a Different Color" which sold millions of copies. 120 line drawings, diagrams. Solutions. xx + 167pp. 5⅜ x 8. T498 Paperbound **$1.00**

SYMBOLIC LOGIC and THE GAME OF LOGIC, Lewis Carroll. "Symbolic Logic" is not concerned with modern symbolic logic, but is instead a collection of over 380 problems posed with charm and imagination, using the syllogism, and a fascinating diagrammatic method of drawing conclusions. In "The Game of Logic" Carroll's whimsical imagination devises a logical game played with 2 diagrams and counters (included) to manipulate hundreds of tricky syllogisms. The final section, "Hit or Miss" is a lagniappe of 101 additional puzzles in the delightful Carroll manner. Until this reprint edition, both of these books were rarities costing up to $15 each. Symbolic Logic: Index. xxxi + 199pp. The Game of Logic: 96pp. 2 vols. bound as one. 5⅜ x 8. T492 Paperbound **$1.50**

PILLOW PROBLEMS and A TANGLED TALE, Lewis Carroll. One of the rarest of all Carroll's works, "Pillow Problems" contains 72 original math puzzles, all typically ingenious. Particularly fascinating are Carroll's answers which remain exactly as he thought them out, reflecting his actual mental process. The problems in "A Tangled Tale" are in story form, originally appearing as a monthly magazine serial. Carroll not only gives the solutions, but uses answers sent in by readers to discuss wrong approaches and misleading paths, and grades them for insight. Both of these books were rarities until this edition, "Pillow Problems" costing up to $25, and "A Tangled Tale" $15. Pillow Problems: Preface and Introduction by Lewis Carroll. xx + 109pp. A Tangled Tale: 6 illustrations. 152pp. Two vols. bound as one. 5⅜ x 8. T493 Paperbound **$1.50**

NEW WORD PUZZLES, G. L. Kaufman. 100 brand new challenging puzzles on words, combinations, never before published. Most are new types invented by author, for beginners and experts both. Squares of letters follow chess moves to build words; symmetrical designs made of synonyms; rhymed crostics; double word squares; syllable puzzles where you fill in missing syllables instead of missing letter; many other types, all new. Solutions. "Excellent," Recreation. 100 puzzles. 196 figures. vi + 122pp. 5⅜ x 8. T344 Paperbound **$1.00**

MATHEMATICAL EXCURSIONS, H. A. Merrill. Fun, recreation, insights into elementary problem solving. Math expert guides you on by-paths not generally travelled in elementary math courses—divide by inspection, Russian peasant multiplication; memory systems for pi; odd, even magic squares; dyadic systems; square roots by geometry; Tchebichev's machine; dozens more. Solutions to more difficult ones. "Brain stirring stuff . . . a classic," Genie. 50 illustrations. 145pp. 5⅜ x 8. T350 Paperbound **$1.00**

THE BOOK OF MODERN PUZZLES, G. L. Kaufman. Over 150 puzzles, absolutely all new material based on same appeal as crosswords, deduction puzzles, but with different principles, techniques. 2-minute teasers, word labyrinths, design, pattern, logic, observation puzzles, puzzles testing ability to apply general knowledge to peculiar situations, many others. Solutions. 116 illustrations. 192pp. 5⅜ x 8. T143 Paperbound **$1.00**

MATHEMAGIC, MAGIC PUZZLES, AND GAMES WITH NUMBERS, R. V. Heath. Over 60 puzzles, stunts, on properties of numbers. Easy techniques for multiplying large numbers mentally, identifying unknown numbers, finding date of any day in any year. Includes The Lost Digit, 3 Acrobats, Psychic Bridge, magic squares, triangles, cubes, others not easily found elsewhere. Edited by J. S. Meyer. 76 illustrations. 128pp. 5⅜ x 8. T110 Paperbound **$1.00**

PUZZLE QUIZ AND STUNT FUN, J. Meyer. 238 high-priority puzzles, stunts, tricks—math puzzles like The Clever Carpenter, Atom Bomb, Please Help Alice; mysteries, deductions like The Bridge of Sighs, Secret Code; observation puzzlers like The American Flag, Playing Cards, Telephone Dial; over 200 others with magic squares, tongue twisters, puns, anagrams. Solutions. Revised, enlarged edition of "Fun-To-Do." Over 100 illustrations. 238 puzzles, stunts, tricks. 256pp. 5⅜ x 8. T337 Paperbound **$1.00**

101 PUZZLES IN THOUGHT AND LOGIC, C. R. Wylie, Jr. For readers who enjoy challenge, stimulation of logical puzzles without specialized math or scientific knowledge. Problems entirely new, range from relatively easy to brainteasers for hours of subtle entertainment. Detective puzzles, find the lying fisherman, how a blind man identifies color by logic, many more. Easy-to-understand introduction to logic of puzzle solving and general scientific method. 128pp. 5⅜ x 8. T367 Paperbound **$1.00**

CRYPTANALYSIS, H. F. Gaines. Standard elementary, intermediate text for serious students. Not just old material, but much not generally known, except to experts. Concealment, Transposition, Substitution ciphers; Vigenere, Kasiski, Playfair, multafid, dozens of other techniques. Formerly "Elementary Cryptanalysis." Appendix with sequence charts, letter frequencies in English, 5 other languages, English word frequencies. Bibliography. 167 codes. New to this edition: solutions to codes. vi + 230pp. 5⅜ x 8⅜. T97 Paperbound **$1.95**

CRYPTOGRAPY, L. D. Smith. Excellent elementary introduction to enciphering, deciphering secret writing. Explains transposition, substitution ciphers; codes; solutions; geometrical patterns, route transcription, columnar transposition, other methods. Mixed cipher systems; single, polyalphabetical substitutions; mechanical devices; Vigenere; etc. Enciphering Japanese; explanation of Baconian biliteral cipher; frequency tables. Over 150 problems. Bibliography. Index. 164pp. 5⅜ x 8. T247 Paperbound **$1.00**

MATHEMATICS, MAGIC AND MYSTERY, M. Gardner. Card tricks, metal mathematics, stage mind-reading, other "magic" explained as applications of probability, sets, number theory, etc. Creative examination of laws, applications. Scores of new tricks, insights. 115 sections on cards, dice, coins; vanishing tricks, many others. No sleight of hand—math guarantees success. "Could hardly get more entertainment . . . easy to follow," Mathematics Teacher. 115 illustrations. xii + 174pp. 5⅜ x 8. T335 Paperbound **$1.00**

AMUSEMENTS IN MATHEMATICS, H. E. Dudeney. Foremost British originator of math puzzles, always witty, intriguing, paradoxical in this classic. One of largest collections. More than 430 puzzles, problems, paradoxes. Mazes, games, problems on number manipulations, unicursal, other route problems, puzzles on measuring, weighing, packing, age, kinship, chessboards, joiners', crossing river, plane figure dissection, many others. Solutions. More than 450 illustrations. viii + 258pp. 5⅜ x 8. T473 Paperbound **$1.25**

THE CANTERBURY PUZZLES H. E. Dudeney. Chaucer's pilgrims set one another problems in story form. Also Adventures of the Puzzle Club, the Strange Escape of the King's Jester, the Monks of Riddlewell, the Squire's Christmas Puzzle Party, others. All puzzles are original, based on dissecting plane figures, arithmetic, algebra, elementary calculus, other branches of mathematics, and purely logical ingenuity. "The limit of ingenuity and intricacy," The Observer. Over 110 puzzles, full solutions. 150 illustrations. viii + 225 pp. 5⅜ x 8. T474 Paperbound **$1.25**

MATHEMATICAL PUZZLES FOR BEGINNERS AND ENTHUSIASTS, G. Mott-Smith. 188 puzzles to test mental agility. Inference, interpretation, algebra, dissection of plane figures, geometry, properties of numbers, decimation, permutations, probability, all are in these delightful problems. Includes the Odic Force, How to Draw an Ellipse, Spider's Cousin, more than 180 others. Detailed solutions. Appendix with square roots, triangular numbers, primes, etc. 135 illustrations. 2nd revised edition. 248pp. 5⅜ x 8. T198 Paperbound **$1.00**

MATHEMATICAL RECREATIONS, M. Kraitchik. Some 250 puzzles, problems, demonstrations of recreation mathematics on relatively advanced level. Unusual historical problems from Greek, Medieval, Arabic, Hindu sources; modern problems on "mathematics without numbers," geometry, topology, arithmetic, etc. Pastimes derived from figurative, Mersenne, Fermat numbers: fairy chess; latruncles: reversi; etc. Full solutions. Excellent insights into special fields of math. "Strongly recommended to all who are interested in the lighter side of mathematics," Mathematical Gaz. 181 illustrations. 330pp. 5⅜ x 8. T163 Paperbound **$1.75**

FICTION

FLATLAND, E. A. Abbott. A perennially popular science-fiction classic about life in a 2-dimensional world, and the impingement of higher dimensions. Political, satiric, humorous, moral overtones. This land where women are straight lines and the lowest and most dangerous classes are isosceles triangles with 3° vertices conveys brilliantly a feeling for many concepts of modern science. 7th edition. New introduction by Banesh Hoffmann. 128pp. 5⅜ x 8. T1 Paperbound **$1.00**

SEVEN SCIENCE FICTION NOVELS OF H. G. WELLS. Complete texts, unabridged, of seven of Wells' greatest novels: The War of the Worlds, The Invisible Man, The Island of Dr. Moreau, The Food of the Gods, First Men in the Moon, In the Days of the Comet, The Time Machine. Still considered by many experts to be the best science-fiction ever written, they will offer amusements and instruction to the scientific minded reader. "The great master," Sky and Telescope. 1051pp. 5⅜ x 8. T264 Clothbound **$3.95**

28 SCIENCE FICTION STORIES OF H. G. WELLS. Unabridged! This enormous omnibus contains 2 full length novels—Men Like Gods, Star Begotten—plus 26 short stories of space, time, invention, biology, etc. The Crystal Egg, The Country of the Blind, Empire of the Ants, The Man Who Could Work Miracles, Aepyornis Island, A Story of the Days to Come, and 20 others "A master . . . not surpassed by . . . writers of today," The English Journal. 915pp. 5⅜ x 8. T265 Clothbound **$3.95**

FIVE ADVENTURE NOVELS OF H. RIDER HAGGARD. All the mystery and adventure of darkest Africa captured accurately by a man who lived among Zulus for years, who knew African ethnology, folkways as did few of his contemporaries. They have been regarded as examples of the very best high adventure by such critics as Orwell, Andrew Lang, Kipling. Contents: She, King Solomon's Mines, Allan Quatermain, Allan's Wife, Maiwa's Revenge. "Could spin a yarn so full of suspense and color that you couldn't put the story down," Sat. Review. 821pp. 5⅜ x 8. T108 Clothbound **$3.95**

CHESS AND CHECKERS

LEARN CHESS FROM THE MASTERS, Fred Reinfeld. Easiest, most instructive way to improve your game—play 10 games against such masters as Marshall, Znosko-Borovsky, Bronstein, Najdorf, etc., with each move graded by easy system. Includes ratings for alternate moves possible. Games selected for interest, clarity, easily isolated principles. Covers Ruy Lopez, Dutch Defense, Vienna Game openings; subtle, intricate middle game variations; all-important end game. Full annotations. Formerly "Chess by Yourself." 91 diagrams. viii + 144pp. 5⅜ x 8. T362 Paperbound **$1.00**

REINFELD ON THE END GAME IN CHESS, Fred Reinfeld. Analyzes 62 end games by Alekhine, Flohr, Tarrasch, Morphy, Capablanca, Rubinstein, Lasker, Reshevsky, other masters. Only 1st rate book with extensive coverage of error—tell exactly what is wrong with each move you might have made. Centers around transitions from middle play to end play. King and pawn, minor pieces, queen endings; blockage, weak, passed pawns, etc. "Excellent . . . a boon," Chess Life. Formerly "Practical End Play." 62 figures. vi + 177pp. 5⅜ x 8. T417 Paperbound **$1.25**

HYPERMODERN CHESS as developed in the games of its greatest exponent, ARON NIMZOVICH, edited by Fred Reinfeld. An intensely original player, analyst, Nimzovich's approaches startled, often angered the chess world. This volume, designed for the average player, shows how his iconoclastic methods won him victories over Alekhine, Lasker, Marshall, Rubinstein, Spielmann, others, and infused new life into the game. Use his methods to startle opponents, invigorate play. "Annotations and introductions to each game . . . are excellent," Times (London). 180 diagrams. viii + 220pp. 5⅜ x 8. T448 Paperbound **$1.35**

THE ADVENTURE OF CHESS, Edward Lasker. Lively reader, by one of America's finest chess masters, including: history of chess, from ancient Indian 4-handed game of Chaturanga to great players of today; such delights and oddities as Maelzel's chess-playing automaton that beat Napoleon 3 times; etc. One of most valuable features is author's personal recollections of men he has played against—Nimzovich, Emanuel Lasker, Capablanca, Alekhine, etc. Discussion of chess-playing machines (newly revised). 5 page chess primer. 11 illustrations. 53 diagrams. 296pp. 5⅜ x 8. S510 Paperbound **$1.45**

THE ART OF CHESS, James Mason. Unabridged reprinting of latest revised edition of most famous general study ever written. Mason, early 20th century master, teaches beginning, intermediate player over 90 openings; middle game, end game, to see more moves ahead, to plan purposefully, attack, sacrifice, defend, exchange, govern general strategy. "Classic . . . one of the clearest and best developed studies," Publishers Weekly. Also included, a complete supplement by F. Reinfeld, "How Do You Play Chess?", invaluable to beginners for its lively question-and-answer method. 448 diagrams. 1947 Reinfeld-Bernstein text. Bibliography. xvi + 340pp. 5⅜ x 8. T463 Paperbound **$1.85**

MORPHY'S GAMES OF CHESS, edited by P. W. Sergeant. Put boldness into your game by flowing brilliant, forceful moves of the greatest chess player of all time. 300 of Morphy's best games, carefully annotated to reveal principles. 54 classics against masters like Anderssen, Harrwitz, Bird, Paulsen, and others. 52 games at odds; 54 blindfold games; plus over 100 others. Follow his interpretation of Dutch Defense, Evans Gambit, Giuoco Piano, Ruy Lopez, many more. Unabridged reissue of latest revised edition. New introduction by F. Reinfeld. Annotations, introduction by Sergeant. 235 diagrams. x + 352pp. 5⅜ x 8. T386 Paperbound **$1.75**

WIN AT CHECKERS, M. Hopper. (Formerly "Checkers.") Former World's Unrestricted Checker Champion discusses principles of game, expert's shots, traps, problems for beginner, standard openings, locating best move, end game, opening "blitzkrieg" moves to draw when behind, etc. Over 100 detailed questions, answers anticipate problems. Appendix. 75 problems with solutions, diagrams. 79 figures. xi + 107pp. 5⅜ x 8. T363 Paperbound **$1.00**

HOW TO FORCE CHECKMATE, Fred Reinfeld. If you have trouble finishing off your opponent, here is a collection of lightning strokes and combinations from actual tournament play. Starts with 1-move checkmates, works up to 3-move mates. Develops ability to look ahead, gain new insights into combinations, complex or deceptive positions; ways to estimate weaknesses, strengths of you and your opponent. "A good deal of amusement and instruction," Times, (London). 300 diagrams. Solutions to all positions. Formerly "Challenge to Chess Players." 111pp. 5⅜ x 8. T417 Paperbound **$1.25**

A TREASURY OF CHESS LORE, edited by Fred Reinfeld. Delightful collection of anecdotes, short stories, aphorisms by, about masters; poems, accounts of games, tournaments, photographs; hundreds of humorous, pithy, satirical, wise, historical episodes, comments, word portraits. Fascinating "must" for chess players; revealing and perhaps seductive to those who wonder what their friends see in game. 49 photographs (14 full page plates). 12 diagrams. xi + 306pp. 5⅜ x 8. T458 Paperbound **$1.75**

WIN AT CHESS, Fred Reinfeld. 300 practical chess situations, to sharpen your eye, test skill against masters. Start with simple examples, progress at own pace to complexities. This selected series of crucial moments in chess will stimulate imagination, develop stronger, more versatile game. Simple grading system enables you to judge progress. "Extensive use of diagrams is a great attraction," Chess. 300 diagrams. Notes, solutions to every situation. Formerly "Chess Quiz." vi + 120pp. 5⅜ x 8. T433 Paperbound **$1.00**

MATHEMATICS: ELEMENTARY TO INTERMEDIATE

HOW TO CALCULATE QUICKLY, H. Sticker. Tried and true method to help mathematics of everyday life. Awakens "number sense"—ability to see relationships between numbers as whole quantities. A serious course of over 9000 problems and their solutions through techniques not taught in schools: left-to-right multiplications, new fast division, etc. 10 minutes a day will double or triple calculation speed. Excellent for scientist at home in higher math, but dissatisfied with speed and accuracy in lower math. 256pp. 5 x 7¼. Paperbound **$1.00**

FAMOUS PROBLEMS OF ELEMENTARY GEOMETRY, Felix Klein. Expanded version of 1894 Easter lectures at Göttingen. 3 problems of classical geometry: squaring the circle, trisecting angle, doubling cube, considered with full modern implications: transcendental numbers, pi, etc. "A modern classic . . . no knowledge of higher mathematics is required," Scientia. Notes by R. Archibald. 16 figures. xi + 92pp. 5⅜ x 8. T298 Paperbound **$1.00**

HIGHER MATHEMATICS FOR STUDENTS OF CHEMISTRY AND PHYSICS, J. W. Mellor. Practical, not abstract, building problems out of familiar laboratory material. Covers differential calculus, coordinate, analytical geometry, functions, integral calculus, infinite series, numerical equations, differential equations, Fourier's theorem probability, theory of errors, calculus of variations, determinants. "If the reader is not familiar with this book, it will repay him to examine it," Chem. and Engineering News. 800 problems. 189 figures. xxi + 641pp. 5⅜ x 8. S193 Paperbound **$2.25**

TRIGONOMETRY REFRESHER FOR TECHNICAL MEN, A. A. Klaf. 913 detailed questions, answers cover most important aspects of plane, spherical trigonometry—particularly useful in clearing up difficulties in special areas. Part I: plane trig, angles, quadrants, functions, graphical representation, interpolation, equations, logs, solution of triangle, use of slide rule, etc. Next 188 pages discuss applications to navigation, surveying, elasticity, architecture, other special fields. Part 3: spherical trig, applications to terrestrial, astronomical problems. Methods of time-saving, simplification of principal angles, make book most useful. 913 questions answered. 1738 problems, answers to odd numbers. 494 figures. 24 pages of formulas, functions. x + 629pp. 5⅜ x 8. T371 Paperbound **$2.00**

CALCULUS REFRESHER FOR TECHNICAL MEN, A. A. Klaf. 756 questions examine most important aspects of integral, differential calculus. Part I: simple differential calculus, constants, variables, functions, increments, logs, curves, etc. Part 2: fundamental ideas of integrations, inspection, substitution, areas, volumes, mean value, double, triple integration, etc. Practical aspects stressed. 50 pages illustrate applications to specific problems of civil, nautical engineering, electricity, stress, strain, elasticity, similar fields. 756 questions answered. 566 problems, mostly answered. 36pp. of useful constants, formulas. v + 431pp. 5⅜ x 8. T370 Paperbound **$2.00**

MONOGRAPHS ON TOPICS OF MODERN MATHEMATICS, edited by J. W. A. Young. Advanced mathematics for persons who have forgotten, or not gone beyond, high school algebra. 9 monographs on foundation of geometry, modern pure geometry, non-Euclidean geometry, fundamental propositions of algebra, algebraic equations, functions, calculus, theory of numbers, etc. Each monograph gives proofs of important results, and descriptions of leading methods, to provide wide coverage. "Of high merit," Scientific American. New introduction by Prof. M. Kline, N.Y. Univ. 100 diagrams. xvi + 416pp. 6⅛ x 9¼.
S289 Paperbound **$2.00**

MATHEMATICS IN ACTION, O. G. Sutton. Excellent middle level application of mathematics to study of universe, demonstrates how math is applied to ballistics, theory of computing machines, waves, wave-like phenomena, theory of fluid flow, meteorological problems, statistics, flight, similar phenomena. No knowledge of advanced math required. Differential equations, Fourier series, group concepts, Eigenfunctions, Planck's constant, airfoil theory, and similar topics explained so clearly in everyday language that almost anyone can derive benefit from reading this even if much of high-school math is forgotten. 2nd edition. 88 figures. viii + 236pp. 5⅜ x 8. T450 Clothbound **$3.50**

ELEMENTARY MATHEMATICS FROM AN ADVANCED STANDPOINT, Felix Klein. Classic text, an outgrowth of Klein's famous integration and survey course at Göttingen. Using one field to interpret, adjust another, it covers basic topics in each area, with extensive analysis. Especially valuable in areas of modern mathematics. "A great mathematician, inspiring teacher, . . . deep insight," Bul., Amer. Math Soc.

Vol. I. ARITHMETIC, ALGEBRA, ANALYSIS. Introduces concept of function immediately, enlivens discussion with graphical, geometric methods. Partial contents: natural numbers, special properties, complex numbers. Real equations with real unknowns, complex quantities. Logarithmic, exponential functions, infinitesimal calculus. Transcendence of e and pi, theory of assemblages. Index. 125 figures. ix + 274pp. 5⅜ x 8. S151 Paperbound **$1.75**

Vol. II. GEOMETRY. Comprehensive view, accompanies space perception inherent in geometry with analytic formulas which facilitate precise formulation. Partial contents: Simplest geometric manifold; line segments, Grassman determinant principles, classication of configurations of space. Geometric transformations: affine, projective, higher point transformations, theory of the imaginary. Systematic discussion of geometry and its foundations. 141 illustrations. ix + 214pp. 5⅜ x 8. S151 Paperbound **$1.75**

A TREATISE ON PLANE AND ADVANCED TRIGONOMETRY, E. W. Hobson. Extraordinarily wide coverage, going beyond usual college level, one of few works covering advanced trig in full detail. By a great expositor with unerring anticipation of potentially difficult points. Includes circular functions; expansion of functions of multiple angle; trig tables; relations between sides, angles of triangles; complex numbers; etc. Many problems fully solved. "The best work on the subject," Nature. Formerly entitled "A Treatise on Plane Trigonometry." 689 examples. 66 figures. xvi + 383pp. 5⅜ x 8. S353 Paperbound **$1.95**

NON-EUCLIDEAN GEOMETRY, Roberto Bonola. The standard coverage of non-Euclidean geometry. Examines from both a historical and mathematical point of view geometries which have arisen from a study of Euclid's 5th postulate on parallel lines. Also included are complete texts, translated, of Bolyai's "Theory of Absolute Space," Lobachevsky's "Theory of Parallels." 180 diagrams. 431pp. 5⅜ x 8. S27 Paperbound **$1.95**

GEOMETRY OF FOUR DIMENSIONS, H. P. Manning. Unique in English as a clear, concise introduction. Treatment is synthetic, mostly Euclidean, though in hyperplanes and hyperspheres at infinity, non-Euclidean geometry is used. Historical introduction. Foundations of 4-dimensional geometry. Perpendicularity, simple angles. Angles of planes, higher order. Symmetry, order, motion; hyperpyramids, hypercones, hyperspheres; figures with parallel elements; volume, hypervolume in space; regular polyhedroids. Glossary. 78 figures. ix + 348pp. 5⅜ x 8. S182 Paperbound **$1.95**

MATHEMATICS: INTERMEDIATE TO ADVANCED

GEOMETRY (EUCLIDEAN AND NON-EUCLIDEAN)

THE GEOMETRY OF RENÉ DESCARTES. With this book, Descartes founded analytical geometry. Original French text, with Descartes's own diagrams, and excellent Smith-Latham translation. Contains: Problems the Construction of Which Requires only Straight Lines and Circles; On the Nature of Curved Lines; On the Construction of Solid or Supersolid Problems. Diagrams. 258pp. 5⅜ x 8. S68 Paperbound **$1.50**

THE WORKS OF ARCHIMEDES, edited by T. L. Heath. All the known works of the great Greek mathematician, including the recently discovered Method of Archimedes. Contains: On Sphere and Cylinder, Measurement of a Circle, Spirals, Conoids, Spheroids, etc. Definitive edition of greatest mathematical intellect of ancient world. 186 page study by Heath discusses Archimedes and history of Greek mathematics. 563pp. 5⅜ x 8. S9 Paperbound **$2.00**

COLLECTED WORKS OF BERNARD RIEMANN. Important sourcebook, first to contain complete text of 1892 "Werke" and the 1902 supplement, unabridged. 31 monographs, 3 complete lecture courses, 15 miscellaneous papers which have been of enormous importance in relativity, topology, theory of complex variables, other areas of mathematics. Edited by R. Dedekind, H. Weber, M. Noether, W. Wirtinger. German text; English introduction by Hans Lewy. 690pp. 5⅜ x 8. S226 Paperbound **$2.85**

THE THIRTEEN BOOKS OF EUCLID'S ELEMENTS, edited by Sir Thomas Heath. Definitive edition of one of very greatest classics of Western world. Complete translation of Heiberg text, plus spurious Book XIV. 150 page introduction on Greek, Medieval mathematics, Euclid, texts, commentators, etc. Elaborate critical apparatus parallels text, analyzing each definition, postulate, proposition, covering textual matters, refutations, supports, extrapolations, etc. This is the full Euclid. Unabridged reproduction of Cambridge U. 2nd edition. 3 volumes. 995 figures. 1426pp. 5⅜ x 8. S88, 89, 90, 3 volume set, paperbound **$6.00**

AN INTRODUCTION TO GEOMETRY OF N DIMENSIONS, D. M. Y. Sommerville. Presupposes no previous knowledge of field. Only book in English devoted exclusively to higher dimensional geometry. Discusses fundamental ideas of incidence, parallelism, perpendicularity, angles between linear space, enumerative geometry, analytical geometry from projective and metric views, polytopes, elementary ideas in analysis situs, content of hyperspacial figures. 60 diagrams. 196pp. 5⅜ x 8. S494 Paperbound **$1.50**

ELEMENTS OF NON-EUCLIDEAN GEOMETRY, D. M. Y. Sommerville. Unique in proceeding step-by-step. Requires only good knowleoge of high-school geometry and algebra, to grasp elementary hyperbolic, elliptic, analytic non-Euclidean Geometries; space curvature and its implications; radical axes; homopethic centres and systems of circles; parataxy and parallelism; Gauss' proof of defect area theorem; much more, with exceptional clarity. 126 problems at chapter ends. 133 figures. xvi + 274pp. 5⅜ x 8. S460 Paperbound **$1.50**

THE FOUNDATIONS OF EUCLIDEAN GEOMETRY, H. G. Forder. First connected, rigorous account in light of modern analysis, establishing propositions without recourse to empiricism, without multiplying hypotheses. Based on tools of 19th and 20th century mathematicians, who made it possible to remedy gaps and complexities, recognize problems not earlier discerned. Begins with important relationship of number systems in geometrical figures. Considers classes, relations, linear order, natural numbers, axioms for magnitudes, groups, quasi-fields, fields, non-Archimedian systems, the axiom system (at length), particular axioms (two chapters on the Parallel Axioms), constructions, congruence, similarity, etc. Lists: axioms employed, constructions, symbols in frequent use. 295pp. 5⅜ x 8. S481 Paperbound **$2.00**

CALCULUS, FUNCTION THEORY (REAL AND COMPLEX), FOURIER THEORY

FIVE VOLUME "THEORY OF FUNCTIONS" SET BY KONRAD KNOPP. Provides complete, readily followed account of theory of functions. Proofs given concisely, yet without sacrifice of completeness or rigor. These volumes used as texts by such universities as M.I.T., Chicago, N.Y. City College, many others. "Excellent introduction . . . remarkably readable, concise, clear, rigorous," J. of the American Statistical Association.

ELEMENTS OF THE THEORY OF FUNCTIONS, Konrad Knopp. Provides background for further volumes in this set, or texts on similar level. Partial contents: Foundations, system of complex numbers and Gaussian plane of numbers, Riemann sphere of numbers, mapping by linear functions, normal forms, the logarithm, cyclometric functions, binomial series. "Not only for the young student, but also for the student who knows all about what is in it," Mathematical Journal. 140pp. 5⅜ x 8. S154 Paperbound **$1.35**

THEORY OF FUNCTIONS, PART I, Konrad Knopp. With volume II, provides coverage of basic concepts and theorems. Partial contents: numbers and points, functions of a complex variable, integral of a continuous function, Cauchy's intergral theorem, Cauchy's integral formulae, series with variable terms, expansion and analytic function in a power series, analytic continuation and complete definition of analytic functions, Laurent expansion, types of singularities. vii + 146pp. 5⅜ x 8. S156 Paperbound **$1.35**

THEORY OF FUNCTIONS, PART II, Konrad Knopp. Application and further development of general theory, special topics. Single valued functions, entire, Weierstrass. Meromorphic functions: Mittag-Leffler. Periodic functions. Multiple valued functions. Riemann surfaces. Algebraic functions. Analytical configurations, Riemann surface. x + 150pp. 5⅜ x 8. S157 Paperbound **$1.35**

PROBLEM BOOK IN THE THEORY OF FUNCTIONS, VOLUME I, Konrad Knopp. Problems in elementary theory, for use with Knopp's "Theory of Functions," or any other text. Arranged according to increasing difficulty. Fundamental concepts, sequences of numbers and infinite series, complex variable, integral theorems, development in series, conformal mapping. Answers. viii + 126pp. 5⅜ x 8. S 158 **Paperbound $1.35**

PROBLEM BOOK IN THE THEORY OF FUNCTIONS, VOLUME II, Konrad Knopp. Advanced theory of functions, to be used with Knopp's "Theory of Functions," or comparable text. Singularities, entire and meromorphic functions, periodic, analytic, continuation, multiple-valued functions, Riemann surfaces, conformal mapping. Includes section of elementary problems. "The difficult task of selecting . . . problems just within the reach of the beginner is here masterfully accomplished," AM. MATH. SOC. Answers. 138pp. 5⅜ x 8.
S159 Paperbound **$1.35**

ADVANCED CALCULUS, E. B. Wilson. Still recognized as one of most comprehensive, useful texts. Immense amount of well-represented, fundamental material, including chapters on vector functions, ordinary differential equations, special functions, calculus of variations, etc., which are excellent introductions to these areas. Requires only one year of calculus. Over 1300 exercises cover both pure math and applications to engineering and physical problems. Ideal reference, refresher. 54 page introductory review. ix + 566pp. 5⅜ x 8.
S504 Paperbound **$2.45**

LECTURES ON THE THEORY OF ELLIPTIC FUNCTIONS, H. Hancock. Reissue of only book in English with so extensive a coverage, especially of Abel, Jacobi, Legendre, Weierstrass, Hermite, Liouville, and Riemann. Unusual fullness of treatment, plus applications as well as theory in discussing universe of elliptic integrals, originating in works of Abel and Jacobi. Use is made of Riemann to provide most general theory. 40-page table of formulas. 76 figures. xxiii + 498pp. 5⅜ x 8. S483 Paperbound **$2.55**

THEORY OF FUNCTIONALS AND OF INTEGRAL AND INTEGRO-DIFFERENTIAL EQUATIONS, Vito Volterra. Unabridged republication of only English translation, General theory of functions depending on continuous set of values of another function. Based on author's concept of transition from finite number of variables to a continually infinite number. Includes much material on calculus of variations. Begins with fundamentals, examines generalization of analytic functions, functional derivative equations, applications, other directions of theory, etc. New introduction by G. C. Evans. Biography, criticism of Volterra's work by E. Whittaker. xxxx + 226pp. 5⅜ x 8. S502 Paperbound **$1.75**

AN INTRODUCTION TO FOURIER METHODS AND THE LAPLACE TRANSFORMATION, Philip Franklin. Concentrates on essentials, gives broad view, suitable for most applications. Requires only knowledge of calculus. Covers complex qualities with methods of computing elementary functions for complex values of argument and finding approximations by charts; Fourier series; harmonic anaylsis; much more. Methods are related to physical problems of heat flow, vibrations, electrical transmission, electromagnetic radiation, etc. 828 problems, answers. Formerly entitled "Fourier Methods." x + 289pp. 5⅜ x 8.
S452 Paperbound **$1.75**

THE ANALYTICAL THEORY OF HEAT, Joseph Fourier. This book, which revolutionized mathematical physics, has been used by generations of mathematicians and physicists interested in heat or application of Fourier integral. Covers cause and reflection of rays of heat, radiant heating, heating of closed spaces, use of trigonometric series in theory of heat, Fourier integral, etc. Translated by Alexander Freeman. 20 figures. xxii + 466pp. 5⅜ x 8.
S93 Paperbound **$2.00**

ELLIPTIC INTEGRALS, H. Hancock. Invaluable in work involving differential equations with cubics, quatrics under root sign, where elementary calculus methods are inadequate. Practical solutions to problems in mathematics, engineering, physics; differential equations requiring integration of Lamé's, Briot's, or Bouquet's equations; determination of arc of ellipse, hyperbola, lemiscate; solutions of problems in elastics; motion of a projectile under resistance varying as the cube of the velocity; pendulums; more. Exposition in accordance with Legendre-Jacobi theory. Rigorous discussion of Legendre transformations. 20 figures. 5 place table. 104pp. 5⅜ x 8. S484 Paperbound **$1.25**

THE TAYLOR SERIES, AN INTRODUCTION TO THE THEORY OF FUNCTIONS OF A COMPLEX VARIABLE, P. Dienes. Uses Taylor series to approach theory of functions, using ordinary calculus only, except in last 2 chapters. Starts with introduction to real variable and complex algebra, derives properties of infinite series, complex differentiation, integration, etc. Covers biuniform mapping, overconvergence and gap theorems, Taylor series on its circle of convergence, etc. Unabridged corrected reissue of first edition. 186 examples, many fully worked out. 67 figures. xii + 555pp. 5⅜ x 8. S391 Paperbound **$2.75**

LINEAR INTEGRAL EQUATIONS, W. V. Lovitt. Systematic survey of general theory, with some application to differential equations, calculus of variations, problems of math, physics. Includes: integral equation of 2nd kind by successive substitutions; Fredholm's equation as ratio of 2 integral series in lambda, applications of the Fredholm theory, Hilbert-Schmidt theory of symmetric kernels, application, etc. Neumann, Dirichlet, vibratory problems. ix + 253pp. 5⅜ x 8. S175 Clothbound **$3.50**
S176 Paperbound **$1.60**

DICTIONARY OF CONFORMAL REPRESENTATIONS, H. Kober. Developed by British Admiralty to solve Laplace's equation in 2 dimensions. Scores of geometrical forms and transformations for electrical engineers, Joukowski aerofoil for aerodynamics, Schwartz-Christoffel transformations for hydro-dynamics, transcendental functions. Contents classified according to analytical functions describing transformations with corresponding regions. Glossary. Topological index. 447 diagrams. 6⅛ x 9¼. S160 Paperbound **$2.00**

ELEMENTS OF THE THEORY OF REAL FUNCTIONS, J. E. Littlewood. Based on lectures at Trinity College, Cambridge, this book has proved extremely successful in introducing graduate students to modern theory of functions. Offers full and concise coverage of classes and cardinal numbers, well ordered series, other types of series, and elements of the theory of sets of points. 3rd revised edition. vii + 71pp. 5⅜ x 8. S171 Clothbound **$2.85**
S172 Paperbound **$1.25**

INFINITE SEQUENCES AND SERIES, Konrad Knopp. 1st publication in any language. Excellent introduction to 2 topics of modern mathematics, designed to give student background to penetrate further alone. Sequences and sets, real and complex numbers, etc. Functions of a real and complex variable. Sequences and series. Infinite series. Convergent power series. Expansion of elementary functions. Numerical evaluation of series. v + 186pp. 5⅜ x 8.
S152 Clothbound **$3.50**
S153 Paperbound **$1.75**

THE THEORY AND FUNCTIONS OF A REAL VARIABLE AND THE THEORY OF FOURIER'S SERIES, E. W .Hobson. One of the best introductions to set theory and various aspects of functions and Fourier's series. Requires only a good background in calculus. Exhaustive coverage of: metric and descriptive properties of sets of points; transfinite numbers and order types; functions of a real variable; the Riemann and Lebesgue integrals; sequences and series of numbers; power-series; functions representable by series sequences of continuous functions; trigonometrical series; representation of functions by Fourier's series; and much more. "The best possible guide," Nature. Vol. I: 88 detailed examples, 10 figures. Index. xv + 736pp. Vol. II: 117 detailed examples, 13 figures. x + 780pp. 6⅛ x 9¼.
Vol. I: S387 Paperbound **$3.00**
Vol. II: S388 Paperbound **$3.00**

ALMOST PERIODIC FUNCTIONS, A. S. Besicovitch. Unique and important summary by a well known mathematician covers in detail the two stages of development in Bohr's theory of almost periodic functions: (1) as a generalization of pure periodicity, with results and proofs; (2) the work done by Stepanof, Wiener, Weyl, and Bohr in generalizing the theory. xi + 180pp. 5⅜ x 8. S18 Paperbound **$1.75**

INTRODUCTION TO THE THEORY OF FOURIER'S SERIES AND INTEGRALS, H. S. Carslaw. 3rd revised edition, an outgrowth of author's courses at Cambridge. Historical introduction, rational, irrational numbers, infinite sequences and series, functions of a single variable, definite integral, Fourier series, and similar topics. Appendices discuss practical harmonic analysis, periodogram analysis, Lebesgue's theory. 84 examples. xiii + 368pp. 5⅜ x 8.
S48 Paperbound **$2.00**

SYMBOLIC LOGIC

THE ELEMENTS OF MATHEMATICAL LOGIC, Paul Rosenbloom. First publication in any language. For mathematically mature readers with no training in symbolic logic. Development of lectures given at Lund Univ., Sweden, 1948. Partial contents: Logic of classes, fundamental theorems, Boolean algebra, logic of propositions, of propositional functions, expressive languages, combinatory logics, development of math within an object language, paradoxes, theorems of Post, Goedel, Church, and similar topics. iv + 214pp. 5⅜ x 8.
S227 Paperbound **$1.45**

INTRODUCTION TO SYMBOLIC LOGIC AND ITS APPLICATION, R. Carnap. Clear, comprehensive, rigorous, by perhaps greatest living master. Symbolic languages analyzed, one constructed. Applications to math (axiom systems for set theory, real, natural numbers), topology (Dedekind, Cantor continuity explanations), physics (general analysis of determination, causality, space-time topology), biology (axiom system for basic concepts). "A masterpiece," Zentralblatt für Mathematik und Ihre Grenzgebiete. Over 300 exercises. 5 figures. xvi + 241pp. 5⅜ x 8. S453 Paperbound **$1.85**

AN INTRODUCTION TO SYMBOLIC LOGIC, Susanne K. Langer. Probably clearest book for the philosopher, scientist, layman—no special knowledge of math required. Starts with simplest symbols, goes on to give remarkable grasp of Boole-Schroeder, Russell-Whitehead systems, clearly, quickly. Partial Contents: Forms, Generalization, Classes, Deductive System of Classes, Algebra of Logic, Assumptions of Principia Mathematica, Logistics, Proofs of Theorems, etc. "Clearest . . . simplest introduction . . . the intelligent non-mathematician should have no difficulty," MATHEMATICS GAZETTE. Revised, expanded 2nd edition. Truth-value tables. 368pp. 5⅜ 8. S164 Paperbound **$1.75**

TRIGONOMETRICAL SERIES, Antoni Zygmund. On modern advanced level. Contains carefully organized analyses of trigonometric, orthogonal, Fourier systems of functions, with clear adequate descriptions of summability of Fourier series, proximation theory, conjugate series, convergence, divergence of Fourier series. Especially valuable for Russian, Eastern European coverage. 329pp. 5⅜ x 8. S290 Paperbound **$1.50**

THE LAWS OF THOUGHT, George Boole. This book founded symbolic logic some 100 years ago. It is the 1st significant attempt to apply logic to all aspects of human endeavour. Partial contents: derivation of laws, signs and laws, interpretations, eliminations, conditions of a perfect method, analysis, Aristotelian logic, probability, and similar topics. xvii + 424pp. 5⅜ x 8. S28 Paperbound **$2.00**

SYMBOLIC LOGIC, C. I. Lewis, C. H. Langford. 2nd revised edition of probably most cited book in symbolic logic. Wide coverage of entire field; one of fullest treatments of paradoxes; plus much material not available elsewhere. Basic to volume is distinction between logic of extensions and intensions. Considerable emphasis on converse substitution, while matrix system presents supposition of variety of non-Aristotelian logics. Especially valuable sections on strict limitations, existence theorems. Partial contents: Boole-Schroeder algebra; truth value systems, the matrix method; implication and deductibility; general theory of propositions; etc. "Most valuable," Times, London. 506pp. 5⅜ x 8. S170 Paperbound **$2.00**

GROUP THEORY AND LINEAR ALGEBRA, SETS, ETC.

LECTURES ON THE ICOSAHEDRON AND THE SOLUTION OF EQUATIONS OF THE FIFTH DEGREE, Felix Klein. Solution of quintics in terms of rotations of regular icosahedron around its axes of symmetry. A classic, indispensable source for those interested in higher algebra, geometry, crystallography. Considerable explanatory material included. 230 footnotes, mostly bibliography. "Classical monograph . . . detailed, readable book," Math. Gazette. 2nd edition. xvi + 289pp. 5⅜ x 8. S314 Paperbound **$1.85**

INTRODUCTION TO THE THEORY OF GROUPS OF FINITE ORDER, R. Carmichael. Examines fundamental theorems and their applications. Beginning with sets, systems, permutations, etc., progresses in easy stages through important types of groups: Abelian, prime power, permutation, etc. Except 1 chapter where matrices are desirable, no higher math is needed. 783 exercises, problems. xvi + 447pp. 5⅜ x 8. S299 Clothbound **$3.95**
S300 Paperbound **$2.00**

THEORY OF GROUPS OF FINITE ORDER, W. Burnside. First published some 40 years ago, still one of clearest introductions. Partial contents: permutations, groups independent of representation, composition series of a group, isomorphism of a group with itself, Abelian groups, prime power groups, permutation groups, invariants of groups of linear substitution, graphical representation, etc. "Clear and detailed discussion . . . numerous problems which are instructive," Design News. xxiv + 512pp. 5⅜ x 8. S38 Paperbound **$2.45**

COMPUTATIONAL METHODS OF LINEAR ALGEBRA, V. N. Faddeeva, translated by C. D. Benster. 1st English translation of unique, valuable work, only one in English presenting systematic exposition of most important methods of linear algebra—classical, contemporary. Details of deriving numerical solutions of problems in mathematical physics. Theory and practice. Includes survey of necessary background, most important methods of solution, for exact, iterative groups. One of most valuable features is 23 tables, triple checked for accuracy, unavailable elsewhere. Translator's note. x + 252pp. 5⅜ x 8. S424 Paperbound **$1.95**

THE CONTINUUM AND OTHER TYPES OF SERIAL ORDER, E. V. Huntington. This famous book gives a systematic elementary account of the modern theory of the continuum as a type of serial order. Based on the Cantor-Dedekind ordinal theory, which requires no technical knowledge of higher mathematics, it offers an easily followed analysis of ordered classes, discrete and dense series, continuous series, Cantor's transfinite numbers. "Admirable introduction to the rigorous theory of the continuum . . . reading easy," Science Progress. 2nd edition. viii + 82pp. 5⅜ x 8. S129 Clothbound **$2.75**
S130 Paperbound **$1.00**

THEORY OF SETS, E. Kamke. Clearest, amplest introduction in English, well suited for independent study. Subdivisions of main theory, such as theory of sets of points, are discussed, but emphasis is on general theory. Partial contents: rudiments of set theory, arbitrary sets, their cardinal numbers, ordered sets, their order types, well-ordered sets, their cardinal numbers. vii + 144pp. 5⅜ x 8. S141 Paperbound **$1.35**

CONTRIBUTIONS TO THE FOUNDING OF THE THEORY OF TRANSFINITE NUMBERS, Georg Cantor. These papers founded a new branch of mathematics. The famous articles of 1895-7 are translated, with an 82-page introduction by P. E. B. Jourdain dealing with Cantor, the background of his discoveries, their results, future possibiilties. ix + 211pp. 5⅜ x 8.
S45 Paperbound **$1.25**

NUMERICAL AND GRAPHICAL METHODS, TABLES

JACOBIAN ELLIPTIC FUNCTION TABLES, L. M. Milne-Thomson. Easy-to-follow, practical, not only useful numerical tables, but complete elementary sketch of application of elliptic functions. Covers description of principle properties; complete elliptic integrals; Fourier series, expansions; periods, zeros, poles, residues, formulas for special values of argument; cubic, quartic polynomials; pendulum problem; etc. Tables, graphs form body of book: Graph, 5 figure table of elliptic function sn (u m); cn (u m); dn (u m). 8 figure table of complete elliptic integrals K, K′, E, E′, nome q. 7 figure table of Jacobian zeta-function Z(u). 3 figures. xi + 123pp. 5⅜ x 8. S194 Paperbound **$1.35**

TABLES OF FUNCTIONS WITH FORMULAE AND CURVES, E. Jahnke, F. Emde. Most comprehensive 1-volume English text collection of tables, formulae, curves of transcendent functions. 4th corrected edition, new 76-page section giving tables, formulae for elementary functions not in other English editions. Partial contents: sine, cosine, logarithmic integral; error integral; elliptic integrals; theta functions; Legendre, Bessel, Riemann, Mathieu, hypergeometric functions; etc. "Out-of-the-way functions for which we know no other source." Scientific Computing Service, Ltd. 212 figures. 400pp. 5⅝ x 8⅜. S133 Paperbound **$2.00**

MATHEMATICAL TABLES, H. B. Dwight. Covers in one volume almost every function of importance in applied mathematics, engineering, physical sciences. Three extremely fine tables of the three trig functions, inverses, to 1000th of radian; natural, common logs; squares, cubes; hyperbolic functions, inverses; $(a^2 + b^2)$ exp. ½a; complete elliptical integrals of 1st, 2nd kind; sine, cosine integrals; exponential integrals; Ei(x) and Ei(−x); binomial coefficients; factorials to 250; surface zonal harmonics, first derivatives; Bernoulli, Euler numbers, their logs to base of 10; Gamma function; normal probability integral; over 60pp. Bessel functions; Riemann zeta function. Each table with formulae generally used, sources of more extensive tables, interpolation data, etc. Over half have columns of differences, to facilitate interpolation. viii + 231pp. 5⅜ x 8. S445 Paperbound **$1.75**

PRACTICAL ANALYSIS, GRAPHICAL AND NUMERICAL METHODS, F. A. Willers. Immensely practical hand-book for engineers. How to interpolate, use various methods of numerical differentiation and integration, determine roots of a single algebraic equation, system of linear equations, use empirical formulas, integrate differential equations, etc. Hundreds of shortcuts for arriving at numerical solutions. Special section on American calculating machines, by T. W. Simpson. Translation by R. T. Beyer. 132 illustrations. 422pp. 5⅜ x 8. S273 Paperbound **$2.00**

NUMERICAL SOLUTIONS OF DIFFERENTIAL EQUATIONS, H. Levy, E. A. Baggott. Comprehensive collection of methods for solving ordinary differential equations of first and higher order. 2 requirements: practical, easy to grasp; more rapid than school methods. Partial contents: graphical integration of differential equations, graphical methods for detailed solution. Numerical solution. Simultaneous equations and equations of 2nd and higher orders. "Should be in the hands of all in research and applied mathematics, teaching," Nature. 21 figures. viii + 238pp. 5⅜ x 8. S168 Paperbound **$1.75**

NUMERICAL INTEGRATION OF DIFFERENTIAL EQUATIONS, Bennet, Milne, Bateman. Unabridged republication of original prepared for National Research Council. New methods of integration by 3 leading mathematicians: "The Interpolational Polynomial," "Successive Approximation," A. A. Bennett, "Step-by-step Methods of Integration," W. W. Milne. "Methods for Partial Differential Equations," H. Bateman. Methods for partial differential equations, solution of differential equations to non-integral values of a parameter will interest mathematicians, physicists. 288 footnotes, mostly bibliographical. 235 item classified bibliography. 108pp. **5⅜ x 8.** S305 Paperbound **$1.35**

Date D